# MECHANICAL TECHNOLOGY
## in Agriculture

# DONALD M. JOHNSON

Associate Professor, Agricultural Education
University of Arkansas
Fayetteville, Arkansas

# JOE HARPER

Professor, Agricultural Biological Engineering
Clemson University
Clemson, South Carolina

# DAVID E. LAWVER

Associate Professor, Agricultural Education
Texas Tech University
Lubbock, Texas

# PHILIP BURIAK

Associate Professor, Agricultural Engineering
University of Illinois
Urbana, Illinois

## AgriScience & Technology Series

**Jasper S. Lee, Ph.D.**
Series Editor

## Interstate Publishers, Inc.
Danville, Illinois

# MECHANICAL TECHNOLOGY

## in Agriculture

# MECHANICAL TECHNOLOGY
## in Agriculture

*Library of Congress Catalog Card No. 96-77359*

ISBN 0-8134-3017-8

2 3 4 5 6 7 8 9 10    03 02 01 00 99

Order from

**Interstate Publishers, Inc.**

510 North Vermilion Street
P.O. Box 50
Danville, IL 61834-0050

Phone: (800) 843-4774
Fax: (217) 446-9706
Email: info-ipp@IPPINC.com

# Preface

Agricultural production, processing, and distribution relies on mechanical technology. From large four-wheel drive tractors to hand-held global positioning receivers and from robotics to hydraulics, mechanical technology drives the agricultural industry. All of our lives are improved through the application of mechanical technology to agriculture.

*Mechanical Technology in Agriculture* emphasizes important areas of agricultural technology including electricity and electronics, internal combustion engines, hydraulics, and construction and maintenance. In addition, emphasis is placed on the development, role, and scope of mechanical technology in agriculture.

*Mechanical Technology in Agriculture* places equal emphasis on the practical applications and theoretical understandings necessary for both occupational success and advanced education in the field of agricultural technology. A major goal of the book is to show the relationship between science, mathematics, and mechanical technology. A second major goal is to apply mathematics, science, and mechanical technology in the solution of agricultural problems.

This book is intended for use by advanced secondary school agricultural education students, community college students, lower division university students, and their teachers. In addition, this book should be of benefit to farmers, agribusiness persons, and others interested in learning about mechanical technology in agriculture.

# Acknowledgments

The authors are indebted to colleagues at their respective institutions who have provided assistance and encouragement in the completion of this textbook. Dr. Glen C. Shinn, Texas A&M University and Dr. J. Anthony Blair, Mississippi State University are given special thanks for their technical review of the content. In addition, the authors are grateful to Dr. Jasper S. Lee for his design, coordination, and assistance with photographs.

The assistance of the staff at Interstate Publishers, Inc. is gratefully acknowledged. President Vernie Thomas who encouraged and supported the completion of this book in so many ways, Mary E. Carter for the art work, and Kim Romine for the layout and typesetting are especially acknowledged.

Don Johnson expresses his appreciation to Leslie, Reid, and Russell Johnson for their constant love and support. Thanks for understanding when I was "at the office." Dr. Robert M. Schneider is also acknowledged for awakening an interest in things mechanical and for his encouragement, support, and friendship over the years.

Joe Harper acknowledges the never-ending love and support of Matthew and Kathy Harper, without which this task would have been impossible.

David Lawver extends special gratitude to Donna for her love and willingness to support this effort. Thank you for encouraging me to work on this book. Also, a special thanks goes to Andrew and Kaitlin for their love and for just being there. All of you are special to me.

Phil Buriak expresses appreciation to his wife, Carol, for her support.

# Contents

## PART THREE—Internal Combustion Engine Technology in Agriculture

## PART FOUR—Hydraulics Technology in Agriculture

## PART FIVE—Construction and Maintenance Technology in Agriculture

# 1

# TECHNOLOGY IN AGRICULTURE

Agriculture has undergone major changes in the United States. Today, less than 2 percent of the labor force works on farms and ranches. Compare this with 1800 when 70 percent of the labor force worked on the farm! Major changes have occurred, including the development of a large agribusiness sector.

Technology has played a big role in the changes. Developments in production practices, such as improved seed, pest control, and mechanization have been important.

1-1. Advances in machinery, fertilizers and pesticides, irrigation and drainage, and structures have reduced human labor requirements and increased the productivity of American agriculture. (Upper right and lower left photos courtesy of L. Bode, Ag. Eng., University of Illinois. Lower right photo courtesy of T. Funk, Ag. Eng., University of Illinois)

# OBJECTIVES

This chapter provides an overview of technology in agriculture. After completing this chapter, you will:

1. Explain the early development of mechanical technology in agriculture.

2. Identify the individuals involved in the evolution of the plow.

3. Identify the individuals involved in the evolution of grain harvesting equipment.

4. Explain the importance of the internal combustion engine to agricultural productivity.

5. Discuss the advances in the design and use of agricultural structures and farm electrification.

6. Explain the concepts of precision farming and site specific crop management.

7. Describe the contribution of mechanical technology to the industrial society.

8. Explain the relationships of science and mathematics to mechanical technology.

**TERMS**

agrarian
agricultural mechanization
Leonard Andrus
bar chart
J. I. Case
combine
commodities
cradle scythes
John Deere
design function
geographic information
    system (GIS)
global positioning system
    (GPS)
internal combustion engine
landsat
laser
line graph
mathematics
Cyrus McCormick
Charles Newbold
plow
precision farming
reaper
remote sensing
science
sickle
site specific crop
    management (SSCM)
squatting
sulky
unit factors
variable rate technology (VRT)
velocity

# MECHANIZATION AND TECHNOLOGY

*Agricultural mechanization* is the use of power and machinery to produce food and fiber. This has included the development of agricultural tools and machine, energy and power, irrigation and drainage, structures for animal housing and crop storage, and electrification.

The innovations resulting from the new technology have changed how people live. These innovations have had great impact on economic, social, industrial, and cultural development in the United States.

## *EARLY DEVELOPMENTS*

Land resources for farming have always been plentiful in the United States. In the 19th century, acquiring land for agricultural development (farming) could be done at very low cost or no cost, by *squatting*, settling on public or unoccupied land, or later, homesteading. Land availability was not a problem. Labor, however, was a problem. The human labor needed to develop the abundant land resources was in short supply. In the early 1800s, the amount of land a farmer could put into production was limited by the size of the labor force in the family. The lack of an available labor force prevented farmers from expanding the size of their farms, from increasing the productivity of their farms, and from gaining wealth from the sale of the *commodities*, plant and animal products, grown on their farms. The farmers of the 19th century had to find ways to extend their capacity to do work.

**1-2. Horses replaced humans as a power source on 19th century farms in the United States.**

The development of machines in the first half of the 19th century allowed the American farmer to increase his/her work output with a reduction in human energy input. These early machines used animal power to replace human power. Later in the century, steam and the development of the internal combustion engine replaced animal power.

Throughout the 1800s, technological advancements in tools and machinery expanded for all aspects of agriculture. The early machines were typically designed and built by local blacksmiths who lived in the farm communities and had a good understanding of the needs of the farmer. The evolution of two machine types, the plow and grain harvesting equipment, will be traced as examples of technological innovation and advancement. The adoption of the internal combustion engine, the refinement of structural systems, and the impact of farm electrification will also be presented in the following sections.

## EVOLUTION OF THE PLOW

*Charles Newbold* won the first United States patent for a plow in 1797. A *plow* is an implement used to break or turn soil in preparation for planting. The one-piece plow, made of cast iron, was not received well by farmers. Many farmers thought the cast iron would contaminate the soil, and in truth, the plow did not perform well. Numerous other inventors patented plows, but it was not until 1837 that *John Deere*, a blacksmith in Illinois, began making steel plows from saw steel and smooth wrought iron. The Deere plow scoured (self-cleaned) well and proved highly effective in the dark, heavy soils of the Midwest. John Deere formed a partnership with *Leonard Andrus* and began producing steel plows. By the 1850s, the

1-3. Larger implements increased operational efficiency. (Courtesy of J. Siemens, Agricultural Engineering, University of Illinois)

John Deere Company was producing more than 10,000 plows annually. As the mechanical technology of the plow advanced, riding (sulky) plows were developed. A ***sulky*** is a light, two-wheeled carriage, seating one person. Gang plows, similar to those used today, soon followed.

## EVOLUTION OF GRAIN HARVESTING EQUIPMENT

The technological advancements in equipment to harvest grain were more dramatic than those in development of the plow. Sickles and cradle scythes were the traditional tools used for grain harvesting until the 1800s. The ***sickle*** is a sharp, curved metal blade fitted with a short handle. ***Cradle scythes*** are hand-held implements with a long curved blade attached to a long, bent handle. The mechanical reaper, developed in the 1830s, was one of the most significant farming inventions of the 19th century. The mechanical ***reaper***, an implement used for cutting and gathering a crop, reduced the time required to harvest grain by more than one-half.

***Cyrus McCormick*** patented a horse-drawn reaper, made many improvements, and moved to Chicago—a location closer to the grain farmers of the Midwest. By 1851, McCormick was producing more than 1,000 reapers each year. John Deere plows and McCormick reapers were among the first farming tools to move from production in the blacksmith's shop to the industrial manufacturing plant.

Grain threshing machinery development occurred concurrently with the development of the reaper. In the 1850s, ***J.I. Case*** began to manufacture and sell a *"combine"*—combination thresher–separator–winnower—that threshed the grain, separated the grain from the straw, and removed the chaff from the grain. This combine allowed for a more timely harvest and

**I-4. The horse-drawn mechanical reaper was one of the most significant farming developments of the 19th century. (Courtesy of J. Siemens, Agricultural Engineering, University of Illinois)**

reduced crop losses. The machine also significantly reduced the time requirements for the grain harvesting operation.

The late 19th century was a period of machine improvement, increases in machine capacity, and widespread adoption. Human labor inputs declined as worker productivity increased. As agricultural machines increased in size and capacity, the need for a more reliable, a more powerful, and a more efficient power source became apparent. Animal power could no longer be a sufficient power source and the power source of choice.

## POWER: TRACTORS, TRUCKS, AND THE INTERNAL COMBUSTION ENGINE

The tractor powered by an internal combustion engine was developed in the late 19th century. An ***internal combustion engine*** converts the chemical energy from the fuel into heat energy, which is converted into mechanical power. The first tractors were simply an engine bolted to a

**Table 1-1.**
**Adoption of Internal Combustion Engine Powered Tractors and Trucks on Farms in the United States; 1910–1988**

| Date | Tractors (thousands) | Horsepower (millions) | Trucks (thousands) |
|---|---|---|---|
| 1910 | 1 | na | 0 |
| 1920 | 246 | 10 | 139 |
| 1930 | 920 | 25 | 900 |
| 1940 | 1567 | 42 | 1045 |
| 1950 | 3394 | 93 | 2207 |
| 1960 | 4688 | 153 | 2834 |
| 1970 | 4619 | 203 | 2984 |
| 1980 | 4780 | 304 | 3377 |
| 1988 | 4609 | na | 3437 |

Adapted from: Cochrane, William. The Development of American Agriculture, 2nd Edition. The University of Minnesota Press, 1993.
na: data not available.

**1-5. The internal combustion engine powers many different machine systems in contemporary agriculture.**

wheeled, steel frame. By 1910, mass-produced tractors were widespread—the result of the critical need for reliable and efficient mobile power. Farmers quickly adopted tractors as their farm power source. Table 1-1 shows the history of tractor and truck adoption and the horsepower gains on farms in the United States.

Tractors, trucks, and self-propelled machinery powered by the internal combustion engine revolutionized American agriculture. All aspects of production—preparing the seed bed, planting and spraying, harvesting, and distribution of farm products—are performed by internal combustion powered equipment. Agricultural machinery advances in the 1900s were the direct outgrowth of the development and the adoption of the internal combustion engine and its agricultural applications. The internal combustion engine eliminated the hard, human, physical labor and the need for animal power, and increased the capacity to do work. The development of agricultural machine systems was possible because of the internal combustion engine. A more reliable, efficient, and mobile source of power was now available.

# ADVANCES IN STRUCTURAL SYSTEMS

Early farm structures were designed and constructed from locally available materials to provide shelter for livestock and storage for farming inputs and harvested crops. These structures did little to control their internal environments other than keeping out snow, rain, sun, and wind. They also did little to differentiate function, i.e., one design, one barn, satisfied all of the shelter and storage needs for the farming enterprise.

**1-6. Early barns were built from locally available materials to provide shelter for livestock and storage for crops and farming inputs.**

Modern farm structures are no longer general purpose buildings, and are built for a specific function. Internal environments can be controlled to suit the design function, and operations within the structure can be mechanized. A ***design function*** is the purpose for which a structure has been created. Design and construction are not limited by locally available materials. New materials and new construction techniques increase the ease of construction, reduce construction and maintenance costs, increase the useful life of the structure, and improve the flexibility and utilization of the structure. Today's agricultural structures add profitability to the production enterprise.

**1-7. Modern agricultural structures are no longer general purpose. Structures are designed and built for a specific function—top, livestock production facility; bottom, storage facility. (Courtesy of T. Funk, Agricultural Engineering, University of Illinois)**

# FARM ELECTRIFICATION

Electricity and electrical appliances have been a relatively recent addition to agricultural production enterprises. The expansion of electrical technologies has been quite rapid however, with electrical systems, electric motors, and controls now used in all aspects of the agricultural industry. Electricity has had an impact on agriculture equal to or greater than that of the internal combustion engine. Electric power has replaced much of the hand labor required on the farm and at a reasonable cost. The use of electrical systems will continue to dominate agricultural mechanization.

# SITE SPECIFIC CROP MANAGEMENT

*Site specific crop management (SSCM)* involves using technology to apply the correct amount of appropriate inputs to crops, to apply that amount to a specific field location, and to apply inputs to cost-effectively produce a crop. To do this, quality machinery and equipment that can be accurately calibrated and capable of changing application rates during various cropping practices, such as applying fertilizer, must be maintained. The operator will be required to know the exact location of the machinery and equipment in the field at all times through global positioning systems—GPS. Finally, the operator will need complex and detailed maps of the field measuring numerous physical characteristics for a spatially well-defined area—geographic information systems (GIS).

## PRECISION FARMING

*Precision farming* is using cropping practices that improve yields based on the needs of the land. Fields are divided into small areas on the basis of information collected with satellite systems using global positioning. Pests, soil fertility and compaction, and other features are studied. Records of yields are kept for the small areas within fields. Computer-controlled equipment applies the needed fertilizer and other inputs to grow a crop.

Precision farming includes satellite positioning, grid soil sampling, spatial mapping, variable rate applications, and real-time yield monitoring. The goal of precision farming is to apply seed, fertilizer, and agricultural chemicals where they are needed in the amounts needed; not to apply uniform rates fence row to fence row as farmers traditionally have done and many continue to do. Precision farming is farming by the foot rather than farming by the field.

1-8. Global positioning systems are used in precision farming. This shows a global positioning unit being used to study soil salinity (top left), global positioning unit being installed on a tractor (top right), data collected by remote sensing being used to study soil fertility (bottom left), and examining sample of corn from the grain flow sensor of a combine (bottom right). (Courtesy Agricultural Research Service, USDA)

## REMOTE SENSING

*Remote sensing* involves gathering and recording data from a great distance. Most remote sensors are on satellites some 500 miles above the earth. Some of the methods used are extremely accurate.

*Landsat* is the term applied to United States satellites that make photographs of the earth and plot the earth's resources. These photographs are used to make maps that provide meaningful information. The photographs aren't made with regular cameras that record light. They are made with remote sensors that view the earth in both visible and infrared light. Not only is the earth mapped but sea-floor (bottom) elevations are also mapped.

Remote sensing is beneficial in forecasting the weather, locating natural resources, detecting crop disease, and protecting the environment.

## GEOGRAPHIC INFORMATION SYSTEMS—GIS

The development of computerized GIS and data collection technologies have progressed to where small areas of a field can be uniquely identified. The ***Geographic Information Systems (GIS)*** partitions fields into grids and then maps them for physical attributes per grid segment. Individual maps can be made for fertility (N, P, K), pesticide residues, soil type and texture, drainability and water holding capacity, and last year's (or past year's) yield data. Computerized GIS allows the layering of these maps giving a site-specific picture of a field on a meter by meter basis. Management decisions regarding application rates of chemical fertilizers and pesticides and seeding rates can be made for each grid segment of the field.

I-9. Dividing a large field into grids is a part of mapping in a geographic information system. (Courtesy, Agricultural Research Service, USDA)

Once the maps are compiled, they serve as a computerized database. The data is loaded into an on-tractor computer so the operator can view the maps of the field and see the inputs needed for each grid segment. The next requirement for site-specific crop management is to locate the tractor and implement on the field and key them to the map. The operator must know the exact position of the tractor and implement at any moment. Global positioning systems provide the means to do this.

## GLOBAL POSITIONING SYSTEMS—GPS

A ***Global Positioning System (GPS)*** is a system of satellites orbiting the earth at very high altitudes. This technology is accurate enough to provide exact locations anywhere in the world. GPS was first developed as a defense system. But with today's integrated technology, GPS receivers are small enough and inexpensive enough to be practical for many other applications, including agriculture.

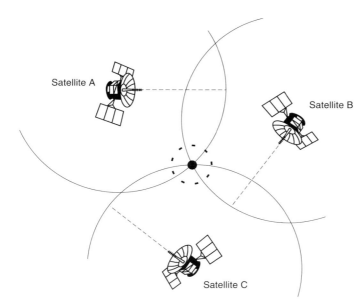

**1-10. Knowing the distances from satellites to a point on the earth allows us to accurately determine positions by triangulation.**

The principles explaining GPS are not difficult, even though the system uses some of the most high technology equipment ever developed. The most basic concept is satellite ranging, or triangulation. Positions on the earth are determined by measuring the distance from a group of satellites in space. The satellites serve as reference points. When distances are known from four different satellites, a single point on the earth's surface can be defined. The fourth satellite is used for error correction; theoretically only three are needed to trigonometrically locate a point in three-dimensional space.

Measurement of the distance to a satellite is equally simple in concept, and again, high technology in application. Distances are determined by timing how long it takes for a radio signal to reach the earth from the satellite. Radio waves travel at the speed of light. By multiplying the time interval (the time it takes for the signal to travel from the satellite to the earth) by the speed of light we can determine exact distances from the satellite to the earth.

## VARIABLE RATE TECHNOLOGY—VRT

Once the needs are known for each field grid location, technology is used to vary application rates. Varying the rate of application of all production inputs (seed, fertilizer, pesticide) in a field without stopping is called *variable rate technology (VRT)* or spatially variable application.

**1-11. Variable rate technology requires receivers and controllers that operate properly to be able to vary the rate of application of all production inputs on the go.**

Uniform application at the different desired rates for each grid segment is critical to gaining the full benefits of site-specific crop management systems.

## LASER TECHNOLOGY

A *laser* is a device that produces a special kind of light known as coherent light. Lasers are sometimes called "electric eyes." An intense, narrow beam of light is produced that is useful in many ways.

Lasers have many uses in mechanical technology. They can be used in land forming to shape land to a certain contour. Lasers are used in laying out rice fields, terraces, and fish ponds. The line of light does not bend

**1-12. A laser-guided system is being used to form this land.**

and cause unwanted changes in elevation. The laser beam guides the tractor as it lays out the land.

Laser beams can be used to "watch" processes in manufacturing plants and other facilities. The light will detect changes in movement or other things indicating a problem. This saves humans from trying to watch high-speed processes in a factory.

Lasers can beam light to scan codes on merchandise, known as bar codes. Garden centers and hardware stores, among others, use scanners that help determine how much to charge customers for purchases. The scanner is hooked to a computer that has all of the prices.

# CONTRIBUTION OF MECHANICAL TECHNOLOGY

Agricultural mechanization in the United States developed as the result of abundant land resources and a limited labor force. Advances in mechanical technologies substituted machines for human labor. This replacement extended human capacity to do work while reducing the overall

### Table 1-2.
### Labor Requirements to Produce Wheat Using Typical United States Production Systems of the Period

| Date | Man-Hr/ac | Man-Hr/bu | Avg Yield (bu/ac) | Production System |
|------|-----------|-----------|-------------------|-------------------|
| 1830 | 50–60 | 2.5–3 | 20 | Walking plow, brush for harrow, hand broadcast of seed, side and flail. |
| 1895 | 8–10 | 0.4–0.5 | 20 | Gang plow, seeder, harrow, binder, thresher, wagons and horses. |
| 1932 | 3–4 | 0.15–0.2 | 20 | 3-bottom gang plow, tractor, 10-foot tandem disc, harrow, 12-foot combine, trucks. |
| 1968 | 1.5 | 0.05 | 30 | Tractor, 12-foot one way plow, 14-foot drill, 14-foot self-propelled combine, trucks. |
| 1990 | 0.25 | 0.007 | 35 | 4-wheel drive tractor, 50-foot field cultivator, 36-foot drill, 24-foot self-propelled combine, trucks. |

Source: USDA

## Table 1-3.
## Labor Requirements to Produce Corn Using
## Typical United States Production Systems of the Period

| Date | Man-Hr/ac | Man-Hr/bu | Avg Yield (bu/ac) | Production System |
|---|---|---|---|---|
| 1750 | 60–70 | 3–3.5 | 20 | Till with hoe, cultivate with hoe, hand plant, hand harvest. |
| 1894 | 14–16 | 0.35–0.4 | 40 | Horse-drawn 2-bottom gang plow, disc, peg-tooth harrow, 2-row planter, hand harvest |
| 1932 | 6–8 | 0.15–0.2 | 40 | Horse-drawn 2-bottom gang plow, 7-foot tandem disc, 4-section harrow, 2-row planter, cultivator, 2-row picker. |
| 1965 | 1–2 | 0.0125–0.025 | 80 | 5-bottom plow, 15-foot tandem disc, 8-row cultivator, 8-row planter, 4-row combine. |
| 1990 | 0.5–1 | 0.005–0.01 | 100 | 4-wheel drive tractor, 10-bottom plow, 24-foot tandem disc, 16-row planter, 8-row corn combine. |

Source: USDA

human labor requirements on the farm. The direct result of advances in agricultural mechanization was an increase in farm size and an increase in farm output. Innovations and technological advancement of the innovations in agricultural mechanization have increased the efficiency of farm operations. Advances in mechanical technologies have reduced human labor requirements in production agriculture. People were available to work in agribusinesses and non-agriculture areas. The United States grew from an **agrarian**, agricultural, society to an industrial society and now an information society. Tables 1-2 and 1-3 show changes in the labor productivity for wheat and corn production from 1750 to 1990 in the United States.

Advancements in agricultural technology have allowed the United States to develop stability in food production, to produce a high quality and diverse food supply at a competitive price, and to aid the undernourished peoples of the world with production surpluses. Agricultural technologies have made the United States the worlds' leader in agriculture.

# RELATIONSHIP OF SCIENCE AND MATHEMATICS TO MECHANICAL TECHNOLOGIES

Technological advancement combines resources in new ways or new configurations to increase efficiency (output per unit input; output/input). In the 19th century, farmers and blacksmiths made technological advances in plow design and construction, grain harvesting equipment, and numerous other agricultural machine systems. These advances were made by the "tinkering" (trial and error) of craftspeople. The need for labor savings in production agriculture was their motivation. The machines were not highly sophisticated, but did improve the efficiency of farming operations. As farming technology continued to develop and advance, machines and machine systems became more sophisticated.

As technology becomes more sophisticated, the links to science become stronger. A "tinkerer" can no longer continue to advance the mechanical technology of agriculture. *Science*, the understanding of a body of knowledge, became a prerequisite for continued technological advancement. Advancement in agricultural mechanical technology continues today as the systematic application of scientific knowledge directed to some specific problem or purpose. Science underpins the technology providing the fundamental basis for its application. Science and technology are inseparable when used to understand and solve practical problems.

*Mathematics* is the symbolic language of science and technology. Agricultural mechanical technology is based on the application of quantitative data and the analysis of relationships between variables. Mathematics provides the tools needed to quantify data, to summarize data, and to describe the relationships demonstrated by the data. Knowledge of mathematics and science is essential for the continued advancement in agricultural mechanical technologies.

## *QUANTIFYING AND SUMMARIZING DATA*

Numerical data may be quantified and/or summarized many ways. Averages, frequency distributions, and percentages are some common examples. Often, data are collected in units not commonly understood. For example, tractor speed (*velocity*) may be measured in ft/sec, but, velocity is better understood in mi/hr. Unit conversions (dimensional analysis) can be used to manipulate the data. *Unit factors* are ratios whose actual value equals unity (one), e.g., 5280ft/1mi = 1; 12in/1ft = 1; 43560ft²/ 1ac = 1. The numbers and the units in the numerator are equal to the numbers and the units in the denominator. The value of the unit factor is one, therefore, we can multiply any number by a unit factor without changing the true value of the number. Only the units are changed.

Using the tractor velocity example, suppose the tractor was traveling 50ft/10 sec. What is the velocity of the tractor in mi/hr? The data manipulation is one of converting the basic data given to the appropriate units.

$$\underline{3.41 \text{ mi/hr}} = 50\text{ft/10sec} \times 1\text{mi/5280ft} \times 60\text{sec/1min} \times 60\text{min/1hr}$$

After the units have been canceled, the units remaining on the right side of the expression must equal the units remaining on the left side of the expression. If the units match, the conversion has been set up properly.

Charts and graphs are additional arithmetic tools used to represent quantitative information (data). Well-designed charts and graphs are simple and effective methods used to describe numerical data and the relationships between variables. Line graphs and bar charts are common graphics used in the study of mechanical technologies in agriculture.

A *line graph* is a coordinate graph. The limits of the data set the scale for the abscissa (x-axis) and for the ordinate (y-axis). The independent

**Relationship Between Pressure and Volume**

**Data**

| Pressure (kPa) | Volume (cm³) |
|---|---|
| 10 | 225.0 |
| 20 | 110.0 |
| 30 | 74.9 |
| 50 | 44.6 |
| 70 | 32.0 |
| 100 | 22.4 |

Data Source: Agriscience Laboratory Champaign, IL

Prepared by: J. B. Student

**1-13. Line graphs are simple to read and are commonly used to plot continuous data.**

variable "X" (the variable affecting change) should be placed on the horizontal axis and the dependent variable "Y" (the variable changed by the action of the independent variable) should be placed on the vertical axis. Plot the data points and draw the curve. Be sure to label the axes and title the graph. Figure 1-13 shows an example of a complete line graph.

In a **bar chart,** the bars represent values and amounts by the relative size/length of the bars. Bars should be the same width with equal spacing between them. The microcomputer can be an effective tool to assist in the construction of bar charts and line graphs. Figure 1-14 shows an example of a properly constructed bar chart.

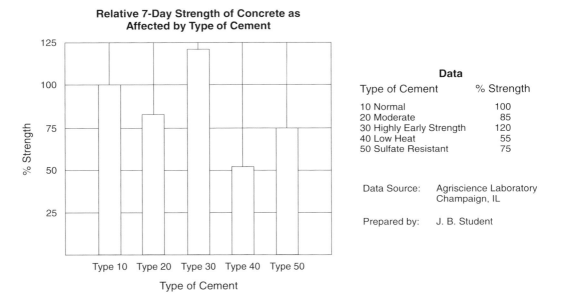

**1-14. Bar charts represent amounts by the relative length of the bars. Discrete data are best shown by bar charts.**

Mathematics is a tool of the mechanical technologist. Mathematics is used to quantify data, to summarize data, and to assist in interpreting physical relationships. Data can be organized, manipulated mathematically, and displayed graphically to better show an effect or a relationship that describes or controls some aspect of agricultural mechanical technology. Unit factor analysis describes a method often used for mathematical manipulation of data when studying mechanical technologies used in agriculture.

# SUMMARY

The early development of technologies for agriculture in the United States came about in response to a limited human labor force and abundant land resources. Farmers of the 19th cetury had to find ways to minimize human labor requirements while maximizing production.

Invention and advancement occurred in all areas of agricultural mechanical technologies, e.g., tillage, planting, harvesting, handling, and storage. Human power was replaced by animal power, which was replaced by mechanical power—the internal combustion engine and electricity. Farmers extended their ability to do work and production per farmer increased.

Early advancements in mechanical technologies were made by innovative farmers and blacksmiths living in farming communities. Trial and error was the method most used in designing and constructing agricultural machines and production systems. As the technologies became more sophisticated, science and mathematics became the necessary method used to design and construct the machines and systems. Science and mathematics (the language of science) guide all contemporary technological advancements. Advancements in agricultural mechanical technologies continue as the systematic application of scientific knowledge directed to some specific agricultural problem or purpose.

# REVIEW QUESTIONS

1. Describe the factors (in the 19th century) that forced the early development of mechanical technologies for agriculture.

2. Trace the evolution of the plow (grain harvesting equipment), identify the people involved, and describe the impact on agricultural production in the United States.

3. Discuss the adoption rate and importance of the internal combustion engine as a power source for American agriculture.

4. How did early farm structures differ from the agricultural structures of today?

5. Discuss the impact of electrification on agricultural production and processing.

6. What is meant by the term "site specific crop management"?

7. How have advances in agricultural mechanical technologies contributed to social, economic, and industrial development in the United States?

8. Explain the relationships of science and mathematics to the design, understanding, and utilization of agricultural mechanical technologies?

# APPLYING THE CONCEPTS

1. Using the data shown in Table 1-1, plot graph/s of tractors, trucks, and horsepower versus time. Observe the curves and discuss the trends. NOTE: Methods of constructing line graphs and bar charts are discussed in a section of this Chapter.

2. Using the data shown in Tables 1-2 and 1-3, plot graphs of man-hr/ac, man-hr/bu, and yield (bu/ac) versus the time period (date). Review the tables and your graphs and discuss the trends observed. NOTE: Methods for constructing line graphs and bar charts are described in a section of this chapter.

# 2

# CHARACTERISTICS OF ELECTRICITY

Modern agriculture depends on electricity. Each year, about three billion dollars are spent for the electricity used in producing crops and animals in the United States. Uses of electricity in agriculture are numerous. These range from cooling milk to warming baby pigs, and from powering irrigation systems to controlling environmental conditions in greenhouses.

While production agriculture is a major consumer of electricity, on-farm electrical consumption pales compared to the use of electricity in agribusiness. The production of farm inputs, such as machinery, feed, seed, fertilizer, and pesticides, requires large amounts of electricity. Industries that process and distribute farm products, such as canneries and frozen food plants, are also heavy users of electricity.

Because all phases of agriculture depend on electricity, you should develop a sound understanding of its characteristics and uses. Careful study of the information in this chapter should serve as a basis for wise use of electricity in agriculture.

2-1. Safety is a major consideration when working with electricity.

# OBJECTIVES

This chapter provides basic information on electricity. After completing this chapter, you will:

1. Relate electricity to the structure of elements and atoms.

2. Explain conductors, insulators, and semiconductors.

3. Explain the conventional and electron theories of electrical current flow.

4. Describe how electricity can be generated by friction, heat, light, pressure, chemical reactions, and magnetism.

5. Describe the difference between and applications of direct current (DC) and alternating current (AC) electricity.

6. Define and safely measure voltage, amperage, resistance, watts, kilowatts, kilowatt-hours and power factor.

7. Solve circuit problems requiring the use of Ohm's Law.

8. Describe the mathematical relationship between voltage, amperage, resistance, watts and power factor in AC and DC electrical circuits.

## TERMS

alternating current (AC)
ammeter
ampere (A)
apparent power
atom
battery
capacitive reactance
clamp-on ammeter
conductor
conventional theory
cosine
cycle
direct current (DC)
electricity
electrodes
electrolyte
electromagnet
electromotive force
electron
electron theory
element
energy
free electrons
friction
fuel cell
germanium
hertz
hydroelectric
impedance
inductive reactance
in-phase
insulator
ion
kilowatt (kW)
kilowatt-hour (kW-hr)

load
magnetic induction
milliampere (mA)
multimeters
neutron
ohm
ohmmeter
Ohm's Law
phase angle
photovoltaic effect
piezoelectric effect
polarity
power
power factor
primary battery
proton
quartz crystal
resistance
root mean square (rms)
secondary battery
semiconductor
silicon
single-phase electricity
solar cell
synchronous alternator
thermocouple
thermopile
three-phase electricity
true power
valence ring
volt (V)
volt meter
wattmeter
watt (W)
work

# ELEMENTS AND ATOMS

Understanding electricity begins with a basic knowledge of elements and atoms.

## Periodic Table of the Elements

**2-2. Periodic table showing 109 elements.**

## ELEMENTS

*Elements* are substances that cannot be broken down into simpler substances using ordinary chemical methods. Scientists have discovered and named 109 elements; 92 of these elements are natural (occur in nature) while the remaining 17 are artificial (created by humans). All matter (anything that has mass and weight) is composed of one or more elements.

## ATOMS

*Atoms* are the smallest units of an element. Atoms cannot be divided further without losing physical and chemical properties. Atoms are composed of protons, neutrons, and electrons.

### Protons and Neutrons

**Protons** have a positive electrical charge. **Neutrons** have no electrical charge. Together, protons and neutrons make up the nucleus, or center, of each atom. Since protons have a positive electrical charge and neutrons have no electrical charge, the nucleus of each atom has a positive electrical charge.

### Electrons

**Electrons** have a negative electrical charge and orbit the nucleus of an atom in rings (or shells). Unlike electrical charges attract each other. Negatively charged electrons are held in orbit by the positively charged protons in the nucleus. The outer ring of electrons is called the **valence** ring.

## COPPER: AN EXAMPLE ELEMENT

Figure 2-3 reinforces and expands what we have already learned about elements and atoms. As you look at the copper atom, you should note three things. First, you should notice that the drawing of the copper atom looks very similar to drawings of our solar system. In our solar system, the planets orbit the sun; in an atom, the electrons orbit the nucleus.

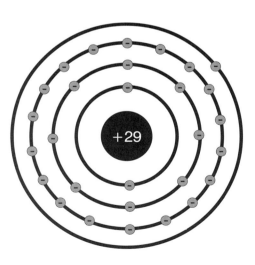

2-3. The atomic structure of the copper element.

Second, notice that the copper atom has 29 protons in its nucleus. If you count the number of electrons, you will find there are also 29 electrons orbiting the nucleus. Since the copper atom has an equal number of protons and electrons, it has no electrical charge. The positively charged protons and the negatively charged electrons cancel each other out.

Third, notice there are four rings of electrons orbiting the nucleus of the copper atom. Each ring has a definite limit to the number of electrons that it can hold. For all elements, the first ring (closest to the nucleus) can hold a maximum of 2 electrons; the second ring can hold a maximum of 8 electrons; the third ring,

18 electrons; the fourth ring, 32 electrons; the fifth ring, 50 electrons; and the sixth ring, 72 electrons.

As a rule, the rings closest to the nucleus are completely filled before additional rings are started. Thus, four rings are required to accommodate the 29 electrons found in the copper atom $(2 + 8 + 18 + 1 = 29)$. Notice that the valence ring is only partially full since it contains only one electron. No known element has more than eight electrons in its valence ring. The number of electrons in the valence ring has a key role in determining the electrical characteristics of the element.

# CONDUCTORS, INSULATORS, AND SEMICONDUCTORS

Conductors, insulators, and semiconductors are important in electricity and electronics. For this reason, it is important to develop a basic understanding of these materials.

## CONDUCTORS

Some materials allow electricity to flow through them easily. These materials are called **conductors**. Copper, aluminum, silver, and gold are all conductors. All of these materials are metals. Almost all metals are good electrical conductors. Any element or material having atoms with three or fewer electrons in its valence ring will be a conductor.

Conductors (usually copper or aluminum wire) in electrical circuits may be thought of as the "highways" over which electrical current flows.

## INSULATORS

An **insulator** is a material that does not allow electricity to flow through it under normal conditions. Rubber, porcelain, and glass are all good electrical insulators. Any element or material composed of atoms having five or more electrons in the valence ring will be an insulator. Insulators are used in electrical circuits to direct the flow of electrical current.

## SEMICONDUCTORS

A *semiconductor* is a material that is neither a good conductor nor a good insulator. Semiconductors are manufactured from elements having atoms with four electrons in their valence rings. The elements **silicon** and **germanium** are widely used in making semiconducting materials. Semiconductors will be described in greater detail in the study of electronics in Chapter 7.

# ELECTRICAL CURRENT FLOW: CONVENTIONAL AND ELECTRON THEORIES

*Electricity* is the flow of electrons from atom to atom in a conductor. Two different theories have been developed to describe electricity. These theories are called the conventional theory and the electron theory.

## CONVENTIONAL THEORY

The conventional theory is the older of the two theories of electricity. It was developed before scientists discovered the existence of electrons.

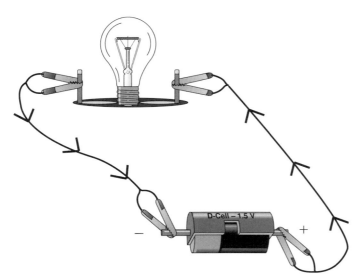

**2-4. The direction of current flow according to the conventional theory.**

According to the ***conventional theory***, electricity is the flow of positively charged particles through a conductor.

Like electrical charges repel each other while unlike electrical charges attract each other. Since the conventional theory assumed that electricity was the flow of positively charged particles through a conductor, current flow in an electrical circuit was assumed to be from positive to negative.

## ELECTRON THEORY

Electricity is actually the flow of negatively charged particles (electrons) through a conductor. Since like charges repel each other and unlike charges attract each other, the flow of electrons (and thus the flow of electricity) in a circuit is from negative to positive.

The ***electron theory*** is the accepted model of electrical current flow. However, because of tradition, the conventional theory of electrical current flow is still widely used. This is especially common in electrical schematics (drawings). Either theory may be used as long as it is used consistently.

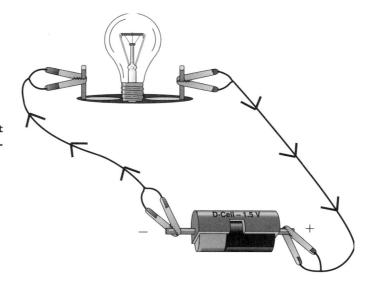

**2-5. The direction of current flow in a simple circuit according to the electron theory.**

## ELECTRON FLOW

Electricity is the flow of electrons through a conductor. While this is a good definition, you may wonder, "Why do the electrons flow through the conductor in the first place?"

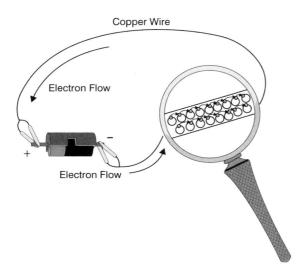

**2-6. A piece of copper wire connected to the negative (–) and positive (+) terminals of a battery. Also shown is a greatly magnified section of the wire showing the wire's individual copper atoms. For clarity, only the atoms' valence electrons are shown.**

A conductor is any material composed of atoms having three or fewer electrons in the valence ring. In such atoms, the valence electrons are not tightly held in their orbit. Thus, these electrons (commonly called *free electrons*) can be dislodged if sufficient external force is applied.

Earlier the element copper was used to explain the composition of atoms. In this section a piece of copper wire will be used to help explain the basis for electron flow.

Chemical reactions within the battery cause the negative terminal to contain more electrons than protons. Similarly, the positive battery terminal contains more protons than electrons. Like electrical charges repel each other while unlike electrical charges attract each other while opposite charges attract.

When the copper wire is attached to the terminals of the battery (Figure 2-6), the loosely held free electrons in the wire are repelled by the negative terminal of the battery and are attracted by the positive terminal. This repulsion and attraction will dislodge free electrons and cause them to flow through the wire to the positive terminal. The flow of electrons will continue until the wire is removed from one or both battery terminals or until the battery discharges (difference in charge between terminals is dissipated).

This explains why free electrons move through a conductor when an external force is applied. Several methods are used in generating the external force.

# METHODS OF GENERATING ELECTRICITY

An external force must be applied to cause free electrons to flow through a conductor. The external force required to cause electrons to flow is the production or generation of electricity. Electricity can be generated by friction, temperature differences, light, pressure, chemical reaction, and magnetism.

## FRICTION

Have you ever walked across a thick carpet on a cold day, touched a metal doorknob, and received an electrical shock? If so, you have used friction to produce static electricity.

*Friction* is caused when two (or more) materials rub against each other. During contact, certain nonmetallic materials either lose or gain electrons. If a glass rod is rubbed with a silk handkerchief, some of the electrons from the rod will be transferred to the handkerchief. Once this happens, the rod will have a positive electrical charge while the handkerchief will have a negative electrical charge. Electrons flow from areas of high electron concentration to areas of low electron concentration. When the negatively charged handkerchief touches a second object having either a neutral or a positive charge the excess electrons in the handkerchief will flow into the second object.

How does this explain why you get shocked when you walk across the carpet and then touch the doorknob? As you walked across the carpet, the soles of your shoes rubbed over the carpet. This transferred electrons from the carpet to your body. When you touched the doorknob, the excess electrons in your body discharged through your hand; thus, producing the familiar static electrical shock.

Electricity produced by friction (static electricity) is an interesting phenomena. But, friction is not a practical method of generating electricity.

## TEMPERATURE DIFFERENCES

Temperature differences can be used to generate electricity using a simple device called a *thermocouple*. A thermocouple consists of two dissimiliar metals (for example, iron and nickel) joined together to form two junctions. See Figure 2-7.

When heat is applied to one of the junctions, the difference in temperature between the two junctions causes free electrons to flow from the iron wire into the nickel wire and away from the hot junction toward the cold junction. A thermocouple generates only a small amount of electricity. To increase output, several thermocouples are often combined to form a device called a *thermopile*. Thermocouples (and thermopiles) are used as

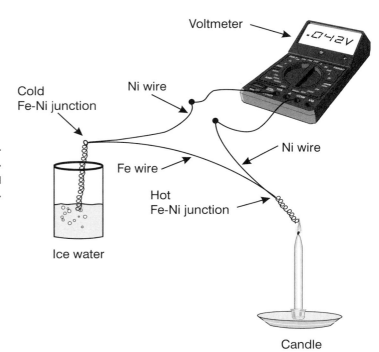

**2-7. A thermocouple consists of two dissimilar metals (for example, iron and nickel) joined in two junctions.**

**2-8. Water for these horses is provided by a 100-watt solar-powered pump. (Courtesy, Agricultural Research Service, USDA)**

flame detectors, furnace safety valves, and in precision heat measurement devices.

## LIGHT

The sun is the major source of natural energy. It has been estimated that the sun produces thermal energy at the continuous rate of 177 trillion kilowatts. (One kilowatt is the amount of electrical energy required to operate ten, 100-watt light bulbs). The sun is a virtually limitless source of energy. Unfortunately, much of this energy is not harnessed for productive use.

A **solar (or photo) cell** is a device for converting light into electricity through a process known as the photovoltaic effect. Certain materials (such as gallium, silicon, and cadmium sulfide) will convert light energy into electrical energy through the **photovoltaic effect**.

The solar cell is made of a thin disk of silicon to which other chemicals have been added. When light strikes the disk, electrons move from one side to the other side. The electrons move through the conductors and provide electrical energy to power the circuit load(s). Solar cells are used to provide electricity for applications ranging from solar calculators to electric fence controllers.

## PRESSURE

When a *quartz crystal* is subjected to pressure, it will produce electricity through a process known as the *piezoelectric effect*. Increasing the pressure on the crystal will increase the amount of electricity produced, while decreasing the pressure will decrease the amount of electricity produced.

The piezoelectric effect is the basis for the operation of the crystal microphone. As you speak into a crystal microphone, sound waves exert varying pressures on the microphone's crystal element. The crystal element reacts to these varying pressures by producing variable electrical outputs. These variable electrical outputs are then transmitted, amplified, and converted back into sound waves by other parts of the sound system. Phonograph needles and some pressure sensors also function due to the piezoelectric effect.

## CHEMICAL REACTIONS

The reactions between certain chemicals can be used to produce electricity. Batteries and fuel cells are two devices that produce electricity in this manner.

### Batteries

A *battery* is made of two or more chemical cells connected together. Each cell is composed of two dissimilar metal plates (called *electrodes*). They are separated from each other and immersed in an electrolyte. An *electrolyte* is a chemical solution (mixture) that contains positively and negatively charged atoms (called *ions*). A chemical cell for producing electricity is shown in Figure 2-9. The cell is composed of a zinc plate, a copper plate, and an electrolyte solution of sulfuric acid and water.

The acid/water solution (electrolyte) reacts with the zinc plate causing it to lose positively charged ions. Each positive ion lost leaves behind two

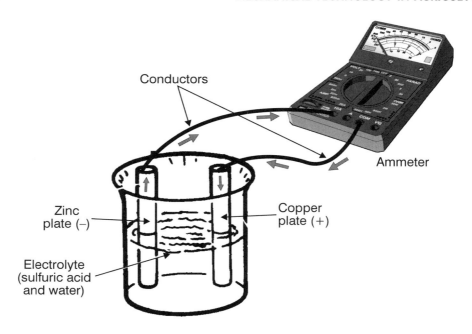

Conductors

Ammeter

Zinc plate (–)

Copper plate (+)

Electrolyte (sulfuric acid and water)

**2-9. A chemical cell for producing electricity.**

electrons. Thus, the zinc plate soon takes on a negative charge. It then becomes the negative terminal of the cell.

As the positive ions move through the electrolyte, they collide with the copper plate. The positive ions attract free electrons from the copper plate. Thus, the copper plate soon takes on a positive charge due to this loss of electrons and becomes the positive terminal of the cell.

If a conductor (a piece of aluminum wire, for example) is connected to the terminals, electrons will flow through the conductor from the zinc plate (negative terminal) to the copper plate (positive terminal). This flow of electrons will continue until the difference in charge between the two plates has dissipated. Once this happens, the cell will be discharged.

All batteries work on the basis of the chemical principles just described. Different combinations of chemicals (metals and electrolyte solution) can be used in a battery. You will often hear people talk about alkaline batteries, mercury batteries, magnesium batteries, lead-acid batteries, and nickel-cadmium batteries. All of these types of batteries are different ways of using chemicals to produce electricity.

A battery may be classified as either a primary or a secondary battery depending on whether the battery can be recharged. ***Primary batteries*** (carbon-zinc; alkaline; and mercury batteries) cannot be recharged. ***Secondary batteries*** (lead-acid and nickel-cadmium batteries) can be recharged.

## FUEL CELLS

A ***fuel cell*** is similar to a battery. It uses chemical reactions to produce electricity. The difference between a fuel cell and a battery lies in the manner in which the chemicals are supplied. In a battery, the chemicals necessary for the reactions are built in. In a fuel cell, the chemicals required for the reactions are pumped into the cell from an external source.

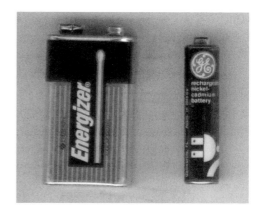

**2-10. A primary battery (left) and a secondary battery (right).**

Currently, the use of fuel cells is limited to military and space applications. However, fuel cells show promise as a power source for electrical automobiles and similar equipment.

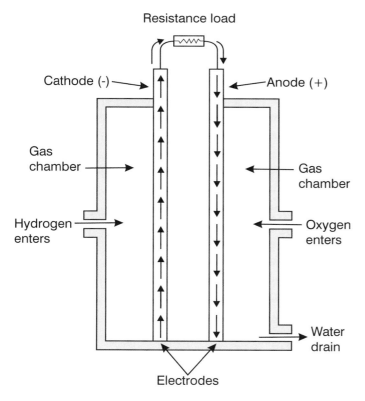

**2-11. The components of a hydrogen-oxygen (Hydrox) fuel cell.**

## MAGNETISM

Have you ever coiled a wire around a nail and connected the ends of the wire to the terminals of a battery? What happened when you touched the nail to a small metal object, such as a paperclip? The nail picked up the paper clip. This happened because you used electricity to make a special type of magnet called an ***electromagnet***. What does all of this have to do with generating electricity? If electricity can be used to produce magnetism, doesn't it seem logical that magnetism can be used to produce electricity? Using magnetism to produce electricity is the most common method of accomplishing this task. In this section, we will review the basic principles involved in using magnetism to produce electricity.

### Basic Principles

If a bar magnet is suspended freely from a string, the magnet will turn until one end points north and the other end points south. If this process is repeated a number of times, the same results will occur. Thus, a magnet is said to have a north-seeking end and a south-seeking end. These two ends are called the north pole and the south pole.

Although you cannot see it, a magnetic field exists between the north and south poles of a magnet. A simple experiment will show the effects of this unseen magnetic field. Place a bar magnet under a pane of glass and sprinkle iron filings on the glass. Gently tap the glass several times. The iron filings align in a distinctive pattern similar to the one shown in Figure 2-12. The alignment of the iron filings is due to the effects of the magnetic field.

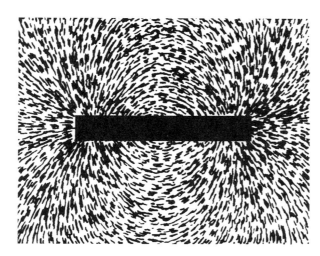

2-12. The effects of a magnetic field.

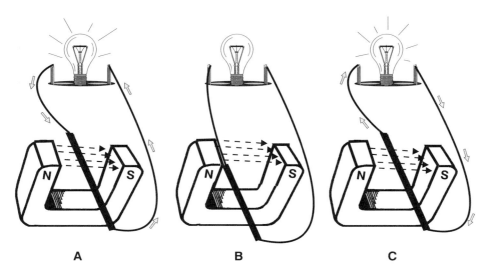

**2-13. A horseshoe magnet, conductor, and light bulb used to illustrate the process of magnetic induction.**

The process of generating electricity using magnetism can be summed up in one sentence. **Any time a conductor cuts across a magnetic field (or a magnetic field cuts across a conductor), electricity will flow in the conductor.** Electricity generated in this manner is produced through the process of *magnetic induction*.

Figure 2-13 A shows the conductor moving downward through the magnetic field. This movement relative to the magnetic field, causes electricity to flow in the direction indicated by the arrows. The electricity flows through the light bulb causing it to glow.

In Figure 2-13 B, the conductor has reached the bottom of its downward movement prior to beginning its upward movement. Since the conductor is not cutting through the magnetic field, no electricity is produced and the bulb does not glow.

The conductor is moving up through the magnetic field in Figure 2-13 C. Since it is again cutting through the magnetic field, electricity is produced and the bulb glows. The arrow shows the electricity flowing in the opposite direction from what it was before (Figure 2-13 A). This is because the conductor is also moving in the opposite direction.

Electricity will be generated as long as the process illustrated in Figure 2-13 is continued. However, this is a very impractical method of generating large amounts of electricity.

## Commercial Electrical Production

This section builds on the basic principles of magnetic induction. First, how electricity can be generated using a rotating motion of the conductor rather than an up and down motion is presented. Next, how generating plants produce electricity is covered. Finally, different sources of energy used in commercial production of electricity are presented

**Generating Electricity with a Rotating Conductor.** In the previous example, a conductor was moved up and down through a magnetic field to produce electricity by magnetic induction. The same can be done by either rotating a magnetic field around a stationary conductor or by rotating a conductor inside a stationary magnetic field.

In Figure 2-14, a looped conductor turns clockwise within a magnetic field. The ends of the conductor are attached to slip rings and brushes that slide over the looped conductor as it rotates. Wires connect the slip rings to a light bulb. The electricity produced as the conductor rotates can be used to operate the light bulb.

In Figure 2-14 A, the looped conductor is moving parallel to the magnetic field. Since the conductor is not cutting across the magnetic field, no electricity is produced and the light bulb does not glow.

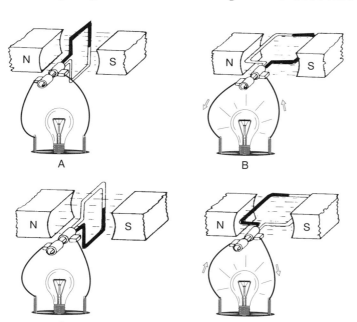

A

B

C

D

2-14. Electricity is generated by rotating a conductor within a stationary magnetic field.

As the looped conductor turns clockwise, it cuts across the magnetic field at a maximum rate when it reaches the position shown in Figure 2-14 B. At this point, the maximum rate of electrical generation has been achieved. Electricity is being produced and the light bulb glows. Notice the direction of electrical flow (indicated by the arrows) during this half of the conductor's rotation.

Electrical generation will continue at a decreasing output (and in the same direction of flow) as the looped conductor moves from position 2-14 B to 2-14 C. Once the looped conductor reaches the position shown in Figure 2-14 C, it is again parallel to the magnetic field. Since the looped conductor is no longer cutting across the magnetic field, no electricity is generated and the light bulb does not glow.

As the looped conductor continues to turn clockwise, it will again cut across the magnetic field and electricity will be generated. However, because the looped conductor's orientation with respect to the poles of the magnet has changed, electricity will flow in the opposite direction.

When the looped conductor reaches the position shown in Figure 2-14 D, it will be cutting across the magnetic field at the maximum rate. Thus, maximum electrical output will be achieved once again.

Electrical generation will continue at a decreasing rate until the looped conductor reaches its original position. At this point, the looped conductor is again parallel to the magnetic field. No electricity is generated and the light bulb does not glow. This process will repeat itself as long as the conductor continues to rotate.

**Commercial Generation of Electricity.** In an electrical power plant, a *synchronous alternator* is used to produce electricity. This device gen-

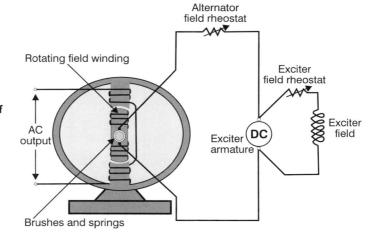

**2-15. A simplified drawing of a synchronous alternator.**

erates electricity using the same principles illustrated using the looped conductor. The primary parts of the alternator are the rotating field windings and the stationary windings.

In operation, a relatively small amount of electricity is supplied to the alternator's field windings. As electricity flows through the field windings, a magnetic field builds around the windings (the field windings become an electromagnet). As the field windings are turned (by a turbine driven by an external power source), the magnetic field also turns, cutting across the alternator's stationary windings. Since the conductors are cutting across a magnetic field, electricity is induced into the stationary conductors.

**Energy Sources Used in Generating Electricity.** An external power source is required to drive the turbine that turns the alternator's field windings. Electrical power plants are often classified based on the source power that drive the turbines. In a **hydroelectric** power plant, the kinetic energy of falling water turns the turbine.

In other electric power plants, water is heated to produce steam that is used to turn the turbines. Nuclear power plants use nuclear reactions to produce steam. As might be expected, coal-fired power plants burn coal to produce steam.

# DIRECT AND ALTERNATING CURRENT ELECTRICITY

There are two types of electricity. Each is based on the pattern of flow of the electrons in the circuit. These types of electricity are called direct current and alternating current.

## DIRECT CURRENT

In **direct current** or DC electricity, the electrons flow in only one direction. Since electrons always flow from the negative terminal to the positive terminal in an electrical circuit, sources of DC electricity must have a fixed **polarity**. This means one specific terminal is always negative while the other is always positive.

Thermocouples and thermopiles, solar cells, piezoelectric crystals, batteries and fuel cells all produce direct current electricity. In addition, magnetism can be used to produce DC electricity using a machine called a DC generator.

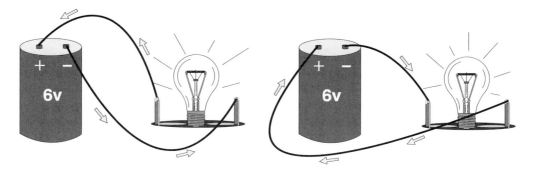

**2-16. A typical DC electrical circuit and the direction of electron flow using electron theory. Notice the direction of current flow can be changed by reversing the two conductors.**

## ALTERNATING CURRENT

With ***alternating current*** or AC, electricity flows first in one direction, stops, reverses and flows in the opposite direction. Once this occurs, the electricity is said to have completed one ***cycle***.

AC electricity is the type generated by electric power plants. One cycle of electrical flow is produced with each revolution of the plant's synchronous alternator. Synchronous alternators used in the United States turn at a speed of 60 revolutions per second (rps). For this reason, AC electricity

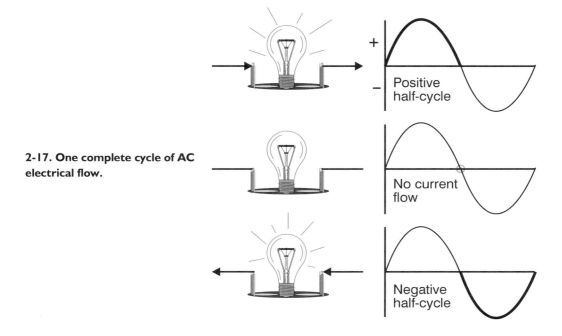

**2-17. One complete cycle of AC electrical flow.**

+
−
Positive
half-cycle

No current
flow

Negative
half-cycle

generated in the United States completes 60 cycles per second. The term *hertz* (Hz) represents one cycle per second. So, in the United States, our AC electricity is generated and delivered at 60 Hz. In many other countries, 50 Hz AC electricity is the standard.

# SINGLE-PHASE AND THREE-PHASE AC ELECTRICITY

Two types of AC electrical service may be available: single-phase or three-phase.

Single-phase service is most commonly available and is widely used in homes, farms, and businesses. With **single-phase electricity,** one complete electrical cycle occurs every 1/60th of a second.

When available, three-phase service is used for large electrical loads, such as on large farms and in factories. **Three-phase electricity** is a combination of three single-phase currents combined so that peak voltages are equally spaced.

The remainder of the discussion of AC electricity deals only with single-phase service.

# VOLTAGE, AMPERAGE, AND RESISTANCE: DEFINITIONS AND MEASUREMENT

## *VOLTAGE*

Voltage is the **electromotive force** (emf) that causes electrons to flow through a conductor. Put differently, voltage is the electrical pressure that causes electron flow.

A DC electrical source produces a constant voltage with respect to time.

By virtue of the way AC electricity is generated, AC voltage varies during each cycle. Voltage is zero at the beginning of the cycle, builds to a maximum positive value, decreases to zero, then builds to a maximum negative value before again returning to zero. Figure 2-19 presents a graphic representation of AC voltage during one cycle of electrical power generation.

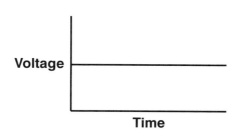

**2-18. Direct current voltage–time relationship.**

The unit of measurement for voltage is the **volt**. One volt is defined as the amount of electrical pressure required to cause one ampere of current to flow in a circuit having one ohm of total resistance.

## MEASURING VOLTAGE

A **voltmeter** is used to measure voltage in an electrical circuit. Most voltmeters have different settings that allow the meter to be used in measuring either AC or DC

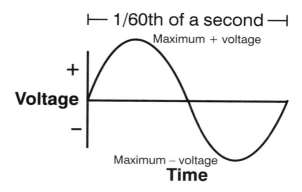

**2-19. AC voltage during one cycle of electrical power generation (60 Hz).**

voltage. Set the meter for the correct type of electrical voltage before connecting the voltmeter to the circuit. Figure 2-20 shows analog and digital AC-DC multimeters used to measure voltage and other electrical characteristics.

Voltmeters are always connected to a circuit between two different conductors or across the terminals of a device that uses electricity (any device that uses electricity is called a **load**).

### Measuring DC Voltage

When measuring DC voltage, the probes of the voltmeter must be connected to the circuit to maintain the correct polarity. The voltmeter's

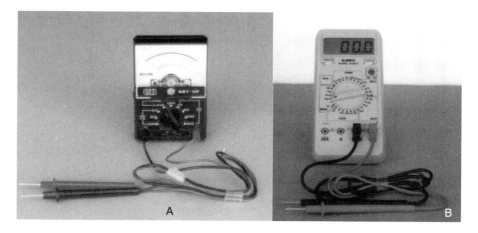

**2-20. An analog AC-DC multimeter (A) and a digital AC-DC multimeter (B).**

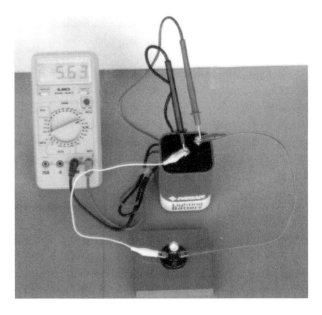

**2-21. Correct polarity connections.**

positive (+) probe, usually red, must be connected to the positive side of the circuit. The negative (−) probe, usually black, must be connected to the negative side of the circuit. See Figure 2-21.

Warning: Failure to observe correct polarity may damage or destroy an analog meter. Usually, when a digital meter is connected with the wrong polarity, the meter will display a negative voltage and no damage will be done to the meter. However, good work practices dictate that DC meters be connected following correct polarity.

## Measuring AC Voltage

An AC voltmeter measures and displays what is known as the *root mean square (rms)* voltage of an AC circuit. The rms voltage in an AC circuit is .707 times the peak voltage. When you hear people speak about 120 volt or 240 volt AC electricity, they are referring to the rms voltage.

Since AC electricity does not have a constant polarity, this factor is not considered in connecting a voltmeter to an AC circuit. Thus, the

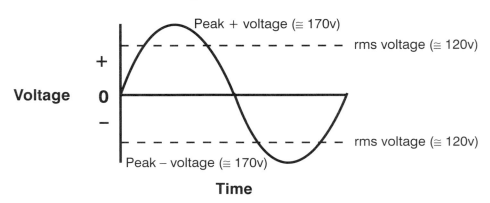

**2-22. The relationship between peak voltage and rms voltage during one cycle of 120 volt alternating current.**

positive and negative meter probes can be connected interchangeably and the same reading will be obtained.

## AMPERAGE

Electrical current is the flow of electrons through a circuit. The rate of electrical current flow is measured in *amperes (A)*. One ampere of electrical current flows in a circuit when $6.25 \times 10^{18}$ (6,250,000,000,000,000,000) electrons flow past a certain point each second.

One ampere can also be defined as the amount of current that will flow in a circuit having one volt of electrical pressure and one ohm of total resistance.

The *milliampere (mA)* is also a commonly used measure of current flow. The metric prefix milli means one-thousandth (1/1000), so one milliampere is equal to one one-thousandths (.001) of an ampere. Stated differently, 1000 mA is equal to one ampere.

## MEASURING AMPERAGE

An *ammeter* is used to measure amperage in a circuit. Amperage in a DC circuit is measured with a DC ammeter, while amperage in an AC circuit is measured using an AC ammeter. As with voltmeters, single ammeters are available that will measure both DC and AC amperages.

### Measuring DC Amperage

For a DC ammeter to measure the rate of current flow in a circuit, the current must flow through the meter (Figure 2-23). This is accomplished by de-energizing the circuit (turning the power "off"), opening the circuit, and connecting the meter probes so the ammeter completes the circuit (meter in series with the load). Once the meter is connected, the circuit is energized (power is turned "on") and the meter reading is obtained. After the reading is made, the circuit is again de-energized, the ammeter is removed, the original circuit is reconnected and the circuit is re-energized.

Proper polarity must be observed when making DC amperage readings. The positive ammeter probe (usually red) must be placed toward the circuit's positive terminal. The negative ammeter probe (usually black) must be placed toward the circuit's negative terminal. Warning: Failure to observe proper polarity may damage or ruin an ammeter.

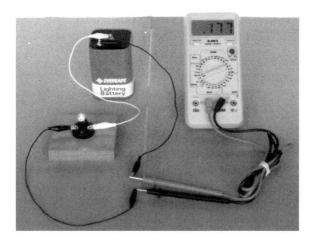

2-23. Proper placement of meter for making amperage reading in a DC circuit.

## Measuring AC Amperage

Current flow in an AC circuit is usually measured with a ***clamp-on ammeter***. This type of ammeter is clamped around one of the circuit's conductors and an amperage reading is obtained. With a clamp-on ammeter, it is not necessary to connect the meter directly into the circuit.

In Figure 2-24, one circuit conductor passes through the jaws of the clamp-on ammeter. Since no current actually flows through the meter, how is an amperage reading obtained? Whenever current flows through a conductor, a magnetic field is produced around the conductor. The more current that flows through the conductor, the stronger the magnetic field. The clamp-on ammeter is calibrated to sense the strength of this magnetic field and convert it to an amperage reading.

2-24. Proper placement of a clamp-on ammeter in an AC circuit.

Analog meters produce the most accurate readings when the values being measured fall near the center of the scale. Readings near zero are difficult to make and are sometimes inaccurate. Generally, this problem can be avoided by selecting the appropriate meter scale. An example of proper scale selection would be using an ammeter's 0–5 A setting to measure a 3 A value rather than using the meter's 0–30 A setting.

You may work with a circuit where even your ammeter's smallest setting fails to produce a reading near the center of the scale. In such cases, you can obtain an accurate reading by coiling the conductor around the ammeter several times and then reading the scale. To determine amperage, divide the reading obtained by the number of times the conductor was coiled around the ammeter.

This procedure works because the strength of the magnetic field around a coiled conductor varies in direct proportion to the number of turns in the coil. See Figure 2-25.

**2-25. Determining amperage by coiling the conductor around the ammeter.**

## RESISTANCE

*Resistance* is that characteristic of any material that opposes the flow of electricity. All materials, even the best conductors, have some resistance to the flow of electrons. The difference between conductors and insulators is the magnitude or degree of resistance. Conductors, like copper and aluminum, have very low resistances while insulators, like rubber and porcelain, have very high resistances.

The unit of measurement for resistance is the **ohm**. The Greek letter omega ($\Omega$) is the symbol for ohm. One ohm is the amount of total resistance that will limit current flow to one ampere in a circuit having one volt of electrical pressure. The resistance of a specific conductor will vary based on its length, cross-sectional area and temperature.

## Length

If all other factors are held constant, the resistance of a specific conductor is directly proportional to the conductor's length. As the length of a conductor doubles, the conductor's resistance will also double. This is why electrical circuits are generally kept as short as possible.

## Cross-Sectional Area

If all other factors are kept constant, the resistance of a specific conductor will be inversely proportional to the conductor's cross-sectional area. Put differently, as the area of a conductor doubles, resistance decreases by 50 percent. A conductor having a cross-sectional area of 1 in$^2$ will have half the resistance of a conductor having a cross-sectional area of ½ in$^2$.

## Temperature

The resistance of a specific conductor increases as the temperature of the conductor increases. The effect of temperature on resistance is not as pronounced as the effects of conductor length and size. For instance, doubling the temperature of a piece of aluminum wire will only increase the wire's resistance by about 32 percent.

# MEASURING RESISTANCE

Resistance is measured using an **ohmmeter**. Resistance measurements are always made with the circuit (or electrical component) disconnected from the voltage source (circuit de-energized). Once the circuit or component has been de-energized, the ohmmeter can be connected and the resistance reading can be made. Warning: Resistance measurements cannot be made on a "live" circuit. Attempts to do so will likely result in equipment damage and/or personal injury.

An ohmmeter contains a battery that sends a small amount of current through the circuit or component being measured. Most ohmmeters actually measure the current flow that occurs in the circuit or component under

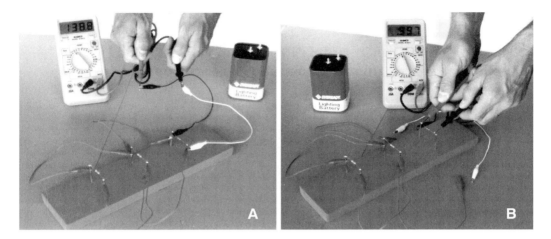

**2-26. The correct ohmmeter connections for measuring resistance in a circuit (A) and in a circuit component (B).**

test and transform this amperage measurement into the corresponding resistance value expressed in ohms.

## MULTIMETERS

Meters that measure two or more electrical characteristics are commonly available. Such devices are called **multimeters**. A multimeter capable of measuring voltage, resistance, and current flow in milliamperes is commonly called a VOM (volt-ohm-milliammeter).

**2-27. This VOM can be pur-chased for less than 20 dollars.**

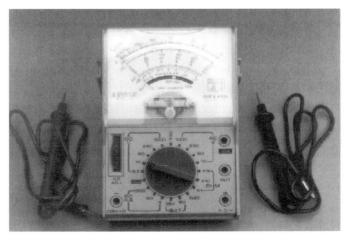

## *SAFETY*

Safety should be a major consideration when working with electricity. Failure to observe safe working practices can be fatal! Warning: If you are unsure of how to perform a job safely, do not attempt the job. Trial-and-error learning has no place in dealing with electricity.

This section has described general procedures for measuring voltage, amperage and resistance. When measuring voltage, amperage or resistance, always read and follow the specific safety and procedural instructions provided by the meter manufacturer.

# OHM'S LAW

In the previous section, voltage, amperage, and resistance were defined in terms of their relationship to each other. For example, one volt was defined as the amount of electrical pressure required to cause one ampere of current to flow in a circuit having one ohm of resistance. This relationship between voltage, current, and resistance serves as the basis for *Ohm's Law*.

Ohm's Law allows you to determine an unknown third value if the remaining two values are known (or can be measured). The Ohm's Law equation is presented below as Formula 2-1.

$E = I \times R$ | Formula 2-1. |

where,

    E = Voltage
    I = Current (measured in amperes)
    R = Resistance (measured in ohms)

Assume that 6 A of current flows in a circuit having a total resistance of 20 ohms. What is the circuit's source voltage?

By inserting the known values for current and resistance into the formula, it is determined that the circuit has a 120 volt source. This completed formula is shown below.

$E = I \times R$
$E = 6 \text{ A} \times 20 \text{ ohms}$
$E = 120 \text{ volts}$

The Ohm's Law equation can be rearranged to solve for any of the three values as long as the other two values are known. For example, assume that you want to know how much current will flow in a 240 V circuit containing a total resistance of 45 ohms. Formula 2-1 can be rearranged as shown below to provide the answer.

$$I = \frac{E}{R}$$

$$I = \frac{240 \text{ V}}{45 \text{ ohms}}$$

$$I = 5.3 \text{ A}$$

If voltage and current are known, the Ohm's Law equation can also be rearranged to solve for resistance. For example, what is the resistance in a 12 V circuit, if 1.2 A of current is flowing in the circuit? The rearranged formula and solution are shown below.

$$R = \frac{E}{I}$$

$$R = \frac{12 \text{ V}}{1.2 \text{ A}}$$

$$R = 10 \text{ ohms}$$

Ohm's Law is based on and describes the relationship between voltage, current and resistance in an electrical circuit. The Ohm's Law formula has many practical uses in working with electricity. Because you will use Ohm's Law so often, you should soon memorize the formula.

# ELECTRICAL POWER: TERMS, MEASUREMENTS AND RELATIONSHIPS

Electricity is important in agriculture because of the power it provides. In this section, you will learn about the terms, measurements and relationships that describe electrical power.

## WORK

Electricity is used to do work. **Work** is defined as the movement of a force through a distance. When electrons move through a circuit, work is accomplished. If, the electrons cause a light bulb, heater, motor or other device to operate, useful work has been done.

## POWER

**Power** is the rate at which work is done. As the time required for doing a certain amount of work decreases, the power required will increase. For example, twice as much power is required to do a certain amount of work in 10 minutes as would be required to do the same amount of work in 20 minutes.

## WATT

Electrical power is measured in **watts (W)**. The number of watts of electrical power in DC and single-phase AC electrical circuits can be calculated using Formula 2-2.

$$W = E \times I \times pf$$ | **Formula 2-2.** |

where,

$W$ = power, in watts
$E$ = voltage
$I$ = current, in amperes
$pf$ = power factor

In all DC circuits, power factor is equal to one (1). Also, in AC circuits containing loads having resistance only (e.g. incandescent lights and heaters) power factor is equal to one (1).

Since multiplying any number by one (1) does not change the value of the original number, the power factor term may be deleted from Formula 2-2 when calculating the wattage for DC circuits and for AC circuits containing only resistance. Deleting the power factor term produces the simplified power equation given as Formula 2-3.

$$W = E \times I$$ | **Formula 2-3.** |

where,

  W = power, in watts
  E = voltage
  I = current, in amperes

Assume that a 12 V DC electrical circuit has a current flow of 2 A. How many watts of electrical power are being used? Inserting the values from the problem into Formula 2-3 as shown below, we find that 24 W are being used by the circuit.

W = E × I
W = 12 V × 2 A
W = 24 W

The power used by an electrical load can be measured directly using a *wattmeter*. A wattmeter measures both circuit voltage and current, and displays the wattage of the circuit on a specially calibrated meter dial or digital readout.

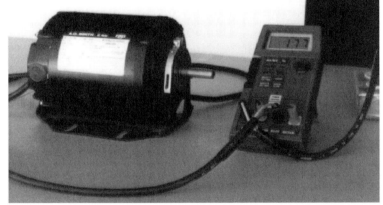

**2-28. A wattmeter correctly connected for measuring the power used by an electric motor.**

## KILOWATT

One watt is a very small amount of electrical power. In fact, 746 watts of electrical power are required to equal one horsepower (hp) of mechanical power. Stated differently, one watt is equal to 1/746 hp.

Since the watt is such a small unit of power, the kilowatt (kW) is often used instead. The metric prefix kilo means 1000, so one *kilowatt* is equal to 1000 watts. If the number of watts being used in a circuit is known, the number of kilowatts can be determined by dividing the watts by 1000.

Assume that an electric space heater draws 15 A when connected to a 120 V AC circuit. How many kilowatts of electricity is the heater using? As shown below, 1.8 kW are being used.

kW = W / 1000 or (E × I) / 1000
kW = (120 V × 15 A) / 1000
kW = 1800 / 1000
kW = 1.8

## *KILOWATT-HOUR*

Electrical power, given either as watts or kilowatts, does not include the element of time. In the previous example, we determined that the heater was using 1.8 kW of electrical power. However, because no time element was involved, we do not know if this power was used for one minute or for one year!

*Energy* is different from power in that energy includes the element of time. Electrical energy use is measured by the *kilowatt-hour (kW-hr)*. One kW-hr is the equivalent of using 1 kW of electrical power for a one hour period of time. The amount of electrical energy being consumed in an electrical circuit can be calculated using Formula 2-4.

kW-hr = kilowatts × hours of use      | **Formula 2-4.** |

Assume the 1.8 kW electric heater from the previous example is used for 40 hours. How many kW-hrs of electrical energy will be consumed? By inserting the known values into Formula 2-4 as shown below, we can determine that 72 kW-hrs of electrical energy will be used.

kW-hrs = kilowatts × hours of use
kW-hrs = 1.8 kW × 40 hrs
kW-hrs = 72

Electricity is sold by the kilowatt-hour. Utility companies install a kilowatt-hour meter (Figure 2-29) at each billing site to measure the amount of electrical energy used at that location during the billing period. Most utility companies bill customers each month.

**2-29. A kilowatt-hour meter.**

Kilowatt-hour meters display cumulative readings (like the odometer of an automobile). To determine the number of kW-hrs of electricity used during a month, the previous month's reading must be subtracted from the current reading.

In Figure 2-30, notice that the current (July 31) meter reading is 51,329 kW-hrs, while the previous (June 30) meter reading was 46,958 kW-hrs.

**2-30. Sample meter readings.**

By subtracting the previous reading from the current reading, we find that 4371 kW-hrs of electrical energy were used during July. Once you know how many kW-hrs of electrical energy have been used, you can determine the cost by multiplying the number of kW-hrs times the charge per kW-hr. For example, if the utility company charges 6.75 cents ($.0675) per kW-hr, the 4371 kW-hrs from the example above will cost $295.04 (4371 kW-hrs × $.0675 per kW-hr = $295.04).

## POWER IN AC CIRCUITS

### Power in AC Circuits
### Containing Resistance Only

When an AC circuit contains loads having only resistance (e.g., incandescent lights and heaters), the voltage and amperage are *in-phase*. This means that circuit voltage and amperage are together during each electrical cycle as they pass from zero to maximum positive value, back to zero, then to maximum negative value and, finally, back to zero.

*Phase angle* is the term used to describe the degree of shift between voltage and amperage during one electrical cycle. Since the voltage and amperage are in-phase in AC circuits having resistance only (as shown in Figure 2-31), there is no shift and the phase angle is zero (0).

*Power factor* is defined as the *cosine* of the phase angle. As shown in Table 2-1, the cosine of zero (0) is one (1). Therefore, when voltage and

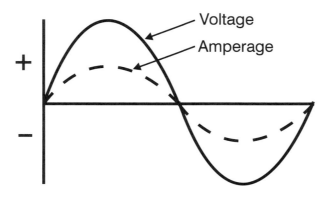

2-31. The relationship between voltage and amperage for an AC circuit containing only resistance.

## Table 2-1
## Relationship Between Phase Angle and Power Factor

| Phase Angle (degrees) | Power Factor (Cosine of the Phase Angle) | Phase Angle (degrees) | Power Factor (Cosine of the Phase Angle) |
|---|---|---|---|
| 0 | 1.000 | 32 | 0.848 |
| 2 | 0.999 | 34 | 0.829 |
| 4 | 0.997 | 36 | 0.809 |
| 6 | 0.995 | 38 | 0.788 |
| 8 | 0.990 | 40 | 0.766 |
| 10 | 0.985 | 42 | 0.743 |
| 12 | 0.978 | 44 | 0.719 |
| 14 | 0.970 | 46 | 0.695 |
| 16 | 0.961 | 48 | 0.669 |
| 18 | 0.951 | 50 | 0.643 |
| 20 | 0.940 | 52 | 0.616 |
| 22 | 0.927 | 54 | 0.588 |
| 24 | 0.914 | 56 | 0.559 |
| 26 | 0.899 | 58 | 0.530 |
| 28 | 0.883 | 60 | 0.500 |
| 30 | 0.866 | | |

amperage are in-phase, power factor is equal to one and may be disregarded when calculating wattage.

Figure 2-31 shows that the voltage and amperage at any point during the cycle always have the same mathematical sign. Whenever numbers having the same sign are multiplied, the product is always positive. Thus, only "positive" (or productive) power is produced in resistive AC circuits.

## Power in AC Circuits
## Containing Inductive Reactance

Whenever current flows through a wire, a magnetic field builds up around the wire. Coiling the wire increases the strength of the magnetic field. In AC electrical loads containing coils of wire (e.g. motors, transformers, fluorescent lights) this magnetic field induces current flow into the conductors. The induced current opposes the normal change in direction of current flow in an AC circuit. This opposition is known as *inductive reactance*. The flow of current in an AC circuit having coils of wire is opposed both by normal resistance and by inductive reactance. When combined, these two types of opposition to current flow (plus capacative reactance, to be discussed later) are known as the *impedance* of the circuit.

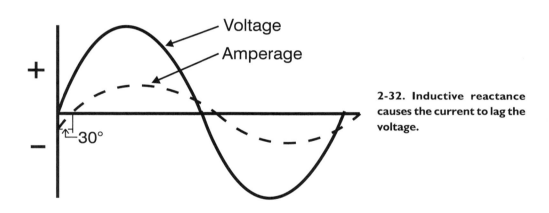

**2-32. Inductive reactance causes the current to lag the voltage.**

The net effect of inductive reactance in a circuit is to cause a phase shift between the voltage and amperage. Because the induced current flow opposes the normal change in direction of current flow, inductive reactance causes the current to lag the voltage. See Figure 2-32.

Notice in Figure 2-32 that, because of the phase shift, the voltage and amperage do not always have the same mathematical sign at any given point. Since multiplying numbers with unlike signs produces a negative product, "negative" (or non-productive) power is produced during part of each electrical cycle. Increasing the phase shift results in a higher percentage of negative power being produced during each cycle.

The phase angle in Figure 2-32 is 30 degrees. As you recall, power factor is the cosine of the phase angle. Thus, examination of Table 2-1 shows power factor to be .866 (or 86.6 percent) for this circuit. This means that positive power is produced during 86.6 percent of each cycle. Negative power is produced during the remaining 13.4 percent of the cycle.

Assume the circuit voltage is 120 V and the current flow is 11 A. By inserting these values as well as the value for power factor into Formula 4-2, we can determine the power in the circuit to be 1143 W. These calculations are shown below.

$$W = V \times A \times pf$$

$$W = 120 \text{ V} \times 11 \text{ A} \times .866$$

$$W = 1143$$

## Improving Power Factor

Electric utility companies prefer to serve customers having electrical systems with high circuit power factors. Here is why:

In the example, 1143 W of electrical power was consumed in the motor circuit. The customer's electric bill would be based on this figure. Yet, because the circuit power factor was .866, the utility company actually had to generate and transmit 1320 W (120 V × 11 A = 1320 W) of power to operate the motor.

Serving customers with low circuit power factors requires utility companies to generate and distribute more electrical power than they are paid for. In addition, serving customers with low power factors may require the installation of larger utility company distribution wires. Because of the additional costs, utility companies may add a penalty charge to the bills of customers with low power factors.

Adding a capacator to an AC circuit causes the current to lead the voltage, a phenomena called ***capacitive reactance.*** Since capacitive reactance is the opposite of inductive reactance, it can be used to cancel out the effects of inductive reactance. Thus, the power factor can be improved by adding carefully sized capacitors to a circuit having a low power factor. Utility company representatives should be contacted for advice and technical assistance in this area.

## Measuring Power Factor

When the phase angle is known, circuit power factor can either be calculated (pf = cosine of the phase angle) or determined from Table 2-1. However, in most cases the phase angle is not known, so power factor must be determined using other methods.

If the voltage, amperage and power (watts) in a circuit can be measured, power factor can be calculated by rearranging Formula 2-2.

$$W = E \times I \times pf$$

or

$$pf = \frac{W}{E \times I}$$

In the rearranged formula, the product of voltage and amperage (E × I) represents ***apparent power***, while the wattage (W) represents ***true power***. Thus, power factor is the ratio of true to apparent power (pf = true power / apparent power).

Assume a voltmeter, an ammeter, and a wattmeter are inserted into the circuit as shown in Figure 2-33. Using the readings indicated, determine the power factor of the circuit.

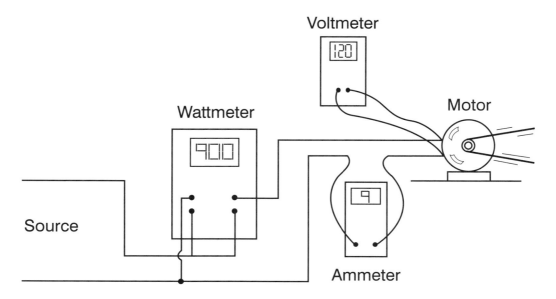

**2-33. Set-up for determining power factor in a motor circuit.**

Inserting the meter readings into the power factor formula reveals that the circuit power factor is .833. The necessary calculations are shown below.

$$pf = \frac{W}{E \times I}$$

$$pf = \frac{900\ W}{120\ V \times 9\ A}$$

$$pf = .833$$

In many cases an electrician will have access to a voltmeter and an ammeter, but not to a wattmeter. In such cases, the wattage (or true power) can be determined using the utility company's kilowatt-hour meter. Once the value for wattage has been obtained in this manner, power factor can be determined using the above procedure.

To measure watts using a kilowatt-hour meter, first determine the meter's $K_h$ factor. This factor will be printed on the face of the meter. Next, shut off all circuits except for the circuit being measured. Operate the circuit load(s) in question and count the number of meter disk revolutions during one minute of operation. Insert the values obtained into Formula 2-5 to determine the watts of power used.

$$W = disk\ rpm \times K_h\ factor \times 60 \qquad \boxed{\textbf{Formula 2-5.}}$$

where,

$$
\begin{aligned}
W &= \text{watts of power used} \\
disk\ rpm &= \text{number of meter disk revolutions per minute} \\
K_h\ factor &= \text{number of watt hours per meter disk revolution} \\
60 &= \text{a constant}
\end{aligned}
$$

Assume that a kilowatt-hour meter with a $K_h$ factor of 7.2 is being used. All loads except for the load in question are disconnected from the voltage source. The meter makes five (5) revolutions in one minute. By inserting these values into Formula 2-5, we find that the load is using 2160 W of electrical power. The necessary calculations are shown below.

$$W = disk\ rpm \times K_h\ factor \times 60$$
$$W = 5\ rpm \times 7.2 \times 60$$
$$W = 2160$$

# SUMMARY

Electricity is widely used in agriculture. Because of this widespread use, agricultural workers need a basic understanding of and appreciation for electricity.

Electricity is the flow of electrons from atom to atom in a conductor. Friction, temperature differences, light, pressure, chemical reactions, and magnetism can all be used to cause electrons to flow.

Direct current (DC) electricity flows in only one direction, and is commercially produced by temperature differences, light, pressure, chemical reactions, and magnetic induction. Alternating current (AC) electricity changes direction of flow 120 times per second, and is produced by magnetic induction.

Voltage is the force that causes electrons to flow. The rate of current flow is measured in amperes. Resistance to the flow of electrons is measured in ohms. Meters for measuring each of these electrical characteristics are available.

Ohm's Law describes the relationship between voltage, amperage, and resistance in an electrical circuit. An understanding of Ohm's Law is extremely valuable in working with electricity.

Electricity is used to do work. Power is the rate at which work is done. Electrical power is measured in watts and kilowatts. Electricity is sold by the kilowatt-hour.

Power in an electrical circuit is the product of voltage, amperage and power factor (watts = voltage × amperage × power factor). In DC circuits and in AC circuits containing resistance only, power factor is equal to one (1). In AC circuits containing inductive reactance power factor will be less than one (<1).

# REVIEW QUESTIONS

1.  How would life in America be different if there was no electricity? For farmers? For off-farm agricultural workers? For consumers?

2.  Sketch an atom. Show the relative location (and electrical charge) of the proton, neutron, and electron.

3.  Explain the conventional and electron theories of current flow.

4. Describe the basic manner in which the atoms of conductors, insulators and semiconductors differ.

5. List the five different methods of generating electricity. For each method, tell if DC or AC electricity (or both) can be generated.

6. Define the following terms: voltage, amperage, resistance, watts, kilowatts, kilowatt-hours, and power factor.

7. What voltage is required to cause 2 amperes of current to flow in a circuit having a total resistance of 60 ohms?

8. How many amperes of current would flow in the circuit described in Question 7, if the circuit voltage is doubled?

9. Assume the following measurements are made in an AC motor circuit: 2.5 amperes; 119 volts; and 250 watts. Determine the power factor of the circuit.

10. Sketch an electrical circuit containing a battery and a lamp fixture and bulb. Draw the proper meter connections to measure (a) circuit voltage and (b) current flow. Also show the proper connections to measure the resistance of the load (lamp fixture and bulb). For each meter connection, write a short explanation of what steps must be completed in connecting the meter.

11. A kilowatt-hour meter had a January 31 reading of 12,005 kW-hrs and a February 28 reading of 13,232 kW-hrs. How many kilowatt-hours of electricity were used during the February billing period? Assuming a rate of 6.5 cents per kilowatt-hour, how much will the electric bill be?

# APPLYING THE CONCEPTS

1. Develop a list of electrical appliances and machines found in your home or school. Describe how your life would be different without these items.

2. Locate the kilowatt-hour meter for your school. Make readings to determine the amount of electricity used in your school each day. Determine local electrical rates and estimate the school's monthly electric bill. If possible, check the accuracy of your estimate by obtaining the actual figure from school officials.

3. Generate electricity using each of the methods described in this chapter. You should be able to obtain all of the required materials in your local community.

4. After you have received proper instruction and have passed required safety tests, demonstrate the proper use of a volt meter, ammeter and ohm meter to your instructor.

5. Determine the resistance of various small loads by inserting them into a 6-volt DC battery circuit, measuring voltage and current, and solving for resistance using Ohm's Law.

6. With your instructor's guidance and permission, set up a test circuit (as in Figure 2-33) and determine the power factor of an electric motor circuit. Note: If you do not have access to a watt meter, use a kilowatt-hour meter to determine true power, following the procedures outlined in this chapter.

7. Use the Internet and World Wide Web to collect information about electricity and electric power. Several web sites with useful information are listed here.

Tennessee Valley Authority — http://www.tva.gov/

Princeton Plasma Physics Laboratory — http://www.pppl.gov/

Energy Information Administration — http://www.eia.doe.gov/

Electric Power Research Institute — http://www.epri.com/

USDA Rural Utilities Service — http://www.rurdev.usda.gov/

Federal Energy Management Program — gopher://tmn.com/11/FEMP

Solar Evaluation — http://www.pathcom.com~sunone/

# 3

# UNDERSTANDING ELECTRICAL CIRCUITS

To use electricity for productive work, a pathway for the flow of electrons must be provided. This pathway is called an electrical circuit. Understanding how electrical circuits function is essential in working with electricity.

A basic electrical circuit has five components necessary for a convenient, safe, and functional circuit. Understanding specific circuit conditions and types of electrical circuits is essential to the use of electricity in agricultural applications. These influence how voltage, amperage, and resistance behave in each type of circuit.

3-1. Electrical circuits light our offices and homes, and supply power for our computers.

# OBJECTIVES

This chapter covers the kinds of electrical circuits. After completing this chapter, you will:

1. Define the term electrical circuit and list the five components of a safe, convenient electrical circuit and explain the function of each circuit component.

2. Describe the two types of overcurrent protection devices used in electrical circuits.

3. Explain the relationship between heat production and overcurrent protection.

4. Identify and describe five different circuit conditions.

5. Identify and describe four different types of electrical circuits.

6. Describe the voltage, amperage, and resistance characteristics of different types of electrical circuits.

7. Analyze different types of electrical circuits to determine voltage, amperage, and resistance.

**TERMS**

ampacity
circuit
circuit breaker
circuit overload
closed circuit
conductor
electrical circuit
equivalent simple circuit
fuse
ground-fault
load
open circuit
overcurrent
parallel circuit
series circuit
series-parallel circuit
simple circuit
switch
voltage source

# THE BASIC ELECTRICAL CIRCUIT

An *electrical circuit* is a pathway for the flow of electrons. At a minimum, a circuit must contain a voltage source, a load, and conductors. For safety and convenience, a circuit should also contain a switch and an overcurrent protection device.

## VOLTAGE SOURCE

An external force is required to cause free electrons to flow. This external force is called voltage. The source of this voltage may be a thermocouple, a solar cell, a piezoelectric crystal, an AC generator, a fuel cell or a battery. The specific type of voltage source selected will depend on the situation. The important thing to remember is a circuit will not function without a *voltage source*.

## LOAD

A *load* is any device that uses electricity during its normal operation. Electric lights, motors, and heaters are all examples of electrical loads.

Loads serve two primary functions in an electrical circuit. First, the load(s) is the reason for the existence of the circuit! The only reason to

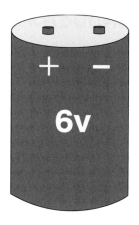

## Source

3-2. A 6 V dry-cell battery is used as the voltage source in this circuit. The batteries supply DC electricity.

## Source

## Load

3-3. A light bulb is one type of electrical load.

install a lighting circuit is to supply electricity to operate lights. It would be foolish to install a lighting circuit and then never connect any lights (bulbs or lamps) to the circuit.

Second, the load(s) supplies resistance to the flow of current. According to Ohm's Law, the amount of current flow (amperage) in a circuit with a fixed voltage is determined by the total resistance of the circuit (I = E/R). Since the circuit conductors and other devices should have little resistance, the primary resistance in a circuit is provided by the load(s). If total circuit resistance is too low, a dangerous level of current will flow in the circuit.

## CONDUCTORS

*Conductors* form the path for the flow of electrons in a circuit. Without a complete electrical pathway, electrons cannot flow from the source to the load and back to the source again. Thus, conductors are an essential element in an electrical circuit.

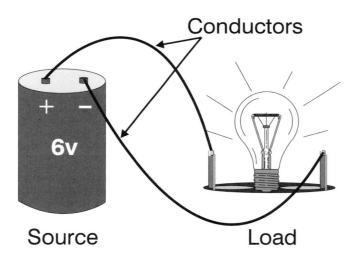

3-4. A circuit with the conductors added between the source and the load. Notice that the light bulb now glows.

## SWITCH

As the circuit is presently constructed (Figure 3-4), the only way to turn the light bulb off is to either unscrew the bulb or to disconnect one of the conductors. Neither of these methods is very convenient.

A *switch* is a device used to control the operation of the load(s) in a circuit. Opening the switch opens the circuit, causing the load to go off. Closing the switch closes the circuit, causing the load to come on.

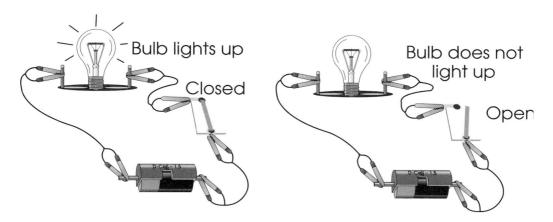

**3-5. A closed circuit (left) and an open circuit (right). Adding a switch to the circuit provides a convenient method of controlling the light.**

## OVERCURRENT PROTECTION DEVICE

An **overcurrent** condition exists when the current flow in a circuit exceeds the amperage rating of the circuit's conductors, load(s) or other device(s). The excessive heat caused by an overcurrent condition may burn or damage a conductor's insulation and cause a fire.

An overcurrent protection device serves as a safety valve by limiting current flow in the circuit to a safe level. **Fuses** and **circuit breakers** are two common types of overcurrent protection devices.

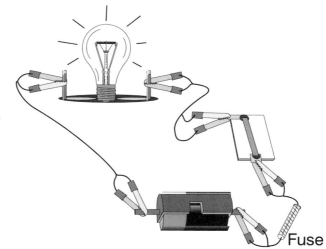

**3-6. A circuit with a fuse added for overcurrent protection.**

**3-7. A 20 A fuse (left) and a 20 A circuit breaker (right).**

If the current flow in a circuit exceeds the overcurrent device's amperage rating, the excess heat produced will cause the protection device to open the circuit, causing current flow to stop. Fuses contain a heat-sensitive link (or element) that melts when current flow exceeds the fuse's amperage rating. Circuit breakers function as heat-sensitive switches that open when current flow exceeds the circuit breaker's amperage rating.

# HEAT PRODUCTION IN AN ELECTRICAL CIRCUIT

Heat is produced any time current flows against the internal resistance of a conductor. The amount of heat produced depends on the amount of current, the resistance of the conductor, and the length of time the current flows. As shown in Formula 3-1, heat production in a conductor increases with increases in any of these three factors.

$$\text{Heat} = I^2 \times R \times t \times 3.413 \qquad \boxed{\text{Formula 3-1.}}$$

where,

Heat = heat, in BTU
  I = current, in amperes
  R = resistance, in ohms
  t = time, in hours

Examination of Formula 3-1 shows that heat production will double if either resistance or time is doubled. But, because heat production is proportional to the square of the current ($I^2$), doubling the current will result in four times more heat being produced. Thus, heat production in a conductor is especially sensitive to the rate of current flow.

Overcurrent protection devices operate based on the heating effect just described. As current flow in a circuit increases past the overcurrent device's amperage rating, the excess heat produced causes the device to operate, disconnecting the circuit from the voltage source.

# CIRCUIT CONDITIONS

## CLOSED CIRCUIT

In a *closed circuit*, a complete electrical pathway exists from the voltage source through the load(s) and back to the voltage source. A closed circuit is necessary for the circuit load(s) to operate. (See Figure 3-5 left.)

## OPEN CIRCUIT

In an *open circuit*, the electrical pathway is not complete from the voltage source through the load(s) and back to the voltage source. The circuit load(s) will not operate when the circuit is open. (See Figure 3-5 right.)

Usually, an open circuit condition is intentionally created to stop a load from operating. An example would be opening a switch to cause a light to go off. At other times, open circuit conditions are unintentional, resulting from conductor or equipment damage. An example of this would be automobile lights that do not work caused by a broken circuit wire.

## CIRCUIT OVERLOAD

A *circuit overload* occurs whenever too much current flows through a circuit. An example would be the use of a 15 A rated extension cord to supply electricity to a 20 A load. If this overload continues for an extended period, the extension cord will get very hot. This may damage the cord's insulation (producing a shock hazard) or cause a fire. Circuit overloads are dangerous and should be avoided.

## *SHORT CIRCUIT*

A short circuit occurs when current flows outside of its intended path, bypassing the normal circuit load(s). Short circuits usually occur due to insulation break-down, or because of faulty or incorrect circuit connections. Short circuits are extremely dangerous.

One of the primary functions of a circuit load is to limit current flow in the circuit. Figure 3-8 shows what can happen to current flow when a short circuit occurs. The bulb does not glow because the short circuit allows current to bypass the load.

According to Ohm's Law, the amount of current that will flow in a circuit having a fixed voltage depends on the total resistance of the circuit.

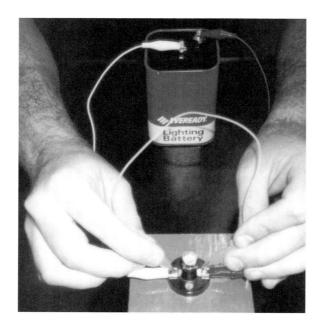

**3-8. A short circuit condition.**

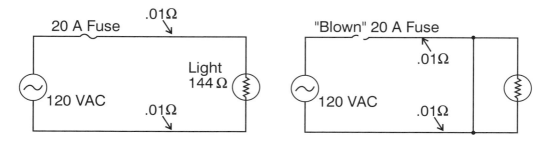

**3-9. A circuit during normal conditions (left) and a circuit during a short circuit condition (right).**

Using the values listed in Figure 3-9 (left), apply Ohm's Law to determine how many amperes of current will flow in the circuit under normal operating conditions.

First, determine the total circuit resistance. In this circuit, the total resistance is composed of the light bulb (144 ohms) and the conductors (.01 ohm + .01 ohm = .02 ohm). Thus, the total circuit resistance is 144.02 ohms (144 ohms + .02 ohm).

By rearranging the Ohm's Law equation and inserting the known voltage and resistance values, we find that .83A of current will flow in the circuit under normal operating conditions. Calculations are shown below.

$$E = I \times R$$

or

$$I = \frac{E}{R}$$

$$I = \frac{120\ V}{144.02\ ohms}$$

$$I = .83\ A$$

Assuming the conductors have a current carrying capacity (*ampacity*) of at least 20 A, it is apparent that a flow of .83A in the circuit does not present an overcurrent hazard. Since the current flow is less than the amperage rating of the overcurrent protection device, the device will remain closed and the circuit will continue to operate.

Figure 3-9 (right) shows a circuit under a short circuit condition. Since the current now bypasses the light bulb, the bulb's resistance is no longer a factor in limiting circuit amperage. Assuming the short circuit itself has no resistance, the total circuit resistance is the .02 ohms provided by the conductors. A quick review of Ohm's Law shows that up to 6000 A of current could flow in the circuit (120 V / .02 ohms = 6000 A).

The 20 A overcurrent protection device would open immediately, disconnecting the circuit from the voltage source. This would stop the flow of current, and prevent a costly and dangerous electrical fire or explosion.

## *GROUND-FAULT*

A *ground-fault* occurs when any current-carrying wire makes electrical contact with a conductive object that is grounded. Current flows outside its intended path during a ground-fault. In Figure 3-10, a current-carrying conductor is in electrical contact with the metal motor casing, producing a ground-fault condition.

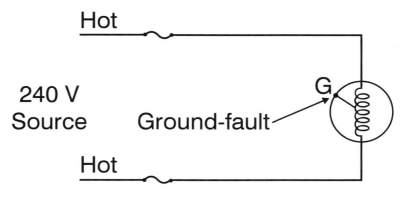

**3-10. A ground-fault condition.**

Ground-faults are especially dangerous because they produce a voltage potential on objects (or parts of objects) that are not normally electrified. Since electricity always seeks a path to ground, a person touching such an object will experience a shock if the body completes the electrical circuit between the energized object and the ground. Grounding wires and ground-fault circuit interrupters are two commonly used methods of protecting people from the hazards of ground-faults.

# FOUR TYPES OF
# ELECTRICAL CIRCUITS

A functional electric circuit must include a voltage source, one or more loads, and properly connected conductors. Depending on how these three components are arranged, four different types of circuits can be constructed. These four types of circuits are the: (a) simple circuit, (b) series circuit, (c) parallel circuit, and (d) series-parallel circuit.

## SIMPLE CIRCUIT

A *simple circuit* contains only one load. Since the circuit has only one load, electrons flow along the same pathway, pass through the load, and return to the voltage source.

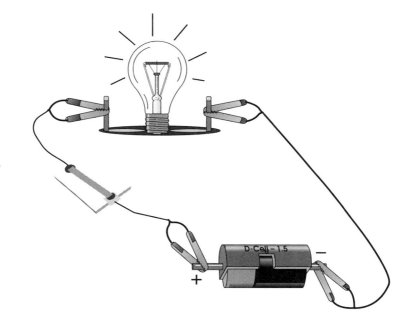

3-11. A simple circuit.

## SERIES CIRCUIT

A *series circuit* (Figure 3-12) contains two or more electrical loads. These loads are connected so only one path for the flow of electrons exists. Since only one electrical pathway exists, each electron must flow through each load. When one load in a series circuit is either removed or fails to function, an open circuit is created and no current will flow in the circuit.

## PARALLEL CIRCUIT

A *parallel circuit* (Figure 3-13) also contains two or more electrical loads. In a parallel circuit, these loads are connected so more than one pathway exists for the flow of electrons. Since more than one electrical pathway exists, electrons branch off and only part of the total current flowing in the circuit flows through each load. If one load in a parallel

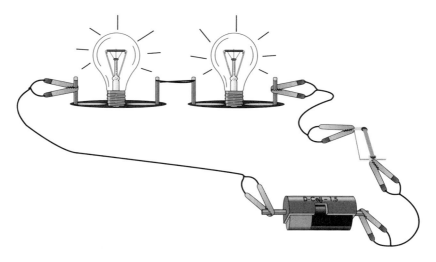

**3-12. A series circuit.**

**3-13. A parallel circuit.**

circuit either fails to function or is removed, the remaining load(s) in the circuit will not be affected.

## SERIES-PARALLEL CIRCUIT

A **series-parallel** (or combination) **circuit** must contain three or more loads. At least one of these loads is connected in series while the remaining loads are connected in parallel.

Examine Figure 3-14 to gain a better understanding of series-parallel circuits. Notice that all of the current flowing in the circuit must flow

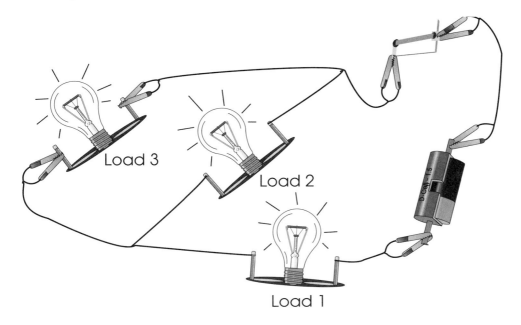

**3-14. A series-parallel circuit.**

through Load 1. If Load 1 is removed from the circuit, an open circuit condition will exist. These two facts show that Load 1 is the series load in this circuit.

Once the current flows through Load 1, the current can divide and flow through either Load 2 or Load 3. Thus, in this portion of the circuit, alternate pathways for the flow of current exist. Notice that if either Load 2 or Load 3 is removed from the circuit, the remaining loads will be unaffected. These two observations indicate that Load 2 and Load 3 are the parallel loads in these circuits.

Figure 3-14 represents a fairly simple series-parallel electrical circuit. However, careful study of this example helps in understanding more complex series-parallel circuits.

# ELECTRICAL CHARACTERISTICS OF SIMPLE, SERIES, PARALLEL, AND SERIES-PARALLEL ELECTRICAL CIRCUITS

Just as simple, series, and parallel electrical circuits have different physical characteristics, they also have different electrical characteristics.

In other words, voltage, amperage and resistance measurements in two circuits containing the exact same components may differ depending on how the components are connected. (Note: In the following sections, voltage drop due to resistance in the circuit conductors will be ignored.)

## SIMPLE CIRCUIT

A simple circuit contains only one load. In this type of circuit, the voltage measured at any point will be equal to the source voltage. Since there is only one path for the flow of electrons, the current flowing in the circuit is the same throughout. The total resistance in a simple circuit is the sum of the load resistance and the resistance of the circuit conductors.

## SERIES CIRCUIT

A series circuit contains two or more loads and only one path for the flow of electrons. This arrangement causes the series circuit to have different electrical characteristics than does a simple circuit.

### Voltage

In a series circuit, the source voltage divides across each load. In other words, if voltage measurements are made across the terminals of each load (as shown in Figure 3-12) the sum of these measurements will be equal to the source voltage. Formula 3-2 expresses the mathematical relationship between the source voltage and the voltage across each load in a series circuit.

$$E_S = E_1 + E_2 + E_3 + ... E_n$$

| Formula 3-2. |

where,

$E_S$ = Source voltage

$E_1-E_n$ = Voltage across each load in the circuit

### Amperage

As in the simple circuit, current only has one path to flow through in a series circuit. Therefore, the current flow in a series circuit will be the same regardless of where in the circuit amperage measurements are made. Mathematically, current flow in a series circuit is expressed by Formula 3-3.

$$I_T = I_1 = I_2 = I_3 = ... I_n$$   | **Formula 3-3.** |

where,

$I_T$ = Total circuit amperage

$I_1$–$I_n$ = Amperage at each load

## Resistance

Since each electron must pass through each load in a series circuit, the total circuit resistance is equal to the sum of each individual load's resistance. Formula 3-4 summarizes the relationship between the total resistance in a series circuit and the resistance of each circuit load.

$$R_T = R_1 + R_2 + R_3 + ... R_n$$   | **Formula 3-4.** |

where,

$R_T$ = Total circuit resistance

$R_1$–$R_n$ = Resistance of each load

## SERIES CIRCUIT EXAMPLE

The example circuit (Figure 3-15) has a 12 VDC source and contains two loads wired in series. Load one has 10 ohms of resistance and load two has 20 ohms of resistance. By applying knowledge of Ohm's Law and series circuits, this circuit can be analyzed to determine its electrical characteristics.

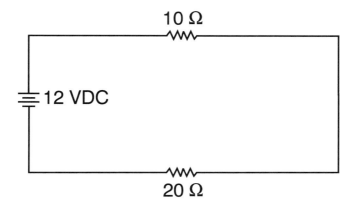

**3-15. An illustration of the relationship between voltage, amperage, and resistance in a series circuit.**

## Resistance

Solving for the circuit's total resistance is presented here. (In this example, the resistance of the conductor will be ignored.) According to Formula 3-4, the total resistance in a series circuit is the sum of each individual resistance. Therefore, the example circuit contains 30 ohms of total resistance, as shown.

$R_T = R_1 + R_2$

$R_T = 10$ ohms $+ 20$ ohms

$R_T = 30$ ohms

## Amperage

Since the source voltage is known and the circuit's total resistance has been determined, use Ohm's Law to calculate the circuit's amperage. As shown by the calculations, the total current flow in this circuit will be .4 amperes.

$$I = \frac{E}{R}$$

$$I = \frac{12\ V}{30\ ohms}$$

$I = .4$ amperes

Since this is a series circuit, the amperage is uniform throughout the circuit (see Formula 3-4). Thus, load one receives .4 amperes of current flow and .4 amperes will also flow through load two.

## Voltage

Since the amperage flowing through each load (which is the same as the total circuit amperage) and the individual resistances are known, Ohm's Law can be used to calculate the voltage across each load. These calculations are as follows:

Load 1.        $E = I \times R$
               $E = .4 \text{ A} \times 10 \text{ ohms}$
               $E = 4 \text{ volts}$

Load 2.        $E = I \times R$
               $E = .4 \times 20 \text{ ohms}$
               $E = 8 \text{ volts}$

In a series circuit, the total circuit voltage is equal to the sum of the voltages across each load (Formula 3-2). In the example, the total circuit voltage is 12 volts. The sum of the voltage across load one (4 volts) and the voltage across load two (8 volts) is 12 volts. This shows that the calculations are correct.

## PARALLEL CIRCUITS

A parallel circuit contains two or more loads connected so alternative paths for the flow of electrons are provided. The presence of these alternative paths causes parallel circuits to have different electrical characteristics than either simple or series circuits.

### Voltage

In a parallel circuit, the total source voltage is present across the terminals of each load. Stated differently, voltage measurements made across the terminals of each load in a parallel circuit will be equal to the voltage measurement at the source.

$$E_S = E_1 = E_2 = E_3 = ... E_n \qquad \boxed{\textbf{Formula 3-5.}}$$

where,

$E_S$ = Source voltage

$E_1 - E_n$ = Voltage across each load in the circuit

### Amperage

Since alternate paths for the flow of electrons are provided in a parallel circuit, each electron does not have to flow through each load in the circuit. Thus, total current flow in a parallel circuit is determined by summing the amperages flowing through each load in the circuit. Formula 3-6 shows this relationship mathematically.

$$I_T = I_1 + I_2 + I_3 + \ldots I_n$$     **Formula 3-6.**

where,

$I_T$ = Total circuit amperage
$I_1–I_n$ = Amperage through each load

## Resistance

The total resistance in a parallel circuit is always less than the resistance of the smallest individual load (Figure 3-16). For any parallel circuit, total resistance can be calculated using Formula 3-7.

$$R_T = \cfrac{1}{\cfrac{1}{R_1} + \cfrac{1}{R_2} + \cfrac{1}{R_3} + \cfrac{1}{R_n}}$$     **Formula 3-7.**

where,

$R_T$ = Total circuit resistance
$R_1–R_n$ = Resistance of each load

Formula 3-7 may look difficult. But, with the aid of a calculator, the formula can be easily used to determine the total resistance in any parallel circuit. An example circuit analysis problem for a parallel circuit follows.

## PARALLEL CIRCUIT EXAMPLE

By applying knowledge of Ohm's Law and parallel circuits, the parallel circuit shown in Figure 3-16 can be analyzed and its electrical characteristics determined.

## Resistance

The analysis begins by determining the circuit's total resistance. By inserting known values into Formula 3-7, the circuit has a total resistance of 6.7 ohms. These calculations are shown below. Notice that, as expected, the total circuit resistance for the parallel circuit is less than the resistance of the smallest individual load ($10\Omega$).

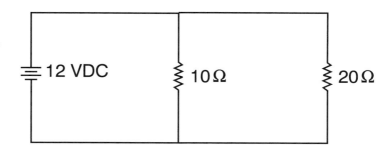

**3-16. An illustration of the relationship between voltage, amperage, and resistance in a parallel circuit.**

$$R_T = \cfrac{1}{\cfrac{1}{R_1} + \cfrac{1}{R_2}}$$

$$R_T = \cfrac{1}{\cfrac{1}{10} + \cfrac{1}{20}}$$

$$R_T = \cfrac{1}{.10 + .05}$$

$$R_T = \cfrac{1}{.15}$$

$$R_T = 6.7 \text{ ohms}$$

## Voltage

In a parallel electrical circuit, the voltage across each load is equal to the source voltage (Formula 3-5). Thus, since our circuit has a 12 volt source, the voltage across load one will be 12 volts and the voltage across load two will also be 12 volts.

## Amperage

Since the source voltage and total resistance for the example circuit are known, Ohm's Law is used to determine the total circuit amperage. As shown by the calculations below, the total current flow in the circuit is 1.8 amperes.

$$I = \frac{E}{R}$$

$$I = \frac{12\,V}{6.7\ \text{ohms}}$$

$$I = 1.8\ \text{amperes}$$

Formula 3-6 shows that the total amperage in a parallel circuit is equal to the sum of the current flowing through each individual load. Thus, an alternate method of determining total circuit amperage is to use Ohm's Law to determine the current flow through each load and then add these values together.

Applying Ohm's Law to load one indicates that 1.2 amperes of current will flow in this branch of the circuit.

$$I = \frac{E}{R}$$

$$I = \frac{12\,V}{10\ \text{ohms}}$$

$$I = 1.2\ \text{amperes}$$

Applying Ohm's Law to load two indicates that .6 amperes of current will flow in this branch of the circuit.

$$I = \frac{E}{R}$$

$$I = \frac{12\,V}{20\ \text{ohms}}$$

$$I = .6\ \text{amperes}$$

The sum of the current flowing in load one (1.2 amperes) and the current flowing in load two (.6 amperes) is equal to 1.8 amperes. Thus, the two methods produce the same results. In solving for current flow in parallel circuits, use either one of these two methods. Or, solve using both methods and compare answers to check accuracy.

## SERIES-PARALLEL ELECTRICAL CIRCUITS

A series-parallel circuit contains three or more electrical loads. At least one of these loads is connected in series while two or more loads are connected in parallel.

## SERIES-PARALLEL CIRCUIT EXAMPLE

A series-parallel circuit is analyzed by changing the circuit (on paper) into an equivalent simple circuit. In an ***equivalent simple circuit*** all loads (both series and parallel) are combined to form one load containing the same (equivalent) resistance as the original series-parallel circuit. Once the circuit's total resistance has been determined, Ohm's Law can be used to determine other electrical characteristics of the circuit. Use Figure 3-17 to illustrate this process.

**3-17. In this series-parallel circuit, the 10 ohm and 15 ohm loads are wired in series while the 20 ohm and 30 ohm loads are wired in parallel.**

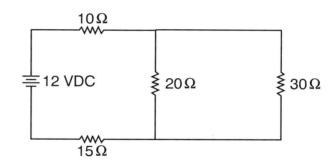

### Resistance

The total resistance of series loads can be found by adding the resistances together (Formula 3-4). Thus, the total resistance of the series component of the example circuit is equal to 25 ohms (10 ohms + 15 ohms).

Look at the parallel loads found in the example circuit. The total resistance of parallel loads in a circuit can be determined using Formula 3-7. By inserting the resistance values from the example circuit into this formula, the parallel component of our circuit has 12 ohms of total resistance.

$$R_T = \cfrac{1}{\cfrac{1}{R_1} + \cfrac{1}{R_2}}$$

$$R_T = \cfrac{1}{\cfrac{1}{20} + \cfrac{1}{30}}$$

$$R_T = \cfrac{1}{.05 + .033}$$

$$R_T = \cfrac{1}{.083}$$

$$R_T = 12 \text{ ohms}$$

Up to this point, knowledge about resistance in series and parallel circuits has been used to combine like loads (series with series and parallel with parallel). Next, these two types of loads will be combined to determine the circuit's total resistance. Figure 3-17 has been redrawn so that it shows the equivalent circuit that has been created. This is shown as Figure 3-18.

Notice that Figure 3-18 shows the two series loads combined to form one 25 ohm load. The two parallel loads are combined to form one 12 ohm load. Also notice that Figure 3-18 shows these two loads connected in series. This is appropriate because all electrons must flow across the 25 ohm series component of the circuit. Likewise, when flowing through the parallel circuit component, an individual electron must overcome 12 ohms of total resistance.

Since the combined loads in Figure 3-18 are in series, the total circuit resistance for the example circuit can be determined using the series resistance formula (Formula 3-4). As shown in the calculations below, the example series-parallel circuit has 37 ohms of total resistance (Figure 3-19).

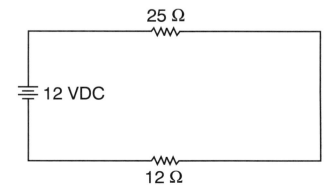

25 Ω

12 VDC

12 Ω

**3-18. Equivalent series and parallel circuit loads.**

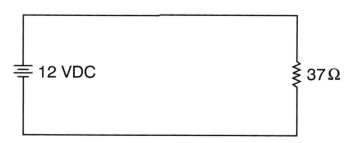

**3-19. The equivalent simple circuit developed from the original series-parallel circuit as shown in Figure 3-17.**

12 VDC

37 Ω

$R_T = R_1 + R_2$

$R_T = 25\ ohms + 12\ ohms$

$R_T = 37\ ohms$

## Total Amperage

The total resistance of the example circuit is 37 ohms. Using Ohm's Law and two known values (source voltage and total resistance), the total current flow in the circuit is calculated to be 0.324 amperes.

$$I = \frac{E}{R}$$

$$I = \frac{12\ V}{37\ ohms}$$

$$I = 0.324\ A$$

## Voltage

In a series circuit, the source voltage divides across each load. Stated differently, the source voltage in a series circuit is equal to the sum of the voltages across each load (Formula 3-2). Thus, in the example circuit, each of the loads will receive only a portion of the 12 volts available at the source.

Ohm's Law can be used to determine the voltage across each load in our original example circuit (Figure 3-17). The voltage across the 10 ohm series load will be 3.24 V.

$$E = I \times R$$

$$E = .324\ A \times 10\ ohms$$

$$E = 3.24\ V$$

Likewise, the voltage across the 15 ohm series resistor will be 4.86 volts.

I × R
E = .324 A × 15 ohms
E = 4.86 V

In a parallel circuit, the voltage is the same across each load (Formula 3-5). Since the two parallel loads have a total resistance of 12 ohms, the voltage across each of these two loads will be 3.89 volts.

E = I × R
E = .324 A × 12 ohms
E = 3.89 V

The sum of the load voltages must equal the source voltage. So, addition of the calculated load voltages will check accuracy. Since 3.24 V + 4.86 V + 3.89 V = 12 V (rounding error accounts for the .01 volt difference), the calculations are accurate.

### Load Amperages

Earlier, the total current in the example circuit was determined to be 0.324 amperes. However, because the individual load voltages were not known, the number of amperes flowing through each load could not be determined. With this information, these last unknown values can be calculated.

Use Ohm's Law to determine the current flowing through each load. Solve for the two series loads first. By rearranging Ohm's Law to solve for amperage and inserting known values into the equation, it is determined that .324 amperes will flow through the 10 ohm series load.

$$I = \frac{E}{R}$$

$$I = \frac{3.24 \text{ V}}{10 \text{ ohms}}$$

I = 0.324 A

Using the same process, it is determined that .324 amperes will also flow through the remaining 15 ohm series load.

$$I = \frac{E}{R}$$

$$I = \frac{4.86\ V}{15\ ohms}$$

$$I = 0.324\ A$$

Notice that the current flowing through both series loads is the same. At first this may appear to be an error; however, examine Figure 3-16 again. By tracing the flow of current through the circuit, it should be obvious that the total circuit amperage must flow through both series loads for the circuit to function.

Now, the current flow through each of the two parallel loads can be determined. Again, rearranging Ohm's Law to solve for amperage, it is determined that the current flow through the 20 ohm parallel load is 0.195 amperes.

$$I = \frac{E}{R}$$

$$I = \frac{3.89\ V}{20\ ohms}$$

$$I = 0.195\ A$$

Finally, the current flowing through the remaining 30 ohm parallel resistor can be determined. Inserting known values into the equation indicates that 0.13 amperes will flow through the 30 ohm load.

$$I = \frac{E}{R}$$

$$I = \frac{3.89\ V}{30\ ohms}$$

$$I = 0.13\ A$$

The sum of the current flowing through the parallel loads is equal to the total source voltage (.195 A + .13 A = .325 A). Thus, all the current flowing into the parallel component of the example circuit is accounted for. (Rounding accounts for the .001 A difference.)

## A FINAL WORD ABOUT SERIES-PARALLEL CIRCUITS

Series-parallel circuits are most commonly found in electronic devices and components. They are occasionally encountered in special applications in agricultural wiring and electrification.

Analyzing a series-parallel electrical circuit is a challenging task. However, a good understanding of the electrical characteristics of series circuits and parallel circuits and following a systematic process will help with most series-parallel circuits.

# SUMMARY

Three components are necessary to have a working electrical circuit—a voltage source, a load, and conductors to connect them. An overcurrent device and a switch are necessary to make the circuit both safe and convenient. Heat is produced in an electrical circuit and heat production is related to the operation of overcurrent devices.

Five specific circuit conditions are closed, open, overload, short, and ground-fault circuits. Under certain conditions, both the closed and open circuit conditions may be desirable. However, overload, short, and ground-fault circuit conditions are always potentially dangerous.

Types of circuits include simple, series, parallel, and series-parallel circuits. Knowledge of the identification, operation, and characteristics of different electrical circuits is essential to working with electricity.

# REVIEW QUESTIONS

1. List and explain the functions of the five essential components of a safe, convenient electrical circuit.

2. Explain how a fuse protects an electrical circuit from an overcurrent condition.

3. Draw a sketch of each of the following circuit conditions: (a) closed circuit, (b) open circuit, (c) short circuit, and (d) ground-fault circuit.

4. Explain the difference between a short circuit and a ground-fault circuit.

5. Determine the current flow in the short circuit illustrated below. Assume the short itself has no resistance.

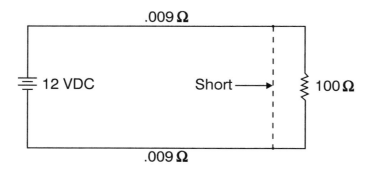

6. Sketch each of the following circuit types: (a) simple circuit, (b) series circuit, (c) parallel circuit, and (d) series-parallel circuit.

7. Write the equations that explain the voltage, amperage, resistance characteristics of (a) series circuits and (b) parallel circuits. Under each equation, write a sentence or two that explains the equation.

8. Analyze each circuit below. Determine the unknown values for each circuit.

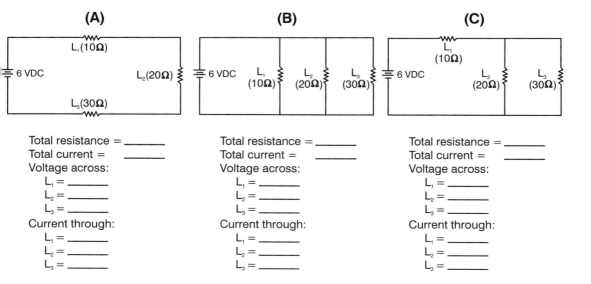

| (A) | (B) | (C) |
|---|---|---|
| Total resistance = _____ | Total resistance = _____ | Total resistance = _____ |
| Total current = _____ | Total current = _____ | Total current = _____ |
| Voltage across: | Voltage across: | Voltage across: |
| $L_1$ = _____ | $L_1$ = _____ | $L_1$ = _____ |
| $L_2$ = _____ | $L_2$ = _____ | $L_2$ = _____ |
| $L_3$ = _____ | $L_3$ = _____ | $L_3$ = _____ |
| Current through: | Current through: | Current through: |
| $L_1$ = _____ | $L_1$ = _____ | $L_1$ = _____ |
| $L_2$ = _____ | $L_2$ = _____ | $L_2$ = _____ |
| $L_3$ = _____ | $L_3$ = _____ | $L_3$ = _____ |

# APPLYING THE CONCEPTS

1. Obtain a 6 volt battery, several conductors, a fuse, a switch and a small load of some type and construct a safe, convenient electrical circuit like the one shown in Figure 3-6.

2. Using a 6 volt battery, lamp fixture, and conductors, construct a simple circuit. Use another conductor to momentarily produce a short circuit condition as shown in Figure 3-8. Observe the lamp fixture when the circuit is shorted. What happens? Why? Next, place a small fuse (250 mA or so) in the circuit. Short the circuit again and observe the fuse. What happens and why?

3. Using a small (6 volt or less) permanent magnet DC motor, conductors and a 6 volt battery, create a ground-fault condition by making the connections shown below.

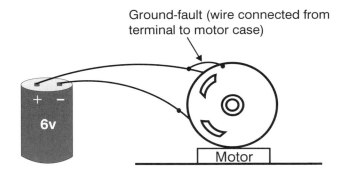

Attach one end of another conductor to the negative terminal of the battery. Attach the other end of the conductor to the terminal of a 6 volt lamp fixture. Take a second conductor and attach one end to the other terminal of the lamp fixture. Touch the free end of the second conductor to the metal frame of the motor and observe the lamp fixture. What happens? Why does this happen? Why is a ground-fault on a piece of high voltage equipment potentially fatal?

4. Using a 6 volt battery, lamp fixtures, and conductors, assemble simple, series, parallel, and series-parallel electrical circuits. Observe the brightness of the lamps in each type of circuit. How do they differ?

5. Using a 6 volt battery, power resistors (available at local electronics store), and conductors, assemble simple, series, parallel, and series-parallel electrical circuits as before (Activity 4). Use a multimeter to take voltage, amperage and resistance measurements on each circuit. Verify the relationships expressed in Formulas 3-2 to 3-7 in this chapter. (Note: Source voltage measurements should be made with the circuit connected to the battery since different voltage readings will be obtained for the same battery under different load conditions.)

# 4

# PLANNING ELECTRICAL SERVICE

Electricity must be where it is needed in order to provide power to do work. This requires important planning activities built on a good understanding of the principles of electricity.

Planning safe, efficient electrical service for production agriculture involves several areas. Good communication with utility company representatives and electrical contractors is essential. This will help ensure the best service possible.

Studying this chapter will develop an understanding of the system by which electricity is transmitted and distributed from the generating plant to the main service entrance of the farm or agribusiness. Once accomplished, various aspects of planning the on-farm electrical system must be considered.

4-1. Electricity is required in many locations on a modern farm.

# OBJECTIVES

This chapter presents considerations in planning the electrical service for a farm. After completing this chapter, you will:

1. Describe the major components of the electrical distribution system from the electrical power plant to the service entrance of a farm building.

2. Explain the advantages and disadvantages of a central point distribution system.

3. Describe the functions and primary components of a building service entrance panel.

4. Define the term "electrical grounding" and explain the purpose(s) of system grounding and equipment grounding.

5. Describe three- and four-wire 120/240 volt single-phase electrical service.

**TERMS**

ampacity
branch circuit
building service conductors
central point distribution system
connected load
demand load
double-pole circuit breaker
equipment grounding
grounding
grounding electrode
main disconnect
messenger
neutral bar
nominal voltage
service conductor
service drop conductors
service entrance equipment
service entrance panel
service laterals
service point
single-pole circuit breaker
stray voltage
system grounding
triplex cable
voltage drop
with diversity
without diversity

6. Plan the farmstead electrical service, including the total connected load and demand load for a non-residential farm building, and size a service entrance panel.

7. Locate and size the main service entrance for a farm having a central point distribution system.

8. Select and size building service conductors based on use conditions and ampacity and voltage drop criteria.

# ELECTRICAL POWER GENERATION AND DISTRIBUTION

Electricity generated at a power plant typically has a voltage of approximately 13,800 volts. This electricity is fed into a nearby system of step-up transformers that increases the voltage to a much higher level (250,000 to 750,000 volts) for initial transmission. Transmitting electricity at high voltages allows for a proportional decrease in current, thus reducing voltage drop in the transmission lines.

From the step-up transformer, the electricity is sent through high voltage transmission lines to distribution substations, strategically located within the utility's service area. At the substation, the high voltage is reduced (using a step-down transformer) and the electricity is divided and sent to load centers within each major use area by way of secondary transmission lines.

The secondary transmission lines carry electricity to the electrical substations at various locations in the country or on the outskirts of a town. These substations are also transformer points at which voltage is again reduced (usually to 7,200 volts) for final distribution to service transformers located near individual customers. The service transformer reduces the voltage again for safe distribution to an individual farm, agribusiness, or residence.

The most common electrical service supplied to farms and residences is 120/240 volt single-phase electricity. These voltage designations are called **nominal voltages**. This means that the actual measured voltages may vary *slightly* from these figures. This chapter will be limited to this type of electrical service.

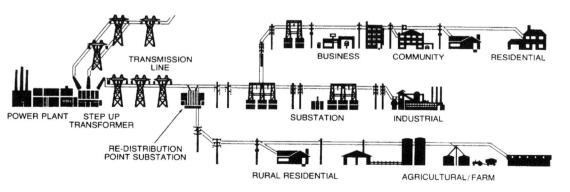

**-2. Example of an electrical transmission and distribution system from the power plant to the service transformer.**

# CENTRAL POINT DISTRIBUTION SYSTEMS

On-farm electrical service originates at the utility company's service transformer. In rural areas, the service transformer is usually located on a pole, and the conductors coming from the service transformer are overhead. These overhead conductors are called ***service drop conductors***. (In towns and cities, service transformers are often at ground level on concrete pads. The conductors supplying electrical service to individual residences and businesses are underground, and are called ***service laterals***.)

The service drop conductors connect to the customer's wiring system at the service point. From there, electrical service extends to the farm's main distribution point and then through service conductors to a service entrance at each individual building or load center.

## *SERVICE DROP*

For 120/240 volt single-phase electrical service, the service drop will consist of three individual conductors—two "hot" and one "neutral." The neutral conductor is connected to the earth (grounded) at the service transformer. The voltage between either hot conductor and the neutral conductor will be 120 volts. The voltage between the two hot conductors will be 240 volts. The hot conductors will always be insulated; the neutral conductor may be uninsulated in overhead installations.

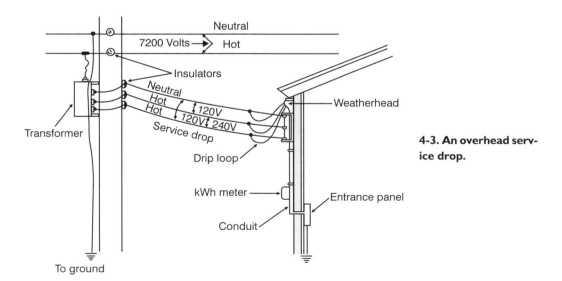

4-3. An overhead service drop.

The service drop conductors may be installed individually or together as a loosely twisted bundle (called **triplex cable**). The *National Electrical Code® (NEC®)** specifies minimum conductor sizes and minimum overhead clearances for service drop conductors. Installation and maintenance of the service drop conductors are the responsibility of the utility company. The *NEC* standards assure hazard-free wiring.

## SERVICE POINT TO MAIN DISTRIBUTION CENTER

The **service point** is the point of connection between the service-drop conductors (which are the utility's responsibility) and the individual customer's wiring system. **Service conductors** attach to the service-drop conductors at the service point and run to a main distribution center. The utility company's kilowatt-hour meter is located between the service point and the main distribution center, and meters the amount of electrical energy consumed. The neutral service conductor will be connected to the earth at the main distribution center by a grounding conductor attached to a grounding electrode buried in the ground.

The customer owns and is responsible for the service conductors and associated hardware, such as the service head, meter socket, and conduit or raceway. A qualified electrician should install all hardware and complete all necessary wiring for this portion of an electrical service.

In some cases, the service entrance panel in the residence serves as the farm's main distribution center. With this system, other farm buildings receive their electrical supply from feeder circuits originating at the residence's service entrance panel. For small farms with limited electrical loads, this system is both efficient and economical. However it is generally inadequate for larger farms with greater electrical loads.

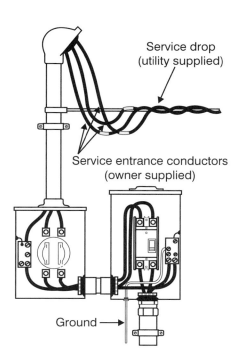

4-4. **A typical installation between the service transformer and the main service entrance. (Note the grounding electrode conductor at the main service entrance.)**

---

**National Electrical Code® and NEC® are registered trademarks of the National Fire Protection Association, Inc., Quincy, MA 02269.

Farms with larger electrical loads generally use a ***central point distribution system***. The main distribution center is at a pole located in the farmyard. A kilowatt-hour meter is attached to the pole and meters electrical consumption for the entire farm. Approved conductors, either in-air or underground, supply electrical service from the distribution center to each building or service area on the farm. The *NEC* (230-21) considers the conductors supplying electricity from the meter pole to individual buildings to be service drops (if overhead) or service laterals (if underground) (*NEC* 230-30). In this text, the term ***building service conductors*** will be used to describe both service drops and service laterals.

A ***main disconnect*** may be provided at the main distribution center to disconnect electrical service from all on-farm loads (except the water pump) in case of an emergency. Separate disconnects for each building or service area may also be provided.

The central distribution pole must meet the specifications of the electrical power supplier. In most locations, the utility will set the pole and bill the customer if there is a charge. A qualified electrician should install all equipment and wiring on the pole, according to the power supplier's specifications. Since the equipment on the central distribution pole is exposed to the weather, only raintight equipment should be used.

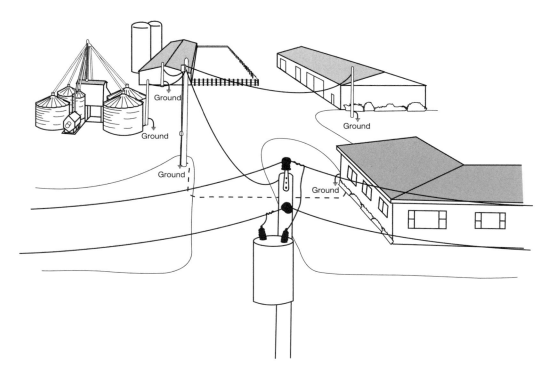

**4-5. A central point distribution system.**

# BUILDING SERVICE CONDUCTORS

Most farms have several electrical load centers (buildings, grain handling systems, pumps, etc.). Thus, the electrical power supplied to the farm's main service point must be distributed to each of these load centers. Building service conductors perform this function.

In a central point distribution system, the service conductors supplying power to a building originate at the main distribution center and terminate at the service entrance of the building. On occasion, a building may be provided with electricity by a feeder circuit that originates at the service entrance of one building and

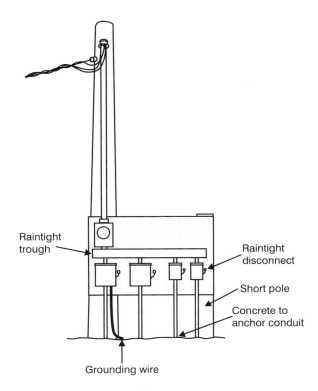

4-6. A meter pole and distribution center (**NEC** 547-8(b)).

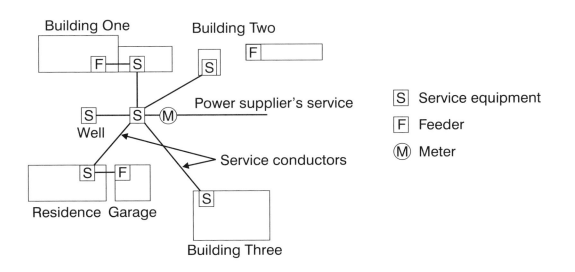

4-7. Service and feeder conductors in a central point distribution system.

terminates at a subpanel in another building or load center. Both of these situations are shown in Figure 4-7.

Building service conductors can either be installed underground or overhead, using conductors properly sized and approved for such use conditions. Installing feeder conductors underground eliminates damage resulting from inclement weather or possible contact with high clearance farmstead equipment. Building service conductors should be installed by a qualified electrician.

# BUILDING SERVICE ENTRANCE

The *service entrance equipment* includes the components of the electrical system needed to carry current from the building service conductors to the branch circuits within the building. For a typical overhead service (Figure 4-8), these components include: (a) the service entrance wires, (b) the weather head, and (c) the building service entrance (breaker or fuse panel). The building service entrance must be grounded. All building service entrance equipment should be installed by a qualified electrician.

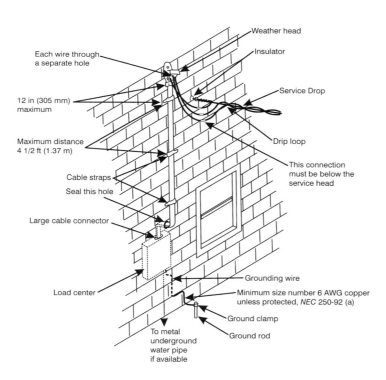

Each wire through a separate hole

12 in (305 mm) maximum

Maximum distance 4 1/2 ft (1.37 m)

Cable straps

Seal this hole

Large cable connector

Load center

Weather head

Insulator

Service Drop

Drip loop

This connection must be below the service head

Grounding wire

Minimum size number 6 AWG copper unless protected, *NEC* 250-92 (a)

Ground clamp

Ground rod

To metal underground water pipe if available

**4-8. A typical overhead service.**

The *service entrance panel* is considered the source for every electrical circuit within the building. Circuits originating at the service entrance panel branch out to provide electrical service to the various areas of the building. Most of the circuits originating at the service entrance panel are called **branch circuits.** Service entrance panels may use either fuses or circuit breakers to provide branch circuit overcurrent protection, although breakers are used almost exclusively in new installations.

The service entrance panel has several important functions. It provides:

- a safe means of disconnecting all electrical power in the building;
- a means of limiting, to a safe level, the amount of current that can enter the building;
- a safe means of subdividing the electrical supply to serve individual loads or load groups within the building; and
- a common point of connection to earth or ground for electrical equipment in the building.

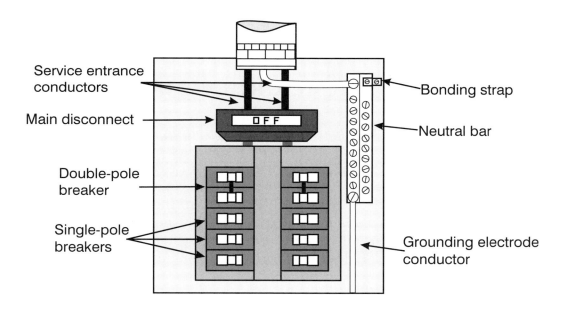

**4-9. The major components of a breaker-type service entrance panel.**

The major components of the service entrance panel:

- ***Main disconnect*** is a circuit breaker that serves to limit current flow into the building to a predetermined, safe level. The main disconnect can also be opened manually to disconnect electrical service from all branch and feeder circuits supplied through the service entrance panel.

- *Single-pole circuit breakers* provide overcurrent protection for individual 120 volt circuits. The hot (ungrounded) conductor of a 120 volt branch (or feeder) circuit is connected to a single-pole circuit breaker.

- *Double-pole circuit breakers* provide overcurrent protection for individual 240 volt circuits. The two hot (ungrounded) conductors of a 240 volt branch (or feeder) circuit are connected to a double-pole circuit breaker.

- The *neutral bar* is connected to earth. The neutral (grounded) conductor of a 120 volt branch circuit is connected to the neutral bar. Other connections at the neutral bar differ depending on whether a three-wire or four-wire electrical service is provided.

- Service entrance panels may be equipped with a separate grounding bar. If so, the branch circuit equipment grounding conductors are attached under screw terminals at the grounding bar. The grounding bar is bonded to the service entrance panel.

# ELECTRICAL GROUNDING

When working with electricity, the term *grounding* means either direct or indirect connection to the earth. The purpose of grounding is safety. Two distinct types of grounding are encountered in electrical wiring—system grounding and equipment grounding. *System grounding* is connecting current-carrying portions of the electrical system to the earth. *Equipment grounding* is connecting conductive equipment not normally intended to carry current (such as metal conduit, device boxes, motor frames, etc.) to the earth. These types of grounding serve different functions.

## SYSTEM GROUNDING

An electrical wiring system must have one conductor (the neutral conductor) connected to a grounding electrode connected to earth. This is called system grounding. The primary purpose of system grounding is to limit the voltage between any hot conductor and the earth to the minimum possible level.

Figure 4-10 shows a 120/240 volt single-phase electrical system. Notice that the neutral conductor is connected to the earth. Thus, if the voltage is measured between either hot conductor and the ground, the voltage will be 120 volts. This is the minimum possible voltage to ground for a 120/240 volt system.

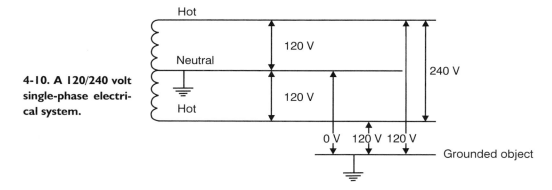

**4-10. A 120/240 volt single-phase electrical system.**

System grounding promotes safety by limiting higher than normal voltages that might be caused by lightening, line surges, or unintentional system contact with high voltage lines. Also, system grounding stabilizes the voltage to ground during normal operation of the electrical system.

A ***grounding electrode*** serves as a terminal or connection to the earth for an electrical grounding system. The *NEC* [250-81(a)(b)(c)(d)] specifies that, if available, each of the following should be bonded together to form the grounding electrode system:

- a metal underground water pipe having at least 10 ft. in the earth;
- metal frame of the building, if the frame is effectively grounded;
- a concrete-encased electrode(s) (2 inch minimum encasement) totaling 20 feet or more in length buried in the earth;
- a ground ring encircling the building buried at least 30 inches below the earth's surface.

If none of the electrodes listed above is available at a building, one or more made grounding electrodes must be installed. The most common made electrode is a metal pipe or rod driven into the ground and having a minimum of 8-ft. of soil contact. If the resistance to ground of a single made electrode is greater than 25 ohms, a second grounding electrode must be installed. The second grounding electrode must be at least 6-ft. from the other electrode, and both electrodes must be bonded together.

A grounding system for a typical farm was shown in Figure 4-5. Note that each building or load center is grounded.

Proper electrical system grounding is essential for safe electrical service. Numerous code requirements must be met to assure proper system grounding. Thus, only a qualified electrician should install and connect the electrical system grounding components.

## EQUIPMENT GROUNDING

Equipment grounding refers to the bonding (electrical connection) of conductive materials that enclose electrical conductors or equipment (such as metal conduit, motor and/or equipment frames, metal device boxes, etc.) back to the system grounding electrode. The purpose of equipment grounding is to help protect property and persons from damage or injury in case of a ground-fault condition. The following examples should help you to understand the purpose and importance of equipment grounding.

In Figure 4-11, a 120-volt electric motor is supplied with electricity by two wires [the ungrounded conductor (connected to the circuit breaker) and the grounded conductor (connected to the neutral bar)]. The motor is in good electrical repair. Thus, a person touching the metal motor frame does not receive an electrical shock.

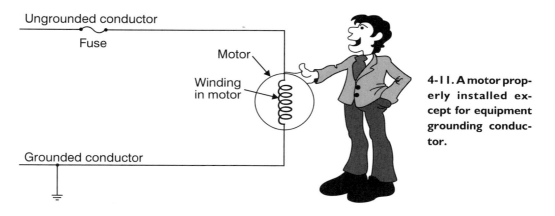

4-11. A motor properly installed except for equipment grounding conductor.

Figure 4-12 shows the same motor circuit, with one difference. Because of incorrect installation, abuse, or deterioration of the motor's internal wiring, the ungrounded conductor has come in electrical contact with the metal motor frame. Because of this, a 120-volt electrical potential exists between the motor housing and earth. A person touching the motor frame completes the ground-fault circuit, and could easily receive an extremely painful or fatal electrical shock.

Figure 4-13 shows the motor circuit with an equipment grounding conductor included. Notice that the grounding conductor connects the motor frame to the system grounding electrode at the service entrance panel. Under normal operating conditions, no electrical current flows in the grounding conductor.

The motor circuit with the ungrounded conductor in electrical contact with the metal motor frame energizes the motor frame. However, this

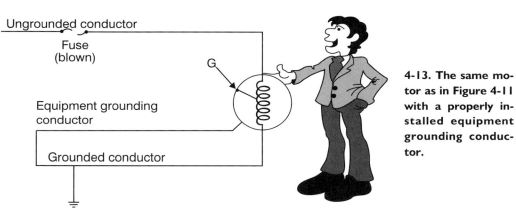

4-12. The same motor as in Figure 4-11 with a ground-fault condition.

Ungrounded conductor
Fuse (not blown)
G
Grounded conductor

Ungrounded conductor
Fuse (blown)
G
Equipment grounding conductor
Grounded conductor

4-13. The same motor as in Figure 4-11 with a properly installed equipment grounding conductor.

time the equipment grounding conductor provides a low resistance path back to the source (service entrance panel). The fault current should be high enough to blow the fuse (or cause the circuit breaker to trip) the instant the motor frame is energized. Thus, as shown, a person touching the motor frame will not receive an electrical shock, since the blown fuse has de-energized the circuit.

To function correctly, the overall resistance of the equipment grounding system must be minimized. This can be accomplished by following proper installation and maintenance procedures. Figure 4-14 will be used to illustrate the dangers of a grounding system having a high resistance.

Note in Figure 4-14, that because of a poor connection, 9 ohms of resistance is present between the motor frame and the equipment grounding wire. Since this is a 120-volt circuit, the maximum fault current is 13.3 amperes (120 volts / 9 ohms). This level of current flow is too small to blow the 20 ampere fuse.

The situation just described could cause two problems. First, because the fuse did not blow, a 120 volt potential still exists between the motor frame and ground. A person touching the motor frame could receive a

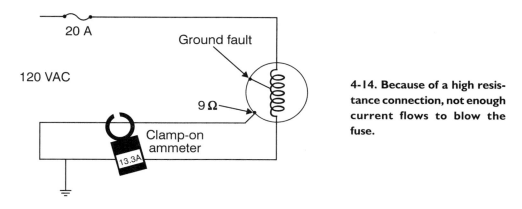

4-14. Because of a high resistance connection, not enough current flows to blow the fuse.

painful or fatal electrical shock. Second, electrical arcing or excessive heating could occur, possibly resulting in a building fire.

# 120/240 VOLT SINGLE-PHASE ELECTRICAL SERVICES

*NEC* Article 250-24 allows two different systems to be used to provide 120/240 volt electrical service from a central distribution point to individual buildings. These two systems are commonly known as: (a) 120/240 volt 3-wire and (b) 120/240 volt 4-wire service.

## 3-WIRE SERVICE

In a 120/240 volt 3-wire service, two hot (ungrounded) conductors and one neutral (grounded) conductor provide electricity from the farm's main distribution center to the service entrance panel of a building. The two hot service conductors terminate at the service entrance panel's main disconnect. The neutral service conductor is connected to the neutral bar of the service entrance panel. In turn, the neutral bar is connected to earth by a grounding conductor attached to a grounding electrode installed at the building. The metal cabinet of the service entrance panel is bonded to the neutral bar using either a bonding screw or a bonding jumper. If a separate equipment grounding bar is present at the service entrance panel, it will be bonded to the neutral bar and to the service entrance panel and the grounding electrode conductor will attach to the grounding bar. A 120/240 volt 3-wire electrical service is shown in Figure 4-15.

An equipment grounding conductor is not run with the service conductors to the building service entrance panel in a 3-wire system. Instead, as shown in Figure 4-15, the branch circuit equipment grounding conductor must be connected to the neutral bar at the service entrance panel.

If a 3-wire system is properly sized and installed, it will provide long, dependable service. However, if resistance develops in the neutral, voltage drop will occur, resulting in a neutral-to-earth voltage (commonly called **stray voltage**) at one or more buildings on the farm.

A stray voltage is a small voltage difference that exists between two surfaces (stanchions, waterers, floor, etc.). Since some animals can sense voltages as small as 0.5 volts, a stray voltage problem can cause significant production losses by causing livestock to avoid feeders and waterers. A stray voltage problem can also agitate dairy cattle, interfering with milk let-down. Figure 4-16 illustrates a stray voltage problem in a dairy facility.

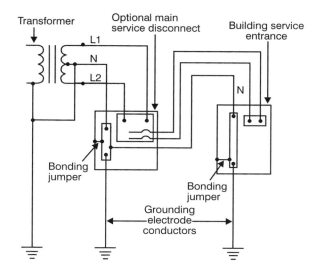

4-15. A 120/240 volt 3-wire service.

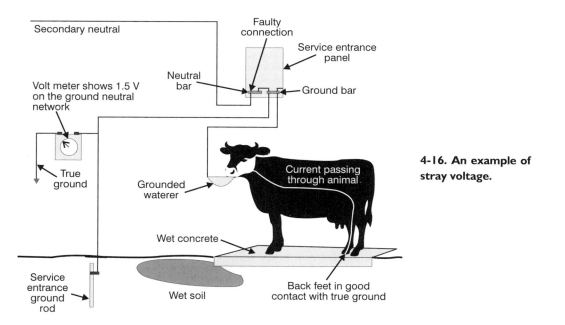

4-16. An example of stray voltage.

A full description of stray voltage, its sources and correction is beyond the scope of this book. However, the use of a 120/240 volt 4-wire electrical service can prevent some stray voltage problems. For this reason, 4-wire electrical service is recommended on livestock farms.

## 4-WIRE SERVICE

In a 120/240 volt 4-wire service, two hot (ungrounded) conductors, one neutral (grounded) conductor, and one equipment grounding conductor run from the main distribution center to the service entrance panel of a building. The *NEC* requires an insulated or covered equipment grounding conductor to be used in a 4-wire service supplying livestock facilities [Article 250-24(a) Exception No. 2].

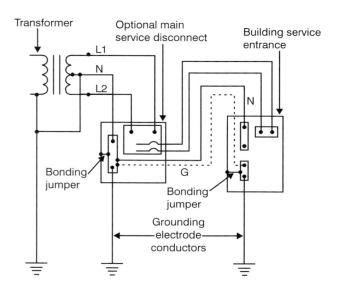

**4-17. A 120/240 volt 4-wire service.**

As with the 3-wire service, the two hot service conductors terminate at the building service entrance panel's main disconnect. Also, as before, the neutral service conductor is attached to the neutral bar of the service entrance panel. But, in a 4-wire service, the neutral bar is not connected to the building's grounding electrode. Instead, the building grounding electrode is connected to a separate grounding bar (by way of the grounding electrode conductor). The incoming equipment grounding conductor terminates at this grounding bar. The metal cabinet of the service entrance panel is also bonded to the grounding bar. Figure 4-17 illustrates a 120/240 volt 4-wire service.

Since, in a 4-wire service, the neutral is not bonded to the grounding electrode at the building, a voltage drop in the neutral does not affect the equipment grounding conductors. Thus, a 4-wire service provides protection against stray voltage problems caused by resistance in the neutral conductor. However, if 120/240 volt 3-wire service is provided elsewhere on the farm (to the home, for example), a voltage drop in the neutral of the 3-wire service may result in a stray voltage problem at a livestock facility, even though the livestock facility has a 4-wire service.

Regardless of whether 3-wire or 4-wire service is used, the *NEC* [547-8(b)] requires that an equipotential plane be provided in confinement livestock buildings having concrete floors. An equipotential plane is an area where wire mesh is embedded in the concrete floor, bonded to all conductive surfaces, and connected to the building's grounding electrode system. The purpose of an equipotential plane is to prevent exposure to stray voltages.

# PLANNING THE ELECTRICAL SERVICE

As repeatedly emphasized, a qualified electrician should install all customer-owned electrical wiring and associated equipment, including the service entrance panels at individual buildings or load centers. However, understanding the planning process, helps provide valuable assistance to utility company personnel and the electrician in designing a safe, efficient farmstead electrical system.

This section describes the farmstead electrical system planning process. The steps in this process include determining the demand load for farm buildings or service areas; locating and sizing the farm's main service; and selecting and sizing service conductors to each building or load center. (Note: The term building will be used to denote both farm buildings and service areas. This section will be limited to non-residential farm buildings.)

## DETERMINING THE DEMAND LOAD FOR A NON-RESIDENTIAL FARM BUILDING

The **connected load** is the sum of all the electrical loads in a building. The **demand load** for a building is the maximum electrical load expected to operate at any one time.

Electrical loads in a building that are likely to operate at the same time (e.g. lights and ventilation fans) are considered to be loads **without diversity.** Electrical loads that are not likely to operate at the same time (e.g. heaters and air conditioners) are considered to be loads **with diversity**. A knowledge of agricultural practices is necessary to identify loads that operate with and without diversity.

Service entrance panels are commonly available with main breakers having the following amperage ratings: 30, 40, 60, 70, 100, 125, 150, and 200 and above. A farm building containing only one branch circuit may be served by a 15 ampere or larger service disconnect. If the building has only two branch circuits, a 30 ampere (or larger) service disconnect may be used. For all other farm buildings, the service disconnect must be rated at 60 amperes or more. To provide for future electrical loads, it is generally recommended that the service disconnect for a farm building be rated at no less than 100 amperes. Most should have larger service panels for future expansion.

The first step in determining the demand load for a farm building is to make a list of all current and anticipated electrical equipment and its amperage. Loads may be listed and estimated as described:

- Duplex convenience outlets (DCOs, commonly called receptacles). Use 1.5 amperes per DCO in calculations at 120 volts. This will account for all plug-in appliance loads, such as power tools and portable fans.

- Lighting outlets. Use 1.5 amperes per light fixture in calculations at 120 volts for normal lighting.

- Motors. Use an amperage value equal to 125 percent of the full-load current for the largest motor plus 100 percent of the full-load current for all remaining motors. (Note: Use *NEC* table values for full-load motor current. *NEC* Table 430-148, for use with single-phase AC motors, can be found on page 218.)

- All other permanently connected equipment. Use 100 percent of the rated full-load current. If an electric resistance heater is rated in watts instead of amperes, divide the wattage by the service voltage (120 or 240 volts) to determine the heater's amperage.

- Continuous loads. The amperage of any continuous load(s) should be increased by 125% in calculating the building demand load [220-10(b)]. The *NEC* defines a continuous load as any load which, under normal conditions, is expected to operate for more than 3 hours at a time.

## Table 4-1.
## Demand Factors for Calculating Demand Load for
## Non-residential Farm Buildings

| Ampere Load at 240 Volts | Demand Factor Percent |
|---|---|
| Loads expected to operate without diversity, but not less than 125% full-load current of the largest motor and not less than the first 60 amperes of load. | 100 |
| Next 60 amperes of all other loads. | 50 |
| Remainder of other loads. | 25 |

Source: *NEC* Table 220-40. Reprinted with permission from NFPA 70-1996, the *National Electrical Code*, Copyright © 1995, National Fire Protection Association, Quincy, MA 02269. This reprinted material is not the complete and official position of the National Fire Protection Association on the referenced subject, which is represented only by the standard in its entirety.

The next step in determining a farm building's demand load is to convert all 120 volt amperages to a 240 volt basis using the following formula:

$$\text{Amperage at 240 volts} = \frac{\text{Amperage at 120 volts}}{2}$$

Conversion to a 240 volt basis is necessary because 240 volt electrical service is provided to the service entrance panel.

The final step in determining demand load is to apply the demand factors presented in Table 4-1 to the building loads in question.

To illustrate the use of this process for determining the demand load for a building, work through an example. In this example, determine the demand load for a service center having the following electrical loads.

| Service Center Loads | Amperage at 240 Volts |
|---|---|
| 27 lights (120 volts) . . . . . . . . . . . . . . . . . | (27 × 1.5A) / 2 = 20.3A |
| 20 DCOs (120 volts) . . . . . . . . . . . . . . . . . | (20 × 1.5A) / 2 = 15.0A |
| Three $1/3$ hp motors (240 volts)* . . . . . . . . . | (3.6A × 1.25) + (2 × 3.6A) = 11.7A |
| Arc welder, 50 amperes (240 volts) . . . . . . . . | 50 A |
| One 3000 watt electric heater (240 volts) . . . . | (3000W / 240V) = 12.5A |
| Total Connected Load (@ 240V) . . . . . . . . | 109.5A |

*Full-load current values taken from *NEC* Table 430-148. See page 218 of this text. Increase the table value of one of the motors by 125 percent.

Once the service center's total connected load has been determined, identify loads that will operate without diversity (at the same time). It is possible that all lights, the exhaust fan, the heater, and the arc welder will all operate at the same time. Totaling these loads results in a sum of 87.3 amperes of loads operating without diversity. All remaining loads (totaling 22.2A) are considered to operate with diversity.

Applying the demand factors listed in Table 4-1 to our service center results in a calculated demand load of 98.4A. These calculations are shown below.

### Service Center Demand Load Calculations

| | |
|---|---|
| Loads expected to operate without diversity, but no less than 125 percent full-load current of the largest motor and not less than the first 60 amperes of load . . . . . . . . . . . . . . . . . . . . . . . . | 100% × 87.3A = 87.3A |
| Next 60 amperes of all other loads . . . . . . . . . | 50% × 22.2A = 11.1A |
| Total Calculated Demand Load . . . . . . . . . | 98.4A |

## SELECTING BUILDING SERVICE PANELS

Once the building's demand load has been determined, the building service entrance panel can be selected from standard ratings. Since the calculated demand load does not match a standard rating, select a larger standard rating. Selection of a 100A service entrance panel would meet the minimum building requirements; however, this would leave virtually no capacity for additional electrical loads.

For the example building, select a 150A service entrance panel. This panel will not cost much more to purchase and install, and will give enough capacity to accommodate future loads. In the long run, it is always less expensive to build extra capacity into the wiring system than it is to replace the system with a larger one at a later date.

# LOCATING AND SIZING
# THE MAIN SERVICE ENTRANCE

The most common type of agricultural electrical distribution system is central point distribution. In this system, all electrical service to the farm enters and is distributed from a central point, usually a meter pole located in the courtyard. Determining the exact location of this point and the size

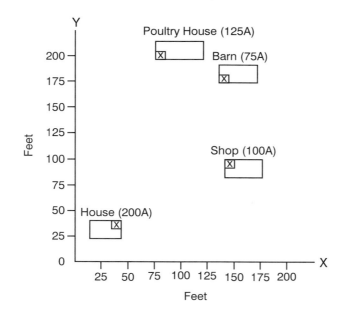

4-18. A scaled map of the farm-stead showing the location for each building.

of the main service are important considerations in planning an on-farm electrical system.

The optimum location of the central distribution point and main service equipment is at the electrical load center. To determine the load center, draw a scaled map that shows the location and the demand load for each building. Next, draw two perpendicular baselines (X and Y) along two sides of the farmstead. An example drawing is shown in Figure 4-18.

Once the drawing has been made, the Y and X coordinates for the central distribution point can be determined using the following formulas. The point of intersection of the calculated Y and X coordinates is the electrical load center of the farmstead.

$$\text{Load Center (Y Coordinate)} = \frac{\text{Sum of each load} \times \text{its Y- distance}}{\text{Sum of loads}}$$

$$\text{Load Center (X Coordinate)} = \frac{\text{Sum of each load} \times \text{its X- distance}}{\text{Sum of loads}}$$

By applying these formulas to the example farmstead in Figure 4-18, it is determined that the optimum location for the central distribution point is at the 113Y by 89X coordinate as shown in Figure 4-19.

| Building | Load | X-distance | X-distance × Load | Y-distance | Y-distance × Load |
|---|---|---|---|---|---|
| Poultry house | 125A | 80-ft. | 10,000 | 200-ft. | 25,000 |
| Shop | 100A | 150-ft. | 15,000 | 100-ft. | 10,000 |
| Barn | 75A | 140-ft. | 10,500 | 180-ft. | 13,500 |
| House | 200A | 45-ft. | 9,000 | 40-ft. | 8,000 |
| Totals | 500A | | 44,500 | | 56,500 |

$$\text{Load Center Y- Coordinate} = \frac{\text{Sum of each load} \times \text{its Y- distance}}{\text{Sum of loads}} = \frac{56,500}{500} = 113\text{-ft.}$$

$$\text{Load Center X- Coordinate} = \frac{\text{Sum of each load} \times \text{its X- distance}}{\text{Sum of loads}} = \frac{44,500}{500} = 89\text{-ft.}$$

**The optimum location calculation for the central distribution point in Figure 4-18.**

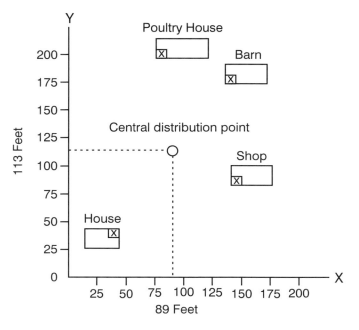

**4-19. The location of the central distribution point for the example farmstead.**

Once the location of the central distribution point has been established, the size of the main service entrance can be determined. Since it is not likely that all buildings on a site will draw their maximum rated amperage at the same time, the *NEC* allows the main service entrance to be smaller than the sum of the building services. Table 4-2 lists the demand factors to be used in determining the minimum size for a farm's main service.

## Table 4-2
## Determining Main Service Capacity

| Individual Building Demand Load | Demand Factor Percent |
| --- | --- |
| Residence load | 100 |
| Largest load (other than residence) | 100 |
| Second largest load | 75 |
| Third largest load | 65 |
| Remaining loads | 50 |

Source: *NEC* Table 220-41. Reprinted with permission from NFPA 70-1996, the *National Electrical Code*, Copyright © 1995, National Fire Protection Association, Quincy, MA 02269. This reprinted material is not the complete and official position of the National Fire Protection Association on the referenced subject, which is represented only by the standard in its entirety.

By applying these demand factors to the example farmstead in Figure 4-18 it is determined that a 449A main service is required. Since service equipment comes in only standard ratings—100A, 200A, 300A, 400A, 500A, 600A, etc.—a larger standard sized service would be selected. For our example farm, we might select a 500A or 600A main service.

# SELECTING AND SIZING BUILDING SERVICE CONDUCTORS

Building service conductors are used to supply electricity from the main service to the service entrance of various farm buildings. These conductors can either be underground or overhead. Regardless of the method of installation, the conductors must be of the correct type and size for the particular use.

**Building Service Conductor Types.** Since building service conductors are outside, they are subjected to harsh environmental conditions. Because overhead feeder conductors are exposed to the weather, they must be rated for use in wet conditions. Underground service conductors must either be protected from soil contact by the use of approved conduit, or they must be approved for direct burial in the soil.

Overhead service conductors are usually made of aluminum, because aluminum is lighter and less expensive than copper. Most overhead aluminum services consist of two insulated wires and an uninsulated neutral wire wrapped together. The neutral wire is called a *messenger*, and contains one steel strand for strength. The three wire set is referred to as triplex conductor. Another type, called quadruplex, consists of three insulated conductors and a messenger. The insulation on overhead conductors is usually Type XHHW, which is listed for use in wet locations.

Building service conductors are often placed underground. Underground conductors eliminate the hazards of machinery contact and weather damage associated with overhead installations. The *NEC* approves Types UF and USE cable, as well as Type USE individual conductors for direct burial.

**Sizing Building Service Conductors.** The size of commonly used electrical wire is expressed by American Wire Gauge (AWG) numbers. AWG numbers range from No. 40 for a wire about the diameter of a

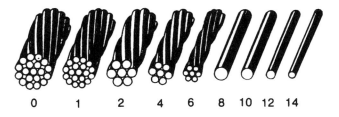

**4-20. Actual size of electric wires.**

human hair to No. 0000 or 4/0 for a wire about ½ inch in diameter. (Larger wires, measured in circular mills, are also available.)

Building service conductors, like all other conductors, must be sized with two concerns in mind. First, the conductor must have sufficient *ampacity*, or current carrying capacity, to supply current to the building being served. Using a conductor with insufficient ampacity will result in insulation and/or conductor damage. This can result in a fire.

Second, conductors should be sized so voltage drop in the circuit will not be excessive. *Voltage drop* is the term used to describe the decrease in voltage that occurs any time electricity flows through a conductor. Since voltage is the "electrical pressure" that causes current to flow through resistance, voltage drop can be thought of as the voltage "used" in pushing current through the resistance of the circuit conductors.

Voltage drop is the product of two factors: (a) the resistance of the circuit conductors and (b) the amount of current flowing in the circuit. Voltage drop in a circuit will increase with increases in conductor resistance and/or circuit amperage. The relationship between voltage drop, conductor resistance and circuit amperage is given by Formula 4-1, which is based on Ohm's Law.

$$E_d = I \times R$$

| **Formula 4-1.** |

where,

$E_d$ = voltage drop
$I$ = circuit amperage
$R$ = resistance of the conductors, in ohms

According to Formula 4-1, the voltage drop in a 240 volt circuit having a load current of 45 amperes, and a conductor resistance of 0.18 Ω would be 8.1 volts (45A × .18 Ω = 8.1V). Figure 4-21 shows the voltmeter readings that would be expected at the source and at the load in this circuit. The difference between these two readings is equal to the calculated voltage drop of 8.1 volts.

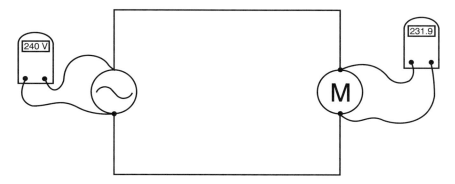

**4-21. Motor circuit with two volt meters—one at source and one at load.**

Excessive voltage drop has a negative effect on circuit loads. For example, at 90 percent of rated voltage (10 percent voltage drop), an electric motor will produce only 81 percent of its rated horsepower. In addition to inefficient load operation, the energy lost is dissipated as heat. Thus, excessive voltage drop may cause overheating of circuit wiring.

Voltage drop can be decreased by reducing the resistance of the circuit conductors, reducing the amperage of the load, or a combination of the two methods. Reducing the resistance of circuit conductors may be accomplished by decreasing the length of the circuit and/or increasing the size of conductors used to wire the circuit. Load amperage can be reduced by carefully selecting equipment and by connecting dual-voltage loads for high-voltage operation.

The *NEC* 215-2(b) recommends that voltage drop in building service circuits should not exceed 3 percent. Likewise, voltage drop in branch circuits should not exceed 3 percent. Furthermore, according to the *NEC*, the maximum combined voltage drop for building service and branch circuits should not exceed a total of 5 percent.

Several tables have been developed for use in selecting circuit conductors. Correct use of these tables will ensure that the conductors selected will meet circuit ampacity and voltage drop requirements. Table 4-3 shows an example table. The heading on this table indicates that it can be used to select aluminum conductors that will limit voltage drop to 2 percent when used to provide single-phase 230-240 volt electricity to loads of 5 to 400 amperes located up to 800 feet away from the source.

Using a table to select the correct size building service conductors is a fairly simple process. The steps include:

## Table 4-3.
## NFEC-AWH Table 17

Minimum allowable size of conductor | Aluminum up to 400 amperes, 230-240 volts, single phase, based on 2 % voltage drop

Length of run in feet — Compare size shown below with size shown to left of double line. Use the larger size

| Load in Amps | In air cable or conduit UF | RH,RHW THW,THWN USE,NM,SE | THHN | Direct burial UF | Direct burial USE | Overhead Single | Overhead Triplex | 50 | 60 | 75 | 100 | 125 | 150 | 175 | 200 | 225 | 250 | 275 | 300 | 350 | 400 | 450 | 500 | 550 | 600 | 650 | 700 | 750 | 800 |
|---|---|---|---|---|---|---|---|---|---|---|---|---|---|---|---|---|---|---|---|---|---|---|---|---|---|---|---|---|---|
| 5 | 12 | 12 | 12 | 12 | 12 | 8 | 8 | 12 | 12 | 12 | 12 | 12 | 12 | 12 | 10 | 10 | 10 | 10 | 8 | 8 | 8 | 6 | 6 | 6 | 6 | 6 | 6 | 4 | 4 |
| 7 | 12 | 12 | 12 | 12 | 12 | 8 | 8 | 12 | 12 | 12 | 12 | 12 | 10 | 10 | 10 | 8 | 8 | 8 | 8 | 6 | 6 | 6 | 6 | 4 | 4 | 4 | 4 | 4 | 4 |
| 10 | 12 | 12 | 12 | 12 | 12 | 8 | 8 | 12 | 12 | 12 | 10 | 10 | 8 | 8 | 8 | 8 | 6 | 6 | 6 | 6 | 4 | 4 | 4 | 4 | 3 | 3 | 3 | 2 | 2 |
| 15 | 12 | 12 | 12 | 12 | 12 | 8 | 8 | 12 | 12 | 10 | 8 | 8 | 8 | 6 | 6 | 6 | 4 | 4 | 4 | 4 | 3 | 3 | 2 | 2 | 2 | 1 | 1 | 1 | 0 |
| 20 | 10 | 10 | 10 | 10 | 10 | 8 | 8 | 10 | 10 | 8 | 8 | 6 | 6 | 6 | 4 | 4 | 4 | 4 | 3 | 3 | 2 | 2 | 1 | 1 | 0 | 0 | 0 | 00 | 00 |
| 25 | 10 | 10 | 10 | 10 | 10 | 8 | 8 | 10 | 8 | 8 | 6 | 6 | 4 | 4 | 4 | 4 | 3 | 3 | 2 | 2 | 1 | 1 | 0 | 0 | 00 | 00 | 00 | 000 | 000 |
| 30 | 8 | 8 | 8 | 8 | 8 | 8 | 8 | 8 | 8 | 6 | 4 | 4 | 4 | 3 | 3 | 2 | 2 | 1 | 0 | 0 | 00 | 00 | 00 | 000 | 000 | 000 | 000 | 000 | 4/0 |
| 35 | 6 | 8 | 8 | 6 | 8 | 8 | 8 | 8 | 8 | 6 | 6 | 4 | 4 | 3 | 3 | 2 | 2 | 1 | 1 | 0 | 0 | 00 | 00 | 000 | 000 | 000 | 4/0 | 4/0 | 4/0 |
| 40 | 6 | 8 | 8 | 6 | 8 | 8 | 8 | 8 | 6 | 6 | 4 | 4 | 3 | 3 | 2 | 2 | 1 | 1 | 0 | 0 | 00 | 00 | 000 | 000 | 4/0 | 4/0 | 4/0 | 250 | 250 |
| 45 | 4 | 6 | 8 | 4 | 6 | 8 | 6 | 8 | 6 | 6 | 4 | 4 | 3 | 2 | 2 | 1 | 1 | 0 | 0 | 00 | 00 | 000 | 000 | 4/0 | 4/0 | 250 | 250 | 250 | 300 |
| 50 | 4 | 6 | 6 | 4 | 6 | 8 | 6 | 6 | 6 | 4 | 4 | 3 | 2 | 2 | 1 | 1 | 0 | 0 | 00 | 00 | 000 | 000 | 4/0 | 4/0 | 250 | 250 | 300 | 300 | 300 |
| 60 | 3 | 4 | 6 | 3 | 4 | 6 | 4 | 6 | 6 | 4 | 3 | 2 | 2 | 1 | 0 | 0 | 00 | 00 | 000 | 4/0 | 4/0 | 250 | 250 | 300 | 300 | 300 | 350 | 350 | 350 |
| 70 | 2 | 3 | 4 | 2 | 3 | 6 | 4 | 6 | 4 | 4 | 3 | 2 | 1 | 0 | 0 | 00 | 00 | 000 | 000 | 4/0 | 4/0 | 250 | 300 | 300 | 350 | 350 | 400 | 400 | 500 |
| 80 | 1 | 2 | 3 | 1 | 2 | 4 | 3 | 4 | 4 | 3 | 2 | 1 | 0 | 0 | 00 | 00 | 000 | 000 | 4/0 | 4/0 | 250 | 300 | 300 | 350 | 350 | 400 | 500 | 500 | 500 |
| 90 | 0 | 2 | 2 | 0 | 2 | 4 | 3 | 4 | 4 | 3 | 2 | 1 | 0 | 00 | 00 | 000 | 000 | 4/0 | 4/0 | 250 | 300 | 300 | 350 | 400 | 400 | 500 | 500 | 500 | 600 |
| 100 | 0 | 1 | 2 | 0 | 1 | 4 | 2 | 4 | 3 | 2 | 1 | 0 | 00 | 00 | 000 | 000 | 4/0 | 4/0 | 250 | 300 | 300 | 350 | 400 | 400 | 500 | 500 | 600 | 600 | 600 |
| 115 | 00 | 0 | 1 | 00 | 0 | 3 | 1 | 4 | 3 | 2 | 1 | 0 | 00 | 000 | 000 | 4/0 | 4/0 | 250 | 300 | 300 | 350 | 400 | 500 | 500 | 600 | 600 | 600 | 700 | 700 |
| 130 | 000 | 00 | 0 | 000 | 00 | 2 | 0 | 3 | 2 | 1 | 0 | 00 | 000 | 000 | 4/0 | 250 | 300 | 300 | 350 | 400 | 500 | 500 | 600 | 700 | 700 | 750 | 800 | | |
| 150 | 4/0 | 000 | 00 | 4/0 | 000 | 1 | 00 | 2 | 2 | 1 | 00 | 000 | 000 | 4/0 | 250 | 250 | 300 | 300 | 350 | 400 | 500 | 500 | 600 | 600 | 700 | 750 | 800 | 900 | 900 |
| 175 | | 4/0 | 000 | | 4/0 | 0 | 000 | 2 | 1 | 0 | 00 | 000 | 4/0 | 250 | 300 | 300 | 350 | 400 | 400 | 500 | 600 | 600 | 700 | 750 | 800 | 900 | 900 | 1M | |
| 200 | | 250 | 4/0 | | 250 | 00 | 4/0 | 1 | 0 | 00 | 000 | 4/0 | 250 | 300 | 300 | 350 | 400 | 500 | 500 | 600 | 600 | 700 | 700 | 750 | 900 | 900 | 1M | | |
| 225 | | 300 | 250 | | 300 | 000 | 250 | 1 | 0 | 00 | 000 | 4/0 | 250 | 300 | 350 | 400 | 500 | 500 | 500 | 600 | 700 | 750 | 900 | 1M | 1M | | | | |
| 250 | | 350 | 300 | | 350 | 4/0 | 250 | 0 | 00 | 000 | 4/0 | 250 | 300 | 350 | 400 | 500 | 500 | 600 | 700 | 700 | 900 | 1M | | | | | | | |
| 275 | | 500 | 350 | | 500 | 4/0 | 300 | 0 | 00 | 000 | 4/0 | 250 | 300 | 400 | 400 | 500 | 500 | 600 | 600 | 750 | 900 | 1M | | | | | | | |
| 300 | | 500 | 400 | | 500 | 250 | 350 | 00 | 00 | 000 | 250 | 300 | 350 | 400 | 500 | 500 | 600 | 600 | 700 | 800 | 900 | 1M | | | | | | | |
| 325 | | 600 | 500 | | 600 | 300 | 400 | 00 | 000 | 4/0 | 250 | 300 | 400 | 500 | 500 | 600 | 600 | 700 | 750 | 900 | 1M | | | | | | | | |
| 350 | | 700 | 500 | | 700 | 300 | 500 | 00 | 000 | 4/0 | 250 | 300 | 350 | 400 | 500 | 600 | 600 | 700 | 750 | 800 | 900 | | | | | | | | |
| 375 | | 700 | 600 | | 700 | 350 | 500 | 000 | 000 | 4/0 | 300 | 350 | 400 | 500 | 500 | 600 | 700 | 700 | 800 | 900 | 1M | | | | | | | | |
| 400 | | 900 | 700 | | 900 | 400 | 600 | 000 | 4/0 | 250 | 300 | 400 | 500 | 600 | 600 | 700 | 750 | 900 | 900 | | | | | | | | | | |

Source: *NFEC Agricultural Wiring Handbook.* National Food and Energy Council, 601 Business Loop 70 W, Ste 216D, Columbia, Missouri 65203. Phone: (573) 875-7155.

1. Determine the building's demand load (amperage) in accordance with *NEC* Section 220-40.

2. Determine the total one-way distance (in feet) from the farm's main service to the building's service entrance.

3. Choose a suitable type of conductor to serve the building based on the type of installation (overhead or underground, single conductors or cable, etc.), availability, and cost.

4. Select the proper conductor size table based on: wire material (copper or aluminum), service voltage (120V, 240V, etc.), and acceptable voltage drop.

5. Determine proper wire size (based on voltage drop) from the right-hand columns in accordance with the load amperage (building demand load) and distance. If no table value for load amperage and/or distance exactly matches your situation, use the next highest table value.

6. Determine proper wire size (based on ampacity) from the left-hand columns in accordance with the load amperage (building demand load), type of conductor to be used, and type of installation.

7. Compare the wire sizes selected in Step 5 and Step 6. If different sizes were selected, choose the largest of the two sizes.

As an example, select the correct size building service conductor to provide 240 volt service to a building with a 110 ampere demand load. The building service entrance is located 160 feet away from the farm's main service. Assume that the voltage drop is to be limited to 2 percent using aluminum Type UF cable buried directly in ground. (Note: In describing the example situation, Steps 1–3 have been completed.)

Based on the situation described, use Table 4-3 to select the correct conductor size. Since the demand load for the building (110A) does not match any of the values listed under "Load in Amps," use the next highest table value of 115 amperes. Also, since the distance of 160 feet does not exactly match any of the values listed under the "Length of Run in Feet," use the next highest table value of 175 feet. By locating the intersection of these two values (115A and 175-ft.) on the right-hand side of the table, AWG #000 wire can be used to meet our voltage drop requirement (2 percent maximum).

By going to the left-hand side of the table and finding the point of intersection between the load value (115A) and the conductor type and installation (Type UF cable, direct burial), AWG #00 wire will meet the ampacity requirements.

Since different AWG wire sizes were selected to meet ampacity and voltage drop requirements, select the largest of the two wires. Thus, Type UF cable having AWG #000 aluminum conductors will be used for the building service conductor.

# SUMMARY

Electricity generated at an electrical power plant must be transmitted and distributed to individual customers. The electric utility company transmits electricity from the power plant to a site's service point. Installation and maintenance of this part of the electrical system is the responsibility of the utility.

Electricity delivered by the electric company to the service point must be made available to the buildings and load centers on the site. On most farms, the electricity is distributed using a central point distribution system. With this system, the main service entrance is generally located on a pole in the farmyard. Building service conductors carry electricity from this main service entrance to the individual building service entrances. Wiring for this part of the electrical system is the responsibility of the customer. A qualified electrician should install or inspect all electrical work from the service point on.

Proper grounding is essential for a safe, functional electrical system. Two types of grounding are important: system grounding and equipment grounding. System grounding means that current carrying portions of the electrical system are connected to the earth. Equipment grounding means that conductive equipment not normally intended to carry electrical current is connected to earth. The purpose of both equipment grounding and system grounding is safety.

An operator can supply valuable assistance to utility company representatives and electricians in planning the electrical system. The operator can help determine the demand load for various buildings, help locate and size the main service entrance, and provide information necessary for sizing building service conductors. A knowledgeable person is an asset in planning a wiring system. However, utility company employees and qualified electricians may complete the actual installation.

# REVIEW QUESTIONS

1. Describe the electrical power distribution system from the power plant to the service entrance of a farm building.

2. What are the primary advantages and disadvantages of a central point distribution system?

3. List the primary functions of a building service entrance panel.

4. Define system grounding and describe its purpose.

5. Define equipment grounding and describe its purpose.

6. Explain the difference between a 3- and 4-wire 120/240 volt single-phase electrical service.

7. Define stray voltage and explain why a stray voltage problem may decrease production if present in a livestock or dairy building.

8. Define the terms "total connected load" and "demand load" as applied to a farm building.

9. Define ampacity and voltage drop and explain why these factors must be considered in sizing electrical conductors.

## APPLYING THE CONCEPTS

1. If possible, have a representative of a local electrical power utility speak to your class, describing the electrical power distribution system serving your community.

2. Identify the components of the electrical system serving your school, home or farm. (Note: Do this visually; do not come into physical or electrical contact with any component.)

3. Set up the ground-fault circuit illustrated below. Close the switch and observe the fuse. Describe what happened and explain why it happened

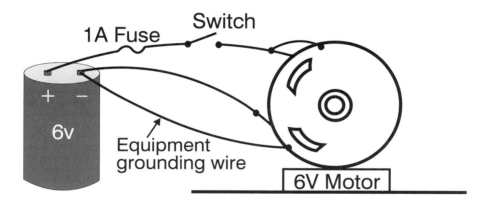

4. Determine the (a) total connected load and (b) demand load for a non-residential farm building containing the following electrical loads. Assume that the lights, the 1 hp motor, and the electric heater operate without diversity.

    15 lights (120 volts)
    20 DCOs (120 volts)
    One, 1 hp electric motor (240 volts)
    Four, 1/2 hp motors (240 volts)
    One, 4000 Watt electric heater (240 volts)

5. Assuming no additional electrical loads are expected, what is the minimum size service entrance panel that should be selected for the building described in Problem 4?

6. Determine the electrical load center of the farmstead illustrated below. Also, select a main service entrance for the farm. Demand loads are given above each building. Location of each building service entrance is marked with an **X**. (Note: You may wish to develop a computer spreadsheet to use in solving this problem.)

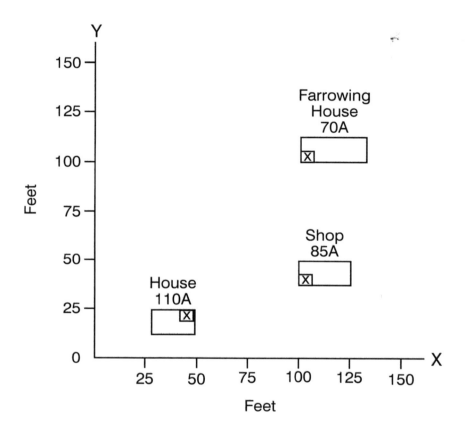

7. Size building service conductors for each of the buildings in Problem 6. Assume 240 volt service with underground Type USE aluminum conductors. Limit voltage drop to 2 percent. (Note: Estimate distances based on the scaled drawing of the farmstead and the placement of the meter pole.)

# 5

# ELECTRICAL WIRING: MATERIALS, DEVICES, AND PROCEDURES

Safe and efficient use of electric power is important in agriculture. This requires both the selection of approved wiring materials and devices and correct installation. As always, only qualified individuals should perform electrical wiring jobs.

All large electrical wiring jobs should be approved by local authorities prior to being placed in service. Applicable electrical and building code requirements should be strictly followed by any person doing an electrical wiring job.

**5.1. This greenhouse is just one of the many agricultural structures requiring specialized wiring materials and methods.**

121

# OBJECTIVES

This chapter covers important principles of electrical wiring. After completing the chapter, you will:

1. Explain the importance of safety in using electricity, including the effects of shock and safety precautions.

2. Name organizations concerned with electrical safety and explain the importance of the *National Electrical Code* and UL label.

3. Describe the three agricultural building environments and list general requirements for wiring and materials used in these environments.

4. Differentiate between branch and feeder circuits and describe the wiring of 120 volt and 240 volt branch and feeder circuits, including color coding and polarity requirements.

**TERMS**

backwiring
balanced load
branch circuits
cable
cable ripper
circuit breaker
conduit
duplex convenience outlet (DCO)
electric shock
equipment grounding conductor
feeder circuit
fibrillation
fluorescent light
4-way switch
fuse
grounded conductor
ground-fault circuit interrupter (GFCI)
hand hacksaw
incandescent light

individual branch circuit
inverse-time characteristic
metallic conduit
*National Electrical Code (NEC)*
National Fire Protection Association (NFPA)
nondelay
nonmetallic conduit
pole
special purpose outlet (SPO)
switch loop
3-way switch
throw
time-delay
Type S fuse
Underwriters' Laboratories, Inc. (UL)
ungrounded conductor
wire nuts
wire stripper

5. Differentiate between building service entrance panels and subpanels and describe how the wiring of subpanels differs based on location.

6. Describe different types of overcurrent and ground-fault protection devices.

7. Explain wiring materials and installation methods.

8. Plan and wire branch circuits to function as specified.

9. Describe the use of incandescent, fluorescent, and high intensity discharge lighting.

10. Correctly size and use electrical boxes based on *NEC* requirements.

11. Demonstrate the correct use of tools and equipment to perform basic wiring tasks.

# ELECTRICAL SAFETY

AC electricity is potentially hazardous and can be fatal. (DC electricity also poses similar hazards.) This section will describe the effects of 60 Hz AC electricity on the human body, present general electrical safety precautions, and discuss organizations concerned with electrical safety.

## *EFFECTS OF ELECTRICITY ON HUMANS*

***Electric shock*** occurs when electrical current passes through the body. Electric shock can occur due to poor equipment design, electrical faults, human error, or a combination of factors. The severity of an electric shock varies somewhat based on the age, gender, and physical condition of the victim. The amount of current flow through the body required to kill a person is remarkably small.

Most people can feel a tingling sensation when as little as one milliampere (1 mA or .001 ampere) of current flows through their body. Currents of up to 5 mA are felt more strongly, but do not usually cause severe pain. However, this level of current may contribute to injury by startling a person and causing a fall or other accident.

Ten mA and above passing through the body is extremely painful. Despite this pain, victims are often unable to release the conductor because of involuntary muscle contractions. For obvious reasons, this level of current flow is known as the "can't let go current." Prolonged current flow of this level may lead to fatigue, collapse, and even death.

If current flow through the body exceeds 100 mA, it begins to interfere with the operation of the heart. ***Fibrillation*** prevents the heart from pumping blood, causing death within minutes unless the fibrillation is stopped. At currents of over 300 mA, the contraction of the heart muscles is so severe that fibrillation is prevented. If the victim is removed from the circuit quickly enough, the heart will likely resume its normal rhythm. Since breathing may have ceased, artificial respiration may be required.

Based on the preceding information, it is concluded that: (a) any amount of current flow through the body is potentially dangerous and (b) current flow through the body of between 100 and 300 mA is most likely to cause death. (By way of comparison, a 100 watt light bulb operating on 120 volt current draws 830 mA of current.) Figure 5-2 shows the effects of various levels of current (60 Hz) flowing through the human body.

| Effects of 60 H$_z$ Electric Shock | |
|---|---|
| **Current intensity—<br>1 second contact** | **Effect** |
| 1 milliampere | Threshold of perception. |
| 5 milliamperes | Accepted as maximum harmless current intensity. |
| 10-20 milliamperes | Maxiumum "let-go" current before sustained muscular contraction. |
| 50 milliamperes | Pain.  Possible fainting, exhaustion, mechanical injury, heart and respiratory functions continue. |
| 100-300 milliamperes | Ventricular fibrillation will start but respiratory center remains intact. |
| 6 amperes | Sustained myocardial contraction followed by normal heart rhythm. Temporary respiratory paralysis. Burns if current density is high. |

Source: Wolf, S. and R. Smith. *Student Reference Manual for Electronic Instrumentation Laboratories.* Prentice-Hall. 1990.

**5-2. Effects of various current levels on the human body.**

Current, not voltage, shocks (or kills) people and other animals. According to Ohm's Law, in a circuit with a constant voltage, the amount of current flow is determined by the resistance of the circuit. In the case of electrical shock, the human body becomes a conductor in the electrical circuit. Researchers have determined that dry skin may have as much as 500,000 $\Omega$ (500 k$\Omega$) of resistance. On the other hand, wet skin may have as little as 1000 $\Omega$ (1 k$\Omega$) of resistance.

Thus, on a cool, dry day a person might use a tool having an electrical fault and, because of high skin resistance, receive only a slight tingle. On a hot, humid day, the same person using the same faulty electrical tool might receive a fatal electrical shock due to decreased skin resistance. For this reason, any electrical tool that causes a tingle, no matter how slight, should be removed from service and repaired.

Time of contact, as well as magnitude of current flow, is a key factor in determining the severity of electrical shock. Researchers have determined that, in 5 percent of cases, electrical contact can be fatal if it exceeds the current value specified in Formula 5-1.

$$I = \frac{116}{\sqrt{t}}$$

$\boxed{\textbf{Formula 5-1.}}$

Where,

  $I$ = current flow through the body, in mA

  $t$ = time duration of current flow, in seconds

  116 = a constant

Based on Formula 5-1, there is a 5 percent chance of fatality when a current of 116 mA flows through a human body for one second. The necessary calculations are shown below.

$$I = \frac{116}{\sqrt{t}}$$

$$= \frac{116}{\sqrt{1 \text{ sec.}}}$$

$$= 116 \text{ mA}$$

## ELECTRICAL SAFETY PRECAUTIONS

When electrical devices are properly installed and used, electricity is a safe source of energy. In fact, most of our lives are spent surrounded by electricity and electrical devices without ill effects. However, when wiring or electrical devices are not properly installed or used, a very real possibility for injury or death exists. All people working with or using electricity should know basic electrical safety precautions. Several important safety precautions follow.

**De-energize electrical branch circuits before making any repairs or connections.** Always de-energize the circuit by removing the fuse(s) or switching the circuit breaker to the "off" position. To make sure that you de-energize the correct circuit, turn on a light or other load known to be on the circuit to be repaired. As an alternative to this, check the circuit with a voltmeter both before and after de-energizing. (Note: It is essential to verify that the load or voltmeter works before de-energizing the circuit.

If either is defective, and you only check after you think the circuit is de-energized, you may wind up working on a live circuit!)

**Place a tag on the panel** indicating that circuit repairs are being made and that the circuit should not be re-energized. If possible, lock the panel door to prevent someone from accidentally re-energizing the circuit. (Note: Circuit tagging and lock-out may be required by law, code, or policy.)

**Shut off power at the service entrance panel's main disconnect before making any connections at the service entrance panel.** This will de-energize the "load side" of the service. Be aware that the "line side" of the service is still energized, so be extremely careful not to make contact with any service entrance conductor.

Always remember, **circuits are de-energized only on the load side past the point where they have been opened or disconnected.**

**Do not attempt to do any wiring job or electrical repair work if you have any doubts as to safety or proper procedures.** When in doubt, do not guess! Get the services of a qualified electrician.

**Have wiring jobs inspected prior to placing them in service.** In many locations, this is a legal requirement. In all cases, this is a good idea. If the inspection reveals sub-standard work, problems can be corrected before they endanger either people or property. If the inspection indicates that the work meets all applicable standards, the nominal inspection fee is a small price to pay for the peace of mind.

Following proper safety precautions in working with electricity is of the utmost importance. Failure to follow proper safety precautions may result in serious injury or death. A sound understanding of electricity, safe work habits, and common sense are essential.

# ORGANIZATIONS CONCERNED WITH ELECTRICAL SAFETY

Many groups ranging from insurance companies to farm organizations are concerned with electrical safety. Two of these organizations are the National Fire Protection Association and the Underwriters' Laboratories, Inc. These have an important role in electrical safety codes and standards.

The *National Fire Protection Association (NFPA)* is a nonprofit organization devoted to promoting and improving the science and methods of fire protection.

Since 1897, the NFPA has published the **National Electrical Code® (NEC®)**\*. The purpose of the *NEC* is to assure safe installation of electrical wiring and devices for the protection of life and property. The *NEC* is not law. However, many state and local electrical codes (which do have the force of law) are based on the *NEC*, either in whole or in part. Thus, indirectly, the *NEC* serves as a national standard. A new, revised edition of the *NEC* is published every three years.

The **Underwriters' Laboratories, Inc. (UL)** is a nationally recognized nonprofit organization that provides a voluntary product testing and list-

**5-3. National Electrical Code (NEC).**

ing program. Manufacturers submit electrical materials, devices, and equipment to UL. UL scientists and engineers conduct tests on the products to determine if they operate safely and prevent electrical shock and/or fire.

If a product passes the UL tests, the item is listed in a UL listing publication. Once listed, the manufacturer is permitted to display the UL label on the product. Follow-up testing of listed products ensures continued compliance with UL standards.

When selecting materials for electrical use, select only materials that are UL listed. Figure 5-4 shows a UL label on a fused switch package.

The UL label indicates that a product meets minimum standards for

**5-4. Arrow points to the UL label.**

---

\**National Electrical Code®* and *NEC®* are registered trademarks of the National Fire Protection Association, Inc., Quincy, MA 02269.

safety and quality only when the product is used for its intended purpose. A UL listed product may pose a serious safety hazard if used for a purpose or in a situation for which the product was not intended.

# BUILDING GROUPS AND WIRING REQUIREMENTS

Agricultural buildings often present adverse environmental conditions that must be considered in planning and installing electrical circuits. Excessive dust, moisture, and corrosive environments are common. *NEC* Article 547 specifically deals with agricultural buildings.

## BUILDING GROUPS

As a general rule, agricultural buildings can be divided into three groups: dry buildings, dusty and/or damp buildings, and corrosive environment buildings.

### Dry Buildings

Dry buildings are not normally subject to damp or wet conditions. Typical dry buildings include shops, machinery storage buildings, and detached garages. Buildings in this group are exempt from *NEC* Article 547. However, other applicable *NEC* and/or local requirements must be followed.

### Dusty and/or Damp Buildings

Buildings in this group are those where excessive dust and moisture may accumulate. Typical buildings include poultry, livestock, and fish confinement facilities.

### Corrosive Environment Buildings

Buildings in this group include areas where poultry and livestock excrement may cause corrosive vapors, areas where corrosive particles might combine with water, and areas that are damp and wet due to periodic washing.

## NEC ARTICLE 547

Article 547 of the *NEC* requires that special wiring materials, devices, and procedures be used in agricultural building having dusty/damp and/or corrosive environments. Type UF cable (among others) is approved for use in these two building groups (547-4). Dustproof and weatherproof boxes, fittings, and wiring devices are required in dusty and/or damp buildings [547-4(a) and 547-5(a)]. Enclosures appropriate for the conditions encountered are required in corrosive environment buildings [547-5(b)]. Electric motors for these two building groups must be totally enclosed or otherwise designed to minimize the entrance of dust, moisture, and corrosive materials (547-6).

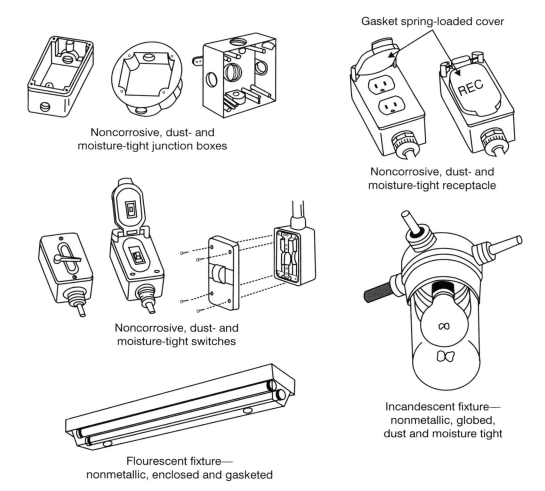

Noncorrosive, dust- and
moisture-tight junction boxes

Gasket spring-loaded cover

Noncorrosive, dust- and
moisture-tight receptacle

Noncorrosive, dust- and
moisture-tight switches

Incandescent fixture—
nonmetallic, globed,
dust and moisture tight

Flourescent fixture—
nonmetallic, enclosed and gasketed

**5-5. Noncorrosive and moisture-tight junction boxes, receptacles, switches, and light fixtures.**

Lighting fixtures used in dusty/damp and/or corrosive buildings must be installed to minimize the entrance of dust, foreign material, moisture, and corrosive material [547-7(a)]. Appropriate guards must be provided if lighting fixtures are exposed to physical damage [547-7(b)]. Watertight lighting fixtures are required where they are exposed to moisture [547-7(c)]. Figure 5-5 shows several devices and boxes for use in dusty/damp or corrosive building environments.

*NEC* Section 547 contains other requirements for agricultural buildings having dusty, damp, and/or corrosive environments. All applicable *NEC* requirements should be followed when planning and installing electrical wiring in these buildings.

# BRANCH AND FEEDER CIRCUITS

All circuits in a building originate at the building's service entrance panel. These circuits can either be branch circuits or feeder circuits.

## *BRANCH CIRCUITS*

**Branch circuits** originate at the service entrance panel (or at a subpanel) and serve individual loads or groups of loads. The circuit breaker (or fuse) in the service entrance panel (or in the subpanel) serves as the overcurrent protection device for branch circuit conductors. Typical branch circuits have a nominal voltage of either 120 or 240 volts. Actual voltages may vary slightly.

### *120-Volt Branch Circuits*

These circuits normally serve general purpose receptacle outlets and lighting fixtures rated for operation at this voltage. No more than 10 duplex convenience outlets (DCOs) or 10 light fixtures (150 watt maximum) should be wired on a single 20 ampere, 120-volt branch circuit. DCOs and lights can be wired on the same circuit, but a heavy load on a DCO may cause lights on the circuit to flicker.

Included in a 120-volt branch circuit is one ungrounded (hot) conductor, one grounded (neutral) conductor, and one equipment grounding conductor. [Note: In a 120-volt circuit, the grounded (neutral) conductor carries the same level of current as does the ungrounded (hot) conductor.] The grounded conductor is white or natural gray, and the equipment grounding conductor is either bare, solid green, or green with one or more yellow

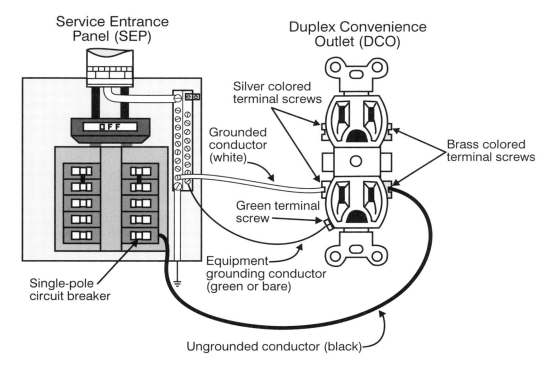

Service Entrance Panel (SEP)

Duplex Convenience Outlet (DCO)

Silver colored terminal screws

Grounded conductor (white)

Brass colored terminal screws

Green terminal screw

Single-pole circuit breaker

Equipment grounding conductor (green or bare)

Ungrounded conductor (black)

**5-6. Wiring connections between service entrance panel and 120 V DCO (duplex convenience outlet).**

stripes [*NEC* 210-5(a)]. The *NEC* does not require that the ungrounded conductor be of any specific color, except that it may not be of any color reserved for either the grounded or equipment grounding conductor. In practice, the ungrounded conductor is usually black or red. Figure 5-6 shows the wiring schematic for a 120 volt branch circuit serving a single DCO.

120-volt circuits should be planned and installed so the total load is balanced at the building's service entrance panel. ***Balanced load*** means the 120-volt load between one ungrounded (hot) service conductor and the grounded (neutral) service conductor should be approximately equal to the 120-volt load between the second ungrounded service conductor and the grounded service conductor. Unbalanced 120 volt loads may cause tripping of the main disconnect—even though the service is of adequate size.

As an example, assume that four 120-volt circuits are to be connected to a building's service entrance panel. Two are lighting circuits having a load of 12 amperes each. The other two are motor circuits each with a 16 ampere load. If the two lighting circuits are connected between one

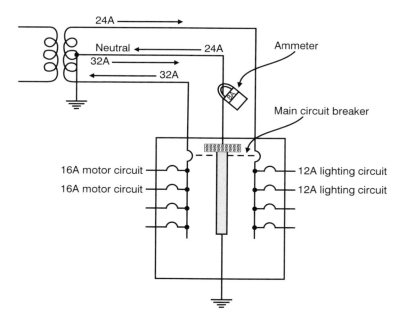

**5-7. Unbalanced 120 V electrical loads.**

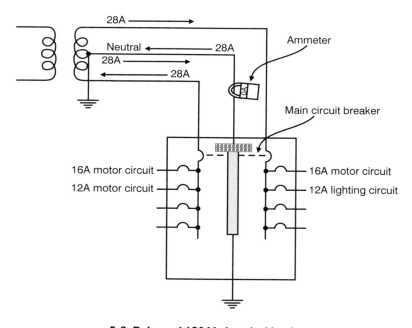

**5-8. Balanced 120 V electrical loads.**

ungrounded service conductor and the grounded service conductor, and the two motor circuits are connected between the second ungrounded service conductor and the grounded service conductor, the 120-volt loads will not be balanced. Note in Figure 5-7 that the grounded (neutral) service conductor carries 8 amperes, which is the difference in the total load on each ungrounded service conductor.

If one lighting circuit and one motor circuit are connected between each ungrounded service conductor and the grounded service conductor, the 120-volt loads will be balanced (Figure 5-8). When the 120-volt loads are perfectly balanced, the ungrounded (neutral) service conductor carries no current. While it is usually not possible to exactly balance 120-volt loads, circuits should be planned to be as closely balanced as possible.

## 240-Volt Branch Circuits

Generally, 240-volt branch circuits serve specific loads, such as stationary motors and appliances, or special purpose outlets. A *special purpose outlet (SPO)* is a receptacle outlet sized and installed to serve a specific plug-and-cord connected appliance.

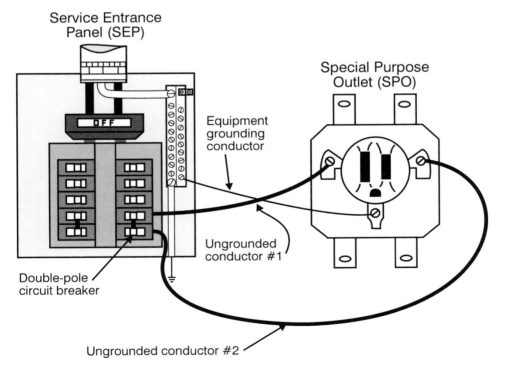

**5-9. Wiring connections between service entrance panel and 240 v SPO.**

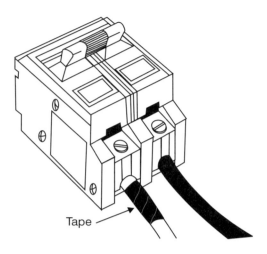

Tape

**5-10. A white conductor identified by wrapping it with black tape.**

Circuits operating at 240 volts have two ungrounded (hot) conductors and an equipment grounding conductor. A grounded (neutral) conductor is not required in a regular 240-volt circuit. Figure 5-9 shows the wiring schematic for a 240-volt branch circuit serving a SPO. Notice, the two ungrounded (hot) conductors are connected to a double-pole circuit breaker at the service entrance panel and to the two brass-colored terminal screws at the SPO. The equipment grounding conductor is connected to the neutral bar of the service entrance panel and to the green grounding screw at the SPO.

When wiring a 240-volt branch circuit using cable, the white conductor is used as an ungrounded (hot) conductor. The *NEC* allows this use as long as the white conductor is permanently identified as an ungrounded (hot) conductor at each location where it is visible and accessible (200-7 Exception No. 1). The conductor can be identified by painting a black band around it or by wrapping it with black tape (Figure 5-10).

Since 240 volt circuits are connected to both ungrounded conductors at the service entrance panel, load balancing is not a problem—240 volt circuits are always balanced.

## FEEDER CIRCUITS

A *feeder circuit* originates at the service entrance panel and supplies (or feeds) electrical power to a sub-panel. Overcurrent protection devices in the service entrance panel are sized to protect the feeder circuit conductors. Properly sized fuses or circuit breakers in the sub-panel provide overcurrent protection for the branch circuit(s) that originate at the sub-panel.

At the service entrance panel, the circuit connections for a feeder circuit are the same as for a 240-volt branch circuit. The two ungrounded (hot) conductors attach under separate terminals of a double-pole breaker. The equipment grounding conductor attaches to a terminal on the service entrance panel's neutral bar.

The feeder circuit connections at the sub-panel differ, depending on whether the sub-panel is in the same or a different building than the service entrance panel.

# SERVICE ENTRANCE PANELS AND SUBPANELS

Branch and feeder circuits originate at either the building service entrance panel or at a sub-panel. The sub-panel may be either in the same building as the service entrance panel or in a separate, nearby building.

## *SERVICE ENTRANCE PANELS*

Building service conductors supply electrical power to the service entrance panel of each building. A building provided with 120/240 volt service may have either 3-wire or 4-wire electrical service.

Each building should have only one service entrance. This allows all electrical power to be shut off by opening a single main disconnect. This enhances safety during maintenance and service.

Ideally, the service entrance panel should be surface-mounted on an interior wall of a clean, dry room. Surface-mounting on the interior of an insulated outside wall is the second best choice. Weatherproof service equipment surface-mounted on an outside wall is a third option. A service entrance panel should never be recessed into an outside wall. Condensation and corrosion will shorten its service life, reduce reliability, and may lead to unsafe conditions.

All service conductors should enter the service entrance panel from or near the bottom of the panel. All branch and feeder circuit conductors should also exit from the bottom or near the bottom of the panel. This minimizes the possibility of moisture damaging components of the service entrance panel.

## *SUB-PANELS*

Sub-panels receive electrical power from feeder circuits originating at a service entrance panel. A sub-panel may be located in the same building as the service entrance panel or in a different building. The feeder circuit connections that should be made at the sub-panel differ for these two situations.

## Sub-panel in Same Building

If the sub-panel is located in the same building as the service entrance panel, a separate grounding bar must be installed in the sub-panel and bonded to the metal cabinet. The sub-panel's neutral bar must not be electrically connected (or bonded) to the panel's metal cabinet. Also, there must be no electrical connection between the sub-panel's neutral bar and the separately installed grounding bar. The correct feeder circuit connections for a sub-panel located in the same building as the service entrance panel are shown in Figure 5-11.

In wiring a 120-volt branch circuit from the subpanel just described, the following connections would be made:

■ The ungrounded (hot) circuit conductor would be attached at the terminal of a single-pole circuit breaker.

■ The grounded (neutral) conductor would be connected to the neutral bar.

■ The equipment grounding conductor would be attached to the grounding bar.

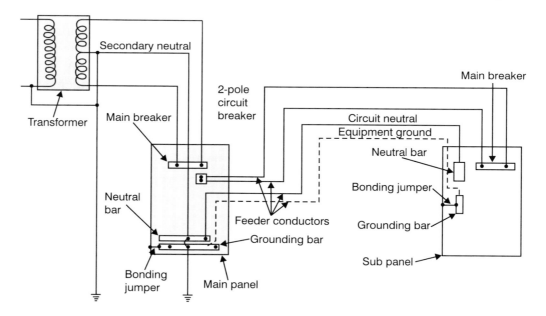

**5-11. Correct feeder circuit connections for a sub-panel located in the same building as the service panel.**

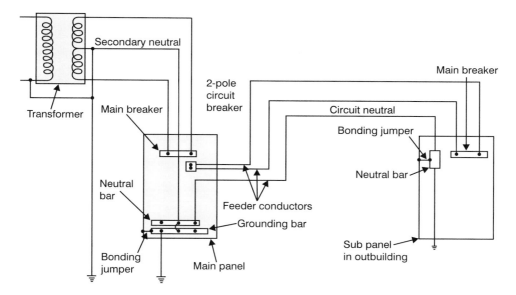

**5-12. Correct feeder circuit connections for a sub-panel located in another building.**

## Sub-panel in a Separate Building

If the sub-panel is located in a separate building from the main service entrance panel, the sub-panel is considered to be the service entrance for the building in which it is located. In this case, the sub-panel's neutral bar must be connected to a grounding electrode at the building. A separate grounding bar is not required. The metal sub-panel must be bonded to the neutral bar. Figure 5-12 shows the wiring of a sub-panel in a separate building.

## Sizing Sub-panels

A sub-panel should be sized to have sufficient capacity to serve all the branch circuits that will be connected to it. The same procedures used in sizing the service entrance panel (see Chapter 4) may be used to size a sub-panel.

# OVERCURRENT AND GROUND-FAULT PROTECTION

Overcurrent and ground-fault protection devices are intended to protect people and property from hazards in using electricity.

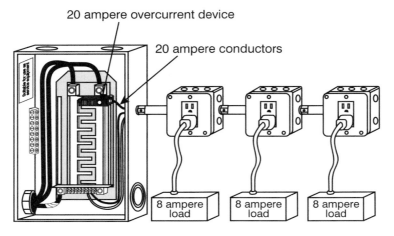

20 ampere overcurrent device

20 ampere conductors

5-13. Overcurrent pro-
tection from overloads.

8 ampere load    8 ampere load    8 ampere load

**24 ampere total load**

## OVERCURRENT PROTECTION DEVICES

Conductors have a certain maximum current-carrying capacity or ampacity. A properly sized overcurrent protection device (fuse or circuit
breaker) is installed in series with the hot (or ungrounded) conductor(s)
to ensure that the current flow in the circuit does not exceed the ampacity
of the circuit conductors (Figure 5-13). If current flow exceeds the overcurrent device's amperage rating, the device will open the circuit, causing
current flow to cease.

### Sizing Overcurrent Protection Devices

The general rule for sizing fuses or circuit breakers for non-motor branch
circuits is: **The overcurrent device must have a rating in amperes that
is not greater than the allowable ampacity of the wires that the device
protects.** *NEC* Article 240 covers general requirements for overcurrent
protection.

Table 5-1, based on *NEC* Table 310-16, lists ampacities for selected
sizes and types of copper conductors. Refer to the *NEC* for additional
information on conductor ampacities and overcurrent protection.

### Fuses

A *fuse* is a safety device that contains a short strip of alloy, called the
fuse link or element. The fuse link has a low melting point. When the
fuse is installed in a fuseholder, the fuse link becomes part of the circuit.

## Table 5-1
## Allowable Ampacities for Selected Copper Conductors*
## [30°C (86°F) Ambient Temperature]

| Wire Size AWG No. | Ampacity | |
| --- | --- | --- |
| | UF & NM Cable** | THW, THWN, RHW, XHHW Wire and USE Cable*** |
| 14***** | 15 | 15 |
| 12 | 20 | 20 |
| 10 | 30 | 30 |
| 8 | 40 | 50 |
| 6 | 55 | 65 |
| 4 | 70 | 85 |
| 3 | 85 | 100 |
| 2 | 95 | 115 |
| 1 | 110 | 130 |
| 1/0 | 125 | 150 |
| 2/0 | 145 | 175 |
| 3/0 | 165 | 200 |
| 4/0 | 195 | 230 |

*Applies only to insulated conductors rated 0 through 2000 volts with not more than 3 current-carrying conductors in cable, conduit, or directly buried in earth and prior to all applicable de-rating factors.

**Based on 60°C (140°F) conductor temperature rating.

***Based on 75°C (167°F) conductor temperature rating.

****AWG 14 wire should not be used to wire branch circuits in agricultural buildings.

If the current flow in the circuit becomes greater than the fuse's amperage rating, excess heat will be produced and the fuse link will melt, opening the circuit.

Fuses are of two basic types—plug or cartridge. Plug type fuses are available in sizes ranging from 1 to 30 amperes, with 15 and 20 ampere sizes being most common. Plug fuses may be either Edison base or *Type S* fuses (*NEC* 240-54). The threads on all sizes of Edison base fuses are the same. This is a potentially hazardous situation since nothing prevents an unknowing

5-14. Edison base fuse.

person from replacing a properly sized fuse with one having too high an amperage rating. Because of this hazard, the *NEC* only allows Edison base fuses to be used as replacements in existing installations, where there is no sign of tampering or over fusing [240-51(b)]. Figure 5-14 shows an Edison base fuse.

Type S fuses are often called "non-tamperable fuses" because each fuse size has a different screw thread. A Type S fuse is designed to be used with a special adapter. The adapter has standard Edison base threads on the outside and screws into a regular fuse holder. A spring barb on the outside projects into the fuse holder, preventing removal of the adapter. The adapter has special-sized threads inside. Only Type S fuses of the same (or smaller) amperage rating as the adapter will fit these special threads. This prevents circuit over fusing. A Type S fuse and adapter are shown in Figure 5-15.

**5-15. Non-tamperable fuse and adapter.**

Cartridge fuses are normally used in circuits carrying 30 amperes or more. Ferrule type cartridge fuses are used in circuits of up to 60 amperes. Knife-blade cartridge fuses are used in circuits rated at over 60 amperes. Figure 5-16 shows both types of cartridge fuses.

**5-16. Ferrule (left) and knife-blade cartridge (right) fuses.**

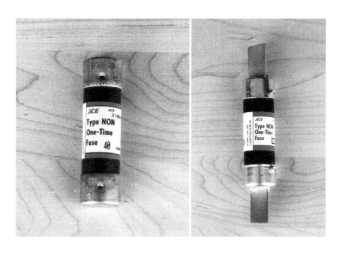

Both nondelay and time-delay plug and cartridge fuses are available. Nondelay (or fast-acting) fuses are designed to blow quickly when current flow exceeds the fuse's amperage rating. A time-delay fuse will carry a momentary overload of several times its rated amperage without blowing. But, a time-delay fuse will blow just like a nondelay fuse if a continuous small overload or a short circuit condition exists. Time-delay fuses are usually used in motor circuits, since an electric motor may momentarily draw up to six or more times its full-load current when starting.

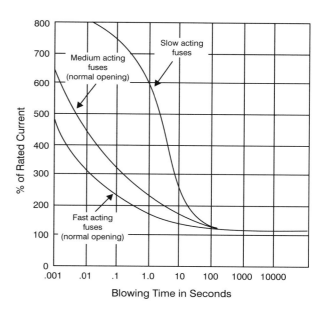

**5-17. Relative blowing time of typical fuses.**

All fuses have an inverse-time characteristic. This means that a fuse will blow faster as the overcurrent increases. Figure 5-17 shows this inverse-time characteristic for typical nondelay and time-delay fuses.

## Circuit Breakers

A *circuit breaker* is a popular and convenient overcurrent protection device. Circuit breakers are not one-time devices as are (most) fuses. When a circuit breaker trips, it can be reset by simply flipping its handle. (Note: The cause of the circuit breaker's tripping should always be determined and corrected before resetting the circuit breaker.)

A circuit breaker works like a combination fuse and switch. Rather than having a melting link as does a fuse, some circuit breakers have a bimetallic strip. When an overload occurs, the bimetallic strip heats. The two metals of the bimetallic strip expand at different rates, causing the strip to bend. This bending action trips the circuit breaker, opening the circuit. After the bimetallic strip has cooled, (and after the cause of the overload has been corrected) the circuit breaker can be reset. Caution: Some bimetallic breakers will re-start after cooling.

Thermal-magnetic circuit breakers are also widely used. This type of circuit breaker has a bimetallic element that causes the circuit breaker to

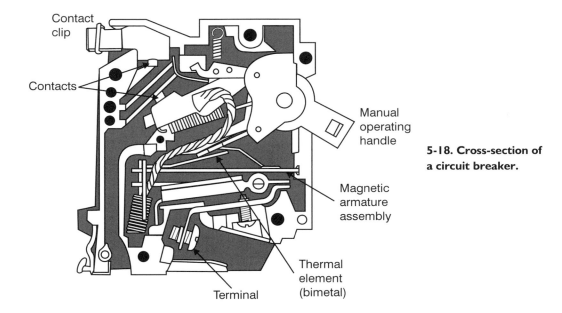

Contact clip

Contacts

Manual operating handle

Magnetic armature assembly

Thermal element (bimetal)

Terminal

**5-18. Cross-section of a circuit breaker.**

trip in case of a continuous overload condition. A magnetic coil inside the circuit breaker causes it to trip in a fraction of a second when subjected to a heavy overload, short circuit, or ground-fault condition. Figure 5-18 shows a cross section of a thermal-magnetic circuit breaker.

## GROUND-FAULT CIRCUIT INTERRUPTERS

A current flow of as little as 10 mA through the human body may be fatal under certain circumstances. While this small level of current flow could be fatal to a human, it would not even begin to trip the circuit breaker or fuse protecting the circuit. A *ground-fault circuit interrupter (GFCI)* is a device intended to protect people by de-energizing a circuit almost instantaneously when a ground-fault current of as little as 5 mA occurs. Thus, GFCIs are people protectors.

A GFCI works on the principle that both wires of a circuit supplying a single-phase electrical load must carry the same amperage if the circuit is functioning correctly. If a ground-fault occurs, some of the current will take an alternate path back to the source, possibly through the grounding wire or through a person. Thus, one of the wires will carry less current than the other when a ground-fault occurs.

The GFCI contains a current transformer sensing coil (Figure 5-19). Both normally current carrying conductors pass through this sensing coil. As long as the amperage in both conductors is the same, the current

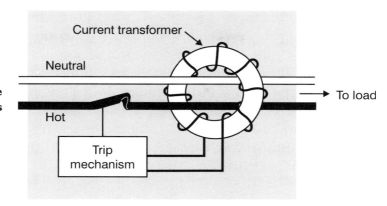

**5-19. Both the hot wire and the neutral wire pass through the GCFI.**

transformer output is zero, and the GFCI does not trip. But, if there is as little as 5 mA difference in current flow between the two wires, the current transformer produces an output, tripping the GFCI and opening the circuit within 25 milli-seconds (.025 second).

The *NEC* (210-8) requires GFCI protection for receptacles installed in several locations. These locations include (but are not limited to) bathrooms, garages (except for receptacles not readily accessible and receptacles for dedicated appliances), and on the outside of dwellings. The purpose of these requirements is to provide ground-fault protection in potentially wet or damp environments.

The *NEC* does not require the use of GFCIs in farm buildings. However, it is a good idea to protect circuits with outlets located in wet areas with

**5-20. Various GFCI devices: GFCI circuit breaker (left), GFCI receptacle (center), and portable GFCI receptacle (right).**

a GFCI. For example, bathrooms, wash areas, shops where floors may be wet, and outside receptacles should be GFCI protected.

GFCI protection can be provided in several ways (Figure 5-20). A GFCI type circuit breaker may be installed to provide ground-fault protection for an entire circuit. A GFCI receptacle will provide ground-fault protection for any load connected to the receptacle. All receptacles from the GFCI receptacle to the end of the circuit also receive ground-fault protection. Finally, a portable GFCI receptacle will provide ground-fault protection for any load connected to it.

# WIRING MATERIALS AND INSTALLATION METHODS

Electrical conductors are made from two different materials: copper and aluminum.

Aluminum is less expensive and weighs less than copper. For these reasons, aluminum conductors (usually triplex cable) are often used as service conductors. Aluminum has a thermal expansion rate approximately 40 percent greater than copper. For this reason, greater expansion and contraction occurs at the terminals of devices connected to aluminum wires. This expansion and contraction may lead to loosened connections and arcing at terminals. In addition, oxidation problems tend to be more severe with aluminum conductors.

To prevent such problems, special materials and procedures must be used when installing aluminum wiring. Only devices (switches, receptacles, etc.) specifically approved for use with aluminum wire should be used. Because of these undesirable characteristics and the special wiring materials and procedures that must be used, the use of aluminum for interior wiring is discouraged.

Copper has generally superior electrical and mechanical characteristics when compared to aluminum. Copper wire offers less resistance to the flow of electricity than aluminum. Thus, it is usually possible to use smaller diameter copper wires to install a given circuit than would be possible with aluminum wires. Because of its lower rate of thermal expansion, expansion and contraction problems are not nearly as severe with copper wire as with aluminum. For these reasons, copper wire is preferred when wiring branch circuits in farm buildings.

# CONDUCTOR DESIGNATIONS AND COLOR CODING

The *NEC* describes three different single-phase branch and feeder circuit conductors and requires that each be identified by color coding.

A **grounded conductor** is a circuit conductor that is intentionally connected to ground. This is accomplished by connecting the grounded conductor to the neutral bar of the service entrance panel. (Many persons refer to this as the "neutral" wire. However, the term grounded conductor is more accurate and is preferred.) In a 120-volt circuit, the grounded conductor is a normally current carrying conductor. *NEC* Article 310-12(a) requires ungrounded conductors AWG #6 or smaller to have either white or natural gray colored insulation. Some specific exceptions to this requirement are permitted.

The **equipment grounding conductor** bonds conductive materials that enclose electrical conductors or equipment back to the system grounding electrode to protect persons and property from damage or injury in case of a ground-fault. During normal circuit operation, the equipment grounding conductor carries no current. *NEC* Article 310-12(b) allows the use of uninsulated (bare) equipment grounding conductors. Where the grounding conductor is insulated, the insulation must either be green or green with one or more yellow stripes.

The **ungrounded conductor(s)** in a branch circuit originate at either a fuse or a circuit breaker. *NEC* Article 310-12(c) does not specify a color for ungrounded conductors. Rather, it specifies that ungrounded conductors may not be of any color reserved for grounded or equipment grounding conductors. In practice, ungrounded conductors are usually (but not always) black or red.

# SIZING CONDUCTORS FOR BRANCH CIRCUITS

Assume that a new machinery storage building will be built with a 50 ampere, 240-volt arc welder near the building's overhead door. The welder will be the only load on this circuit. The one-way circuit length from the service entrance panel to the receptacle serving the welder is 65 feet. Because this is a dry building, wire the circuit using Type NM cable. Voltage drop in the welder branch circuit must be limited to 2 percent. What size conductor should be used? Use the "Load in Amps" column in Table 5-2 to find an exact match for the welder's amperage, 50 amps. Under the "In Air, Cable or Conduit" column for Type NM cable, an AWG #8 conductor will meet ampacity requirements for a 50 ampere

## Table 5-2
## Conductor Size Selection Table

**Minimum Allowable Size of Conductor**

**Copper up to 400 Amperes, 230-240 Volts, Single Phase, Based on 2% Voltage Drop**
**Length of Run in Feet**
Compare size shown below with size shown to left of double line. Use the larger size

| Load in Amps | UF | RH, RHW, THW, THWN, USE, NM, SE | THHN | UF | USE | Single | Triplex | 50 | 60 | 75 | 100 | 125 | 150 | 175 | 200 | 225 | 250 | 275 | 300 | 350 | 400 | 450 | 500 | 550 | 600 | 650 | 700 | 750 | 800 |
|---|---|---|---|---|---|---|---|---|---|---|---|---|---|---|---|---|---|---|---|---|---|---|---|---|---|---|---|---|---|
| | | | | | | In Air Cable or Conduit / Direct Burial / Overhead in Air | | | | | | | | | | | | | | | | | | | | | | | |
| 5 | 14 | 14 | 14 | 14 | 14 | 10 | 8 | 14 | 14 | 14 | 14 | 14 | 14 | 14 | 12 | 12 | 12 | 12 | 10 | 10 | 10 | 10 | 8 | 8 | 8 | 8 | 8 | 6 | 6 |
| 7 | 14 | 14 | 14 | 14 | 14 | 10 | 8 | 14 | 14 | 14 | 14 | 14 | 12 | 12 | 12 | 10 | 10 | 10 | 10 | 8 | 8 | 8 | 8 | 6 | 6 | 6 | 6 | 6 | 6 |
| 10 | 14 | 14 | 14 | 14 | 14 | 10 | 8 | 14 | 14 | 14 | 12 | 12 | 10 | 10 | 10 | 10 | 8 | 8 | 8 | 8 | 6 | 6 | 6 | 6 | 4 | 4 | 4 | 4 | 4 |
| 15 | 14 | 14 | 14 | 14 | 14 | 10 | 8 | 14 | 12 | 12 | 10 | 10 | 10 | 8 | 8 | 8 | 6 | 6 | 6 | 6 | 4 | 4 | 4 | 4 | 3 | 3 | 3 | 3 | 2 |
| 20 | 12 | 12 | 12 | 12 | 12 | 10 | 8 | 12 | 12 | 10 | 10 | 8 | 8 | 8 | 6 | 6 | 6 | 6 | 4 | 4 | 4 | 4 | 3 | 3 | 2 | 2 | 2 | 1 | 1 |
| 25 | 10 | 10 | 10 | 10 | 10 | 10 | 8 | 12 | 10 | 10 | 8 | 8 | 6 | 6 | 6 | 6 | 4 | 4 | 4 | 4 | 3 | 3 | 2 | 2 | 1 | 1 | 1 | 0 | 0 |
| 30 | 10 | 10 | 10 | 10 | 10 | 10 | 8 | 10 | 10 | 10 | 8 | 6 | 6 | 6 | 4 | 4 | 4 | 4 | 4 | 3 | 2 | 2 | 1 | 1 | 1 | 0 | 0 | 0 | 00 |
| 35 | 8 | 8 | 8 | 8 | 8 | 8 | 8 | 10 | 10 | 8 | 8 | 6 | 6 | 4 | 4 | 4 | 4 | 3 | 2 | 2 | 1 | 1 | 0 | 0 | 0 | 00 | 00 | 00 | |
| 40 | 8 | 8 | 8 | 8 | 8 | 8 | 8 | 10 | 8 | 8 | 6 | 6 | 4 | 4 | 4 | 4 | 3 | 3 | 2 | 2 | 1 | 1 | 0 | 0 | 00 | 00 | 00 | 000 | 000 |
| 45 | 6 | 8 | 8 | 8 | 8 | 8 | 8 | 10 | 8 | 8 | 6 | 6 | 4 | 4 | 4 | 3 | 3 | 2 | 2 | 1 | 1 | 0 | 0 | 00 | 00 | 000 | 000 | 000 | |
| 50 | 6 | 8 | 8 | 6 | 8 | 8 | 8 | 8 | 8 | 6 | 6 | 4 | 4 | 4 | 3 | 3 | 2 | 2 | 1 | 1 | 0 | 0 | 00 | 00 | 000 | 000 | 000 | 4/0 | 4/0 |
| 60 | 4 | 6 | 6 | 4 | 6 | 8 | 6 | 8 | 8 | 6 | 4 | 4 | 3 | 2 | 2 | 1 | 1 | 0 | 0 | 00 | 00 | 000 | 000 | 4/0 | 4/0 | 4/0 | 4/0 | 4/0 | 250 |
| 70 | 4 | 4 | 6 | 4 | 4 | 6 | 6 | 8 | 6 | 6 | 4 | 4 | 3 | 2 | 2 | 1 | 1 | 0 | 0 | 00 | 00 | 000 | 000 | 4/0 | 4/0 | 4/0 | 250 | 250 | 300 |
| 80 | 3 | 4 | 4 | 3 | 4 | 6 | 4 | 6 | 6 | 4 | 4 | 3 | 2 | 2 | 1 | 1 | 0 | 0 | 00 | 00 | 000 | 000 | 4/0 | 4/0 | 250 | 250 | 300 | 300 | |
| 90 | 2 | 3 | 4 | 2 | 3 | 4 | 4 | 6 | 6 | 4 | 4 | 3 | 2 | 1 | 1 | 0 | 0 | 00 | 00 | 000 | 000 | 4/0 | 4/0 | 250 | 250 | 300 | 300 | 350 | |
| 100 | 1 | 3 | 3 | 1 | 3 | 4 | 4 | 6 | 4 | 4 | 3 | 2 | 1 | 1 | 0 | 0 | 00 | 00 | 000 | 000 | 4/0 | 4/0 | 250 | 250 | 300 | 300 | 350 | 350 | 400 |
| 115 | 0 | 2 | 2 | 0 | 2 | 3 | 3 | 6 | 4 | 4 | 3 | 2 | 1 | 0 | 0 | 00 | 00 | 000 | 000 | 4/0 | 4/0 | 250 | 300 | 300 | 350 | 350 | 400 | 400 | 500 |
| 130 | 00 | 1 | 2 | 00 | 1 | 2 | 2 | 4 | 4 | 3 | 2 | 1 | 0 | 0 | 00 | 000 | 000 | 4/0 | 4/0 | 250 | 300 | 300 | 350 | 400 | 400 | 500 | 500 | 500 | |
| 150 | 000 | 0 | 1 | 000 | 0 | 1 | 1 | 4 | 4 | 3 | 1 | 0 | 0 | 00 | 000 | 000 | 4/0 | 4/0 | 4/0 | 250 | 300 | 350 | 350 | 400 | 500 | 500 | 500 | 600 | 600 |
| 175 | 4/0 | 00 | 00 | 4/0 | 00 | 0 | 0 | 4 | 3 | 2 | 1 | 0 | 00 | 000 | 000 | 4/0 | 4/0 | 250 | 250 | 300 | 350 | 400 | 400 | 500 | 500 | 600 | 600 | 600 | 700 |
| 200 | | 000 | 000 | | 000 | 00 | 00 | 3 | 2 | 1 | 0 | 00 | 000 | 000 | 4/0 | 4/0 | 250 | 250 | 300 | 350 | 400 | 500 | 500 | 500 | 600 | 600 | 700 | 700 | 750 |
| 225 | | 4/0 | 000 | | 4/0 | 0 | 000 | 3 | 2 | 1 | 0 | 00 | 000 | 4/0 | 4/0 | 250 | 250 | 300 | 300 | 350 | 350 | 400 | 500 | 500 | 600 | 600 | 700 | 700 | 900 |
| 250 | | 250 | 4/0 | | 250 | 00 | 4/0 | 2 | 1 | 0 | 00 | 000 | 4/0 | 4/0 | 250 | 300 | 300 | 350 | 350 | 400 | 500 | 600 | 600 | 700 | 700 | 750 | 800 | 900 | 1000 |
| 275 | | 300 | 250 | | 300 | 000 | 4/0 | 2 | 1 | 0 | 00 | 000 | 4/0 | 4/0 | 250 | 300 | 350 | 350 | 400 | 500 | 600 | 600 | 700 | 700 | 800 | 900 | 900 | 1000 | |
| 300 | | 350 | 300 | | 350 | 000 | 250 | 1 | 1 | 0 | 000 | 4/0 | 4/0 | 250 | 300 | 350 | 350 | 400 | 500 | 500 | 600 | 700 | 700 | 800 | 900 | 900 | 1000 | | |
| 325 | | 400 | 350 | | 400 | 4/0 | 300 | 1 | 0 | 00 | 000 | 4/0 | 250 | 300 | 300 | 350 | 400 | 400 | 500 | 600 | 600 | 700 | 750 | 900 | 900 | 1000 | | | |
| 350 | | 500 | 350 | | 500 | 4/0 | 300 | 1 | 0 | 00 | 000 | 4/0 | 250 | 300 | 350 | 350 | 400 | 500 | 500 | 600 | 700 | 750 | 900 | 900 | 1000 | | | | |
| 375 | | 500 | 400 | | 500 | 250 | 300 | 0 | 0 | 00 | 4/0 | 250 | 300 | 300 | 350 | 400 | 500 | 500 | 600 | 600 | 700 | 800 | 900 | 1000 | | | | | |
| 400 | | 600 | 500 | | 600 | 250 | 400 | 0 | 00 | 000 | 4/0 | 250 | 300 | 350 | 400 | 500 | 500 | 500 | 600 | 700 | 750 | 900 | 1000 | | | | | | |

Source: NFEC Agricultural Wiring Handbook

load. Under the "Length of Run in Feet" column use the next highest table value of 75 feet. According to the table, an AWG #6 conductor is required to limit voltage drop in the circuit to 2 percent.

Since the two conductor sizes based on ampacity and voltage drop are not the same, choose the largest conductor for the welder circuit. Type NM cable having AWG #6 conductors should be used in wiring this circuit.

## CABLE AND CONDUIT WIRING MATERIALS AND PROCEDURES

The *NEC* requires that single wires must be protected from physical damage. In wiring branch circuits, this is generally accomplished by either using cable or by running individual conductors in conduit.

### Cable Wiring Materials and Procedures

A *cable* consists of two or more wires in a protective outer sheath or jacket. All wires in the sheath must be individually insulated, except for the equipment grounding wire, which may or may not be insulated. Figure 5-21 shows the construction of typical cables used in wiring branch circuits

A particular cable can be described based on several factors. These factors include: (a) the cable type, (b) the size of the individual conductors, (c) the number of normally current-carrying conductors within the sheath, and (d) whether or not an equipment grounding conductor is included. This information is stamped on the cable's sheath, listed on the box containing the cable, or both.

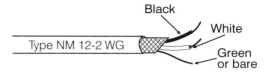

### Nonmetallic sheathed cable

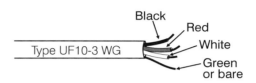

### Underground feeder cable

**5-21. Typical cable construction for wiring used in branch circuits.**

The top cable in Figure 5-21 is designated as a Type NM 12-2 WG cable. In this designation, the Type NM indicates nonmetallic sheathed cable. Article 336 of the *NEC* covers the use, installation and construction specifications for this type of cable. According to the *NEC*, Type NM cable may be used for both concealed and exposed wiring in normally dry locations having less than three floors above grade level.

Following the type designation, the 12 indicates the size of the individual conductors (AWG No. 12). The 2 (following the conductor size) means that there are two normally current-carrying conductors contained in the sheath. Finally, the WG stands for "with ground," indicating that a grounding conductor is also included in the cable.

In Figure 5-21, the designation Type UF 10-3 WG on the lower cable indicates that this is underground feeder cable, having three AWG #10 gauge normally current carrying conductors, and an equipment grounding wire. Type UF cable has an outer covering that is moisture, fungus, and corrosion resistant, as well as flame retardant. For these reasons, Type UF cable is widely used for wiring branch circuits in livestock buildings. *NEC* Article 339 covers the use, installation and construction specifications for Type UF cable. Many other types of cables are available. Table 5-3 describes cables commonly used in agricultural wiring.

Cable should be installed where it cannot be easily damaged. When cable is used to wire livestock buildings, the cable should be run along the inside surface of the walls and ceiling (Figure 5-22). The cable should be secured at least every 4½ feet and within 12 inches of each cabinet,

# Table 5-3
# Cables Commonly Used in Agricultural Wiring

| Material | Type Letter | Description | Use |
|---|---|---|---|
| *Cables*<br>Nonmetallic | NM | Fibrous, flame-retardant, and moisture-resistant sheath | Exposed and concealed work in normally dry locations—may be installed or fished into air voids in masonry block or tile walls not exposed or subject to excessive moisture or dampness |
| | NMC | Flame-retardant and moisture-fungus-corrosion-resistant sheath | Dry, moist, damp, or corrosive locations—inside or outside of masonry and tile walls |
| Underground feeder and branch circuit cable | UF | Sheathed in flame-retardant and moisture-fungus-corrosion-resistant outer cover suitable for direct burial in earth | Underground feeder and branch-circuit cable underground, including direct burial in earth—install minimum 24" deep in earth, reducible to 18" if protection is installed above cable. Permitted for interior wiring in wet, dry, or corrosive locations. |
| Service-entrance cable | SE | Flame-retardant, moisture-resistant cover | Generally as a service-entrance conductor on the outside of building, carrying power to service panel inside; also as branch circuit or feeder if all normally current carrying conductors are insulated with rubber or thermoplastic |
| | USE | Moisture-resistant cover | Underground service entrance—single-conductor cables having rubber insulation specifically approved for the purpose of not requiring outer covering. |
| Service-drop cable | TRI-PLEX | Two individually insulated current-carrying wires twisted together with a bare neutral | Feeder lines between buildings, usually #6 or larger; bare neutral has high tensile strength to carry entire cable between spans. |
| Flexible cables<br>All thermoset<br>    parallel cord | SP-1<br>SP-2 | Thermoset insualted, thermoset covered, with no fabric braid | Pendant or portable cords in damp places—not with hard usage—SP-2 available in #18 and #16; SP-1, #18 only—typical household extension cord |
| All plastic<br>    parallel cord | SPT-1<br>SPT-2 | Thermoplastic insulated and covered, with no fabric braid | Same as thermoset above |
| Lamp cord | C | Thermoset insulated, with cotton braid on each conductor | Pendant or portable uses in dry places not with hard usage—available in #18-10 sizes |
| Junior hard<br>    service cord | SJ | Thermoset insulated and covered, no fabric braid | Pendant or portable uses in damp places with hard usage. |
| | SJO | Thermoset insulated, oil-resistant thermoset cover, no fabric braid | Same as above |
| | SJT | Thermoplastic or thermoset insulated with thermoplastic cover, no fabric braid | Same as above |
| | SJTO | Thermoplastic or thermoset insulated with oil-resistant thermoplastic cover, no fabric braid | Same as above |
| Hard service<br>    cord | S | Thermoset insulatead and covered, no fabric braid | Pendant or portable use in damp places with extra hard usage |
| | SO | Thermoset insulated with oil-resistant thermoset cover, no fabric braid | Same as above |
| | ST | Thermoplastic or thermoset insulated with thermoplastic cover, no fabric braid | Same as above |
| | STO | Thermoplastic or thermoset insulated with oil-resistant thermoplastic cover, no fabric braid | Same as above |

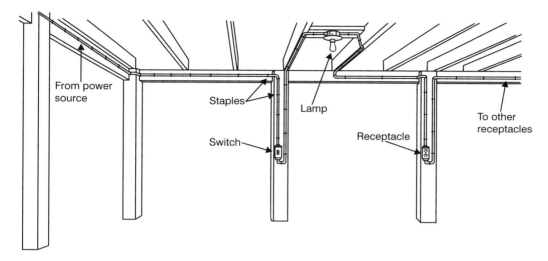

From power source

Staples

Lamp

To other receptacles

Switch

Receptacle

**5-22. Cables and lampholders are installed in protected areas of joists, timbers, and studs.**

box or fitting using approved staples, cable ties, straps, or similar fittings. Sharp bends in the cable should be avoided. The minimum bending radius is five times the largest diameter of the cable.

If a building has exposed joists, run the cable along the joist at least 2 inches from the bottom. When the cable must run perpendicular to joists (or similar building components), 1×2 inch running boards should be installed on the bottom of the joists and the cable attached to the board. *NEC* Article 336 describes the proper installation of cable wiring.

## Conduit Wiring Materials and Procedures

**Conduit** is a channel or tube through which conductors are run in order to provide the conductors with mechanical protection. In conduit wiring, the conduit is installed and individual conductors are "fished" through it to make circuit connections. Because conduit wiring is more expensive and time consuming than cable wiring, use on farms is limited to locations where protection from animal or mechanical damage is necessary.

Various conductors can be installed in conduit. Conductors commonly installed in conduit are described in Table 5-4.

**Types of Conduit.** Conduit can either be metallic or non-metallic. *Metallic conduit* is made of either galvanized steel or aluminum. Rigid

### Table 5-4
### Conductors Commonly Installed in Conduit

| Material | Type Letter | Description | Use |
|---|---|---|---|
| *Insulations* | | | |
| Rubber | RH & RHH | Flame-retardant thermoset | Dry and damp locations |
| | RHW | Flame-retardant, moisture-resistant thermoset | Dry and wet locations |
| Thermoplastic | TW | Flame-retardant, moisture-resistant thermoplastic | Dry and wet locations |
| | THHN | Flame-retardant, heat-resistant thermoplastic | Dry and damp locations |
| | THW | Flame-retardant, moisture- and heat-resistant thermoplastic | Dry and wet locations |
| | THWN | Flame-retardant, moisture- and heat-resistant thermoplastic | Dry and wet locations |

metal conduit, intermediate metal conduit (IMC), and electrical metallic tubing (EMT) are the three primary types of metallic conduit. Rigid metal conduit provides maximum protection, but is expensive, difficult to work with, and subject to corrosion. IMC is similar to rigid metal conduit, but is lighter and less expensive. EMT, commonly called thin wall tubing, is light and easy to work with. However, the use of EMT is not allowed in locations where severe physical damage may occur.

When properly installed and bonded, metallic conduit can serve as the equipment grounding conductor in a branch circuit. Because of the danger of corrosion, metallic conduit should normally not be used in confinement livestock buildings.

***Nonmetallic conduit*** can be used to protect wiring in dry, damp, wet, or corrosive locations (as approved or listed). Nonmetallic conduit is usually made from PVC (polyvinyl chloride), although other materials are available (high density polyethylene, fiberglass, nonmetallic fiber, etc.). When properly installed, PVC conduit is dust-tight, watertight, and noncorrosive.

PVC conduit is available in Schedule 40 and Schedule 80 (heavy wall) wall thicknesses. Schedule 80 PVC conduit should be used in locations where the conduit may be exposed to physical damage. PVC conduit is commonly available in 20 and 40 foot lengths. In farm buildings, PVC conduit should be surface mounted on walls and ceilings.

**Table 5-5**
**Support Spacing for PVC Conduit**

| Conduit Size (inches) | Maximum Spacing Between Supports (feet) |
| --- | --- |
| $1/2 - 1$ | 3 |
| $1 1/4 - 2$ | 5 |
| $2 1/2 - 3$ | 6 |
| $3 1/2 - 5$ | 7 |
| 6 | 8 |

Note: Based on *NEC* Table 347-8.
PVC conduit listed for support at spacings other than as shown may be installed with support as listed (*NEC* 347-8 Exception).

PVC conduit must be supported at regular intervals, depending on its size (Table 5-5). In addition, PVC conduit must be supported within 3 feet of each box or other conduit termination point. Nonmetallic straps are available for conduit support in corrosive environments.

Whenever possible, avoid running conduit through walls and ceilings from a cold area to a warm area. If this must be done, seal the inside of the conduit with a press-in-place putty, called duct sealer, on the warm side of the wall or ceiling. This will prevent moisture in the warm part of the conduit from moving into the cold side.

PVC conduit can be cut with a fine-toothed saw or a special PVC cutter. Cuts should be filed to remove sharp edges, which may damage insulation. Joints should be made with PVC couplers and glued with a PVC solvent-cement. The steps in joining PVC conduit are shown in Figure 5-23.

PVC conduit can be shaped by heating it with a hot box or hot air blower and then bending it by hand. Care must be taken to avoid reducing the

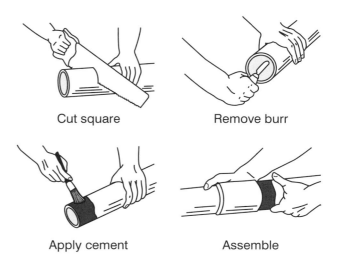

Cut square

Remove burr

Apply cement

Assemble

5-23. Sequence of steps for joining nonmetallic conduit.

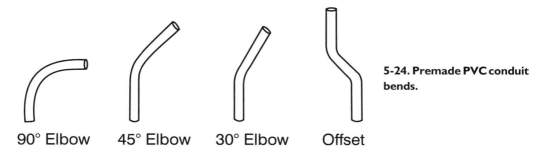

**5-24. Premade PVC conduit bends.**

90° Elbow    45° Elbow    30° Elbow    Offset

conduit's inside diameter when bending. As an alternative, commercially available PVC conduit bends (Figure 5-24) may be used to achieve a desired bend or offset. According to *NEC* Article 347-14, no more than the equivalent of four 90 degree bends may be made between conductor pull points.

PVC expands when heated. Allow for thermal expansion by placing conduit supports at least 1 foot away from all corners (Figure 5-25). If the conduit has few corners, or is exposed to a wide temperature range and is at least 40 feet long, one or more expansion joints must be installed.

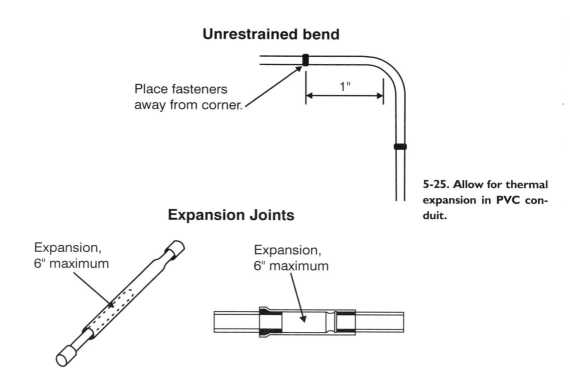

**Unrestrained bend**

Place fasteners away from corner.

1"

**Expansion Joints**

Expansion, 6" maximum

Expansion, 6" maximum

**5-25. Allow for thermal expansion in PVC conduit.**

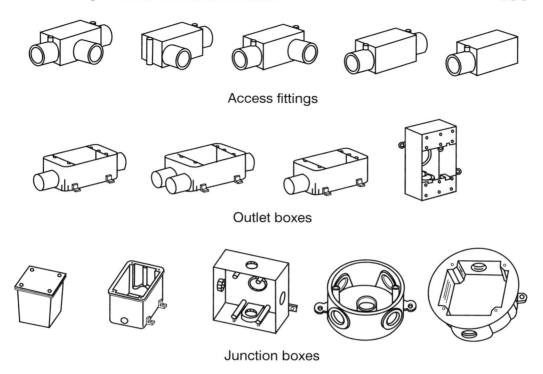

Access fittings

Outlet boxes

Junction boxes

**5-26. PVC molded fittings and boxes used with PVC conduit.**

PVC molded fittings and boxes (Figure 5-26) should be used with PVC conduit. Conduit may be connected to boxes using a conduit-to-box adapter (Figure 5-27). Conduit can be glued directly to a box having a socket fitting.

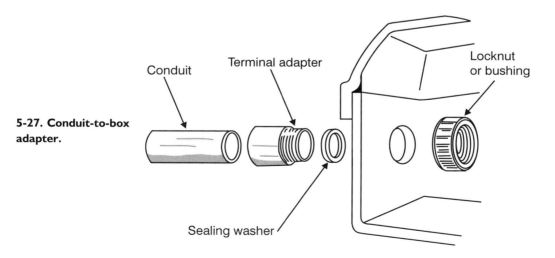

**5-27. Conduit-to-box adapter.**

Conduit

Terminal adapter

Locknut or bushing

Sealing washer

**Sizing Conduit.** The size conduit required for a particular wiring job is determined by four factors: (a) size of the wires, (b) type of insulation on the wires, (c) number of wires to be installed, and (d) if the wires are all of the same type and size. If the wires to be installed are all of the same type and size, the minimum required size of nonmetallic conduit can be selected using Table 5-6.

### Table 5-6
### Maximum Number of Conductors for Common Sizes of Nonmetallic Conduit

| Insulation Type | AWG Wire Size | Minimum Conduit Size (inches) | | |
| --- | --- | --- | --- | --- |
| | | 1/2 | 3/4 | 1 |
| XHHW | 14 | 7 | 13 | 22 |
| | 12 | 5 | 10 | 17 |
| | 10 | 4 | 7 | 13 |
| | 8 | 1 | 4 | 7 |
| THW | 14 | 4 | 8 | 15 |
| RHW (without | 12 | 3 | 7 | 12 |
| outer covering) | 10 | 3 | 5 | 9 |
| | 8 | 1 | 3 | 5 |
| RHW (with outer | 14 | 3 | 6 | 10 |
| covering) | 12 | 2 | 5 | 9 |
| | 10 | 1 | 4 | 7 |
| | 8 | 1 | 1 | 3 |
| THHN | 14 | 10 | 18 | 32 |
| THWN | 12 | 7 | 13 | 23 |
| THWN-2 | 10 | 4 | 8 | 15 |
| | 8 | 2 | 5 | 8 |

Note: Based on information presented in *NEC* Table C2.

# RECEPTACLE OUTLETS: TYPES AND INSTALLATION

Receptacle outlets provide a convenient means of connecting electrical equipment to the wiring system. Most electrical appliances are served through receptacle outlets. Two primary types of receptacle outlets are the duplex convenience outlet and the special purpose outlet. A third type of receptacle outlet, the GFCI outlet, was discussed earlier in this chapter.

## DUPLEX CONVENIENCE OUTLETS

A *duplex convenience outlet (DCO)* is a general purpose outlet having two receptacles built into one device. DCOs are available in 15 and 20 ampere, 120-volt ratings (Figure 5-28). Only install a DCO in a circuit for which it is rated.

The two halves of a DCO are electrically connected by a removable tab between the two brass-colored ungrounded (hot) terminal screws and by a second removable tab between the two silver-colored grounded (neutral) terminal screws.

**5-28. A duplex convenience outlet. (Ungrounded conductor slot is smaller than the grounded conductor slot.)**

### Grounding Type DCOs

Grounding type DCOs have a green grounding screw where the branch circuit equipment grounding conductor is attached. When a metal tool or appliance with a three-prong plug is connected to a correctly wired grounding type receptacle, the metal case of the tool or appliance is electrically connected to ground. This helps to prevent shocks.

The *NEC* requires that grounding type receptacles be installed in new 15 and 20 ampere branch circuits [210-7(a)]. The *NEC* also requires that properly wired grounding receptacles be used when replacing old receptacles. However, the *NEC* makes an exception—if no grounding means is available because of the way the circuit is currently wired [210-7(d)].

Despite the exception permitted by the *NEC*, replacement receptacles should be of the grounding type, even if this requires replacing the conductors serving the receptacle. As an alternative to rewiring, nongrounding receptacles can be replaced with GFCI-protected receptacles. If this method is used, all receptacles fed through a properly wired GFCI receptacle are also GFCI protected. Thus, only the first receptacle on each circuit must be replaced with a GFCI receptacle (Figure 5-29).

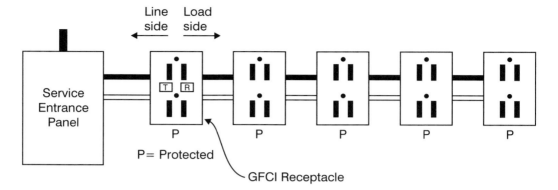

**5-29. A GFCI receptacle installed as the first receptacle in a circuit provides protection to all other receptacles beyond it on the circuit.**

## Common DCO Circuits

Wiring a single DCO on a 120-volt branch circuit is a fairly straight-forward task. The ungrounded (black) conductor attaches to one of the brass-colored terminal screws on the DCO. The grounded (white) conductor attaches to one of the silver-colored terminal screws on the DCO. The equipment grounding conductor (bare or green) attaches to the green grounding screw on the DCO. In addition, if a metal device box is used, the equipment grounding conductor must also be "pigtailed" and attached to the box with a grounding screw or clip [*NEC* 250-114(a)]. (This is not required if a plastic device box is used.)

**Two or More Un-Switched DCOs.** In this circuit, two or more 120-volt DCOs are on the same branch circuit and, since there is no switch in the circuit, the DCOs are "hot" at all times, unless shut off at the service entrance panel. This is an extremely common DCO circuit. Figure 5-30 shows how this circuit would be wired using cable and metal device boxes. (Note: If plastic device boxes were used, the equipment grounding conductor would not be attached to the boxes.)

In Figure 5-30, notice that the first receptacle is connected to the circuit using short pigtail wires. These wires must have the same color insulation as the circuit conductors to which they are spliced. Insulated wire nuts are used to make the splices. At the last receptacle, the circuit conductors attach directly to the appropriate terminals and no pigtails are required, except for the equipment grounding conductor.

As an alternative method of wiring through DCOs, the incoming and outgoing ungrounded conductors can be connected to different brass-colored

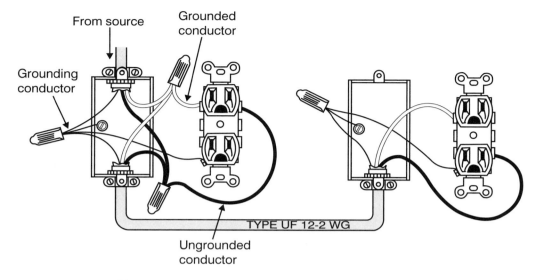

From source

Grounded conductor

Grounding conductor

Ungrounded conductor

TYPE UF 12-2 WG

**5-30. Wiring connections for two or more un-switched DCOs.**

terminal screws. The incoming and outgoing grounded conductors will each be attached to different silver-colored terminal screws. Pigtails would still be required for connecting the equipment grounding conductor. This method is shown in Figure 5-56 (page 178).

**Switched-Controlled Split-Duplex Receptacle.** This DCO circuit is wired so a single-pole switch controls one outlet of the DCO, while the other outlet is always "hot." This circuit is often used in dwellings. Typically, a floor lamp is plugged into the switch-controlled outlet and a clock, television, radio, or other appliance is plugged into the other outlet. Figure 5-31 shows how this circuit would be wired using cable and plastic device boxes.

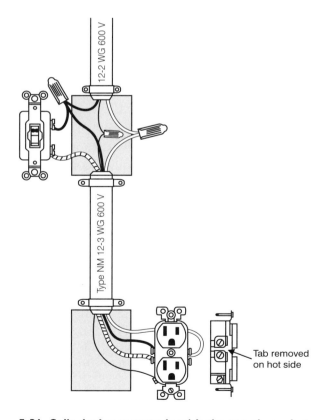

12-2 WG 600 V

Type NM 12-3 WG 600 V

Tab removed on hot side

**5-31. Split duplex receptacle with the top always hot and the bottom controlled by the switch.**

Notice that a 12-2 with ground cable is used between the source and the switch. A 12-3 with ground cable is used between the switch and the receptacle.

At the switch box, the two grounded wires are spliced together using a wire nut. (Note: Grounded wires never attach to a single-pole switch.) Likewise, since this is a plastic device box, the two equipment grounding wires are also spliced together using a wire nut. The incoming ungrounded (black) wire is spliced to a short pigtail wire and to the black wire of the outgoing cable. The pigtail wire is attached to one of the switch's brass-colored terminal screws. The red wire (second ungrounded conductor) from the outgoing cable is connected to the other brass-colored terminal screw at the switch.

At the receptacle outlet, the grounded conductor attaches to the silver-colored terminal screw. The equipment grounding conductor connects to the green grounding screw. Again, since this is a plastic device box, no connection to the box is required.

The tab between the receptacle's two brass-colored terminal screws is removed (see inset). This allows the two outlets to operate separately. The incoming black ungrounded conductor attaches to the top brass-colored terminal screw. Since the black wire is not switched in this circuit, the top outlet will always be "hot." The red ungrounded conductor connects to the bottom brass-colored terminal screw. Since the red ungrounded conductor is switched, the bottom outlet will be controlled by the switch.

**Multiwire DCO Circuit.** A multiwire circuit has two ungrounded conductors, a single grounded conductor, and an equipment grounding conductor. The voltage between either ungrounded conductor and the grounded conductor is 120 volts. The voltage between the two ungrounded conductors is 240 volts. The advantage of a multiwire circuit is that two 120-volt circuits share the same grounded conductor. Thus, rather than the two circuits requiring four normally current-carrying conductors, only three are required. The circuit can be wired with a 3-wire with ground cable.

In Figure 5-32 two ungrounded conductors are attached to a double-pole breaker. The receptacle loads are divided evenly between the two ungrounded conductors. The single grounded conductor is connected to each receptacle. (Note: An equipment grounding conductor is also required, but is not shown for clarity.)

In wiring a multiwire receptacle, special attention must be given to proper installation of the grounded conductor. If, for any reason, the grounded wire should become open, appliances connected to the circuit would become series connected loads in a 240-volt circuit. Thus, the

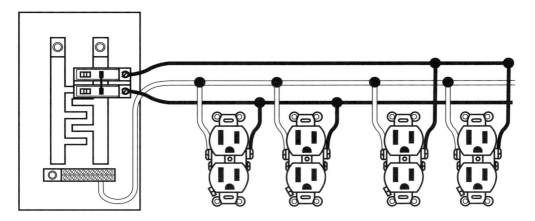

**5-32. A multiwire DCO circuit. Note: Equipment grounding wire not shown for clarity.**

appliances would likely be subjected to incorrect voltages, causing equipment damage and possible safety hazards.

Because of the dangers associated with an open in the grounded conductor of a multiwire DCO circuit, the *NEC* [Article 300-13(b)] requires the grounded conductor to be connected to receptacles so the removal (or failure) of the receptacle will not break continuity of the grounded conductor. In practical terms, this means that the grounded conductor in a multiwire circuit must be connected to receptacles using a pigtail wire (except for the last receptacle on the run, which may be directly connected. This preserves the continuity of the grounded conductor even if a receptacle is removed (or fails).

-33. An SPO recepticle for an air com-
ressor.

## SPECIAL PURPOSE OUTLETS

A special purpose outlet (SPO) is installed to serve a specific machine or appliance, such as a welder, heater, or large motor. An SPO is usually installed on an ***individual branch circuit***. This means that the equipment connected to the SPO is the only load on the circuit. The SPO and the individual branch circuit conductors and overcurrent protection device are selected and sized based on the requirements of the equipment to be connected.

| Configuration for Nonlocking Plugs and Receptacles | | | | | | | | |
|---|---|---|---|---|---|---|---|---|
| Nominal Voltage | Maximum Amperage | | | | | | | |
| | 15 A | | 20 A | | 30 A | | 50 A | |
| | Receptacle | Plug | Receptacle | Plug | Receptacle | Plug | Receptacle | Plug |
| 120 V | 5-15R | 5-15P | 5-20R | 5-20P | 5-30R | 5-30P | 5-50R | 5-50P |
| 240 V | 6-15R | 6-15P | 6-20R | 6-20P | 6-30R | 6-30P | 6-50R | 6-50P |

| Configuration for Locking Plugs and Receptacles | | | | | | |
|---|---|---|---|---|---|---|
| Nominal Voltage | Maximum Amperage | | | | | |
| | 15 A | | 20 A | | 30 A | |
| | Receptacle | Plug | Receptacle | Plug | Receptacle | Plug |
| 120 V | L5-15R | L5-15P | L5-20R | L5-20P | L5-30R | L5-30P |
| 240 V | L6-15R | L6-15P | L6-20R | L6-20P | L6-30R | L6-30P |

5-34. Standard plug and receptacle configurations.

## PLUG AND RECEPTACLE CONFIGURATIONS

The *NEC* [Section 410-56(h)] states that receptacles and attachment plugs must be constructed so the receptacle will not accept an attachment plug with a voltage or current rating different from the receptacle. To meet this requirement, the National Electrical Manufacturers Association (NEMA) has developed standard plug and receptacle configurations.

The configuration of typical plugs and receptacles used in agricultural buildings are shown in Figure 5-34.

## SWITCHES: TYPES AND INSTALLATION

Switches control one or more electrical loads by opening and closing the circuit serving the load(s). For safety reasons, a switch may only be installed in the ungrounded (hot) conductor(s) of a circuit. The only exception to this rule is a switch that opens the grounded (neutral) conductor simultaneously with the ungrounded (hot) conductor is allowed [*NEC* 380-2(b) Exception No. 1).

## SWITCH RATINGS

Each switch is rated for a specific maximum voltage and amperage. In addition, switches designed to control motors, may also be rated for a maximum horsepower. Switch ratings are usually stamped into the switch's metal yoke or mounting strap. A switch should only be installed in a circuit that does not exceed the switch's voltage, current or horsepower rating. In addition, a switch should only be used to control loads for which the switch is approved.

## GROUNDING-TYPE SWITCHES

Switches having a green grounding screw terminal are available. Connecting this terminal to the circuit equipment grounding conductor provides grounding protection for the normally non-current carrying metal components of the switch. Also, any metal part in good electrical contact with the switch is similarly protected.

Grounding-type switches should be used whenever a metal cover plate is used. The grounding type switch, properly installed, will provide grounding protection for the metal cover.

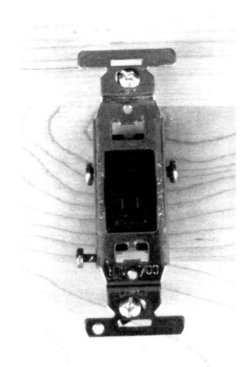

## POLES AND THROWS

A switch is often described based on the number of poles and throws it has. A **pole** is a moveable contact within a switch. The term **throw** indicates the number of paths provided for current to flow through the switch. Thus, a single-pole, single-throw

**5-35. A grounding-type switch.**

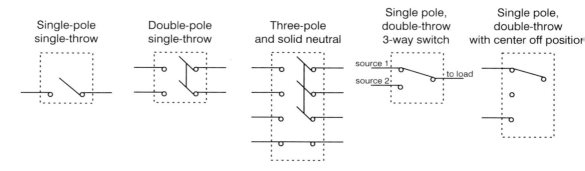

**5-36. Typical switch configurations.**

switch has one moveable contact and provides only one path for current flow through the switch. Figure 5-36 is a schematic showing the configuration of various types of switches.

## SNAP SWITCHES

The flush-mounted toggle switch, often called a snap switch, is the most common switch used in general purpose circuits. When this switch is mounted in a box with a cover plate, only the insulated switch handle is exposed.

### Single-pole Single-throw Switch

A single-pole single-throw (SPST) switch is used to control the load(s) in a circuit from a single location. A SPST switch has two brass-colored screw terminals where the incoming and outgoing ungrounded conductors are attached. The circuit grounded conductors should never attach to a SPST switch.

The switch's "on" and "off" positions are marked. The switch should be installed so that the load is "on" when the handle is up, and "off" when the handle in down. SPST snap switches like the one in Figure 5-35 are used in a variety of circuits.

**SPST Switch Controlling a Light at the End of the Run.** Figure 5-37 shows how a SPST switch circuit would be wired to control a ceiling-mounted lighting fixture located at the end of the circuit.

Notice that only the ungrounded conductors from the incoming and outgoing cables attach to the brass-colored switch terminals. The grounded conductors from the two cables are spliced together with a wire nut at the switch box. Since a plastic box and cover plate with a nonmetallic screw are used at the switch, the equipment grounding conductors from the two cables are also merely spliced together.

At the lighting fixture, the ungrounded conductor connects to the brass-colored terminal screw. The grounded conductor connects to the silver-colored terminal screw. The equipment grounding conductor is connected to the metal fixture box with a grounding clip.

**SPST Controlling a Lighting Fixture in the Middle of the Run.** Often, a lighting fixture to be controlled by a switch is located between the electrical supply and the switch (Figure 5-38). To wire this circuit, the grounded conductor from the source is connected directly to the silver-colored terminal of the lighting fixture. But, the ungrounded conductor must pass through the switch before returning to the light. The wires from the lighting fixture to the switch are called a *switch loop*.

When cable is used to wire a circuit containing a switch loop, a white wire will have to be used as an ungrounded conductor and connected to the switch. The *NEC* (200-7 Exception No. 2) allows this use of a white wire as an ungrounded conductor when cable wiring a switch loop. In such a case, the *NEC* requires that the white wire must supply the switch, and the black wire must return to the load.

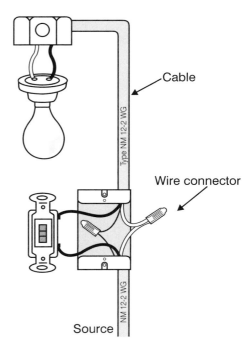

**5-37. A SPST switch controlling a light at the end of the run.**

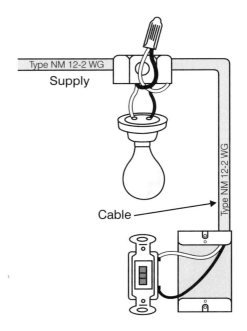

**5-38. SPST switch controlling a light in the middle of the run. Note: Equipment grounding wire not shown for clarity.**

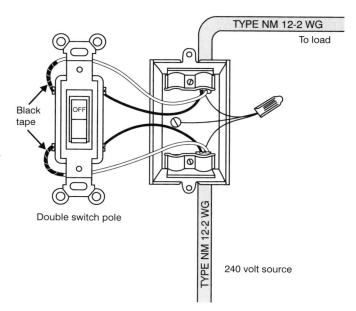

**5-39. DPST switch wired in a 240-volt circuit.**

## Double-pole Single-throw Switch

A double-pole single-throw (DPST) snap switch is used to control one or more loads operating on a 240-volt circuit. The DPST switch has four brass-colored screw terminals where the two incoming and two outgoing ungrounded wires are attached. Like a SPST switch, a DPST switch also has marked "on" and "off" positions. Again, like SPST switches, a DPST switch should be installed so the load is "on" when the switch handle is up and "off" when the switch handle is down. The double-pole single-throw switch opens (or closes) both ungrounded (hot) conductors in a 240-volt circuit.

Figure 5-39 shows how a DPST switch is wired in a 240 circuit using cable. Notice how black tape is used to identify the cable's white wire as an ungrounded conductor in the 240-volt circuit.

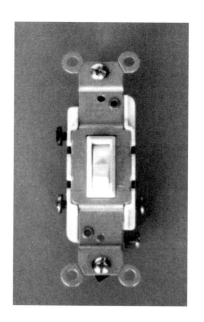

**5-40. A 3-way switch.**

## Single-pole Double-throw Switch

The single-pole double-throw (SPDT) switch is commonly called a *3-way switch* (Figure 5-40). A 3-way switch has three screw terminals: one

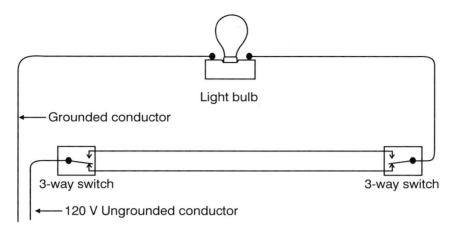

**5-41. A 3-way switch circuit controlling a lighting fixture.**

common terminal and two traveler terminals. The common terminal can be identified by markings on the switch, by its darker color or both. A 3-way switch does not have marked "on" and "off" handle positions.

Three-way switches are always used in pairs. The use of two 3-way switches in a lighting circuit allows the lights to be controlled from two different locations. For this reason, 3-way switches are often used to control lighting fixtures in: (a) rooms having two entrances, (b) long hallways, (c) stairwells, and (d) similar locations. Figure 5-41 shows a schematic of a 3-way switch circuit controlling a lighting fixture.

**Wiring 3-way Switch Circuits.** Three-way switch circuits are easy to wire if four basic points are kept in mind. These are outlined below:

1. The grounded wire from the electrical supply connects directly to the silver- colored terminal of the load. This wire is never switched or interrupted.

2. The ungrounded wire from the electrical supply connects to the common terminal of the first 3-way switch.

3. The ungrounded black wire from the brass terminal of the load connects to the common terminal of the second 3-way switch.

4. To complete the circuit, the traveler terminals of the two 3-way switches are connected together using 3-wire cable (or individual wires in conduit).

**Three-way Switch Circuit Controlling a Lighting Fixture at the End of the Run.** Figure 5-42 shows how this circuit would be wired using cable wiring materials. The four points listed previously were followed in wiring this circuit. Notice that 3-wire cable is required between the two 3-way switches, while 2-wire cable is used for the rest of the circuit.

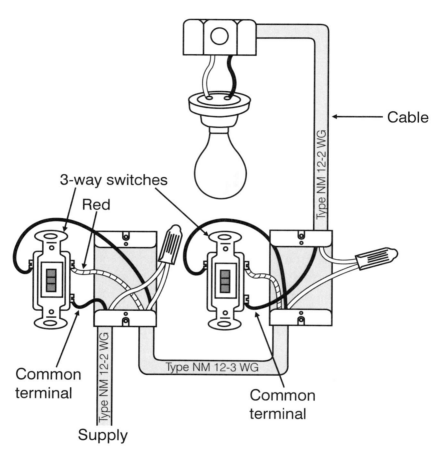

5-42. A 3-way switch controlling a lighting fixture at the end of the run. Note: Equipment grounding wire not shown for clarity.

**Three-way Switch Circuit Controlling a Lighting Fixture in the Middle of the Run.** This circuit is slightly more complex than the previous circuit, since it incorporates a switch loop. However, keeping the same four basic points in mind will also allow us to wire this circuit. The only difference is that the white wire between the lighting fixture and the last 3-way switch is used as an ungrounded conductor (Figure 5-43).

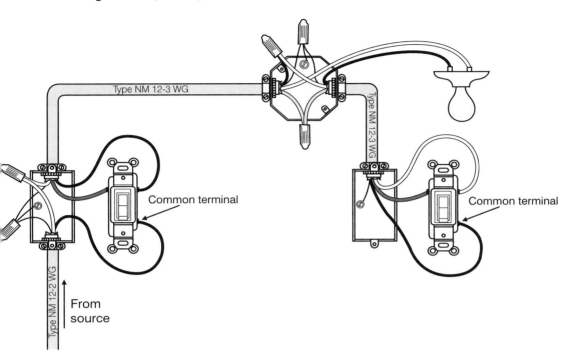

**5-43. A 3-way switch controlling a lighting fixture in the middle of the run.**

The same *NEC* requirements apply to wiring a switch loop in a 3-way switch circuit as to wiring one in a SPST switch circuit. The white wire used as an ungrounded conductor must be used as the supply to the switch. The white wire used as the ungrounded conductor may not be used as the supply to the lighting fixture (*NEC* 200-7 Exception No. 2).

## Double-pole Double-throw Reversing Switch

This type of switch is commonly called a **4-way switch.** A 4-way switch has four screw terminals. All four terminals are travelers. A 4-way switch does not have marked "on" and "off" handle positions (Figure 5-44).

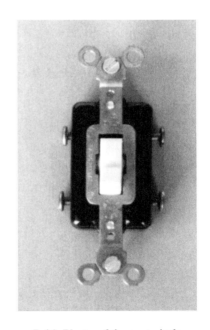

**5-44. Photo of 4-way switch.**

Four-way switches are always used in a circuit containing a pair of 3-way switches. The most common situation is to use one 4-way switch and a pair of 3-way switches to control a lighting circuit from three locations. Additional 4-way switches can be added to this basic circuit to provide additional switching locations. But, because of the extensive wiring requirements for circuits containing multiple 4-way switches, circuits of this type are limited. Figure 5-45 shows a schematic for a 3- and 4-way switch circuit.

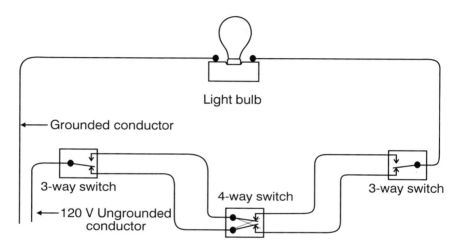

5-45. Schematic of a 3- and 4-way switch circuit.

**Wiring 3- and 4-way Switch Circuits.** Wiring 3- and 4-way switch circuits is made easier if four basic points are kept in mind:

1. The grounded conductor from the electrical supply is connected to the silver terminal of the load.

2. The ungrounded conductor from the electrical supply is connected to the common terminal of one 3-way switch.

3. The traveler terminals of both 3-way switches are connected to the traveler terminals of the 4-way switch. (Note: A wiring diagram provided with the 4-way switch should show the correct connections.)

4. The ungrounded black wire from the brass terminal of the load connects to the common terminal of the other 3-way switch.

**Three- and 4-way Switch Circuit Controlling a Lighting Fixture at the Beginning of the Run.** This circuit (Figure 5-46) represents a fairly common 3- and 4-way switching circuit. The electrical supply enters at a ceiling mounted lighting fixture. The switches are placed at three different locations.

Notice that the circuit below is wired in accordance with the four points previously discussed. The grounded conductor from the incoming cable attaches to the light fixture's silver-colored terminal (Point No. 1). For the remainder of the circuit, the white wire is used as an ungrounded conductor in wiring the switch loop. The ungrounded conductor from the electrical supply connects to the common terminal of one 3-way switch (Point No. 2). The traveler terminals from both 3-way switches are connected to the traveler terminals of the 4-way switch (Point No. 3). Finally, the common terminal of the other 3-way switch is connected to the brass-colored terminal of the lighting fixture (Point No. 4).

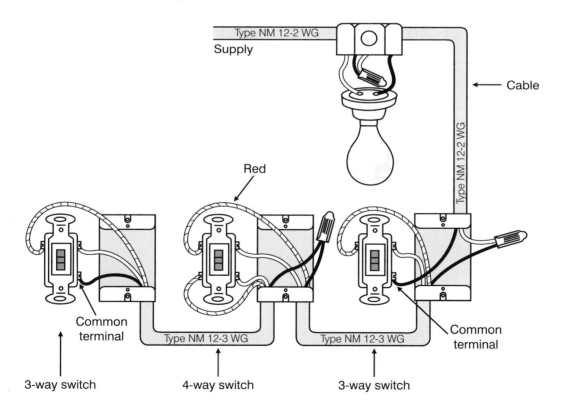

**5-46. 3- and 4-way switch circuit controlling a lighting fixture at the beginning of the run. Note: Equipment grounding wire not shown for clarity.**

# LIGHTING AND LIGHTING FIXTURES

Three primary types of lights are used in agricultural buildings: incandescent, fluorescent, and high intensity discharge.

## *INCANDESCENT LIGHTS AND FIXTURES*

### *Incandescent Lights*

An ***incandescent light*** (Figure 5-47) glows because of the heat (approximately 4700°F) produced as current flows through a high resistance tungsten filament. If the filament was heated in open air, it would quickly burn up due to the combination of oxygen and the hot filament material. To prevent this, the filament is enclosed in a glass bulb. Incandescent bulbs rated at up to 300 watts have standard screw bases.

A typical 100 watt incandescent light converts only about 10 percent of the energy input into visible light. Thus, incandescent lights have a low efficiency compared to fluorescent and high intensity discharge lights and cost more to operate. Incandescent lights have a short service life—only about 750 hours for a typical 100 to 150 watt bulb. In addition, the light output of an incandescent bulb decreases to about 80 to 90 percent of its initial output as the bulb approaches its rated service life.

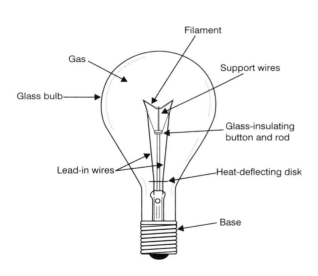

**5-47. Typical incandescent lamp.**

Incandescent lights do offer some advantages. They are inexpensive, widely available, and operate well under most conditions including low temperatures. In addition, incandescent lights do not require a prolonged "warm-up" period as do some types of lights. They reach full illumination almost immediately once energized. Thus, incandescent lights should be considered in situations where light is needed for short periods and/or where lights are frequently turned "on" and "off."

## Fixtures for Incandescent Lights

Permanently mounted incandescent lighting fixtures are typically made of either porcelain or plastic. Because of their higher resistance to heat, porcelain fixtures are recommended for lights rated at over 100 watts.

The silver-colored terminal screw in an incandescent lighting fixture is electrically connected to the screw shell inside the fixture. The fixture's brass-colored terminal screw is electrically connected to the insulated center contact at the bottom of the screw shell. These connections are shown in Figure 5-48.

Incandescent lighting fixtures are mounted on metal or plastic boxes. When used in a damp/dusty or wet building, the fixture and the box must comply with *NEC* 547-7(abc). The fixtures must be installed to minimize the entrance of dust. Where exposed to physical damage, the fixture must be protected by a suitable guard. Finally, fixtures that may be exposed to water must be watertight. Figure 5-49 shows an incandescent lighting fixture approved for use in a damp building.

When wiring incandescent lighting fixtures, make certain that the temperature in the fixture will not exceed the temperature rating of the conductors to be used. This is a special concern when using dust- and watertight fixtures.

## Wiring Incandescent Lighting Fixtures

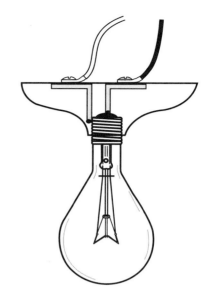

**5-48. Incandescent lighting fixture.**

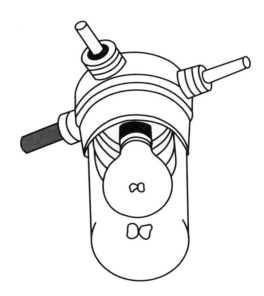

**5-49. Incandescent lighting fixture for damp buildings.**

The wiring of permanently mounted incandescent lighting fixtures is fairly simple. The ungrounded conductor is attached to the fixture's brass-colored terminal screw. The grounded conductor is attached to the fixture's

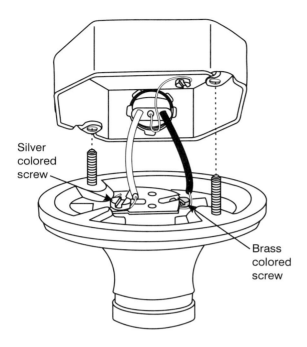

Silver colored screw

Brass colored screw

**5-50. Proper wiring for an incandescent lighting fixture at the end of a run.**

silver-colored terminal screw. If a metal device box is used, the equipment grounding screw must be attached to the box using an approved connector.

Figure 5-50 shows how an incandescent lighting fixture at the end of a run would be wired.

In wiring lighting fixtures, take special precautions to ensure that the ungrounded conductor is connected to the silver-colored screw and that the ungrounded conductor is connected to the brass-colored screw. (In other words, make sure that correct polarity is maintained.) Figure 5-51 (left) shows what would happen to a person making contact with the base of a bulb in a correctly wired lighting fixture. Figure 5-51 (right) shows what would happen in the same situation if the grounded and ungrounded wires were reversed at the lighting fixture.

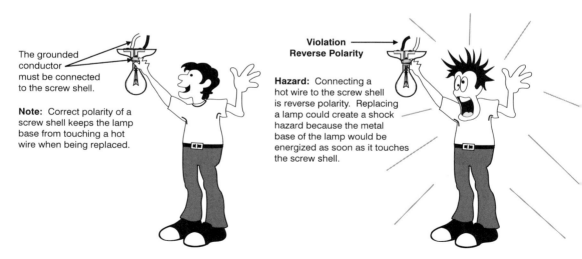

The grounded conductor must be connected to the screw shell.

**Note:** Correct polarity of a screw shell keeps the lamp base from touching a hot wire when being replaced.

Violation — Reverse Polarity

**Hazard:** Connecting a hot wire to the screw shell is reverse polarity. Replacing a lamp could create a shock hazard because the metal base of the lamp would be energized as soon as it touches the screw shell.

**5-51. A correctly wired lighting fixture (left) and incorrectly wired (reverse polarity) lighting fixture (right)**

# FLUORESCENT LIGHTS AND FIXTURES

## Fluorescent Lights

A *fluorescent light* tube is a glass tube filled with a gas and having a small filament in each end. The inside of the tube is coated with a fluorescent material. The gas inside the tube is commonly a mixture of argon gas and mercury vapor. The two filaments are coated with a chemical material that emits electrons when heated. The two filaments are not connected to each other. Rather, each filament is brought out to the two pins on each end of the tube (Figure 5-52).

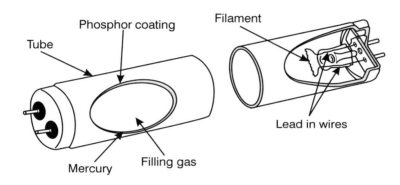

**5-52. A typical fluorescent lamp.**

Fluorescent lights are more efficient than incandescent lights, producing from three to four times more light per watt. Fluorescent lights have a much longer service life than incandescent lights. The use of fluorescent lighting also reduces glare and shadows in a room or building.

Fluorescent lights are more expensive to purchase than incandescent lights. Also, turning fluorescent lights "on" and "off" frequently reduces their service life. Most ordinary types of fluorescent lights are difficult to start at low temperatures (below 50°F) and when the humidity is high (65 percent relative humidity or above). Although they cost more, special fluorescent bulbs and fixtures that provide excellent service in cool, humid environments are available.

## Fluorescent Lighting Fixtures

Special accessories (a ballast and an automatic starter switch) are required in order for a fluorescent light to operate. These accessories are

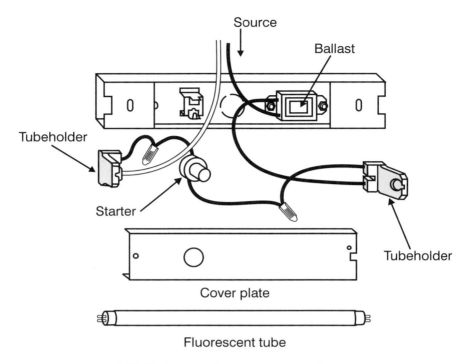

**5-53. Parts of the fluorescent lighting fixture.**

typically part of the fluorescent lighting fixture into which the bulbs are mounted (Figure 5-53).

Fluorescent lighting fixtures are available for use in agricultural buildings having a harsh environment. These fixtures are nonmetallic enclosed fixtures. A special gasket is placed between the fixture and the enclosure to make a watertight seal.

As with incandescent lights, always make sure that the temperature rating of the wiring is sufficient for the fixture. Fluorescent lighting fixtures are purchased prewired. The instructions (and diagrams) provided by the manufacturer should be followed in mounting the fixture and wiring it into an electrical circuit.

## HIGH INTENSITY DISCHARGE LIGHTS

High intensity discharge (HID) lights include mercury, metal halide, high-pressure sodium, and low-pressure sodium lights. HID lights have long service lives, are very energy efficient, and operate well at low temperatures.

HID lights require anywhere between 5 and 15 minutes to start. Therefore, light is not immediately available when the switch is turned "on." Normally, auxiliary incandescent or fluorescent lights are used with interior HID lights to provide illumination while the main HID lights warm up. Once an HID light has been switched "off," it cannot be restarted immediately. It must cool first.

Because of their delayed starting and restarting characteristics, HID lights are best used where lights are left "on" for at least three hours. Also, HID lights tend to function best when mounted at least 12 feet high. For these reasons, HID lights are well suited for outdoor security lights and for interior lighting in shops and other buildings having high ceilings.

# BOXES AND FITTINGS

## BOXES

Boxes have several important functions. They secure the cable or conduit connected to the box, preventing mechanical strain on the wiring connections. Boxes attach to the building structure and provide support for switches, receptacle outlets and fixtures. Finally, boxes enclose all wiring connections, providing protection and preventing accidental contact with uninsulated components.

A box should be approved for the application and environment where it will be used. As previously indicated, noncorrosive, dust- and watertight boxes should be used in environments where these conditions are present.

## FITTINGS

Conduit and cables must be secured to boxes to prevent mechanical strain on wiring connections. A variety of devices are available for securing conduit and cables to boxes. Selection of the proper device depends on the type of conduit or cable and boxes used. Figure 5-54 (left) shows a typical conduit-to-box connection with PVC conduit and a nonmetallic box. Figure 5-54 (right) shows a watertight cable-to-box connection with Type UF cable and a nonmetallic box.

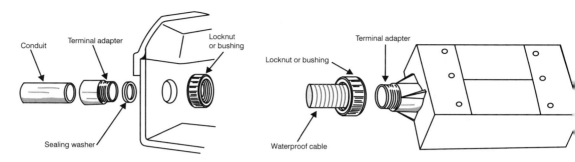

**5-54. Typical PVC conduit-to-box connection (left) and watertight cable-to-box connection (right).**

## SIZING BOXES

A box must have adequate volume for all of the conductors and devices that it will contain (*NEC* 370-16). Using a box that is too small is a violation of the *NEC*, makes work more difficult, increases the time required for wiring tasks, and makes a short circuit more likely.

The minimum cubic inch (in³) volumes for selected trade sizes of metal boxes are listed in *NEC* Table 370-16(a). The *NEC* requires that all nonmetallic boxes be marked by the manufacturer with their volume. This marking requirement also applies to metallic boxes not listed in *NEC* Table 370-16(a).

The *NEC* requirements for box volume are based on the size of the largest conductor entering or leaving the box. These requirements are listed in Table 5-7.

## Table 5-7
## Required Box Volume per Condutor

| Conductor Size (AWG) | Box Volume/Conductor (in³) |
|---|---|
| 14 | 2.00 |
| 12 | 2.25 |
| 10 | 2.50 |
| 8 | 3.00 |
| 6 | 5.00 |

Note: Based on *NEC* Table 370-16(b).

The required volume for a specific box is determined by multiplying the number of equivalent conductors in the box by the value from Table 5-7 for the largest conductor. The following rules are used in determining the number of equivalent conductors in a box [*NEC* 370-16(b)].

1. Each conductor passing through a box without being spliced or connected to a device is counted as one conductor.

2. Each conductor connecting to a splice or a device is counted as one conductor. But, if a conductor is contained completely within the box (such as a pigtail splice), it is not counted.

3. All grounding conductors in a box are counted as only one conductor. [Exception: If a second set of equipment grounding conductors is present in the box (as permitted by *NEC* 250-74 Exception No. 4 for isolated ground receptacles), an additional conductor must be counted.]

4. A switch or receptacle counts as two conductors.

5. Each of the following types of fittings is counted as one conductor: cable clamps, fixture studs, hickeys, and straps (Figure 5-55). Each type of fitting is only counted once, even if two or more of the same fittings are present.

6. Cable connectors with the clamping mechanism located outside of the box <u>do not</u> count as a conductor.

These rules were used to determine the number of equivalent conductors in the receptacle box shown in Figure 5-56. Assume that the largest wire is AWG 10. Table 5-7 indicates that this size conductor requires a box volume of 2.5 in3 per conductor. Thus, based on our equivalent conductor count of eight, the box selected must have a minimum volume of 20 in³. If no box having this exact volume is available, the next largest size should be used.

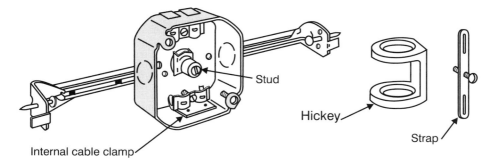

Stud

Hickey

Strap

Internal cable clamp

**5-55. Fittings that count as one conductor in a box.**

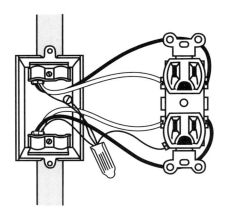

| Conductor, device, fitting | Equivalent conductors |
|---|---|
| 4 wires terminating at DCO | 4 |
| 2 equipment grounding wires | 1 |
| 2 pigtail wires | 0 |
| 2 internal cable clamps | 1 |
| 1 DCO | 2 |

**Total equivalent conductors = 8**

**5-56. Example of counting fittings and conductors in a box.**

# BASIC TOOLS AND PROCEDURES

Many tools and operations are used in electrical wiring. Several tools are shown here. Careful study and supervised practice under the direction of an expert are necessary to develop skills in electrical wiring.

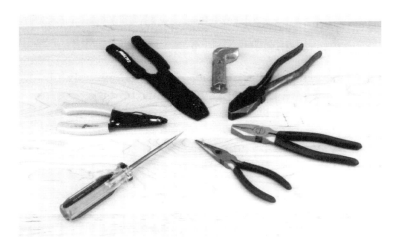

**5-57. Various electrical tools.**

## Cutting Wires and Cables

Smaller wires and cables are usually cut with lineman's pliers or with diagonal cutting pliers. Larger wires and cables are cut with a hand hacksaw. Regardless of the cutting method, wires and cables should be cut straight across (90° angle).

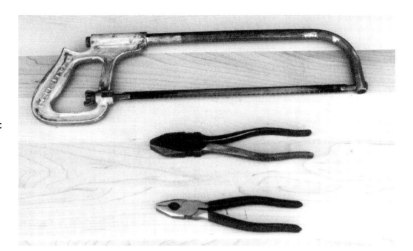

**5-58. Tools used to cut wires and cables.**

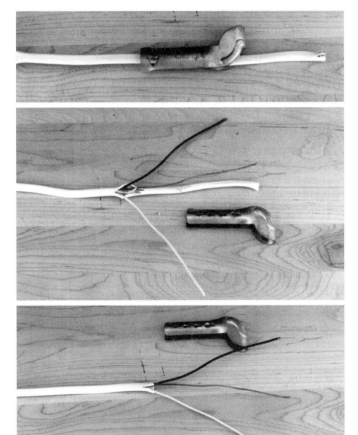

**5-59. A cable ripper is used to slice open the outer jacket from the cable.**

## Removing the Jacket from Cables

A *cable ripper* is used to slice open the outer jacket from flat 2-wire cables (either with or without ground). Cable rippers are made of spring steel and have a small triangular blade inside. When a piece of cable is placed inside the stripper and the handles are squeezed together, the blade penetrates the cable jacket. The jacket is sliced open as the cable ripper is pulled along its length (Figure 5-59). Once the jacket has been opened, it can be removed using either a utility knife or a pair of diagonal cutting pliers.

A 3-wire cable (with or without ground) is round. Under the jacket, the individual conductors are twisted around each other. A utility knife is generally used to slice open the jacket of a round 3-wire cable, since the knife can follow the rotation of the wires. This prevents nicking or cutting the insulation on any of the individual conductors.

The *NEC* (300-14) specifies that at least 6 inches of free conductor must be left at each outlet, junction and switch point to allow for splices or connection to fixtures or devices. When using cable wiring, this means that a minimum of 6 inches of unjacketed cable must be available inside each box (Figure 5-60).

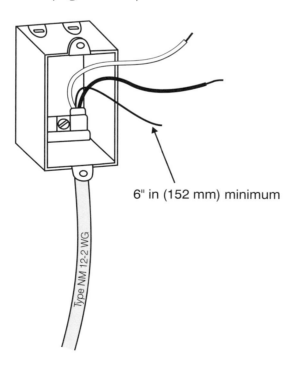

6" in (152 mm) minimum

Type NM 12-2 WG

5-60. Allow 6 inches of unjacketed, free conductor at each outlet box.

## Stripping Insulation from Individual Wires

A *wire stripper* is used to remove insulation from the ends of individual wires. To use a wire stripper, first adjust the stripper for the size (AWG No.) of wire to be stripped. With the stripper jaws open, position the stripper at the point where insulation removal is to begin. Squeeze the stripper handles together, twist the wire and the stripper and pull the stripper toward the end of the wire. The cut insulation should pull off easily, without nicking or otherwise damaging the wire.

A multipurpose tool contains several useful tools, including a wire stripper. For most multipurpose tools, individual stripper notches are provided for each of the common AWG wire sizes. No adjustment is required. Simply place the wire to be stripped in the correct stripper notch. Remove the insulation in the same way as you would when using a wire stripper.

Some people remove insulation from wires using a pocket knife. This is not a good practice since you are likely to nick the wire. A nicked wire has less ampacity and is more likely to break.

## Splicing Wires

Branch circuit wires are usually spliced (joined) together using *wire nuts.* Wire nuts are available in different sizes to accommodate the splicing of different gauges and numbers of wires. Always use the correct wire nut for the size and number of wires to be spliced. This information is given on the wire nut box.

To splice wires using a wire nut follow these steps. First, strip of about ½ to ¾ inch of insulation from the ends of the wires to be spliced. Choose the correct size wire nut in accordance with instructions on the box. Hold all of the wires to be spliced in one hand so the ends of the wires are even. Holding the wires firmly, push the wires into the wire nut while twisting the wire nut. Continue until the wire nut is tight. Test the splice

**5-61. Wire nuts used to splice (join) two or more wires together.**

by holding the wire nut in one hand while pulling firmly on the wires one at a time. If the splice is properly made, you will not be able to pull any of the wires out. Lastly, check to make certain that no uninsulated wire is exposed at the splice.

**Connecting Wires to Devices.** Wires can be connected to most devices (switches, receptacles) in one of two ways, either by connecting the wire to a screw terminal or using the backwiring technique.

To connect a wire to a device terminal, use the following procedure. Strip about $1/2$ to $3/4$ inch of insulation from the end of the wire to be connected. Using a pair of needle nose pliers, form a $2/3$ loop in the bare wire. The loop should be made clockwise in relation to the screw terminal. This causes the wire to be drawn tightly under the screw as it is tightened. A properly made connection should have no insulation under the terminal and no more that $1/16$ of an inch of bare wire exposed at the terminal.

Many switches and receptacles have both screw terminals and special *backwiring* terminals. To wire a backwired device, use the following procedure. Using the molded "strip gauge" on the back of the device, measure the length of insulation to be stripped from the conductors. Strip the recommended length of insulation from the conductors to be inserted using a wire stripper. Insert the wires into the correct backwiring terminal holes so that no uninsulated wire is exposed. Gently pull on each wire to ensure that secure connections have been made. Tighten the unused screw ter-

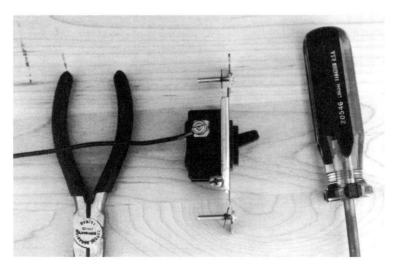

5-62. Ungrounded wire correctly connected to a switch terminal.

minals on the side of the device. (Note: This helps prevent accidental contact between the screw terminals and circuit conductors or metal device boxes.)

A spring leaf inside each backwiring terminal prevents the wires from coming loose. To remove a wire from a backwired terminal, a small screwdriver may be placed in a special slot to depress the spring leaf. With the leaf compressed, the wire can be easily removed.

Note: Regardless of the wiring method used, a conductor may only be attached to devices that are approved for use with that type of wire.

# SUMMARY

The basic materials, devices, and procedures used in electrical wiring have been covered in this chapter. In addition, the effects of electricity on the human body and electrical safety have been stressed.

Electric shock is painful and potentially fatal. Only a fraction of an ampere of current flow through the body may interfere with operation of the heart, causing death. Because of the potential hazards, only knowledgeable persons should work with electricity. Strict safety precautions must be followed to avoid injury.

To enhance electrical safety, the National Fire Prevention Association publishes the *National Electrical Code* (*NEC*). The *NEC* is intended to ensure safe electrical wiring systems. Many local electrical codes are based in whole or in part on the *NEC*. The Underwriters' Laboratories (UL) tests electrical wiring and devices to ensure that they are safe when used as intended. Always purchase UL listed materials and devices.

Agricultural buildings present special problems related to electrical wiring. Many such buildings are dusty, damp, and/or have corrosive environments. Special wiring materials and procedures, as outlined in *NEC* Article 547, are required for these types of buildings.

Electrical branch circuits deliver electricity to individual loads. Single-phase branch circuits have nominal ratings of either 120 or 240 volts. Feeder circuits carry electricity from a service entrance panel to a subpanel and are usually 240-volt circuits.

The wiring system inside a building consists of several components. These components may include the service entrance panel, subpanel(s), overcurrent protection devices, ground-fault circuit interrupters, copper or aluminum conductors in cable or conduit, receptacle outlets, switches, lighting fixtures, and various boxes and fixtures. The entire electrical system must be carefully planned to provide safe, efficient service. Individual circuits and components must be carefully designed and selected.

Electrical wiring materials and devices must be carefully installed following approved procedures. Careful system design, proper materials selection, and correct installation procedures are all required to ensure safe, functional electrical service. Lastly, it must be emphasized that only qualified individuals should do electrical work.

# REVIEW QUESTIONS

1. Describe what is meant by the "let-go" current threshold as related to human contact with a 60 Hz AC electrical current.

2. What are the two key factors in determining the severity of an electrical shock? Explain how these two factors are related.

3. A homeowner is replacing a defective single-pole switch that controls a ceiling lamp. To de-energize the circuit, the homeowner turns the single-pole switch to the "off" position. No other measures are taken to de-energize the circuit. Can the homeowner safely replace the defective single-pole switch? Why or why not? What else, if anything, should be done prior to replacing the switch?

4. List two organizations that are concerned with electrical safety. Describe the primary contribution of each organization to electrical safety.

5. Describe three different building groups common in agricultural wiring. List an example building in each group.

6. What article of the *National Electrical Code* describes the requirements that must be met in wiring dusty/damp and/or corrosive environment buildings?

7. Describe the difference between a branch and a feeder circuit.

8. What connections are made at the building service entrance panel when wiring a 120 volt branch circuit using 2-wire cable with an equipment grounding wire?

9. What connections are made at the building service entrance panel when wiring a 240 volt branch circuit using 2-wire cable with an equipment grounding wire? Indicate any special markings that should be present.

10. Describe how the 120 volt loads listed below should be connected to the service entrance panel so as to balance the electrical loads as closely as possible.

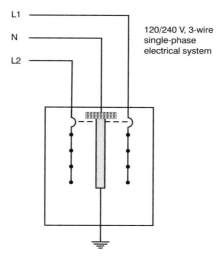

L1

N

L2

120/240 V, 3-wire single-phase electrical system

A. Three, 12 ampere lighting circuits.

B. One, 8 ampere motor load.

C. One, 15 ampere DCO circuit.

D. One, 9 ampere SPO circuit.

11. Determine the current flow on the grounded (neutral) service conductor in a 120/240 volt, 3-wire, single-phase electrical system with loads connected as shown below.

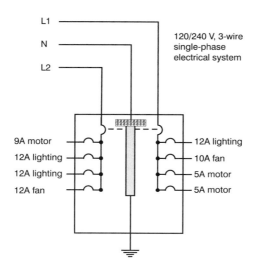

L1

N

L2

120/240 V, 3-wire single-phase electrical system

9A motor

12A lighting

12A lighting

12A fan

12A lighting

10A fan

5A motor

5A motor

12. Describe the difference in the feeder circuit connections made to a sub-panel when (a) the sub-panel is in the same building as the service entrance panel and (b) the sub-panel is in a separate building.

13. Explain the purpose of an overcurrent protection device, and list two different overcurrent protection devices.

14. Overcurrent protection devices have an "inverse-time characteristic." Explain what this means.

15. What is the purpose of a ground-fault circuit interrupter (GFCI)? List two locations where GFCIs are required by the *NEC*.

16. List the correct name for each of the three conductors found in a single-phase branch or feeder circuit. Also indicate the color code requirements for each conductor.

17. A 240 volt 30 ampere special purpose outlet (SPO) is to be installed in a building. The one-way circuit length is 79 feet; voltage drop must be limited to 2 percent. What size Type UF copper cable should be used to wire the SPO?

18. A box of cable has the following information printed on it: Type NM-C 10-3 WG. Explain what each part of this designation means.

19. Three Type THW (AWG #10) conductors are to be run in non-metallic conduit. What is the smallest standard conduit size that can be used?

20. Define the terms "pole" and "throw" as used in describing a switch.

21. Identify the voltage and amperage rating of the receptacle shown below.

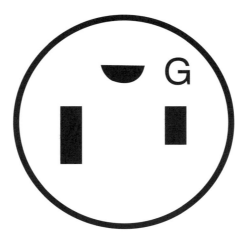

22. Determine the minimum volume (in³) device box required for the situation shown below.

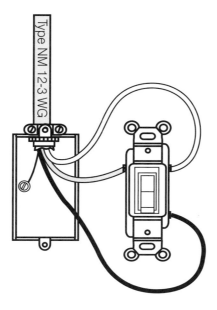

# APPLYING THE CONCEPTS

Under the supervision of your instructor, diagram and wire each of the following circuits. Have each circuit inspected by your instructor upon completion. DO NOT connect your circuit to any electrical source. Note: Use a variety of approved wiring materials and methods (conduit and cable) in completing this assignment.

1. Wire this circuit so that the duplex convenience outlets (DCOs) are on the same circuit and always "hot."

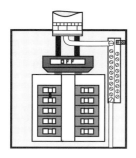    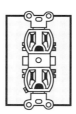    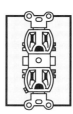

2. Wire this circuit so that the switch controls the bottom half of the DCO. The top half of the DCO should always be "hot."

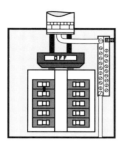   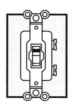   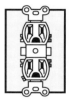

3. Wire this circuit so that the 240 volt special purpose outlet (SPO) is always "hot."

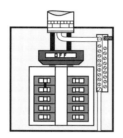

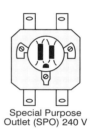

Special Purpose
Outlet (SPO) 240 V

4. Wire this circuit so that the lamp fixture can be controlled by either switch.

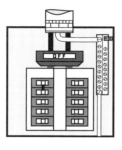   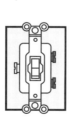   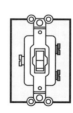   

5. Diagram and wire the circuit below so that either switch will control the lamp fixture.

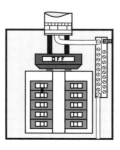   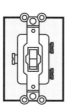      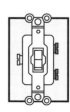

# 6

# SELECTING AND USING ELECTRIC MOTORS

An electric motor is a device for converting electrical power into mechanical power. It has been estimated that electric motors consume approximately 60 percent of all electrical energy generated in the United States.

In the home, electric motors are found in appliances ranging from clocks to garage door openers. Agricultural use of electric motors includes applications such as ventilation fans, grain augers and elevators, water pumps, and mechanized feeding systems. In industry, electric motors power machine tools, presses, and industrial robots to name just a few applications.

6-1. Stepper motors are used in robots. They rotate a specific number of degrees for each pulsing electrical input applied to the motor winding instead of producing continuous shaft rotation. As robots become more common in agricultural production and processing, stepper motors will become more widespread. (Courtesy, Automation International, Inc.)

# OBJECTIVES

This chapter covers the selection and use of electric motors. After completing the chapter, you will:

1. Explain the cost benefit of electric motors in agriculture.

2. Identify and explain the functions of the major components of an electric motor.

3. Explain the principles of operation of DC motors and single-phase AC motors.

4. Identify types of motors used in agriculture and their common applications.

5. Interpret electric motor nameplate information.

6. Select the correct type of motor enclosure for specific use conditions.

7. Interpret motor wiring diagrams and correctly wire dual voltage motors for either low or high voltage operation.

8. Reverse the direction of motor shaft rotation for various types of motors.

9. Analyze the performance of an electric motor to determine motor efficiency and power factor.

10. Plan motor branch circuits that comply with applicable *National Electrical Code* requirements.

## TERMS

ambient (amb.) temperature
ampacity
armature
capacitor-start capacitor-run motor
capacitor-start induction-run motor
centrifugal switch
DC motor
disconnecting means
enclosure
end bell
frame
frame number (FR)
hertz (Hz)
horsepower rating (HP)
induction motor
insulation class
KVA code letter
model number
motor controller
motor duty cycle
motor rotation
motor selection
nameplate
permanent-split capicator motor
repulsion-start induction-run motor
rotor
running winding
service factor (SF)
squirrel cage rotor
split-phase motor
starting winding
stator
terminal board
thermal protection
universal motor
voltage drop

# ELECTRIC MOTOR COST COMPARISON

A person, working steadily for one hour, can produce about $^1/_{10}$ horsepower. This is the approximate amount of energy required to operate a 100 watt light bulb. If a person works at this rate for 10 hours, he will have done one horsepower-hour of work. If the worker is paid $10.00 per hour, the one horsepower-hour of work done will cost his employer $100.00 ($10.00/hr. × 10 hrs.).

A one horsepower electric motor operating continuously for 10 hours will perform 10 horsepower-hours of work. Assuming a motor efficiency of 75 percent, the motor will use 10 kilowatt-hours (kW-hrs) of electrical energy during this period. At a cost of 10 cents per kW-hr, it will cost 1 dollar to operate the electric motor ($0.10/kW-hr × 10 kW-hrs).

Based on the information above, the one horsepower motor will produce 10 times more work than the person (10 hp-hrs vs. 1 hp-hr) at only 1 percent of the cost ($1.00 vs. $100). Thus, it is easy to see, that as a source of power, electric motors are much more cost-effective than humans. On the other hand, electric motors cannot think, coordinate the work of others, or make management decisions. The efficient "muscle" supplied by electric motors allows humans time to devote to other important tasks.

# IDENTIFYING ELECTRIC MOTOR COMPONENTS AND THEIR FUNCTIONS

The *frame* serves as the motor housing, keeps all the internal parts in place, and conducts heat away from the motor to the surrounding air

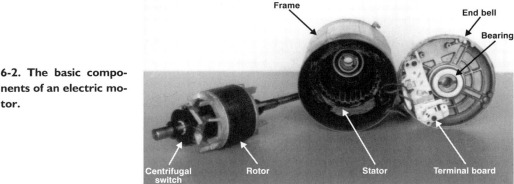

6-2. The basic components of an electric motor.

Frame

End bell

Bearing

Centrifugal switch

Rotor

Stator

Terminal board

where it is dissipated. The frame also protects internal motor components from water, dirt, and other environmental hazards and provides a means for mounting the motor to machinery and equipment. The ***end bells***, located at each end of the motor, can be removed to gain access to internal components.

Bearings, located in the end bells, support the rotating motor component and keep it in proper alignment. Sleeve, roller, or ball bearings may be used in a particular motor, depending on the motor's intended use.

The ***terminal board***, located in one end bell, provides a means of making electrical connections from the motor windings to the motor branch circuit. A wiring diagram, provided with the motor, will show how the wiring connections should be made.

The ***stator*** consists of a laminated steel core that holds coils of copper wire in place. Electricity flowing through these coils produces a strong magnetic field necessary for motor operation.

The term used to name the rotating part of a motor differs for AC and DC motors. In AC motors, the rotating component is called the ***rotor***. In DC motors, it is called the ***armature***. Despite this difference in terms the component rotates because of the interaction of its magnetic field and the stator's magnetic field. A shaft extending from the rotating component (rotor or armature) to the outside of the motor allows equipment to be connected to the motor.

A fan may be used to move air over the motor windings or housing to dissipate heat. In motors designed for use in dry, clean, non-hazardous environments, an internal fan draws air in one end of the motor, forces the air over the windings, and pushes it out the other end. In some totally enclosed motors (used in wet, dusty or hazardous environments), an external fan circulates air over the outside of the motor for cooling. Not all motors are equipped with cooling fans.

In addition to these basic components, some electric motors may have additional parts. Many motors have built-in ***thermal protection*** to automatically disconnect the motor from the electrical circuit in case of overheating. Induction-run motors will be provided with a ***centrifugal switch*** that disconnects the starting windings (located in the stator) from the electrical circuit once the motor approaches full speed. DC motors and wound rotor AC motors have brushes and a commutator to provide current to the armature.

# HOW ELECTRIC MOTORS WORK

All electric motors operate because of the interaction between magnetic fields in the stator and in the rotating motor component (rotor or armature). However, the exact method of operation varies somewhat between different types of motors.

## DC MOTORS

*DC motors* get their name because they are designed to operate on direct current (DC) electricity.

As shown in Figure 6-3, the armature is placed between two permanent magnets. A magnetic field is present between the north and south poles of the two magnets. Direct current electricity flows into the armature through the "A" brush, which rides on one section of the commutator. Current flows out of the armature and back to ground through the "B" brush that rides on the second section of the commutator. Current flow through the armature windings creates a second, strong magnetic field. These two magnetic fields oppose one another, causing the motor to turn. Reversing the direction of current flow through the armature reverses the direction of motor rotation.

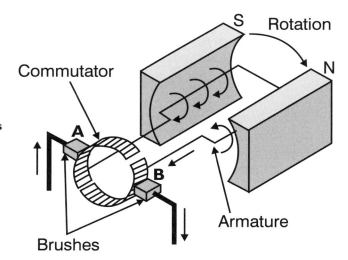

**6-3. The basic operating principles of a DC motor.**

The armature has several segments. Each segment consists of a wire wrapped many times around the armature, with the ends terminating at opposite commutator segments. The stationary brushes continually switch

6-4. A small, disassembled DC motor.

from one pair of commutator segments to the next as the armature rotates. The brushes switch commutator halves with every one-half armature revolution to keep the armature rotating.

Except for very small DC motors, permanent magnets are not used to create the magnetic field surrounding the armature. Rather, coils of wire (called field coils) are wrapped on iron cores (called field shoes) to create powerful electromagnets.

## SINGLE-PHASE AC INDUCTION MOTORS

The single-phase AC induction motor is the most common type of electric motor used in agriculture.

In Figure 6-5, the stator has two poles wrapped with insulated copper wire. Each end of the wire is connected to an AC electrical source. Current flowing through the coils creates a strong electromagnet, having a north pole and a south pole. As the direction of the current flow alternates in

6-5. An example of how the single-phase AC induction motor operates.

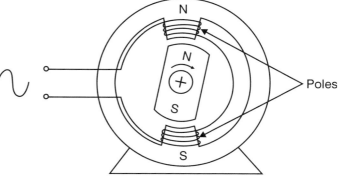

the AC circuit, the polarity of the stator's magnetic poles also alternates. For simplicity in explaining the basic principles of AC motor operation, Figure 6-5 shows the rotor as a permanent magnet.

Since like magnetic poles repel each other, the rotor will turn clockwise as indicated by the arrow in Figure 6-5. As the rotor reaches the horizontal position (90° rotation), the unlike magnetic poles attract, and the rotor continues to turn clockwise as shown in Figure 6-6.

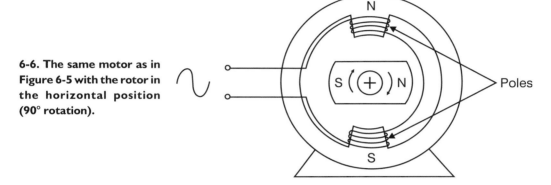

**6-6. The same motor as in Figure 6-5 with the rotor in the horizontal position (90° rotation).**

As the rotor again approaches the vertical position (180° rotation), the AC electricity changes direction of flow, reversing the polarity of the stator poles. Since like magnetic poles repel each other, the rotor continues to turn clockwise (Figure 6-7 left). As the rotor again reaches the horizontal position (270° rotation), the unlike magnetic poles attract and the rotor continues to turn until it has completed one clockwise revolution (Figure 6-7 right). By this time, the polarity of the stator coils has changed again and the motor continues to rotate.

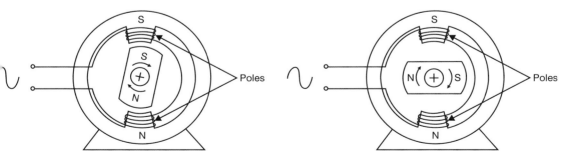

**7. The same motor as in Figure 6-5 at the vertical position (180° rotation) left and at the horizontal position 70° rotation) right.**

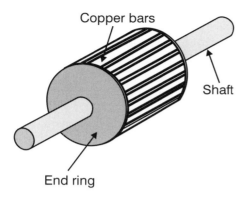

**6-8. The squirrel cage rotor.**

In an actual AC *induction motor,* the rotor is not a permanent magnet. Rather, the rotor, like the stator, is an electromagnet. Since there is no direct electrical connection between the AC voltage source and the rotor, current flow is caused by magnetic induction. Magnetic induction is the process of generating a voltage in a conductor by the relative motion between the conductor and a magnetic field.

The type of rotor most often used in AC induction motors is the squirrel cage rotor. As shown in Figure 6-8, the *squirrel cage rotor* has a cylinder made of a special type of soft steel. Bare copper, aluminum or brass bars are mounted in slots in the cylinder. Two end rings short circuit the individual bars together, creating paths for current flow.

As the AC electricity reverses directions, the north and south poles of the stator windings alternate. Since the rotor is not cutting magnetic lines of flux, no voltage is induced into the rotor, and the motor will not start (Figure 6-9). However, if some means were available to start the rotor turning, the rotor would cut across magnetic lines of flux, inducing a voltage into the rotor. The resulting magnetic field would interact with the stator's magnetic field, causing the rotor to continue turning. Thus, a single-phase induction motor requires a method of starting; once started, it will continue to run.

A starting winding is added to the stator of a single-phase motor for starting. The starting winding has an impedence (total opposition to current

**6-9. The poles alternate in a single-phase induction motor, but the rotor does not turn in either direction. Therefore, a single-phase motor needs a method of starting so it can run by itself on single-phase power.**

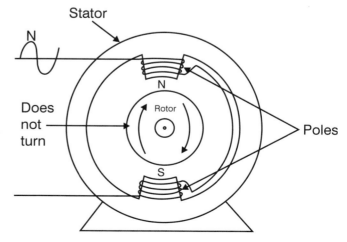

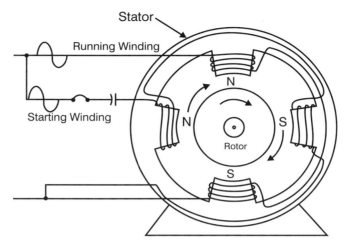

**6-10. The starting process for a single-phase AC induction motor.**

flow) that is different from the main running winding. This difference causes the current in the starting winding to be out of phase with the current in the running winding. Because the two currents are out of phase, a rotating magnetic field develops in the stator windings, inducing voltage into the rotor. The induced voltage creates a second magnetic field around the rotor, causing the rotor to turn.

Once the rotor is turning, the starting winding is no longer needed. In most induction motors, an internal centrifugal switch disconnects the starting winding from the voltage source once the motor reaches approximately 75 percent of its rated speed.

## COMMON TYPES OF ELECTRIC MOTORS

Many different types of electric motors are commercially available, ranging from $1/1000$ horsepower DC motors (about the size of your thumb) to 500 horsepower three-phase AC motors (about the size of an automobile). With such a wide assortment of electric motors available, a functional system for classifying motors is extremely helpful. Understanding the basic operating characteristics of a limited number of motor classes is easier than trying to become familiar with an almost infinite number of individual electric motors.

Electric motors are commonly classified according to three characteristics: (a) type of electrical service required, (b) physical features, and (c) rotation starting method. Based on these criteria, almost any electric motor used in agriculture can be classified.

Reading down Figure 6-11, the first distinction between motors is the type of electrical service required. AC motors require alternating current, DC motors require direct current, and universal motors can operate on either AC or DC electricity. DC motors can be sub-divided based on the type and arrangement of the stator windings. AC motors can be divided into those that require three-phase electrical service and those that operate on single-phase electricity.

Single-phase AC electric motors can be classified as either synchronous or induction run. The induction-run AC motors can be divided into those with wound rotors and those with squirrel cage rotors (a distinction based on physical characteristics). Finally, squirrel cage AC induction motors can be classified as split-phase, capacitor-start or shaded-pole.

While Figure 6-11 includes motors commonly used in agriculture, other types of motors are available. For example, DC stepper motors are widely used in industrial robots. Stepper motors, instead of producing continuous

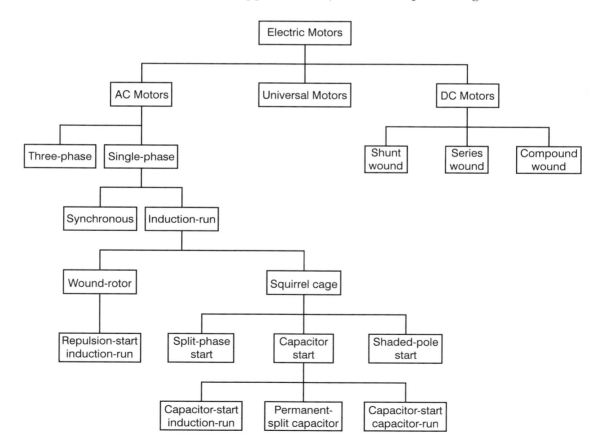

**6-11. Electric Motor Classification System**

shaft rotation, rotate a specific number of degrees for each pulsing electrical input applied to the motor windings. As robots become more common in agricultural production and processing, stepper motors will become more widespread.

# SINGLE-PHASE AC MOTORS

The most common type of electric motor used in agriculture is the single-phase AC motor. In this section you will learn more about single-phase motors.

## *SYNCHRONOUS MOTORS*

AC electricity in the United States is generated and supplied to consumers at a frequency of 60 Hz (cycles per second). Synchronous motors operate at an exact, constant output speed (rpm), that is determined by the design of the motor and the frequency (Hz) of AC electricity used to power the motor. Because of their precise speed, synchronous motors are used to power clocks and timers.

## *WOUND-ROTOR MOTORS*

Wound-rotor motors get their name because their rotors are made of wire windings connected to a commutator ring (similar to the DC motor armature shown in Figure 6-4). During motor starting, carbon brushes riding on the commutator ring connect the wound rotor to the AC power source. Thus, the initial build-up of the magnetic field in the rotor is not due to induction. Rather is a result of the flow of electricity directly from the voltage source. Once a wound rotor motor approaches its normal operating speed, the line voltage is effectively disconnected from the rotor and the motor continues to run as an induction motor.

Although several types of wound-rotor AC motors are manufactured, the repulsion-start induction-run motor is the most common in agriculture. ***Repulsion-start induction-run motors*** are designed to develop a very high starting torque. For this reason, they are used to power hard to start loads, such as silo unloaders, conveyors, and deep-well pumps. Due to their large size and fairly high cost, the use of repulsion-start induction-run motors is becoming less common.

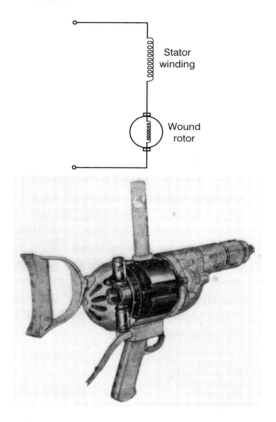

6-12. A cut-away view and an internal wiring schematic for a universal motor used in an electric drill.

Stator winding

Wound rotor

## UNIVERSAL MOTORS

The **universal motor** is a high-speed motor that will operate on either alternating or direct current. Since alternating current is the type most readily available, the vast majority of universal motors operate on AC electricity. A universal motor is sometimes called a series motor because the stator and the rotor are connected in series.

Note from Figure 6-12 that universal motors also use a wound rotor, and have brushes and a commutator like DC motors and repulsion-start induction-run AC motors. Universal motors are generally special-purpose motors, built into portable equipment, such as drills, grinders, sanders, vacuum cleaners, etc. The primary advantages of the universal motor include high starting torque, high power-to-size ratio, and rapid acceleration.

A universal motor does not operate at a constant speed. Rather, the motor will run as fast as the load allows. Under no-load conditions, a universal motor may over-speed and damage itself (unless internal friction limits the motor to a safe speed). Under heavy load conditions, a universal motor will slow to a fraction of its no-load speed as it attempts to power the load.

## SQUIRREL CAGE MOTORS

Several different types of AC squirrel cage induction motors are made, but the three basic types most commonly used in agricultural applications are the: (a) split-phase, (b) capacitor-start, and (c) shaded-pole motors. These classifications are made based on the method used to develop the rotating magnetic field in the stator windings that enables the motor to start.

## Split-Phase Motors

*Split-phase motors,* available in sizes of up to $1/2$ horsepower, are simple in construction and inexpensive. They develop a fairly low starting torque and draw a large amount of current when starting. For these reasons, split-phase motors are commonly used with easy to start loads, such as ventilation fans and centrifugal pumps.

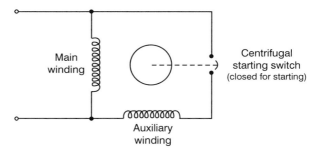

The split-phase motor uses an auxiliary winding in the stator assembly to produce the rotating magnetic field necessary to induce electricity into the rotor. This auxiliary winding, often called the **starting winding**, is made of fewer turns of a smaller wire than is the main stator winding (also called the **running winding**). In a split-

6-13. A cut-away view and an internal wiring schematic for a split-phase motor.

phase motor, the starting winding is wired in parallel with the running winding. A centrifugal switch, placed in series with the starting winding, opens and disconnects the starting winding from the voltage source once the motor reaches approximately 75 percent of its rated speed.

Because the starting winding has less impedence (total resistance to current flow), the magnetic field reaches a maximum in the starting winding before it reaches a maximum in the running winding. As the initial magnetic field in the starting winding declines, the magnetic field in the running winding increases. This alternate peaking and declining of the magnetic fields produces a rotating magnetic field that induces a voltage into the rotor.

Current flow through the rotor produces another magnetic field, which interacts with the stator magnetic field, causing the rotor to turn. Once the motor starts turning, voltage will continue to be induced into the rotor because the rotor is now cutting through the stator's magnetic field. This induced voltage will continue as long as electricity flows through the running winding. The starting winding, which is not needed once the motor begins turning, is disconnected from the voltage source through the centrifugal switch.

The split-phase motor gets its name because the difference in impedence between the running and starting windings has the effect of splitting single-phase AC electricity into two off-set phases during motor starting.

## Capacitor-Start Motors

Capacitor-start motors are similar to split-phase motors. They also split single-phase AC electricity into two off-set phases for motor starting. Capacitor-start motors differ from split-phase motors in that they use a capacitor (device for storing electrical energy) in series with the starting winding to increase starting torque and decrease starting current draw. Three different types of capacitor-start motors are available: (a) capacitor-start induction run, (b) two-value capacitor, and (c) permanent-split capacitor.

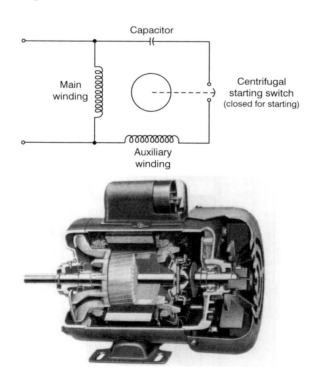

*Capacitor-start induction-run motors* are available in $\frac{1}{8}$ to 10 horsepower sizes. These motors develop a high-starting torque with a moderate starting current draw and are used on hard-to-start loads, such as grain augers and air compressors. Figure 6-14 shows a cut-away view of a capacitor-start induction-run motor and an internal wiring schematic for the same motor. Except for the capacitor in series with the starting winding, the wiring schematic is exactly the same as the schematic for a split-phase motor. As with a split-phase motor, a centrifugal switch disconnects the starting winding from the voltage source once the motor approaches its rated operating speed.

6-14. A cut-away view and an internal wiring schematic for a capacitor-start induction-run motor.

Two-value capacitor motors (also called *capacitor-start capacitor-run motors)* are available in sizes ranging from 2 to 20 horsepower. These motors also develop a high-starting torque with a moderate-starting current draw.

The two-value capacitor motor has both a starting capacitor and a running capacitor. The starting capacitor increases motor torque and reduces current draw during motor starting. The centrifugal switch disconnects the starting capacitor (but not the auxiliary winding) from the voltage source once the motor approaches its rated operating speed. The smaller-value running capacitor remains in series with the auxiliary winding during motor operation, increasing efficiency by lowering the amount of line current required to operate the motor.

Two-value capacitor motors develop a slightly higher starting torque than do capacitor-start induction-run motors. For this reason, they can handle more difficult starting loads. Conveyors, barn cleaners, and silo unloaders or other applications that must start under moderate load are examples of loads likely to be powered by two-value capacitor motors.

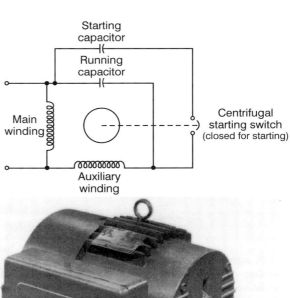

**6-15. A two-value capacitor motor and its internal wiring schematic.**

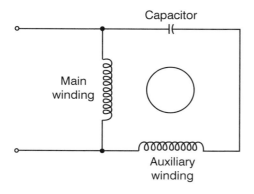

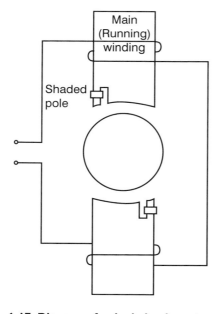

6-16. A permanent-split capacitor motor and its internal wiring schematic.

6-17. Diagram of a shaded-pole motor.

***Permanent-split capacitor motors*** are similar to two-value capacitor except that the same value of capacitance is set for both starting and running. As shown in Figure 6-16, this eliminates the need for both a second capacitor and a centrifugal switch.

Permanent-split capacitor motors are manufactured in sizes ranging from $1/20$ to 1 horsepower. Like split-phase motors, the permanent-split capacitor motor develops a fairly low starting torque. However, starting current draw is much less for a permanent-split capacitor motor. Thus, permanent-split capacitor motors are primarily used to power easy-starting loads, such as ventilation fans.

### Shaded-Pole Motors

Shaded-pole motors are low-cost, simply constructed motors. They are available in ratings of from $1/250$ to $1/2$ horsepower. Shaded-pole motors develop a very low starting torque. For this reason, they are used on easy-to-start loads, such as blowers, fans, and some small appliances.

A diagram of a shaded-pole motor is presented in Figure 6-17. Notice that it does not have a starting winding, only a running winding. The small copper shading loop on each stator pole interacts with the stator magnetic field causing the rotor to begin turning. Once the rotor begins turning, the shaded-pole motor operates in the same fashion as other AC induction motors.

# SELECTING THE RIGHT ELECTRIC MOTOR

With the many types of electric motors available, selecting a motor for a particular application may seem a difficult task. This need not be so. Table 6-1 summarizes the important characteristics of single-phase AC motors commonly used in agriculture.

## Table 6-1.
## Types of Single Phase Motors and Their Characteristics

| Type/Power Range | Load-Starting Ability | Starting Current | Characteristics | Electrically Reversible | Typical Uses |
|---|---|---|---|---|---|
| **Split-Phase** 35 to 370 W 1/20 to 1/2 hp | Easy starting loads. Develops 150 percent of full-load torque. | High; five to seven times full-load current. | Inexpensive, simple construction. Small for a given motor power. Nearly constant speed with varying load. | Yes | Fans, centrifugal pumps; loads that increase as speed increases. |
| **Capacitor-start** 100 W to 7.5 kW 1/8 to 10 hp | Hard starting loads. Develops 350 to 400 percent of full-load torque. | Medium, three to six times full-load current. | Simple construction, long service. Good general-purpose motor suitable for most jobs. Nearly constant speed with varying load. | Yes | Compressors, grain augers, conveyors, pumps. Specifically designed capacitor motors are suitable for silo unloaders and barn cleaners. |
| **Two-value capacitor** 15 to 150 kW 2 to 20 hp | Hard starting loads. Develops 350 to 450 percent of full-load torque. | Medium, three to five times full-load current. | Simple construction, long service with minimum maintenance. Requires more space to accomodate larger capacitor. | Yes | Conveyors, barn cleaners, elevators, silo unloaders. |
| **Permanent-split capacitor** 35 to 750 W 1/20 to 1 hp | Easy starting loads. Develops 150 percent of full-load torque. | Low, two to four times full-load current | Inexpensive, simple construction. Has no starting winding switch. | Yes | Fans and blowers. |

*(Continued)*

## Table 6-1 (Continued)

| Type/Power Range | Load-Starting Ability | Starting Current | Characteristics | Electrically Reversible | Typical Uses |
|---|---|---|---|---|---|
| **Shaded pole** 3 to 370 W 1/250 to 1/2 hp | Easy starting loads. | Medium. | Inexpensive, moderate efficiency, for light duty. | No | Small blowers, fans, small appliances. |
| **Wound-rotor (Repulsion)** 125 W to 7.5 kW 1/6 to 10 hp | Very hard starting loads. Develops 350 to 450 percent of full-load torque. | Low, two to four times full-load current. | Larger than equivalent, size split-phase, or capacitor motor. Running current varies only slightly with load. | No Rev. by brush ring change. | Conveyors, drag burr mills, deep-well pumps, hoists, silo unloaders, bucket elevators. |
| **Universal or series** 5 W to 1.5 kW 1/150 to 2 hp | Hard starting loads. Develops 350 to 450 percent of full-load torque. | High | High speed, small size for a given hp. Usually directly connected to load. Speed changes with load variations. | Yes | Portable tools, kitchen appliances. |
| **Synchronous** Very small, fractional hp | | | Constant speed. | | Clocks and timers. |
| **Soft-start** 7.5 to 560 kW 10 to 75 hp | Easy starting loads | Low, 1.5 to 2 times full-load current. | Excellent for large loads requring low starting torque. | Yes | Crop driers, forage blowers, irrigation pumps, manure agitators. |

Source: Soderholm and Puckett (1974).

## INTERPRETING MOTOR NAMEPLATES

An electric motor has a **nameplate** on which important, specialized information appears. Understanding the information provided is essential when installing, servicing or replacing an electric motor.

The **model number** is a number that allows the manufacturer to identify a specific type of motor. Motors made by the same manufacturer and having the same model number should, for all practical purposes, be identical.

The National Electrical Manufacturers Association (NEMA) has established standard size frames and shaft heights for electric motors. The

6-18. A typical electric motor nameplate.

*frame number (FR)* divided by 16 gives the height (in inches) from the center line of the motor shaft to the bottom of the motor mount. The nameplate in Figure 6-18 lists a frame number of 56. Thus, the centerline of the motor shaft is 3½ inches above the motor mounting (56 / 16 = 3.5 in., or 3½ in.). When replacing a motor, selecting a replacement with the same frame number will ensure a proper fit.

The *horsepower rating (HP)* on the nameplate tells how much power the motor will develop at full-load when supplied with its rated voltage. One horsepower is the ability to do 33,000 foot-pounds of work per minute. Electric motors of less than one horsepower are called fractional horsepower motors. Those over one horsepower are called integral horsepower motors. Very small motors are often rated in watts. One horsepower is equal to 746 watts.

The speed or RPM tells how many revolutions the motor shaft makes per minute under full-load conditions when operated at rated voltage. The speed of a squirrel cage induction motor depends on the number of magnetic poles in the stator's running winding and the frequency (hertz) of the applied AC voltage.

Synchronous speed refers to the rotational speed of the magnetic field created in the stator and can be calculated using Formula 6-1.

$$\text{Synchronous speed (rpm)} = \frac{120 \times \text{Frequency (Hz)}}{\text{\# of Poles}}$$

Formula 6-1.

Where,

120 = a constant

Frequency = cycles per second of AC source

\# of Poles = Number of electromagnetic poles in the stator's running winding.

Use Formula 6-1 to determine that a two-pole induction motor operating on 60 Hz AC electricity will have a synchronous speed of 3600 rpm. A four-pole motor operating from the same electrical source will have a synchronous speed of 1800 rpm, while a six-pole motor will have a synchronous speed of 1200 rpm.

AC induction motors always turn at a slower speed than synchronous speed. When operating at full-load on 60 Hz power, a two-pole induction motor will turn at about 3450 rpm, a four-pole motor at about 1725 rpm, and a six-pole motor at about 1150 rpm. The speed listed on the nameplate is the motor's nominal (or rated) full-load speed, not its synchronous speed. The actual full-load speed of the motor may vary slightly from the nominal speed.

*Ambient (Amb.) temperature* is the temperature of the air directly outside of the motor enclosure. A motor must not be operated in an environment where the temperature will exceed its ambient temperature rating. Most motors are rated at an ambient temperature of 40°C (104°F).

The *insulation class* indicates the maximum safe operating temperature that will not cause the insulation on motor wires to break down prematurely. Common insulation classes are A, B, F, and H. Class A is the lowest temperature rating, meaning that this class of insulation will break down at a lower temperature than will other classes. Most farm-duty motors have either Class A or B insulation.

*Service factor (SF)* is a multiplier that, when applied to the motor's rated horsepower, gives the maximum horsepower the motor can develop (at rated voltage) on a continuous overload basis without overheating. A service factor rating of "1" means that a motor has no continuous overload capacity, and will quickly overheat if overloaded. On the other hand, a motor with a service factor of 1.35 can tolerate a continuous overload 35 percent greater than its rated horsepower. The class of insulation used in a motor is the primary factor in determining its service factor rating.

The voltage listed on the nameplate indicates the nominal voltage(s) at which the motor is designed to operate. If two voltages are listed, the motor is a dual voltage motor and can be operated at either voltage, as long as the proper wiring connections are made. A wiring diagram on the motor will indicate the correct wiring for operation at each listed voltage.

The information on phase (Ph) indicates if the motor is designed for operation on single-phase or three-phase electricity.

The amperage listed tells how much current the motor will draw when operating at rated load and voltage. Dual voltage motors will have two amperages listed, with the large value being twice that of the small value. The small value indicates the current draw when the motor is operated on the higher voltage; the large value indicates the current draw when the motor is operated at the lower voltage.

*Hertz (Hz)* lists the AC frequency in cycles per second for motor operation. In the United States, this is 60 Hz.

*Motor duty cycle* indicates whether the motor is intended for continuous or intermittent operation. Continuous duty motors can be operated indefinitely at rated load. Intermittent duty ratings are based on a fixed operating time (5, 15, 30, or 60 minutes) after which the motor must be allowed to cool.

The *KVA code letter* indicates the approximate kilovolt-amperes (1000 volt-amperes) consumed by the motor per horsepower when in locked-rotor condition. Locked-rotor means the rotor cannot turn. The KVA code letter also indicates how much current a motor would be expected to draw during start-up.

## SELECTING THE CORRECT MOTOR ENCLOSURE

Electric motors are manufactured with several different types of housings called *enclosures*. Since motors used in agriculture may have to operate under adverse environmental conditions, it is extremely important to select one with the correct enclosure. The four motor enclosures commonly used in agriculture are: (a) drip-proof, (b) splash-proof, (c) totally enclosed, and (d) explosion-proof.

### Drip-Proof

Drip-proof enclosures have ventilation openings in each end. They allow the passage of air over and around the windings for cooling. The openings are made so water drops falling at an angle of up to 15° from vertical will not enter the motor. Drip-proof motors should be used indoors in clean, dry locations.

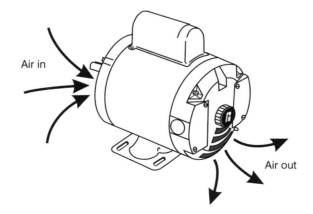

Air in

Air out

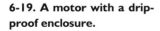

**6-19. A motor with a drip-proof enclosure.**

## Splash-Proof

Splash-proof enclosures also have ventilation openings in each end to allow air to move through the motor. Splash-proof enclosures will protect the motor from liquids or particles that strike the enclosure at angles of not greater than 100° from the vertical. They may be used outdoors, but should be protected from the weather by a suitable cover.

## Totally Enclosed

Totally enclosed motors have no ventilation openings in the housing (but are not air-tight or waterproof). They generally operate at fairly high temperatures. Totally enclosed motors are used in locations that are dirty, damp or dusty. Three different types of totally enclosed motors are available.

Totally-enclosed, fan-cooled (TEFC) motors have an external fan, enclosed in a metal shroud, that blows air over the motor to help cool it. This type of motor is often used in dusty or wet areas in and around agricultural buildings.

Totally-enclosed, non-ventilated (TENV) motors are not equipped with an external cooling fan. The TENV motor depends on convection air for cooling.

Totally-enclosed, air-over (TEAO) motors are not equipped with a fan as part of their construction. Rather, they rely on air flow from an external or driven device for cooling.

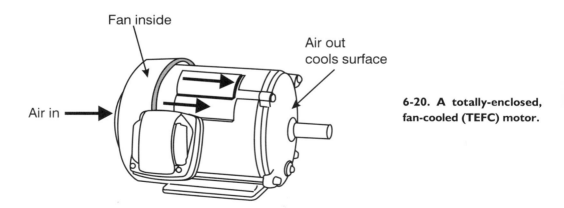

Fan inside

Air out
cools surface

Air in

6-20. A totally-enclosed, fan-cooled (TEFC) motor.

## Explosion-Proof

Explosion-proof motors are actually a fourth type of totally-enclosed motor. They are specially designed to withstand an internal explosion.

Explosion-proof motors must be used in hazardous locations where vapors or dusty conditions could cause an explosion or fire.

## CONNECTING DUAL VOLTAGE MOTORS

Many AC motors rated at $1/2$ horsepower or more can operate at either of two voltage levels. These motors are known as dual-voltage motors. Commonly, for single-phase AC motors, the two voltages are 115 and 230 volts.

Dual-voltage motors have two sets of running windings. For low-voltage operation, the two sets of running windings are connected in parallel. For high-voltage operation, the running windings are connected in series.

Figure 6-21 shows a dual-voltage, capacitor-start, induction-run motor wired for low voltage (115 V) operation. Trace the flow of electricity from the source through the running windings and back to the source to confirm that the running windings are indeed connected in parallel.

6-21. A dual-voltage, capacitor-start, induction-run motor wired for low voltage (115V) operation.

Whenever possible, dual-voltage motors should be operated at the higher voltage. When wired for high voltage operation, the motor will develop the same amount of power, but will draw only one-half the current. Thus, smaller, less-expensive wiring can be used in the motor branch circuit.

At first, it may be difficult to understand why a motor wired for high voltage draws only one-half the current as when wired for low voltage. When the total resistance of the running windings under the two conditions is considered, the reason is obvious.

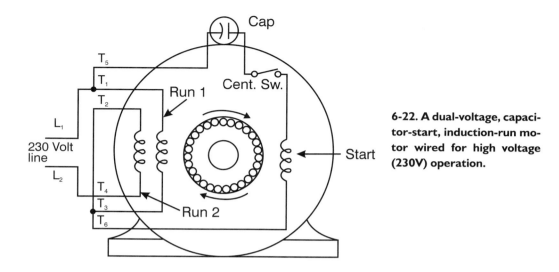

6-22. A dual-voltage, capacitor-start, induction-run motor wired for high voltage (230V) operation.

Assume that each set of running windings of a certain dual-voltage motor has a resistance of 16 ohms. When two resistances are connected in parallel, their total resistance can be calculated as shown below.

$$R_T = \cfrac{1}{\cfrac{1}{R_1} + \cfrac{1}{R_2}}$$

Remember, the running windings of a dual-voltage motor are connected in parallel for low voltage operation. Thus, the total resistance of the two running windings is 8 ohms. These calculations are shown below.

$$R_T = \cfrac{1}{\cfrac{1}{R_1} + \cfrac{1}{R_2}}$$

$$R_T = \cfrac{1}{\cfrac{1}{16} + \cfrac{1}{16}}$$

$$R_T = \cfrac{1}{0.125}$$

$$R_T = 8 \text{ ohms}$$

Since the total resistance of the running windings is 8 ohms, according to Ohm's law, the motor will draw 14.4 amperes of current when wired for low voltage (115 V) operation.

$$\text{Amperes} = \frac{\text{Voltage}}{\text{Resistance}}$$

$$\text{Amperes} = \frac{115 \text{ Volts}}{8 \text{ ohms}}$$

$$\text{Amperes} = 14.4$$

Now, calculate the current draw of the motor when it is wired for high voltage operation (running windings in series). When two resistances are wired in series, their total resistance is the sum of the individual resistances.

$$R_T = R_1 + R_2$$

Quick addition shows the total resistance of the running windings to be 32 ohms when the windings are wired in series for high voltage operation. Again, according to Ohm's Law, the motor will draw 7.2 amperes when connected for high voltage (230 V) operation.

$$\text{Amperes} = \frac{\text{Voltage}}{\text{Resistance}}$$

$$\text{Amperes} = \frac{230 \text{ Volts}}{32 \text{ ohms}}$$

$$\text{Amperes} = 7.2$$

Comparison of the calculated amperages shows that the motor will draw 14.4 amperes when operated on low voltage, compared to 7.2 amperes when operated on high voltage. Thus, whenever possible, connect dual-voltage motors for operation at high voltage.

# REVERSING THE ROTATION OF AC INDUCTION MOTORS

Most AC induction-type electric motors are reversible. This means a change in the internal wiring of the motor will reverse the direction of rotation of the motor shaft. (See Table 6-1.)

**6-23. The two ends of a motor are designated as (a) the "drive end" and (b) the "end opposite the drive end."**

*Motor rotation* is the direction of turn of the shaft and is either clockwise (CW) or counterclockwise (CCW). Since a motor has two ends, confusion sometimes results in the use of these terms.

The terms "clockwise" and "counterclockwise" describe the direction of motor rotation when viewed from the end opposite the drive end. Counterclockwise rotation is considered standard for DC motors and AC single-phase motors.

An AC induction-type motor will continue to rotate in the direction in which it begins rotating. The direction of current flow in the starting windings determines the direction of the initial rotation of the motor. To reverse motor rotation in an AC induction motor, simply interchange the two leads that supply electricity to the starting windings.

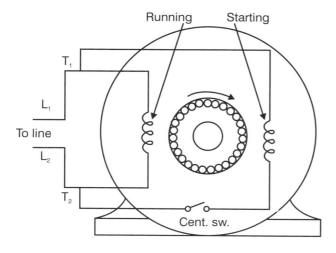

6-24. A split-phase, AC induction-type motor. Notice that connection T1 and T2 lead to the starting winding. Simply reversing the wires at these two points will reverse the direction of motor rotation.

# MEASURING ELECTRIC MOTOR PERFORMANCE CHARACTERISTICS

An electric motor changes electrical power into mechanical power. The efficiency of a motor is a measure of how well the motor accomplishes this task. A highly efficient motor will convert a large percentage of electrical power into mechanical power. A less efficient motor will convert a smaller percentage of electrical power into mechanical power. As a general rule, motor efficiency ranges from about 50 to 80 percent. The efficiency of an electric motor can be calculated using Formula 6-2.

$$\text{Efficiency (\%)} = \frac{\text{Mechanical power output} \times 746}{\text{Electrical power input}} \times 100 \qquad \boxed{\textbf{Formula 6-2.}}$$

where,

Mechanical power output = horsepower developed by the motor
Electrical power input = watts of electricity consumed by the motor
746 = conversion factor (746 watts/horsepower)

When AC circuits include loads having coils of wire (such as a motor), inductive reactance causes a phase shift between voltage and amperage. The current lags the voltage in the circuit. Power factor is defined as the cosine of this phase angle between circuit amperage and voltage.

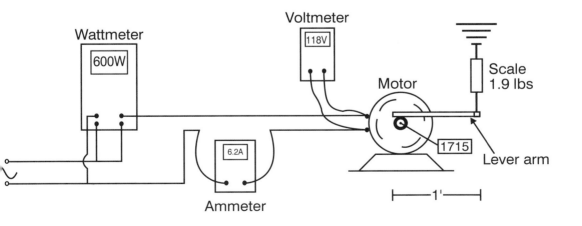

6-25. Test set-up and data to calculate the efficiency and power factor of an electric motor.

Power factor can be calculated as the ratio of true power to apparent power in a circuit. True power can be measured directly with a wattmeter. Apparent power can be calculated as the product of voltage and amperage, measured with a volt meter and an ammeter, respectively.

Use the test set-up and data presented in Figure 6-25 to calculate the efficiency and power factor of the motor shown. First, calculate the motor's efficiency, and then the power factor.

## DETERMINING MOTOR EFFICIENCY

The first step in calculating the motor's efficiency is to determine how much mechanical power is being produced. The horsepower developed by a rotating shaft can be calculated using Formula 6-3.

$$\text{Horsepower} = \frac{\text{To} \times \text{N}}{5252}$$

> **Formula 6-3.**

Where,

$\quad$ To $=$ torque (in pound-feet, lb-ft)
$\quad$ N $=$ shaft speed (in revolutions per minute, RPM)
$\quad$ 5252 $=$ a constant

Torque can be defined as a rotating force. It is calculated as the product of force times lever-arm length (To $=$ F $\times$ LA). In Figure 6-25, the scale reads 1.9 pounds of force acting through a 1 foot lever-arm. Thus, the motor is developing 1.9 lb-ft of torque. The tachometer at the motor shaft indicates that the motor is rotating at 1715 rpm. By inserting these values into Formula 6-8 and solving the equation, we find that the motor is developing .62 horsepower.

$$
\begin{aligned}
\text{Horsepower} &= \frac{\text{To} \times \text{N}}{5252} \\[2mm]
&= \frac{1.9 \text{ lb-ft} \times 1715 \text{ rpm}}{5252} \\[2mm]
&= .62 \text{ horsepower}
\end{aligned}
$$

According to the wattmeter reading in Figure 6-25, the motor is consuming 600 watts of electrical power. Since we know both the mechanical power output (horsepower) and the electrical power input (watts), we can calculate the efficiency of the motor using Formula 6-2. Based on the test data collected, the motor's efficiency is 77 percent.

$$\text{Efficiency (\%)} = \frac{\text{Mechanical power output} \times 746}{\text{Electrical power input}} \times 100$$

$$= \frac{.62\text{-hp} \times 746}{600 \text{ watts}} \times 100$$

$$= 77\%$$

## DETERMINING MOTOR POWER FACTOR

Power factor is the ratio of true power to apparent power. In Figure 6-25, the meters show the following readings: 118 volts, 6.2 amperes, and 600 watts. Thus, the motor power factor is .82.

$$\text{Power Factor} = \frac{\text{True Power (in watts)}}{\text{Apparent Power (in volt-amperes)}}$$

$$= \frac{600 \text{ watts}}{118 \text{ volts} \times 6.2 \text{ amperes}}$$

$$= \frac{600 \text{ watts}}{731.6 \text{ volt-amperes}}$$

$$= .82$$

# SIZING MOTOR BRANCH
# CIRCUIT CONDUCTORS

Selecting the correct size conductors is an important aspect of planning a motor branch circuit. Using conductors larger than required incurs unnecessary expenses. Using conductors that are too small is a much more serious situation. This may lead to excessive voltage drop, improper motor operation and danger to persons and/or property.

Four basic steps must be followed in determining the correct size conductors to use in wiring an electric motor branch circuit. These steps include: (a) determining the total motor current load, (b) determining minimum conductor size based on ampacity requirements, (c) determining the minimum conductor size based on maximum permissible voltage drop, and (d) selecting the size conductor that meets (or exceeds) both ampacity and voltage drop requirements.

## DETERMINING TOTAL MOTOR CURRENT

The total current in a motor branch circuit is calculated according to requirements specified in the *National Electrical Code® (NEC®)**. For a single motor operating on an individual branch circuit, the motor load is calculated as 125 percent of the motor's full-load amperage rating. Table 6-2 lists full-load current values for single-phase AC motors.

Assume that a 1½ horsepower, 230-volt, single-phase, AC motor is to be installed on an individual branch circuit. According to Table 6-2, the full-load current value for this motor is 10 amperes. Thus, the motor

**Table 6-2.
Full-Load Currents in Amperes
Single-Phase Alternating-Current Motors**

The following values of full-load currents are for motors running at usual speeds and motors with normal torque characteristics. Motors built for especially low speeds or high torques may have higher full-load currents, and multispeed motors will have full-load current varying with speed, in which case the nameplate current ratings shall be used.

The voltages listed are rated motor voltages. The currents listed shall be permitted for system voltage ranges of 110 to 120 and 220 to 240 volts.

| HP | 115 Volts | 200 Volts | 208 Volts | 230 Volts |
|----|-----------|-----------|-----------|-----------|
| 1/6 | 4.4 | 2.5 | 2.4 | 2.2 |
| 1/4 | 5.8 | 3.3 | 3.2 | 2.9 |
| 1/3 | 7.2 | 4.1 | 4.0 | 3.6 |
| 1/2 | 9.8 | 5.6 | 5.4 | 4.9 |
| 3/4 | 13.8 | 7.9 | 7.6 | 6.9 |
| 1 | 16 | 9.2 | 8.8 | 8 |
| 1½ | 20 | 11.5 | 11 | 10 |
| 2 | 24 | 13.8 | 13.2 | 12 |
| 3 | 34 | 19.6 | 18.7 | 17 |
| 5 | 56 | 32.2 | 30.8 | 28 |
| 7½ | 80 | 46 | 44 | 40 |
| 10 | 100 | 57.5 | 55 | 50 |

Source: *NEC* Table 430-148. Reprinted with permission from NFPA 70-1996, the *National Electrical Code*, Copyright © 1995, National Fire Protection Association, Quincy, MA 02269. This reprinted material is not the complete and official position of the National Fire Protection Association on the referenced subject, which is represented only by the standard in its entirety.

*National Electrical Code® and NEC® are registered trademarks of the National Fire Protection Association, Inc., Quincy, MA 02269.

current load would be calculated as 12.5 amperes (10 amperes × 1.25 = 12.5 amperes).

If more than one motor operates on the same branch circuit, total motor current is determined by taking 125 percent of the full-load current of the largest motor and adding the full-load current(s) of the remaining motor(s). For example, assume that $1/4$, $1/3$ and $1/2$ horsepower motors operate on the same 240 volt branch circuit. Based on the full-load amperages presented in Table 6-2, the motor load is calculated to be 12.6 amperes.

A. 125% of largest motor's full-load current . . . . . . . (4.9 amperes × 1.25) = 6.1 amperes
B. Full-load current of $1/3$ horsepower motor . . . . . . . . . . . . . . . . . . . 3.6 amperes
C. Full-load current of $1/4$ horsepower motor . . . . . . . . . . . . . . . . . . . 2.9 amperes
Total . . . . . . . . . . . . . . . . . . . . . . . 12.6 amperes

Occasionally one or more motors are permanently connected in branch circuits containing other, non-motor loads. The size of these combination loads is determined by adding the combined non-motor current load to the motor current load.

## DETERMINING CONDUCTOR SIZE BASED ON AMPACITY REQUIREMENTS

The **ampacity** of a conductor is defined as the current (in amperes) that the conductor can carry on a continuous basis under specific conditions without exceeding its temperature rating. The conductors selected for a motor branch circuit must have enough ampacity to carry the current drawn by the motor(s).

Ampacity requirements can be met using a conductor size selection table. A number of such tables are available. Table 6-3 is intended for use in selecting copper conductors for single-phase, 240-volt circuits of up to 400 amperes at a 2 percent voltage drop.

Table 6-3 is divided into two sections by the double line running up and down the table. The information to the left of the line is used in selecting the conductor size that will meet circuit ampacity requirements.

Earlier, we determined that a $1^1/_2$ horsepower, 230-volt, single-phase electric motor has a full-load current rating of 10 amperes (Table 6-2). For this example, let's assume that an individual branch circuit is to be wired for this motor using Type UF cable.

In Table 6-3, locate the "Load in Amps" column (to the far left). Move down this column until you find an entry equal to your calculated motor load (10 amperes × 1.25 = 12.5 amperes). If no entry exactly matches

## Table 6-3.
## Conductor Size Selection Table

| Load in Amps | UF | RH, RHW, THW, THWN, USE, NM, SE | THHN | UF | USE | Single | Triplex | 50 | 60 | 75 | 100 | 125 | 150 | 175 | 200 | 225 | 250 | 275 | 300 | 350 | 400 | 450 | 500 | 550 | 600 | 650 | 700 | 750 | 800 |
|---|---|---|---|---|---|---|---|---|---|---|---|---|---|---|---|---|---|---|---|---|---|---|---|---|---|---|---|---|---|
| | | Minimum Allowable Size of Conductor | | | | | | Copper up to 400 Amperes, 230-240 Volts, Single Phase, Based on 2% Voltage Drop — Length of Run in Feet — Compare size shown below with size shown to the left of the double line. Use the larger size. | | | | | | | | | | | | | | | | | | | | | | |
| | In Air Cable or Conduit | | | Direct Burial | | Overhead in Air | | | | | | | | | | | | | | | | | | | | | | | | | |
| 5 | 14 | 14 | 14 | 14 | 14 | 10 | 8 | 14 | 14 | 14 | 14 | 14 | 14 | 14 | 12 | 12 | 12 | 12 | 10 | 10 | 10 | 10 | 8 | 8 | 8 | 8 | 8 | 6 | 6 |
| 7 | 14 | 14 | 14 | 14 | 14 | 10 | 8 | 14 | 14 | 14 | 14 | 14 | 12 | 12 | 12 | 10 | 10 | 10 | 10 | 8 | 8 | 8 | 8 | 6 | 6 | 6 | 6 | 6 | 6 |
| 10 | 14 | 14 | 14 | 14 | 14 | 10 | 8 | 14 | 14 | 14 | 12 | 12 | 10 | 10 | 10 | 10 | 8 | 8 | 8 | 8 | 6 | 6 | 6 | 6 | 4 | 4 | 4 | 4 | 4 |
| 15 | 14 | 14 | 14 | 14 | 14 | 10 | 8 | 14 | 12 | 12 | 10 | 10 | 10 | 8 | 8 | 8 | 6 | 6 | 6 | 6 | 4 | 4 | 4 | 4 | 3 | 3 | 3 | 3 | 2 |
| 20 | 12 | 12 | 12 | 12 | 12 | 10 | 8 | 12 | 12 | 10 | 10 | 8 | 8 | 8 | 6 | 6 | 6 | 6 | 4 | 4 | 4 | 4 | 3 | 3 | 2 | 2 | 2 | 1 | 1 |
| 25 | 10 | 10 | 10 | 10 | 10 | 10 | 8 | 12 | 10 | 10 | 8 | 8 | 6 | 6 | 6 | 6 | 4 | 4 | 4 | 4 | 3 | 3 | 2 | 2 | 1 | 1 | 1 | 0 | 0 |
| 30 | 10 | 10 | 10 | 10 | 10 | 10 | 8 | 10 | 10 | 10 | 8 | 6 | 6 | 6 | 4 | 4 | 4 | 4 | 4 | 3 | 2 | 2 | 1 | 1 | 1 | 0 | 0 | 0 | 00 |
| 35 | 8 | 8 | 8 | 8 | 8 | 8 | 8 | 10 | 10 | 8 | 8 | 6 | 6 | 4 | 4 | 4 | 4 | 3 | 3 | 2 | 1 | 1 | 0 | 0 | 0 | 00 | 00 | 00 | |
| 40 | 8 | 8 | 8 | 8 | 8 | 8 | 8 | 10 | 8 | 8 | 6 | 6 | 4 | 4 | 4 | 4 | 3 | 3 | 2 | 2 | 1 | 1 | 0 | 0 | 00 | 00 | 00 | 000 | 000 |
| 45 | 6 | 8 | 8 | 6 | 8 | 8 | 8 | 10 | 8 | 8 | 6 | 6 | 4 | 4 | 4 | 3 | 3 | 2 | 2 | 1 | 1 | 0 | 0 | 00 | 00 | 000 | 000 | 000 | |
| 50 | 6 | 8 | 8 | 6 | 8 | 8 | 8 | 8 | 8 | 6 | 6 | 4 | 4 | 4 | 3 | 3 | 2 | 2 | 1 | 1 | 0 | 0 | 00 | 00 | 000 | 000 | 000 | 4/0 | 4/0 |
| 60 | 4 | 6 | 6 | 4 | 6 | 8 | 6 | 8 | 8 | 6 | 4 | 4 | 3 | 2 | 2 | 1 | 1 | 0 | 0 | 00 | 00 | 000 | 000 | 4/0 | 4/0 | 4/0 | 250 | | |
| 70 | 4 | 6 | 6 | 4 | 4 | 6 | 6 | 8 | 6 | 6 | 4 | 4 | 3 | 2 | 2 | 1 | 1 | 0 | 0 | 00 | 00 | 000 | 000 | 4/0 | 4/0 | 4/0 | 250 | 250 | 300 |
| 80 | 3 | 4 | 4 | 3 | 4 | 6 | 4 | 6 | 6 | 4 | 4 | 3 | 2 | 2 | 1 | 1 | 0 | 0 | 00 | 00 | 000 | 000 | 4/0 | 4/0 | 250 | 250 | 300 | 300 | 300 |
| 90 | 2 | 3 | 4 | 2 | 3 | 4 | 4 | 6 | 6 | 4 | 4 | 3 | 2 | 1 | 1 | 0 | 0 | 00 | 00 | 000 | 000 | 4/0 | 4/0 | 250 | 250 | 300 | 300 | 350 | 350 |
| 100 | 1 | 3 | 3 | 1 | 3 | 4 | 4 | 6 | 4 | 4 | 3 | 2 | 1 | 1 | 0 | 0 | 00 | 00 | 000 | 000 | 4/0 | 4/0 | 250 | 250 | 300 | 300 | 350 | 350 | 400 |
| 115 | 0 | 2 | 2 | 0 | 2 | 3 | 3 | 6 | 4 | 4 | 3 | 2 | 1 | 0 | 0 | 00 | 00 | 000 | 000 | 4/0 | 4/0 | 250 | 300 | 300 | 350 | 350 | 400 | 400 | 500 |
| 130 | 00 | 1 | 2 | 00 | 1 | 2 | 2 | 4 | 4 | 3 | 2 | 1 | 0 | 0 | 00 | 00 | 000 | 4/0 | 4/0 | 250 | 300 | 300 | 350 | 400 | 400 | 500 | 500 | 500 | |
| 150 | 000 | 0 | 1 | 000 | 0 | 1 | 1 | 4 | 4 | 3 | 1 | 0 | 0 | 00 | 000 | 000 | 4/0 | 4/0 | 4/0 | 250 | 300 | 350 | 350 | 400 | 500 | 500 | 500 | 600 | 600 |
| 175 | 4/0 | 00 | 00 | 4/0 | 00 | 0 | 0 | 4 | 3 | 2 | 1 | 0 | 00 | 000 | 000 | 4/0 | 4/0 | 250 | 300 | 350 | 400 | 400 | 500 | 500 | 600 | 600 | 600 | 700 | |
| 200 | | 000 | 000 | | 000 | 00 | 00 | 3 | 2 | 1 | 0 | 00 | 000 | 000 | 4/0 | 250 | 250 | 300 | 350 | 400 | 500 | 500 | 500 | 600 | 600 | 700 | 700 | 750 | |
| 225 | | 4/0 | 000 | | 4/0 | 0 | 000 | 3 | 2 | 1 | 0 | 000 | 4/0 | 4/0 | 250 | 300 | 300 | 350 | 350 | 400 | 500 | 500 | 600 | 600 | 700 | 700 | 750 | 800 | 900 |
| 250 | | 250 | 4/0 | | 250 | 00 | 4/0 | 2 | 1 | 0 | 00 | 000 | 4/0 | 4/0 | 250 | 300 | 300 | 350 | 350 | 400 | 500 | 500 | 600 | 600 | 700 | 700 | 750 | 800 | 900 | 1000 |
| 275 | | 300 | 250 | | 300 | 000 | 4/0 | 2 | 1 | 0 | 00 | 000 | 4/0 | 4/0 | 250 | 300 | 350 | 350 | 400 | 500 | 500 | 600 | 700 | 700 | 800 | 900 | 900 | 1000 | |
| 300 | | 350 | 300 | | 350 | 000 | 250 | 1 | 1 | 0 | 000 | 4/0 | 4/0 | 250 | 300 | 350 | 350 | 400 | 500 | 500 | 600 | 700 | 700 | 800 | 900 | 900 | 1000 | | |
| 325 | | 400 | 350 | | 400 | 4/0 | 300 | 1 | 0 | 00 | 000 | 4/0 | 250 | 300 | 300 | 350 | 400 | 500 | 500 | 600 | 600 | 700 | 750 | 900 | 900 | 1000 | | | |
| 350 | | 500 | 350 | | 500 | 4/0 | 300 | 1 | 0 | 00 | 000 | 4/0 | 250 | 300 | 350 | 400 | 400 | 500 | 500 | 600 | 700 | 750 | 800 | 900 | 1000 | | | | |
| 375 | | 500 | 400 | | 500 | 250 | 300 | 0 | 0 | 00 | 4/0 | 250 | 300 | 300 | 350 | 400 | 500 | 500 | 600 | 600 | 700 | 800 | 900 | 1000 | | | | | |
| 400 | | 600 | 500 | | 600 | 250 | 400 | 0 | 00 | 000 | 4/0 | 250 | 300 | 350 | 400 | 500 | 500 | 600 | 700 | 750 | 900 | 1000 | | | | | | | |

Source: NFEC Agricultural Wiring Handbook

your calculated load, use the next highest entry. (In this example, we will use 15 amperes, which is the next highest entry.)

Once you have located the correct amperage value, move straight to the right until you are in the column headed by the conductor type and condition of use that matches your situation. (In our example, this is the "UF" column under the heading "In Air Cable or Conduit.") The number in this column will be the minimum wire size that meets the circuit's ampacity requirement. In this example, number 14 wire would be selected.

# DETERMINING CONDUCTOR SIZE BASED ON VOLTAGE DROP

All conductors have some resistance to the flow of electrical current. The voltage used in overcoming this resistance is dissipated as heat, and is unavailable for use at the circuit load. Thus, the voltage available at the load is less than the source voltage. This difference in the source voltage and the load voltage is called *voltage drop*.

Voltage drop occurs in any electrical circuit. It is critical to limit the voltage drop to an acceptable level, usually 2 to 3 percent. The voltage drop in a circuit can be calculated as: (Voltage drop = Circuit amperage × Conductor resistance). As indicated by this formula, voltage drop can be reduced by decreasing the circuit amperage, by decreasing the resistance of the conductors, or a combination of the two.

Conductor size selection tables also take voltage drop into account. In Table 6-3, the headings to the right of the double lines indicate the one-way length of the circuit (from source to load) in feet. For this example, assume a one-way circuit length of 80 feet. Since no entry is provided for an 80-ft run, the next highest value of 100-ft is used. Follow the 100-ft column down to the same row as the circuit load (15 amperes). Number 10 conductor is required to limit voltage drop in the circuit to 2 percent.

## SELECTING CONDUCTOR SIZE TO MEET BOTH AMPACITY AND VOLTAGE DROP REQUIREMENTS

According to Table 6-2, UF cable with number 14 conductors will meet the ampacity requirements for our motor circuit. However, number 10 conductors are required to limit voltage drop in the circuit to 2 percent. When a difference exists in the size wire needed based on ampacity and voltage drop requirements, always select the size that represents the largest wire. In this example, select UF cable with AWG #10 conductors.

# MOTOR PROTECTION AND CONTROL

An electric motor will attempt to power any load, even if this results in self-destruction. Also, electric motors may draw six to eight times more current when starting than during normal operation. For these reasons, electric motors present some special problems from the standpoint of control, overcurrent, and overload protection.

To provide safe service, every motor branch circuit is required to contain the following items: (a) short-circuit and ground-fault protection for the branch circuit conductors, (b) a disconnecting means, (c) motor overload protection, and (d) a controller to start and stop the motor. These required motor circuit components are shown in Figure 6-26.

In many cases, one or more of these items may be combined into a single device. For example, a fusible switch used as the motor controller can also serve as the motor overload protection.

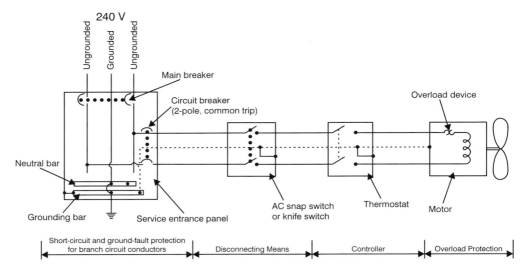

**6-26. Ventilating fan motor circuit.**

The discussion provided in this section is general. Specific information may be obtained by referring to the current edition of the *National Electrical Code (NEC)*, or by consulting with local inspection officials.

## *BRANCH CIRCUIT SHORT-CIRCUIT AND GROUND-FAULT PROTECTION*

A motor branch circuit must have a properly sized fuse or circuit breaker to protect the circuit conductors against short circuits and ground-faults. Since a motor may draw up to six (or more) times its rated full-load current when starting, only time-delay fuses or inverse-time circuit breakers should be used. The motor branch circuit protection device must be capable of carrying the high motor starting current.

For a branch circuit containing a single motor, the maximum allowable overcurrent device is determined based on a percentage of the motor's full-load amperage (Table 6-2). Table 6-4 lists the maximum percentages that can be used in sizing short-circuit and ground-fault devices to protect branch circuit conductors serving various types of motors.

To illustrate this process, assume we are selecting a double-pole circuit breaker to protect a $3/4$ horsepower 230-volt AC (single-phase) motor circuit.

According to Table 6-2, a single-phase, $3/4$ horsepower, 230-volt AC motor has a full-load current rating of 6.9 amperes. For a single-phase motor, an inverse time circuit breaker rated at 250 percent of the motor's full-load current rating is the largest allowed (Table 6-4). Multiplying the

## Table 6-4.
## Maximum Rating or Setting of Motor Branch Circuit Short-Circuit and Ground-Fault Protective Devices

| | Percent of Full-Load Current | | | |
| Type of Motor | Nontime Delay Fuse** | Dual Element (Time-Delay) Fuse** | Instanta-neous Trip Breaker | Inverse Time Breaker* |
|---|---|---|---|---|
| Single-phase motors | 300 | 175 | 800 | 250 |
| AC polyphase motors other than wound-rotor | | | | |
| Squirrel Cage: | | | | |
| Other than Design E | 300 | 175 | 800 | 250 |
| Design E | 300 | 175 | 1100 | 250 |
| Synchronous | 300 | 175 | 800 | 250 |
| Wound rotor | 150 | 150 | 800 | 150 |
| Direct-current (constant voltage) | 150 | 150 | 250 | 150 |

For certain exceptions to the values specified, see Sections 430-52 through 430-54.

*The values given in the last column also cover the ratings of nonadjustable inverse time types of circuit breakers that may be modified as in Section 430-52.

**The values in the Nontime Delay Fuse Column apply to Time-Delay Class CC fuses.

†Synchronous motors of the low-torque, low-speed type (usually 450 rpm or lower), such as are used to drive reciprocating compressors, pumps, etc., that start unloaded, do not require a fuse rating or circuit-breaker setting in excess of 200 percent of full-load current.

Source: *NEC* Table 430-152. Reprinted with permission from NFPA 70-1996, the *National Electrical Code,* Copyright © 1995, National Fire Protection Association, Quincy, MA 02269. This reprinted material is not the complete and official position of the National Fire Protection Association on the referenced subject, which is represented only by the standard in its entirety.

motor's rated full-load current (6.9 amperes) by 250 percent results in a calculated circuit breaker size of 17.25 amperes. Since this is not a standard size, the next largest size (20 amperes) double-pole circuit breaker will be the maximum allowable size [*NEC* 430-52(c), Exception 1].

This process determines the maximum allowable size overcurrent protection device that can be used with a particular motor. It is recommended that the smallest size device that allows the motor to start and operate properly be used. This may be determined using a trial and error procedure. Simply select a device rated at about 115 percent of the motor's rated full-load current. If this device does not allow the motor to operate properly, try the next largest standard size device. Repeat this process until the smallest standard size device that will allow normal operation is identified.

Double-check to confirm that the overcurrent device selected is within the allowable maximum size rating previously determined.

Often the time-delay fuse or circuit breaker selected has a higher amperage rating than the circuit conductors. This is permissible in a motor circuit, since the circuit conductors are protected against a continuous overload by the motor overload protection device.

Generally only one motor is installed per branch circuit. However, more than one motor may be installed on a branch circuit if the either of the following conditions are met.

- Each motor has its own overcurrent protection device in addition to the circuit breaker at the service entrance panel.

- Two or more motors (each not over 1 horsepower and each having a rated full-load current of not over 6 amperes) may be placed on one circuit if the circuit is not protected at over 20 amperes for a 120-volt circuit, or 15 amperes for a 240-volt circuit.

## MOTOR OVERLOAD PROTECTION

An electric motor will attempt to power any load to which it is attached, even if this results in excessive current draw and motor self-destruction. In many instances, the amount of current required to damage a motor is less than the current level required to operate the circuit overcurrent protection device (fuse or circuit breaker). For example, the conductors in a certain motor branch circuit may be protected by a properly sized 20-ampere time-delay circuit breaker. Yet the motor may have a full-load current rating of only 8 amperes. Thus, the motor could be overloaded by 250 percent and still not draw enough current to trip the circuit breaker. For this reason, overload protection for the motor must be provided.

Motor overload protection is intended to open the motor circuit in case of a continuous overload. At the same time, since a motor may draw six or more times as much current when starting as it does during full-load operation, the overload protection device must allow large momentary overloads without opening the motor circuit. For this reason, time-delay overload protection devices are used. Time-delay devices do not trip as a result of momentary overloads. They do trip if the overload is continuous.

Often, and especially in the case of smaller motors, the overload protection is built into the motor itself in the form of a thermal protector. A thermal protector has one or more heat sensing elements that protect the motor. If a motor is equipped with built-in thermal protection, this will be indicated on the motor nameplate.

## Table 6-5.
## Recommended Maximum Overload Protection
## Rating as a Percentage of Full-Load Current

Motors with service factor of not less than 1.15 . . . . . . . . . . ≤125%

Motors with rated temperature rise not over 40°C . . . . . . . . ≤125%

All other motors . . . . . . . . . . . . . . . . . . . . . . . . . . . ≤115%

Source: *NEC* 430-32(a)(1) and 430-32(c)(1). Reprinted with permission from NFPA 70-1996, the *National Electrical Code*, Copyright © 1995, National Fire Protection Association, Quincy, MA 02269. This reprinted material is not the complete and official position of the National Fire Protection Association on the referenced subject, which is represented only by the standard in its entirety.

Thermal protectors may reset either manually or automatically. A manual reset thermal protector must be reset by hand. An automatic reset thermal protector resets itself once the motor has cooled. Manual reset thermal protectors should be used in situations where unexpected motor starting could cause property damage or personal injury. The cause of the motor overload should be determined and corrected before the motor is placed back in service.

If a motor is permanently installed and not equipped with built-in thermal protection, separate overload protection must be provided. Most commonly, this is accomplished using carefully sized thermal overload devices installed in the motor controller. These thermal protection devices may also be either manual or automatic resetting devices.

Overload protection installed in control devices are generally removable items. Their size should be based on the full-load current rating of the motor. Overload protection devices come in a wide range of trip current ratings. However, since a particular application may require a rating that is not available, the use of a device rated higher than the motor's full-load current may be required. Table 6-5 gives the recommended ratings for overload protection devices as a percentage of the motor's full-load amperage for continuous duty motors of more than 1 horsepower and for automatically started motors of 1 horsepower or less. (Note: Actual motor nameplate full-load current values should be used in sizing motor overload protection devices.)

The branch circuit overcurrent protection device can serve as the overload protection for a manually started motor rated at 1 horsepower or less if the overcurrent device is within sight of the motor controller [*NEC* 430-32(b)].

## Disconnecting Means

The **disconnecting means** is defined by the *NEC* (Article 100) as "a device, group of devices, or other means whereby the conductors of a circuit can be disconnected from their source or supply." The disconnecting means must disconnect the motor and controller from all ungrounded ("hot") circuit conductors. This protects individuals working on the motor or controller. The disconnecting means must clearly indicate whether it is "on" or "off." The *NEC* [430-102(a)]specifies that the disconnecting means shall be in sight of the motor controller, the motor, and the machine driven by the motor. ("In sight of" is considered to mean both visible and within a distance of 50 ft. or less.)

The disconnecting means must be a switch rated in horsepower, a circuit breaker or a molded case switch. However, the *NEC* does allow some exceptions to this requirement (*NEC* 430-109). Those with agricultural applications include:

- Stationary motors of less than $^1/_8$ horsepower may use the branch circuit protective device (e.g., circuit breaker).

- For a plug and cord connected motor, a horsepower rated cord and plug with a rating no less than the motor ratings may be used as the disconnect. Motors rated at $^1/_3$ horsepower or less do not require that the plug and cord be horsepower rated.

- Motors of 2 horsepower or less and 300 volts or less may use a general purpose (AC rated only) snap-action switch as the disconnecting means, provided the motor full-load current rating does not exceed 80 percent of the switch's amperage rating. For example, from Table 6-1, a 115-volt, $^1/_2$ horsepower motor has a full-load current rating of 9.8 amperes. A general purpose snap-action switch rated at 15 amperes could be used as the disconnect, since the switch's 80 percent rating of 12 amperes (15 amperes × .80 = 12 amperes) exceeds the full-load current rating of the motor.

- Motors of 2 horsepower or less and 300 volts or less may also use a general purpose (AC and DC rated) snap switch, so long as the switch's amperage rating is two times the motor's full-load current rating.

Each electric motor is required to have its own disconnecting means except when: (a) a number of motors drive several parts of the same machine or (b) a group of motors is located in the same room and all are within sight of the disconnecting means. In such cases, a disconnecting means may serve more than one motor.

## MOTOR CONTROLLER

A **motor controller** is a switch or device that is normally used to start and stop a motor by making and breaking the electrical current to the motor. Motors may be controlled either manually or automatically. Several motor control options are available, depending on the particular motor to be controlled.

The simplest method of motor control is to use the attachment plug and receptacle as the motor controller. This option is allowed only for portable motors rated at $1/3$ horsepower or less.

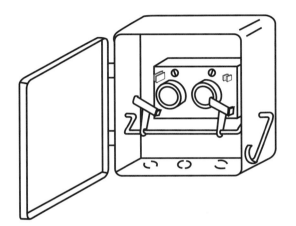 

6-27. A fusible knife switch (left) and a motor snap switch (right).

For stationary motors of $1/8$ horsepower or less that normally operate on a continuous basis and are constructed so they cannot be damaged by overload or failure to start (e.g., clock and timer motors), the branch circuit overcurrent protection device may be used as the motor controller.

A fusible knife switch (Figure 6-27 left) may serve as the motor controller as long as the switch's horsepower rating is sufficient. When a fusible switch is used, time-delay fuses can usually be sized so as to provide motor overload protection and still not blow during motor starting.

Motor snap switches (Figure 6-27 right) with built-in thermal overload protection are available. The switches control motors of up to 2 horse-

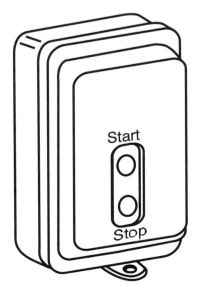

6-28. A manual motor starter.

**6-29. A magnetic motor controller.**

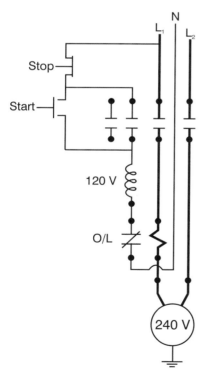

**6-30. Normal connection of a start-stop starter to control a single-phase motor with 120 V holding coil above.**

power. These switches, while more expensive, are preferable to normal snap switches.

Manual motor starters with built-in thermal overload protection are available to control single-phase AC motors of up to 5 horsepower.

A magnetic motor starter uses an electric solenoid coil to close the contacts and start the motor. Magnetic motor starters may either be activated manually or automatically. The ability to automate motor operation in response to signals supplied by various sensing devices (such as thermostats, humidistat, pressure switches, limit switches, etc.) is a primary advantage of the magnetic motor starter. Magnetic motor starters are recommended for all motors rated at over 2 horsepower.

The operating principle that distinguishes the magnetic motor controller from other types of controllers is the use of an electromagnet to open and close the motor circuit. Figure 6-29 shows a magnetic motor controller equipped with a start/stop station. This controller is commonly used where manual motor control is desirable (table saws, wood planers, hydraulic power packs, etc.).

To understand how the magnetic motor controller shown in Figure 6-29 operates, examine a schematic drawing of a motor being controlled by such a device. This schematic is shown in Figure 6-30.

In discussing the schematic in Figure 6-30, it will be helpful to differentiate between the control circuit and the load circuit. The control circuit (drawn with thin lines) includes the coil and all of the components necessary to energize and de-energize the coil (push buttons, control circuit conductors, holding contact, and the overload relay). The load circuit (drawn with thick lines) includes the power supply conductors, the main contacts, the motor power supply conductors, and the motor itself. The job of the control circuit is to control the opening and closing of the main contacts in the load circuit to control the operation of the load (motor).

When the start switch at the start-stop station is momentarily depressed, the control circuit is completed and electricity flows energizing the coil. The energized coil, being an electromagnet, causes the normally-open main contacts to close, completing the load circuit, causing the motor to operate. The energized coil also closes the holding contact in the control circuit. Since the holding contact in the control circuit is wired in parallel with the start switch, the control circuit remains energized even though the start switch is released.

To stop the motor, it is only necessary to momentarily depress the stop switch. The stop switch is a normally-closed push-button switch wired in series ahead of the start switch and the holding contact. Depressing the stop switch opens the control circuit, de-energizing the coil and opening both the holding contact and the main (load) contacts.

The magnetic motor controller represented by the schematic in Figure 6-30 is equipped with motor overload protection. As current flows through the load circuit to the motor, it must flow through a heater element. A normally-closed overcurrent switch is wired into the control circuit in series with the solenoid. The overcurrent switch, which is temperature activated, is in close proximity to the heater element. A sustained overload causes the heater element to give off excessive heat, opening the overcurrent switch. This de-energizes the coil and allows the holding and main load contacts to return to their normally-open condition, disconnecting the motor from the source.

As previously indicated, one of the primary advantages of magnetic motor control is the ability to automate motor operation. Figure 6-31 shows a magnetic motor controller being used with a thermostat and a humidistat to automate the operation of a 120-volt ventilation fan motor.

In Figure 6-31, the thermostat and the humidistat are connected into the control circuit in parallel. Because of this parallel connection, the control circuit will be complete if the contacts in either the thermostat or the humidistat close. Thus, the ventilation fan will operate if either the temperature or the humidity increases above the level set on each device.

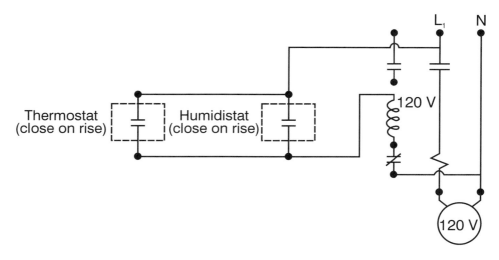

**6-31. The thermostat or the humidistat will cause the motor in this circuit to operate if they close.**

In Figure 6-31, the control circuit holding contact is not connected since we want the thermostat and/or the humidistat to both start and stop the motor. If the holding contact was connected, once started, the fan motor would continue to operate even if both the thermostat and the humidistat contacts opened.

# SUMMARY

Electric motors are the workhorses of the agricultural industry, providing reliable, inexpensive power for a wide range of uses. This chapter has provided information on the different types of electric motors available. These range from fractional horsepower synchronous motors to 100 horsepower three-phase motors.

Many different types of motors are used. The basic principles of motor operation and motor nameplate information tend to be the same with different motors. Dual voltage motors can be connected for operation at either rated voltage. The direction of shaft rotation can be easily reversed for several different types of motors.

Motors vary in efficiency in converting electrical energy into mechanical energy. The power factor of a particular motor circuit is easy to determine.

Motor branch circuits must be carefully planned. Motor branch circuit conductors must meet ampacity and voltage drop requirements. In addition, requirements for: (a) short-circuit and ground-fault protection, (b) motor overload protection, (c) motor disconnecting means, and (d) motor control must be met.

Be careful in studying and/or working with electricity. Become aware of and always comply with *NEC* and local code requirements. Your safety and health, as well as the safety and health of others, are too important to be taken lightly.

## REVIEW QUESTIONS

1. What is the primary function of an electric motor?

2. Identify the parts of the electric motor shown below.

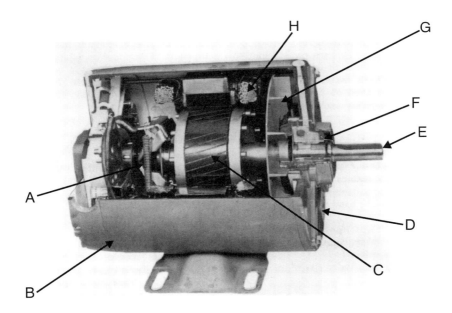

3. Explain how an AC induction motor starts and runs.

4. Assume that you must select an electric motor to power a ventilation fan in a farm service center. The following motor types are available: split-phase, capacitor-start induction-run, and wound-rotor. Which motor would you select? Explain your answer.

5. An electric motor nameplate provides the following information:

      3/4 hp           60 Hz           1 phase           1,725 RPM
          115/230 V      6.9/13.8 A         1.15 SF

Answer the following questions about the motor:

A. How many sets of running windings does the motor have?

B. How many stator poles does the motor have?

C. What is the maximum overload horsepower that this motor can produce on a continuous basis without overheating?

D. How many amperes will this motor draw when connected for low voltage operation?

6. Answer the following questions about the motor in the diagram below.

A. What type of motor is shown in the diagram?

B. Is the motor connected for operation at low or high voltage?

C. Which two wires should be reversed in order to change the direction of rotation of the motor shaft?

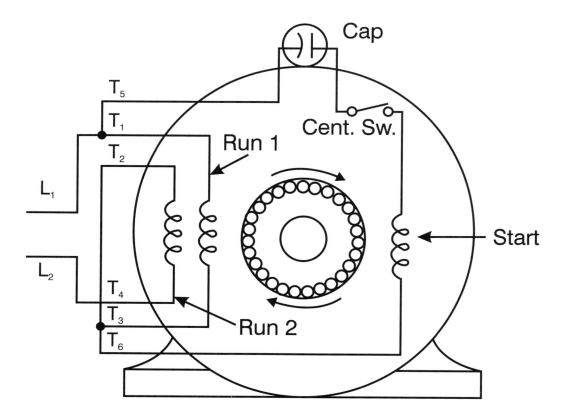

7. During a motor performance test, the following measurements were taken:

|  |  |  |  |
|---|---|---|---|
| Current | 12 A | Speed | 1690 rpm |
| Voltage | 240 V | Torque | 7.1 lb-ft |
| Watts | 2150 | | |

Determine the following:

A. Power factor

B. Horsepower output

C. Motor efficiency

8. An air compressor with a 5 horsepower, 230 volt single-phase motor (code letter E) is to be installed in a farm supply cooperative's service center. The one-way circuit length from the service entrance panel to the air compressor is 35 feet. The air compressor will be the only load on the circuit. Determine the following:

A. The minimum size THWN conductor that can be used (in conduit) to meet ampacity requirements and limit voltage drop to 2 percent.

B. The maximum size (ampere rating) inverse-time circuit breaker that can be used to provide short-circuit and ground-fault protection for the motor branch circuit.

C. The maximum size overload protection device that can be installed in the motor controller to protect the motor from over-heating. (Note: Assume that the full load amperage on the motor nameplate is 28 amperes.)

# APPLYING THE CONCEPTS

1. Develop a list of electric motors found in your home, farm, greenhouse, and/or agricultural mechanics lab. Describe how life would be different without these electric motors.

2. Secure several different types of discarded electric motors. For each motor, identify its type (split-phase, capacitor-start induction-run, etc.). Disassemble each type of motor and identify the individual motor components. Record similarities and differences between each motor type. (Note: With motors having a capacitor(s), make certain that the capacitor(s) is discharged prior to disassembly.)

3. Secure several dual-voltage, reversible motors. Set each motor up for both low and high voltage operation and for clockwise and counterclockwise rotation.

4. For a specific electric motor designated by your instructor, answer the following questions based on the information presented on the motor nameplate.

   A. At what voltage(s) is this motor designed to operate?

   B. What is the full-load amperage(s) of this motor?

   C. What is the motor's horsepower rating?

   D. What is the motor's service factor?

   E. What is the maximum horsepower this motor can produce on a continuous basis without overheating?

   F. If the motor is a dual voltage motor, draw the terminal connections that are necessary to operate the motor at (a) low voltage and (b) high voltage.

   G. If the motor is reversible, draw the terminal connections required to make the motor operate (a) clockwise and (b) counterclockwise.

5. If a dynamometer and watt meter are available, complete this activity under the supervision of your instructor. Set up a motor test circuit similar to the one shown in Figure 6-25. Determine the power factor and efficiency of the motor at (a) no-load, (b) 1/4 load, (c) 1/2 load, (d) 3/4 load, and (3) full-load. Develop a graph plotting efficiency and power factor as a function of load.

# 7

# UNDERSTANDING ELECTRONICS IN AGRICULTURE

Electronic devices have a vital role in modern agriculture. Current electronic applications range from tractor performance monitors to machine vision systems and from computer controlled food processing lines to digital soil pH meters. While today's agriculture is heavily dependant on electronics, present use will quite likely pale in comparison to future use. Electronic devices and applications undreamed of today will become commonplace in the agriculture of the future.

What is electronics? Put simply, *electronics* is the use of semiconductor devices to manipulate electrical signals. The objective of manipulating these electrical signals may be for measurement (for example, to determine the moisture level of stored grain), or to automatically control some operation (for example, fuel injection timing of a diesel tractor engine).

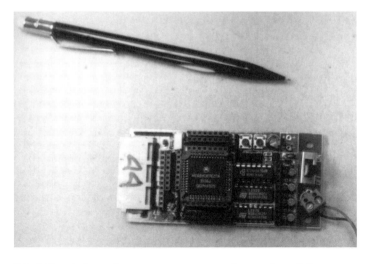

**7-1. This miniboard computer can control up to four DC motors.**

235

# OBJECTIVES

This chapter covers fundamental electronics principles and applications. After completing the chapter, you will:

1. Define electronics and describe common electronics applications in agriculture.

2. Identify various types of resistors, determine the value by reading the color code, and explain how they are used in electronic circuits.

3. Calculate the size resistor required to limit current or voltage in a circuit to a specified level.

4. Describe a capacitor and explain how it functions in DC and AC circuits.

5. Define inductance and explain the effects of inductance in DC and AC circuits.

6. Identify and explain the basic operation of different diodes, transistors, rectifiers, and thyristors.

7. Define integrated circuits and describe the two major types and their basic uses.

8. Identify schematic symbols for common discrete electronic components and interpret electronic circuit schematics.

9. Describe different methods of assembling electronic circuits.

**T E R M S**

analog (linear) integrated circuit
avalanche voltage
bidirectional triode thyristor (TRIAC)
bipolar transistor
breadboarding
bridge rectifier
capacitance (C)
capacitor
continuous signal integrated circuit
counter voltage
covalent bonding
crystal lattice
depletion region
dielectric
digital integrated circuit
discrete semiconductor component
doping
electronics
farad (F)
field-effect transistor (FET)
fixed capacitor
fixed resistor
forward-biased
full-wave rectification
half-wave rectification

henry (H)
inductance (L)
inductor
insulated-gate field-effect transistor (IGFET)
integrated circuit
junction diode
junction field-effect transistor (JFET)
light-emitting diode (LED)
pentavalent element
perforated board (perf board)
pictorial drawing
potentiometer (pot)
printed circuit (PC) board
rectification
resistor
rheostat
reverse-biased
schematic drawing
silicon-controlled rectifier (SCR)
soldering
solid state
thyristor
transistor
trivalent element
variable capacitor
variable resistor
wire wrapping
zener diode

# NON-SEMICONDUCTOR
# ELECTRONIC COMPONENTS

Although the distinguishing feature of electronics is the use of semiconductors to manipulate electricity, almost all electronic circuits and devices require the use of components that are not semiconductors.

## *RESISTORS*

A *resistor* is an electronic circuit component intended to introduce opposition to the flow of current into a circuit. The unit of measurement for resistance is the ohm. Resistors are sized according to their resistance values. Resistors are used in electronic circuits to accomplish one (or both) of the following functions: (a) reduce current to a specified level or (b) cause a desired voltage drop. There are two different types of resistors available: fixed resistors and variable resistors.

### *Fixed Resistors*

*Fixed resistors* have only one set (or fixed) resistance value. Different types of fixed resistors are available, including carbon-composition resistors, wire-wound resistors, metal film resistors, and carbon film resistors. See Figure 7-2.

The resistance value of most fixed resistors is indicated by color code bands on the body of the resistor. Figure 7-3 shows how to read these color bands to determine a resistor's value.

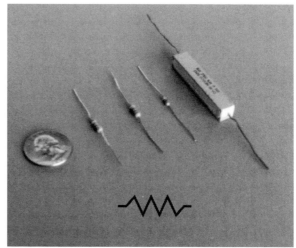

**7-2. Several fixed resistors and the schematic symbol for a fixed resistor.**

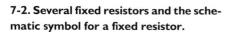

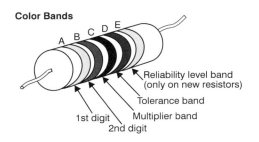

Color Bands

Reliability level band
(only on new resistors)

Tolerance band

1st digit    Multiplier band
2nd digit

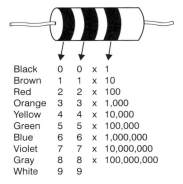

| Black | 0 | 0 | x | 1 |
| Brown | 1 | 1 | x | 10 |
| Red | 2 | 2 | x | 100 |
| Orange | 3 | 3 | x | 1,000 |
| Yellow | 4 | 4 | x | 10,000 |
| Green | 5 | 5 | x | 100,000 |
| Blue | 6 | 6 | x | 1,000,000 |
| Violet | 7 | 7 | x | 10,000,000 |
| Gray | 8 | 8 | x | 100,000,000 |
| White | 9 | 9 | | |

Fourth band indicates tolerance (accuracy)
Gold = ±5%   Silver = ±10%   None = ±20%

**7-3. To determine a resistor's value, you must be able to read the color code bands on the body of the resistors.**

According to the color code, a resistor with the following colored bands, yellow-violet-orange-silver, is a 47,000 Ω resistor having a tolerance of ± 10 percent. The ± 10 percent tolerance means that the resistor's actual value can range between 42,300 Ω (90% of 47,000) and 51,700 Ω (110% of 47,000).

## Variable Resistors

A *variable resistor* does not have a set resistance value. Instead, the resistance can be changed to any specific value within the resistor's range. Some variable resistors (potentiometers and rheostats) change values when a mechanical adjustment is made to the resistor. Other variable resistors change values automatically in response to changes in light level (photoresistors) and temperature (thermistor). Variable resistors are used whenever it is necessary to adjust the resistance in an electronic circuit.

A *potentiometer (pot)* usually has three terminals, as shown in Figure 7-4. The resistance between the two outer terminals does not change. However, the center terminal is attached to a slider, that is controlled by the adjustment knob. Turning the adjust-

**7-4.  A potentiometer (pot) and its schematic symbol.**

ment knob varies the resistance between the center terminal and each of the two outside terminals by altering the distance from each terminal to the slider. A *rheostat* is similar to a potentiometer, except that a rheostat only has two terminals.

Photocells and thermistors also function as variable resistors. The resistance of a photocell varies inversely with light level (i.e., resistance decreases as light level increases). A thermistor's resistance varies inversely with temperature (i.e., resistance increases as temperature decreases).

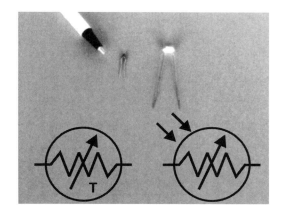

7-5. A thermistor (left) and a photoresistor (right) along with their schematic symbols.

Photoresistors and thermistors both play important roles in automatic sensing and control circuits. Photocells and thermistors are actually semiconductor devices; however, because of their variable resistance characteristics, they are included in this section. Resistors are commonly used in electronic circuits to either reduce current or to reduce voltage.

**Reduce Current.** Ohm's Law specifies the relationship between voltage, amperage, and resistance in electrical circuits. Ohm's Law can be used to determine the size of resistor required to limit current in a circuit to any desired level. The Ohm's Law formula is:

Voltage = Amperage × Resistance

Figure 7-6 shows an electronic circuit that uses a 6-volt battery as the power source. Assume that the load in the circuit is an unspecified elec-

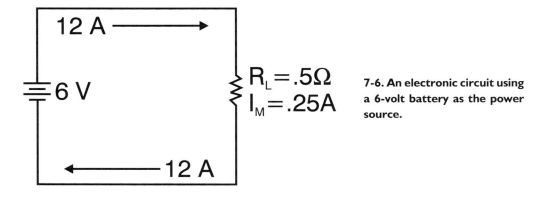

7-6. An electronic circuit using a 6-volt battery as the power source.

tronic component having a resistance of .5 ohms. Further assume that the component has a maximum current rating of .25 amperes (or 250 mA).

What will happen to the electronic component once the circuit is energized? Rearrange the Ohm's Law formula to find out.

$$\text{Amerage} = \frac{\text{Voltage}}{\text{Resistance}}$$

$$= \frac{6 \text{ volts}}{.5 \text{ ohms}}$$

$$= 12 \text{ amperes}$$

Based on these calculations it's pretty certain what will happen to the electronic component once the switch is closed. The component will be destroyed almost instantaneously! This will happen because the electronic component will draw 48 times its rated maximum current. Few if any devices could survive such an overload.

Does this mean that this component cannot be powered by the 6-volt battery? Not necessarily. If an appropriately sized resistor is placed in series with the device, the current flow can be reduced to a permissible level. (Remember, the total resistance in a series circuit is equal to the sum of the individual resistances.)

According to Ohm's Law, 24 ohms of total resistance are required to limit current flow in a 6-volt circuit to .25 amperes. The necessary calculations are shown.

$$\text{Ohm's} = \frac{\text{Voltage}}{\text{Amperage}}$$

$$= \frac{6 \text{ volts}}{.25 \text{ amps}}$$

$$= 24 \text{ ohms}$$

Since the device itself has a resistance of .5 ohms, 23.5 ohms of additional resistance need to be added to the circuit to limit current flow to .25 amperes. Figure 7-7 shows the circuit with the resistor added. (Note: It is not likely that a resistor with a value of exactly 23.5 ohms could be found, so a 24 ohm resistor would be used instead. Such a small difference would not have any appreciable effect on the operation of the circuit.)

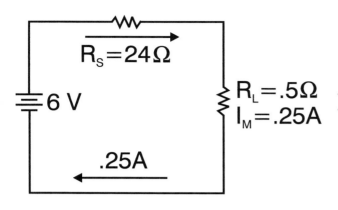

$R_S = 24\Omega$

6 V

.25A

$R_L = .5\Omega$
$I_M = .25A$

**7-7. The circuit depicted in Figure 7-6 with a series resistor added.**

**Reduce Voltage.** In a series circuit, the source voltage is equal to the sum of the voltage drops across each circuit load (resistance). Furthermore, the voltage drop across each individual load in a series circuit is proportional to the load's resistance. The example circuit in Figure 7-8 illustrates these relationships.

The circuit in Figure 7-8 has a 6 volt source ($V_{in}$) and two resistors (5 and 10 ohms, respectively) connected in series. Based on Ohm's Law, it can be determined that .4 amperes of current will flow in the circuit (6 V / 15 ohms = .4 amperes). Since this is a series circuit, the current flow will be the same at any point in the circuit.

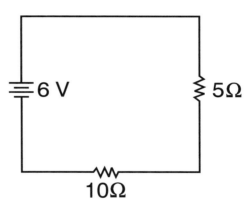

6 V

5Ω

10Ω

**7-8. A circuit with a 6-volt source ($V_{in}$) and two resistors (5 and 10 ohms) connected in series.**

The voltage drop across each resistor can also be calculated using Ohm's Law. These calculations (below) show that the voltage drop across the 5 ohm resistor will be 2 volts, while the voltage drop across the 10 ohm resistor will be 4 volts.

$$\text{Voltage drop}_{5 \text{ ohm resistor}} = \text{Amperage} \times \text{Resistance}$$
$$= .4 \text{ amps} \times 5 \text{ ohms}$$
$$= 2 \text{ volts}$$
$$\text{Voltage drop}_{10 \text{ ohm resistor}} = \text{Amperage} \times \text{Resistance}$$
$$= .4 \text{ amps} \times 10 \text{ ohms}$$
$$= 4 \text{ volts}$$

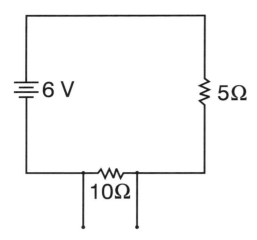

**7-9. The circuit in Figure 7-8 modified by adding two conductors across the terminals of the 10 ohm resistor.**

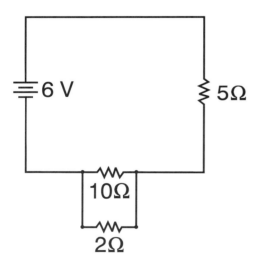

**7-10. A load having a 2 ohm resistance is added across the 10 ohm resistor of the circuit in Figure 7-9.**

[Note that the sum of the voltage drops (4 volts + 2 volts) in the circuit is equal to the source voltage (6 volts)].

Look at Figure 7-9. Notice that the previous circuit (Figure 7-8) has been modified by adding two conductors across the terminals of the 10 ohm resistor. From the calculations just completed, the voltage across this resistor ($V_{out}$) is 4 volts.

You might think that a load connected to the conductors across the 10 ohm resistor would operate at 4 volts. However, this is not correct since the added load and the 4 ohm load will be in parallel. This will change the total circuit resistance, causing a change in the voltage across each resistor. To illustrate this, assume that a load having a 2 ohm resistance is added across the 10 ohm resistor, as shown in Figure 7-10.

Determine the total resistance of the circuit shown in Figure 7-10. Since there is only one series resistor ($R_1$), the total series resistance in the circuit is 5 ohms. The total resistance of the parallel circuit branch (composed of the 2 and 10 ohm resistors) can be calculated using the formula below.

$$R_{parallel} = \cfrac{1}{\cfrac{1}{R_2} + \cfrac{1}{R_3}}$$

$$= \cfrac{1}{\cfrac{1}{4} + \cfrac{1}{2}}$$

$$= \cfrac{1}{.25 + .5}$$

$$= 1.33 \text{ ohm}$$

Since the series branch of the circuit has 5 ohms of resistance and the parallel branch has 1.33 ohms of resistance, the circuit has 6.33 ohms of total resistance. Now that the individual resistances of the series and parallel circuit branches are known, the actual voltage ($V_{out}$) supplied to the 2 ohm load can be determined using Formula 7-1.

$$V_{out} = \frac{V_s \times R_p}{R_t}$$

| Formula 7-1. |
| --- |

Where,

$V_{out}$ = output voltage
$V_s$ = source voltage
$R_p$ = resistance of the parallel circuit branch
$R_t$ = total circuit resistance

By inserting the values into Formula 7-1, the actual voltage ($V_{out}$) supplied to our 2 ohm load is 1.26 volts. The necessary calculations are shown.

$$V_{out} = \frac{V_s \times R_p}{R_t}$$

$$= \frac{6 \text{ volts} \times 1.33 \text{ ohms}}{6.3 \text{ ohms}}$$

$$= \frac{7.98}{6.33 \text{ ohms}}$$

$$= 1.26 \text{ V}$$

The use of carefully sized resistors to produce a desired voltage drop is a common practice in designing electronic circuits. This allows circuit components with different voltage ratings to operate from the same voltage source.

A resistor has a maximum power rating that indicates how much power the resistor can safely dissipate, measured in watts (Watts = Volts × Amperes). Always use a resistor that has a power rating equal or greater than the power to be dissipated.

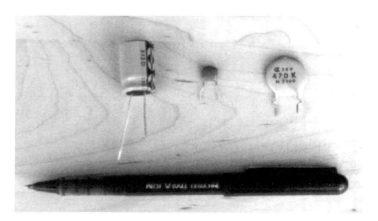

**7-11. Examples of three capacitors.**

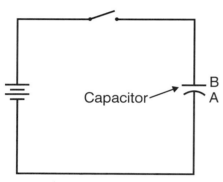

**7-12. A capacitor in a DC circuit.**

# CAPACITORS

A *capacitor* is a device that stores electrical energy in an electrostatic field. Capacitors perform several important functions in electronic circuits. These functions include: (a) storing electrical energy, (b) blocking the flow of current in a DC circuit, and (c) allowing the flow of current in an AC circuit.

A capacitor is shown in the circuit in Figure 7-12. The capacitor has two metal plates separated by an insulating material called a *dielectric.* In the illustration, plate A is connected to the negative terminal of the battery (a DC source) and plate B is connected to the positive terminal. The switch in the circuit is open, so no current flows.

## Capacitor Operation in a DC Circuit

To understand the operation of a capacitor in a DC circuit, assume that the switch in Figure 7-12 is suddenly closed. The negative battery terminal will repel the free electrons in the conductor, driving them to plate A. Electrons will accumulate on plate A because they cannot flow through the dielectric. Thus, plate A will take on a negative charge. At the same time, the free electrons on plate B will be attracted to the positive battery terminal. This will cause plate B to take on a positive charge since it will have more protons than electrons. This creates a potential difference between plate A and plate B. This potential difference will be equal to the source voltage, but will have the opposite polarity.

Once the capacitor has a potential difference equal to the source voltage, the capacitor is fully charged and current flow in the DC circuit will cease. If the capacitor was removed from the circuit, it would retain its charge (potential difference) and could be used as a source of voltage until the capacitor discharged (expended its potential difference). Capacitors used in high voltage circuits can retain dangerously high electrical charges. For safety, capacitors should be discharged prior to handling.

## Capacitor Operation in an AC Circuit

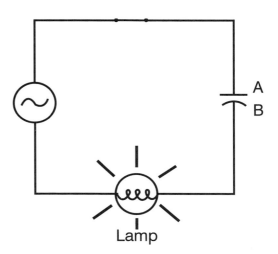

The previous example has shown how a capacitor (a) stores electrical energy and (b) blocks the flow of current in a DC circuit. Figure 7-13 shows how (and why) a capacitor allows current flow in an AC circuit.

When a capacitor is connected in a circuit with an AC voltage source, current does not flow through the capacitor (since the dielectric is still an insulator). Instead, current literally flows around the capacitor! Examine the events during one AC cycle (1/60 of a second) to see how this happens.

**7-13. Same circuit as 7-12, except with AC source and non-polarized capacitor**

Assume that the capacitor in Figure 7-13 is discharged and the switch has just been closed. As the voltage in the AC circuit starts to increase during the positive half-cycle, free electrons begin to accumulate on plate A. But, before the capacitor can become fully charged, the positive half-cycle voltage has peaked and the AC voltage starts to return to zero. Since the capacitor now has a larger charge than the AC voltage source, the capacitor starts to discharge. This discharge from the capacitor tends to oppose the decreasing AC source voltage, thus causing the AC to seem to delay in its return to zero.

Once the AC source voltage has returned to zero, the positive half-cycle is completed. Now the voltage begins to increase during the negative half-cycle. Since the polarity of the AC voltage has reversed, free electrons begin to accumulate on plate B. But again, before the capacitor can become fully charged, the negative half-cycle has peaked and the AC voltage starts to return to zero. Since the capacitor now has a larger charge than the

AC voltage source, the capacitor starts to discharge. Again, this discharge tends to oppose the decreasing AC source voltage, causing the AC to seem to delay in its return to zero. When the AC voltage returns to zero, one AC electrical cycle has been completed and the process is repeated as long as the switch is closed.

In an AC circuit, the electrons travel around the capacitor, through the load and source, then arrive essentially at the other side. This gives the effect of allowing AC electricity to flow in a circuit containing a capacitor.

A capacitor will allow more current to flow in an AC circuit as the frequency of the source voltage is increased. Thus, all other factors being equal, more current will flow in a circuit with a frequency of 500 Hz than in a circuit with a frequency of 60 Hz. This characteristic allows capacitors to be used to filter unwanted frequencies (called noise) from an electronic circuit.

### Capacitance and Its Unit of Measurement

*Capacitance (C)* is the measure of the ability to store an electrical charge. The basic unit of measurement for capacitance is the *farad (F)*. A capacitor rated at one farad (1 F) will store $6.28 \times 10^{18}$ electrons when connected to a one volt supply for one second. The capacitors used in electronics are generally much smaller than 1 F. Thus, most capacitors will be rated in either microfarads ($\mu$F) or in picofarads (pF). A microfarad is equal to $1 \times 10^{-6}$ farads (.000001 F), while a picofarad is equal to $1 \times 10^{-12}$ farads (.000000000001 F).

### Capacitors in Series and Parallel

The total capacitance of two or more capacitors connected in series is different than if they were connected in parallel. Connecting capacitors in series reduces the total capacitance, while connecting capacitors in parallel

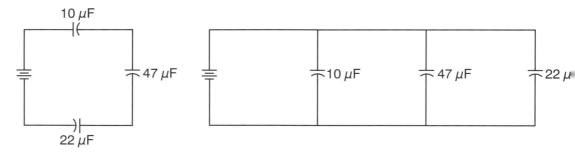

**7-14. Three capacitors connected in series (left) and three capacitors connected in parallel (right).**

increases the total capacitance. Figure 7-14 (left) shows three capacitors connected in series; Figure 7-14 (right) shows the same three capacitors connected in parallel.

The total capacitance for capacitors connected in series can be calculated using Formula 7-2.

$$C_t = \cfrac{1}{\cfrac{1}{C_1} + \cfrac{1}{C_2} + \cfrac{1}{C_3} + \dots \cfrac{1}{C_n}}$$

**Formula 7-2.**

Where,

$C_t$ = Total capacitance
$C_1$ = Value of first capacitor
$C_2$ = Value of second capacitor
$C_3$ = Value of third capacitor
$C_n$ = Value of the $n^{th}$ capacitor

By inserting the capacitor values from Figure 7-14 left into Formula 7-2, it is determined that the circuit has a total capacitance of 6.02 $\mu$F. These calculations are shown.

$$C_t = \cfrac{1}{\cfrac{1}{C_1} + \cfrac{1}{C_2} + \cfrac{1}{C_3} \dots \cfrac{1}{C_n}}$$

$$= \cfrac{1}{\cfrac{1}{10\ \mu F} + \cfrac{1}{47\ \mu F} + \cfrac{1}{22\ \mu F}}$$

$$= \cfrac{1}{.10\ \mu F + .021\ \mu F + .045\ \mu F}$$

$$= \cfrac{1}{.166\ \mu F}$$

$$= 6.02\ \mu F$$

The total capacitance for capacitors connected in parallel can be determined using Formula 7-3.

$$C_t = C_1 + C_2 + C_3 + \dots C_n$$

**Formula 7-3.**

Where,

$C_t$ = Total capacitance
$C_1$ = Value of first capacitor
$C_2$ = Value of second capacitor
$C_3$ = Value of third capacitor
$C_n$ = Value of the $n^{th}$ capacitor

Thus, by inserting known values for the three capacitors connected in parallel (Figure 7-14 right), it is determined that the total circuit capacitance is 79 $\mu$F ($C_t$ = 10 $\mu$F + 47 $\mu$F + 22 $\mu$F = 79 $\mu$F).

## Types of Capacitors and Their Schematic Symbols

Capacitors are often classified based on the material used in their dielectric. These materials include ceramics, mica, and polystyrene. All of these materials produce a capacitor having a fixed, non-adjustable capacitance. These are called *fixed capacitors.*

Electrolytic capacitors, having a dielectric made of an oxide layer formed on aluminum or tantalum foil, are also available. This special dielectric gives electrolytic capacitors a much greater capacitance per volume and a longer service life than non-electrolytic capacitors. Most electrolytic capacitors are polarized. This means that they must be connected into a circuit with the positive lead to the most positive connection point and the negative lead to the most negative connection point. For this reason, polarized capacitors are not suitable for use in AC circuits. Electrolytic capacitors have a fixed capacitance value.

A *variable capacitor* has one or more fixed plates and one or more moveable plates, with air between the plates serving as the dielectric material. Turning a rod affixed to one side of the moveable plate(s) varies the distance between the fixed and moveable plates, and changes the capacitance.

**7-15. The schematic symbols for fixed (left), variable (center), and polarized (right) capacitors.**

## INDUCTORS

*Inductance (L)* is the opposition to any change (increase or decrease) in current flow in a circuit. The unit of measurement for inductance is the *henry* (H). One henry is the inductance required in a circuit to induce one volt in a coil when the current changes its rate of flow by one ampere per second. The henry is too large a unit for practical electronic work, so the millihenry (mH) is more commonly used. One millihenry is equal to one thousandths of a henry (1 mH = .001 H).

An *inductor* is a coil placed in a circuit to produce a desired amount of inductance. Inductors may be used in electronic circuits to (a) change the form of an AC sine wave, (b) filter out specific frequency bands from an electrical signal, or (c) tune a receiver (such as a radio) to pick up a desired signal.

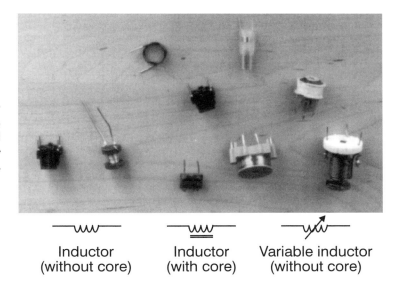

7-16. A variety of inductors used in electronics, as well as the general schematic symbols for fixed and variable inductors.

|  |  |  |
|---|---|---|
| Inductor<br>(without core) | Inductor<br>(with core) | Variable inductor<br>(without core) |

Any time current flows through a conductor, a magnetic field builds up around the conductor. Any time a magnetic field cuts across a conductor, a voltage is induced into the conductor. Whenever the current flow through a conductor changes, the magnetic field surrounding the conductor will change (expanding with an increase in current; diminishing with a decrease in current).

Now, assume that a conductor is wound into a coil and connected to a DC source, as illustrated in Figure 7-17. Notice in Figure 7-17 (left) the

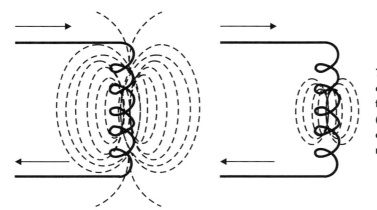

7-17. Increasing current in a circuit expands the magnetic field surrounding the coil (left); decreasing current causes a contraction in the magnetic field (right).

current in the circuit is increasing; in Figure 7-17 (right) the current in the circuit is decreasing.

As the current in the circuit is increasing (Figure 7-17, left), the magnetic field expands. The expanding magnetic field cuts across adjacent coil turns, inducing a voltage into the coil. This induced voltage is called a **counter voltage** because its polarity is opposite to that of the source voltage and tends to oppose any increase in current flow. Once current flow in the circuit has reached its maximum level (determined by the circuit voltage and resistance in accordance with Ohm's Law), current flow will no longer change, the magnetic field will no longer expand, and no further counter voltage will be induced into the circuit.

In Figure 7-17 (right), current flow is decreasing (due to either increased resistance, decreased voltage, or a combination of the two). This causes the magnetic field surrounding the coil to contract. The contracting magnetic field cuts across the adjacent turns of the coil inducing a counter voltage. This induced counter voltage tends to oppose any decrease in current flow. Once the current flow in the circuit has reached its minimum level, current flow will no longer change, the magnetic field will no longer contract, and no further counter voltage will be induced into the circuit.

Normally, in a DC circuit, current flow changes only when the circuit is first energized (as current increases to its maximum) and when the circuit is de-energized (as current decreases to zero). At other times, current flow is constant. Thus, an inductor placed in a DC circuit will produce a counter voltage only when the circuit is first energized or when the circuit is de-energized.

In an AC circuit, current flow is constantly changing as long as the circuit is energized. Thus, an inductor placed in an AC circuit produces a counter voltage as long as the circuit is energized. Since this counter voltage opposes any change in current flow in the circuit, the net effect of an inductor in an AC circuit is to cause the circuit amperage to lag (peak after) the circuit voltage.

To further compare the effects of inductance in DC and AC circuits, imagine that the same lamp and inductor are placed in a 6-volt DC circuit and a 6-volt AC circuit, as shown in Figure 7-18. Once the current stabilizes at its maximum value in the DC circuit, no counter voltage will be induced by the inductor. Thus, the inductor will have a negligible effect on the brightness of the lamp. However, since the current is constantly changing in the AC circuit, a counter voltage is constantly being produced. This counter voltage will decrease the true ɪ  ̛ available to the lamp in the AC circuit, causing it to produce less  .t than the lamp in the DC circuit.

**7-18. A comparison of the effects of inductance in DC circuit (left) and AC circuit (right).**

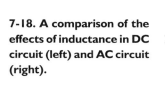
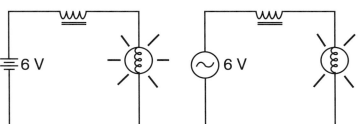

# DISCRETE SEMICONDUCTOR COMPONENTS

A *discrete semiconductor component* is a separate and individual component, made from semiconductor material, that is not part of an integrated circuit. Diodes, transistors, and thyristors are all examples of discrete semiconductor components.

## *BASIC SEMICONDUCTOR THEORY*

An element having four electrons in its valence ring is neither a good insulator nor a good conductor. Such elements are called semiconductors. Silicon and germanium are the two elements most commonly used in

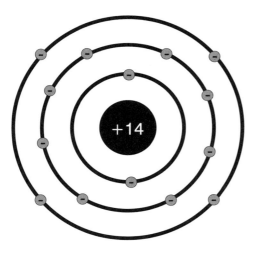

**7-19. The atomic structure of silicon.**

producing semiconductor devices. Gallium arsenide is also becoming an important semiconductor material because of the high speed and low power requirements of devices made from this material.

Silicon, like most solid substances, has a crystalline structure. In a crystal, atoms are arranged in an orderly, repeating, three-dimensional pattern. This pattern is called a *crystal lattice*. Figure 7-20 shows how individual silicon atoms join together to form this crystal lattice. (Note: For clarity, only the valence electrons of each silicon atom are shown.)

**7-20. Crystal structure composed of silicon atoms showing covalent bonding.**

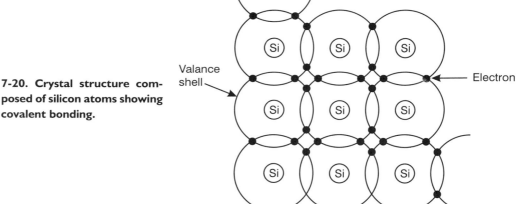

In Figure 7-20, the individual silicon atoms are held together in the crystal lattice through covalent bonding. *Covalent bonding* occurs when atoms share valence electrons. Each of the individual silicon atoms in the crystal shares valence electrons with its neighbors. Through this sharing, each silicon atom achieves a full (eight electron) valence shell. Thus, a silicon crystal will not conduct electricity because there are no free electrons.

Silicon is not very useful in its pure state. But, when certain elements are added to pure silicon in a process called *doping*, the doped silicon takes on extremely useful electrical characteristics. Elements used to dope silicon include aluminum, arsenic, bismuth, boron, gallium, and phosphorus. Doping elements are added to the silicon crystal in extremely small quantities. Depending on the doping element used, either n-type or p-type silicon crystals are produced as a result of doping.

## N-type Crystals

N-type crystals are produced when a pentavalent element is used as the doping material. ***Pentavalent elements*** have five valence electrons and include phosphorus, bismuth, and arsenic.

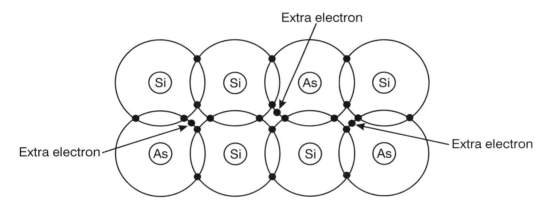

**7-21. The results of doping a silicon crystal with a minute quantity of a pentavalent element.**

Since the doping element has five valence electrons, only four of these enter into covalent bonds with silicon atoms. This leaves one electron that is not joined. This free electron becomes a conduction electron. The n-type crystal gets its name because electrons (with their negative charges) are the primary electrical carriers.

## P-type Crystals

P-type crystals are produced when a trivalent element is used as the doping material. ***Trivalent elements*** have three valence electrons and include aluminum, boron, and gallium.

Notice in Figure 7-22 that the three valence electrons of the doping element join in covalent bonds with the silicon. However, the silicon atom

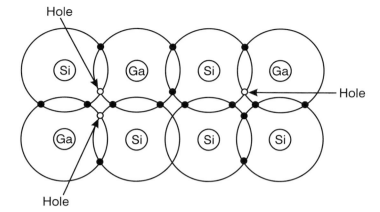

7-22. The results of doping a silicon crystal with a trivalent element.

is not satisfied since one more electron is required to complete its covalent bonding structure. Thus, a hole exists in the silicon atom's valence ring. Since this hole exists due to the lack of a negatively charged electron, the hole itself is considered to have a positive charge. The hole has a strong attraction for an electron.

Conduction through a p-type crystal is through hole movement. As an electron from a neighboring atom is attracted and fills the hole, a hole is transferred to the atom donating the electron. Thus, hole flow is in the opposite direction from electron movement. The p-type crystal gets its name because holes (considered to be positively charged) are the primary electrical carriers.

Alone, neither p-type nor n-type semiconductor material is very useful. However, when combined in different configurations, they form the basis for an assortment of useful electronic devices.

## SEMICONDUCTOR COMPONENTS

Several discrete semiconductor components play important roles in electronics. These components include diodes, transistors, and thyristors.

### Diodes

The junction diode is the simplest semiconductor device. A *junction diode* functions as a one-way valve, allowing electrical current to flow in only one direction.

A junction diode is made by doping one-half of a semiconductor material (silicon or germanium) with p-type dopant and the other half with n-type

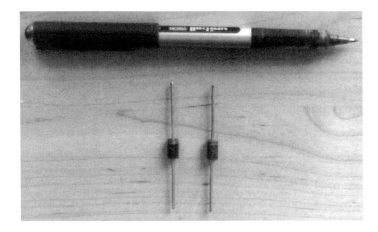

**7-23. Junction diodes.**

dopant. The boundary at the p and n regions is called the p-n junction. Connections made to the p and n regions are referred to as the anode and the cathode, respectively. Figure 7-24 shows the construction of a junction diode as well as its schematic symbol. (Note that the schematic symbol follows the conventional theory of current flow. In other words, the arrow of the symbol points in the direction of positive particle flow. Electron flow is in the direction opposite the arrow.)

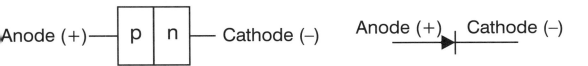

**7-24. The construction of a junction diode (left) and its schematic symbol (right).**

When the anode is connected into a circuit so it is more positive than the cathode, the diode is said to be *forward-biased* (Figure 7-25). When a diode is forward-biased, electrons in the n region will be attracted toward the anode and the holes in the p region will be attracted toward the cathode. If the voltage applied to the diode is greater than the diode's threshold voltage (about 0.6 volts for silicon diodes and 0.25 volts for germanium diode), electrical carriers (electrons and holes) will be able to cross the p-n junction and current will flow in the circuit.

In Figure 7-26, the connections from the battery to the diode have been reversed. Now, the anode is more negative than the cathode, and the diode is said to be *reverse-biased*. In this situation, the battery attracts electrical carriers (electrons and holes) away from the p-n junction, creating what

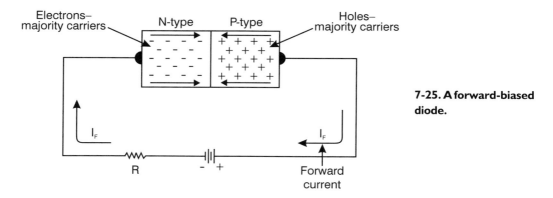

7-25. A forward-biased diode.

is known as a ***depletion region*** (a region depleted of electrical carriers). Since no electrical carriers are available in the depletion region, current cannot flow across the diode's p-n junction. Thus, no current flows in a circuit having a diode that is reverse-biased.

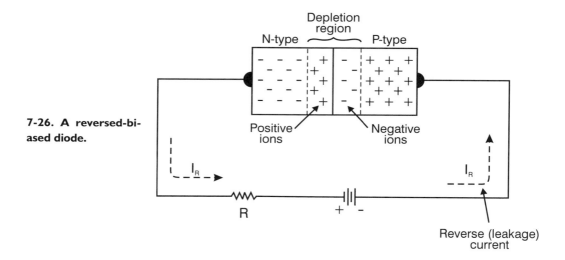

7-26. A reversed-biased diode.

Normally, a junction diode allows current to flow in only one direction. Actual operating characteristics for a diode can be illustrated using Figure 7-27.

The right side of Figure 7-27 shows the operating characteristics of a forward-biased diode. As stated, a diode requires a certain threshold forward voltage ($V_F$) before it will allow current to flow across the p-n junction. Once this threshold voltage is reached, current flow through the diode (forward current, $I_F$) will increase with voltage. If forward current exceeds the diode's maximum current rating, the diode may crack, melt, or explode due to excessive heat buildup.

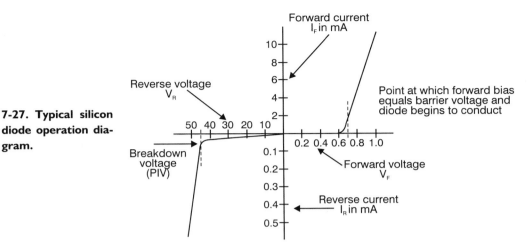

**7-27. Typical silicon diode operation diagram.**

The left side of Figure 7-27 shows what happens to a diode when it is reverse-biased. It will block current flow when reverse-biased as long as the applied voltage ($V_R$) is less than the diode's breakdown voltage ($V_{br}$). However, once breakdown voltage has been reached, excessive reverse current ($I_R$) across the diode may cause it to fail.

Several types of diodes are available, including junction diodes, zener diodes, and light-emitting diodes (LEDs).

Junction diodes are commonly used to transform low-current AC electricity into DC electricity through a process called **rectification**. A single diode placed in an AC circuit will produce what is known as **half-wave rectification.** This is because only one-half of the incoming AC sine wave is allowed to flow through the diode. The other half of the AC sine wave is blocked by the diode.

If four junction diodes are placed in a circuit as shown in Figure 7-29, each half of the AC sine wave is converted into DC electricity. This is

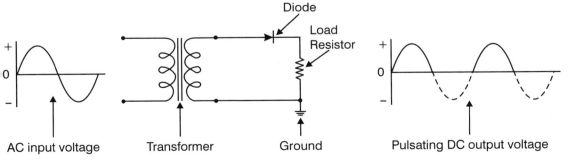

**7-28. The process of half-wave rectification.**

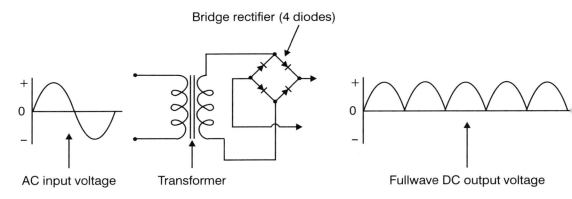

**7-29. The process of full-wave rectification.**

called *full-wave rectification* since both halves of the AC sine wave are used. This network of four diodes is called a *bridge rectifier.* Bridge rectifiers can either be constructed using individual junction diodes or purchased as a unit. Automobile and tractor alternators use bridge rectifiers to change AC electricity into DC electricity.

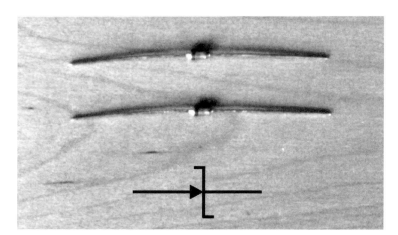

**7-30. A zener diode and its schematic symbol.**

The *zener diode* is a special type of diode designed for reverse-bias operation. In Figure 7-31, the circuit contains a variable voltage DC source, a series resistor (R1), a parallel connected 6.8 volt zener diode, and a parallel connected resistance load (RL). Also, a voltmeter is connected across the terminals of the load.

Operate the circuit in Figure 7-31, gradually increasing the source voltage and observing the readings on the voltmeter. At zero volts the voltmeter will read zero. As the source voltage increases, the voltmeter will read

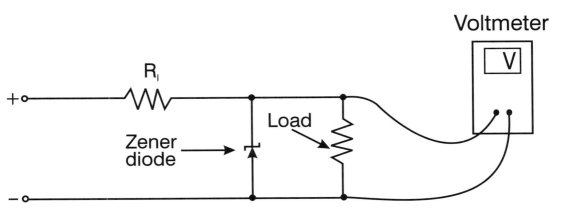

**31.** A circuit containing a variable voltage DC source, a series resistor, a parallel connected zener diode, nd a parallel connected resistance load. A voltmeter is connected across the terminals of the resistance ad.

slightly less than the source voltage (due to a slight voltage drop across R1) and the circuit operates as if the diode is not present.

This situation will hold true until the source voltage exceeds the voltage rating of the zener diode (6.8 volts in our example). This voltage, called the ***avalanche voltage***, is the reverse-bias voltage at which the zener diode begins to conduct. Once avalanche voltage has been reached, current flow through the diode will go from practically zero to a very high value. It is limited only by the low internal resistance of the diode. This low internal resistance is why the series resistor (R1) must be included in the circuit. R1 limits current flow through the zener diode to a safe level.

Because the zener diode diverts any voltage greater than its avalanche voltage back to ground (without flowing through the load), the voltmeter across the load will read no more than 6.8 volts regardless of the source voltage. Thus, a zener diode can be used to limit voltage to a load. A zener diode can also be used to regulate voltage to a load. This ensures that voltage remains relatively constant despite fluctuations in current draw.

Like a junction diode, a ***light-emitting diode*** (**LED**) will allow current to flow in only one direction. But an LED will also emit light when it is forward-biased. When reverse-biased, an LED will not conduct and produces no light.

Most LEDs are designed to operate in low-power circuits. Maximum forward voltage ($V_F$) ratings of 2.5 volts, and maximum forward current ($I_F$) ratings of 25 mA are typical for LEDs. Voltages or currents in excess of an LED's maximum rating may ruin it by melting the p-n junction. A

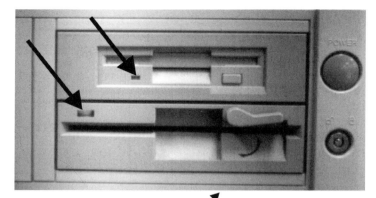

**7-32. Actual light-emitting diodes (LEDs) in computer disk drives and their schematic symbol.**

resistor is usually placed in series with an LED to limit voltage and amperage.

LEDs are widely used as indicating devices. For example, a computer disc drive is operating when the LED on the drive is lit.

## Transistors

**Transistors** are semiconductor devices having three leads that control current flow without use of a vacuum tube. A small current or voltage at one of these leads can control a much larger current flowing through the other two leads. This allows transistors to be used as switches and amplifiers. There are two major families of transistors—bipolar transistors and field-effect transistors.

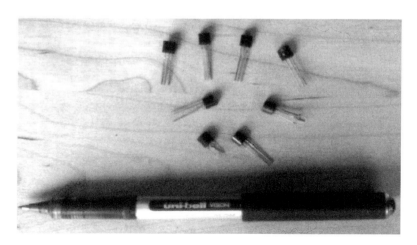

**7-33. An assortment of transistors.**

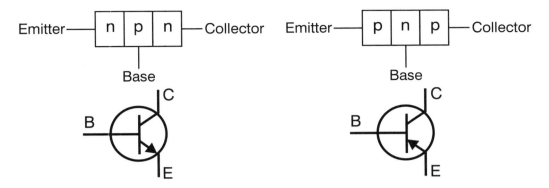

**7-34. The construction of npn and pnp bipolar transistors and the schematic symbol for each.**

*Bipolar transistors* consist of a thin layer of either n-type or p-type semiconductor material sandwiched between two layers of the opposite type of semiconductor material. If p-type material is sandwiched between two layers of n-type material, the transistor is called a npn bipolar transistor. If n-type material is sandwiched between two layers of p-type material, the transistor is called a pnp bipolar transistor. Electrons are the primary electrical carriers in an npn transistor; holes are the primary electrical carriers in a pnp transistor. The pnp transistor is more commonly used than the npn transistor.

The three layers of a bipolar transistor are known as the collector, emitter, and base. The base serves as a gate (or switch) that controls the current moving through the three layers.

Two conditions must be met before a bipolar transistor will allow current flow. First, the emitter-base junction must be forward-biased. Second, the collector-base junction must be reverse-biased. The following example will show how a transistor operates.

In Figure 7-35, a battery is connected to a pnp transistor. When switch one (S1) is closed and switch two (S2) is open, the emitter-base junction

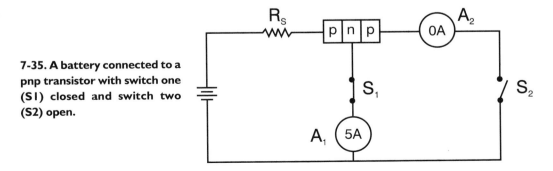

**7-35. A battery connected to a pnp transistor with switch one (S1) closed and switch two (S2) open.**

is forward-biased and holes flow in the emitter-base circuit. Assume that the resistor, R1, limits current flow in the emitter-base circuit to five amperes as shown on ammeter A1. Note that, with S2 open, no current flows through the emitter-collector junction, so ammeter A2 reads zero. In this mode, the transistor functions as a simple pn junction diode.

In Figure 7-36, notice what happens as a result of closing S2. The total current flow in the circuit is the same as before, five amperes. But, now the emitter-base current has decreased from five amperes to .25 amperes (A1). At the same time, the current through the emitter-collector has increased from zero amperes to 4.75 amperes (A2).

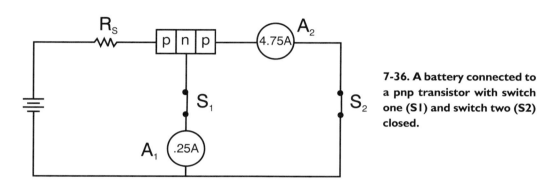

**7-36. A battery connected to a pnp transistor with switch one (S1) and switch two (S2) closed.**

The transistor is constructed so the emitter and collector are closer together than the emitter and the base. Once the emitter-base junction is reverse-biased (by closing S2), most of the holes injected into the emitter travel into and through the collector due to their velocity. The negative potential at the reverse-biased collector also attracts the positively-charged holes through the emitter-base junction.

In this example circuit, current flow through the collector is 19 times the current flow through the base. Thus, our transistor is said to have a current gain of 19:1.

Figure 7-37 shows an example circuit with S1 open and S2 closed. With S1 open, no holes are being injected into the base from the emitter. There are no holes that can be attracted into the collector by its negative potential. Additionally, the negative potential at the collector attracts the holes away from the base-collector junction. These conditions serve to increase the resistance across the base-collector junction to a high level. The net effect is that with S1 open no appreciable current can flow in the circuit. Thus, both ammeters (A1 and A2) read zero.

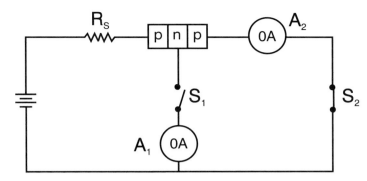

**7-37. A battery connected to a pnp transistor with switch one (S1) open and switch two (S2) closed.**

An npn bipolar transistor will operate exactly like the pnp transistor. The only difference is that in the npn transistor, electrons, not holes, will be the primary electrical carrier.

The important thing to remember about the bipolar transistor is that by controlling a small emitter-base current, a much larger emitter-collector current can be controlled. Bipolar transistors can either be used as *solid-state* (no moving parts) switches or as amplifiers.

Field-effect transistors (FETs) have recently become more important than bipolar transistors. The primary difference between these two types is that *field-effect transistors (FETs)* are voltage controlled. This allows an FET to control a large output current using a small input voltage and practically no input current. FETs are also used both as switches and as amplifiers.

There are two major families of FETs: junction field-effect transistors (JFETs) and insulated-gate field-effect transistors (IGFETs).

The body of a *junction field-effect transistor (JFET)* is a continuous length of one type (n-type or p-type) of semiconductor material. Two small sections of the other type of semiconductor material are placed on either side of the long section. These two small sections are electrically connected. If the body of the JFET is made of n-type material, the device is called an n-channel JFET. If the body of the FET is made of p-type material, the device is called a p-channel JFET.

The three terminals of a JFET are the source, gate, and drain (see Figure 7-38). If a voltage is placed across the source and drain terminals, the JFET will allow current to flow from the source to the drain, as shown in Figure 7-39 left. To stop current flow, a gate voltage (positive for p-channel devices, negative for n-channel devices) must be applied from the gate to the source. A small gate voltage will reduce current flow through the channel (Figure 7-39 center), while a larger voltage (called the cutoff

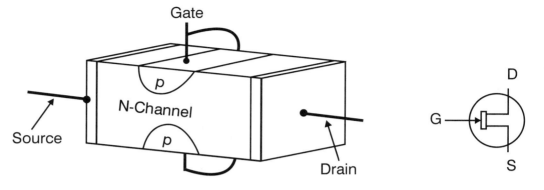

N-Channel/JFET construction

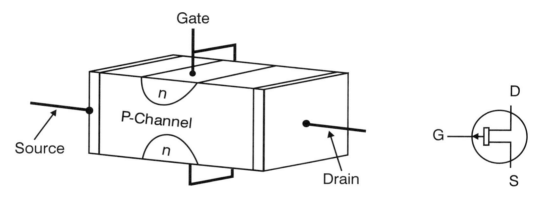

P-Channel/JFET construction

**7-38. The construction and schematic symbols for both n-channel and p-channel field-effect transistors.**

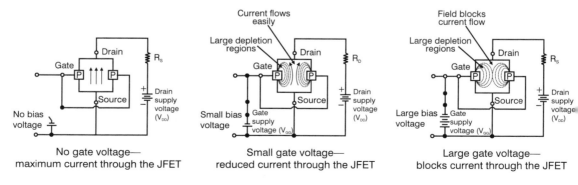

No gate voltage—
maximum current through the JFET

Small gate voltage—
reduced current through the JFET

Large gate voltage—
blocks current through the JFET

**7-39. Operation of an n-channel JFET.**

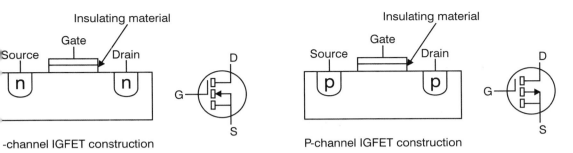

**7-40. The construction and schematic symbol for n-channel IGFET (left) and p-channel IGFET (right).**

voltage) will completely block current flow (Figure 7-39 right). This characteristic allows a JFET to be used as a voltage sensitive variable resistor.

In an ***insulated-gate field-effect transistor (IGFET)***, the gate is insulated by a glass-like layer of silicon-dioxide. Thus, the gate has no electrical contact with the source and the drain. Like a JFET, the body of the IGFET is a continuous length of one type of semiconductor material. Two small sections of the other type of semiconductor material are placed in the body of the IGFET. If these two small sections are made of n-type semiconductor material, the device is called an n-channel IGFET. If the sections are made of p-type semiconductor material, the device is called a p-channel IGFET.

To understand how an IGFET operates, take a closer look at an n-channel IGFET. When no voltage is applied to the IGFET's gate, no current flows between the source and the drain. A small gate voltage creates a thin n-channel in the p-type material allowing some current to flow from the source to the drain. As the gate voltage is increased, the n-channel becomes wider allowing more current to flow from the source to the drain. Thus, increasing the gate voltage effectively reduces the resistance through the n-channel and increases current through the device.

IGFETs are widely used in computers because of their low power requirements and high operating speeds. Also they are used as solid-state switches, amplifiers, and voltage-controlled variable resistors.

## Thyristors

***Thyristors*** are a class of semiconductor switching devices that have three leads. A small trigger current at one lead will allow a much larger current to flow through the other two leads. Once current flow is established, it will continue even when the trigger current is discontinued.

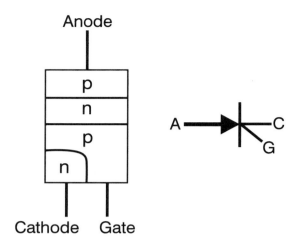

Anode

Cathode    Gate

**7-41. The construction of a silicon-controlled rectifiers (SCR) and its schematic symbol.**

There are two classes of thyristors: silicon-controlled rectifiers (SCRs) and bidirectional triode thyristors (TRIACs). *Silicon-controlled rectifiers (SCRs)* are solid-state switches that allow current flow in only one direction. *Bidirectional triode thyristors (TRIACs)* allow current flow in two directions.

An SCR is similar to the bipolar transistor, except for one important difference. The SCR is made of four layers of semiconducting material (as compared to three layers in the bipolar transistor). Thus, the SCR has three pn junctions.

When an SCR's anode is more positive than the cathode, the two outer pn junctions are forward-biased (Figure 7-42). However, current will not flow through the SCR because the middle pn junction is reverse-biased. A small current applied to the SCR's gate terminal forward-biases this middle pn junction, allowing current to flow through the SCR. The SCR will continue conducting once the gate current is no longer present, as long as the current through the device is greater than some minimum value (called the SCR's holding current). Once current flow through the SCR is interrupted (or reduced to below the holding current value), the SCR returns to its normally non-conducting state and no current will flow until the gate is triggered again.

SCRs are used in a variety of applications. Solid-state ignitions for automobiles and compact equipment items often contain SCRs. The speed

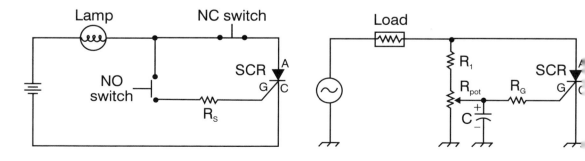

**7-42. Examples of SCR circuits. An SCR switching circuit (left) and an SCR power control circuit (right).**

of universal motors can be controlled using SCRs. SCRs are also used to switch high current DC electricity.

A TRIAC is a solid-state switch that will allow current to flow in two directions. They are widely used in AC circuits. A TRIAC is equivalent to two SCRs in parallel with the anode of one SCR connected to the cathode of the other SCR.

As seen in Figure 7-43, a TRIAC is a five layer (npnpn) sandwich with an additional n-type region. Each of the three terminals makes electrical contact with two adjacent layers. Note that the three terminals of the TRIAC are the gate, main terminal one (A1), and main terminal two (A2). Since a TRIAC can be used in an AC circuit (having a constantly changing polarity), the terms anode (denoting positive terminal) and cathode (denoting negative terminal) are not appropriate for a TRIAC. The TRIAC's gate terminal performs the same function as an SCR's gate, so the same name is used.

**7-43. The physical construction of and schematic symbol for a bidirectional triode thyristors (TRIAC).**

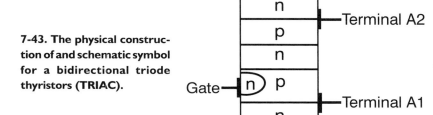

Normally a TRIAC will block current flow in both directions. However, a momentary electrical trigger pulse applied to its gate terminal will allow the TRIAC to conduct in either direction. When used in an AC circuit, the TRIAC will return to its normally non-conducting state during each electrical half-cycle as the current flow between the main terminals drops below the TRIAC's holding current value. At this point, another trigger pulse must be applied to the gate terminal to cause the TRIAC to conduct again.

TRIACs are used for a variety of purposes. A common application is in controlling the speed of AC motors. As shown in Figure 7-44A, an adjustable trigger circuit is used to control current flow to the TRIAC's gate terminal. The setting of the trigger circuit determines the point in each AC half-cycle at which the TRIAC begins to conduct and allow current flow to the motor. Allowing the TRIAC to begin conducting earlier in each half-cycle provides more current to the motor causing it to turn

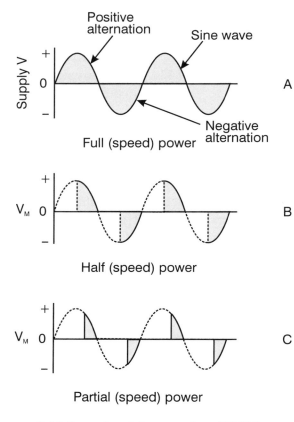

**7-44. Examples of the operation of TRIACs.**

faster Figure 7-44B). Blocking conduction through the TRIAC for a longer part of each half-cycle reduces current flow to the motor, causing it to turn slower (Figure 7-44C). (Note: This same principle also explains the operation of most AC light dimmers.)

# INTEGRATED CIRCUITS

An *integrated circuit (IC)* is a complete electronic circuit contained entirely on a single chip of silicon. A single IC may contain the equivalent of 250,000 individual components on a chip that is only one-quarter inch square! The primary advantages of ICs include smaller size, lower cost, and higher reliability.

The advent of integrated circuits in the late 1950s and their continued development has led to many of the compact electronic marvels we enjoy today. Personal and laptop computers, compact calculators, digital wrist watches, and hand-held video games are just a few of the products made possible by integrated circuit technology.

ICs can be grouped into two major categories. *Analog (linear) integrated circuits* produce, amplify or respond to continuous signals. A *continuous signal integrated circuit* is one that can vary between a range of values. Continuous signals usually represent physical variables, such as temperature, light intensity, sound, voltage, etc. Analog ICs include many different types of timers, amplifiers, voltage regulators, and oscillators (an electronic circuit that produces a sine wave output).

The second category of integrated circuits is the digital IC. *Digital integrated circuits* produce or respond to signals having only two voltage levels. A digital IC is either "on" or "off" depending on the voltage level supplied to it. Digital ICs form the heart of modern computers, with

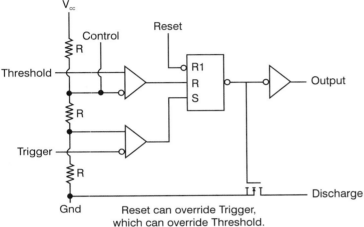

**7-45. An analog timer IC, as well as a block diagram showing the timer's internal circuitry.**

numbers and letters represented by the on-off status of groups of digital switches.

# READING ELECTRONICS SCHEMATICS

The ability to interpret and follow schematic drawings is needed to construct a wide variety of predesigned electronic circuits.

A *pictorial drawing* shows objects as they actually appear. Figure 7-46 is a pictorial drawing of an electrical circuit containing a battery, lamp and fixture, single-pole switch and conductors.

A *schematic drawing* shows objects using symbols. Figure 7-47 shows the previous circuit (Figure

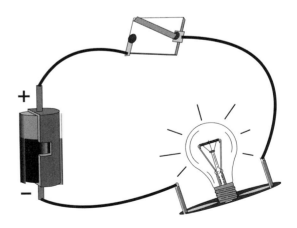

**7-46. A pictorial drawing of an electrical circuit.**

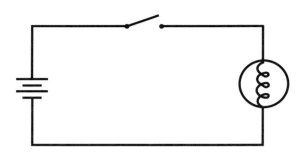

**7-47. A schematic drawing of the circuit depicted in Figure 7-46.**

7-46) represented as a schematic drawing.

Schematic drawings are used instead of pictorial drawings for several reasons. First, schematic symbols are generally easier and quicker to draw than actual objects. Second, the same electronic component made by two different manufacturers may not look exactly the same. This could cause confusion in constructing a circuit based on a pictorial drawing. Since a schematic symbol is not based on the appearance of an object, the potential for confusion is eliminated. Finally, many electronic circuits are made up of dozens or hundreds of individual components. The use of a schematic drawing allows complex circuits to be shown in a smaller diagram than would be possible with a pictorial drawing. Schematic drawings are relatively easy to interpret if a few key points are kept in mind. The placement of any given component in a schematic drawing does not necessarily correspond to that component's location in the actual circuit. The arrangement of the components in a schematic drawing is determined more by the clarity of the diagram than by actual construction details. In Figure 7-48, notice the difference in the location of components in the schematic drawing and in the actual circuit.

Straight lines are used in schematic drawings to represent wires and leads that connect electronic components. Whenever possible, schematics should be drawn so lines do not cross each other unless there is an

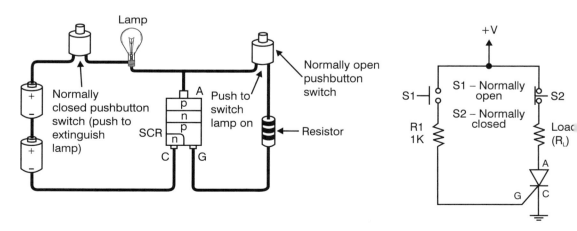

**7-48. A pictorial drawing (left) and the schematic drawing (right) for the same circuit.**

electrical connection between the wires. In complex schematic drawings, a few line crossings are unavoidable. To help avoid confusion in these situations, three systems are commonly used to show whether or not crossing lines represent electrical connections.

In the first system, a dot is used to indicate an electrical connection between two crossing lines. If no dot is present, there should be no electrical connection. Figure 7-49 illustrates this first system.

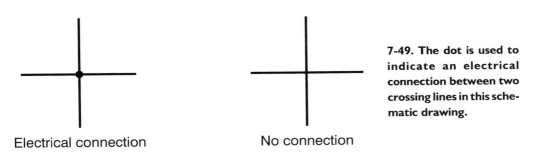

Electrical connection                      No connection

7-49. The dot is used to indicate an electrical connection between two crossing lines in this schematic drawing.

In the second system, it is assumed that the crossing of any two lines represents an electrical connection. If there is no electrical connection, a small loop is made in one of the lines at the point where it crosses the other line. This system is illustrated in Figure 7-50.

7-50. Crossing lines are used to indicate an electrical connection in this schematic drawing. A small loop is made at the intersection to indicate no electrical connection.

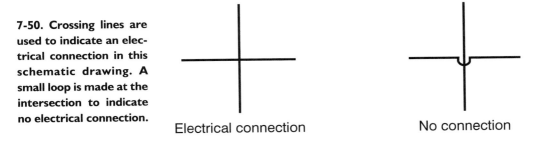

Electrical connection                      No connection

The third system is really a combination of the first two systems. If crossing lines represent an actual electrical connection, a dot is placed at the connection point (as in the first system). If the crossing lines do not represent an electrical connection, a small loop is made in one of the crossing lines (as in the second system). Figure 7-51 illustrates this system.

Sometimes an electronic schematic will have a key that explains the system used to deal with crossing lines. More often, careful study of the schematic is needed to determine which of these systems is being used.

Battery symbols can be confusing when first starting to work with schematic drawings. The schematic symbol for a battery is made from

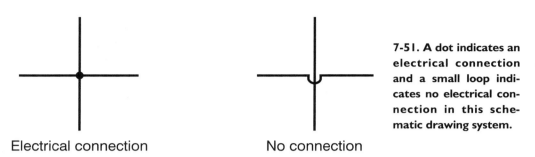

7-51. A dot indicates an electrical connection and a small loop indicates no electrical connection in this schematic drawing system.

Electrical connection                              No connection

either one or two pairs of long and short lines. In all cases, the short line represents the negative battery terminal and the long line represents the positive battery terminal. If only one pair of lines is used (Figure 7-52 left), the battery represented is a 1.5 volt battery. If two pairs of lines are used without any notation (Figure 7-52 center), the battery is a 3 volt battery. If two pairs of lines are used and a notation is present (Figure 7-52 right), the battery voltage is indicated by the notation.

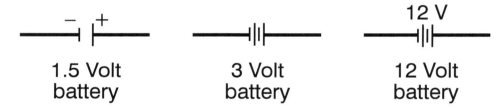

| 1.5 Volt battery | 3 Volt battery | 12 Volt battery |

7-52. The schematic symbol for a 1.5 volt and 3 volt battery, and for battery voltage indicated by a notation.

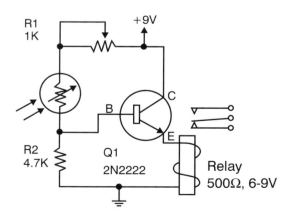

7-53. A light-activated relay circuit schematic.

In working with schematic drawings, be aware of how power supply output and ground terminals are represented. Examine the light-activated relay circuit schematic shown in Figure 7-53. The short arrow (at the top of the schematic) indicates the point where the positive side of the voltage source should be connected. The notation beside the arrow indicates the recommended voltage. The ground symbol (at the bottom of the schematic) indicates where the negative side of the voltage source should be connected.

# ASSEMBLING ELECTRONIC CIRCUITS

Several methods are used to assemble either temporary or permanent electronic circuits.

## *BREADBOARDING*

It is always a good idea to build a temporary version of any circuit before assembling it in permanent form. This allows you to verify that the circuit works and to experiment with potential circuit improvements.

Assembling a temporary circuit is called **breadboarding** because these circuits are usually assembled using a solderless modular breadboard. The breadboard has a number of plug-in sockets into which electronic components and connection wires can be inserted. Various sockets in the breadboard are electrically connected to each other so that circuit connections can be made quickly and easily.

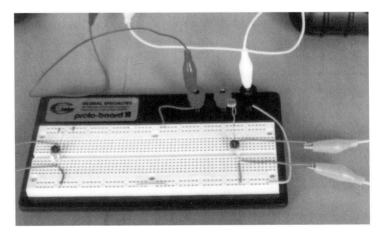

**7-54. A temporary circuit constructed using a breadboard.**

## *SOLDERING*

Most permanent circuit construction methods involve soldering. In **soldering,** a special metal alloy (solder) is melted over the connection point of two or more leads. This binds the leads together, providing a strong, reliable mechanical and electrical connection.

Several types of solder are used in electronics work. The most common type is called 60-40 solder. This means that the solder is 60 percent tin and 40 percent lead. 60-40 solder has a melting point of approximately 370°F. For electronics work, only rosin-core solder should be used. Acid-core

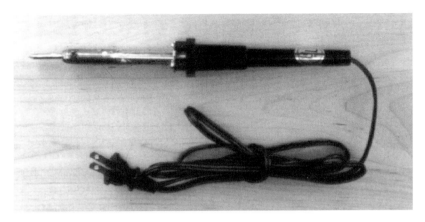

7-55. A soldering iron used to solder electronic components together.

solder, commonly used to join thin metals, is highly corrosive and should never be used to solder electronic circuits.

An electric soldering iron is used as the heat source for soldering. For electronic circuit assembly, use a low-power soldering iron rated at about 20 to 30 watts.

The ability to solder well is a skill that must be developed. This will require practice. The following points should be kept in mind.

- Solder does not adhere to dirty surfaces. Be sure to remove dirt, grease, oil, wax, and other foreign material from all components to be soldered. Steel wool, fine sandpaper, or solvent can be used to clean materials. If soldering to a printed circuit board, always buff the board's copper foil with steel wool before soldering.

- Keep the tip of the soldering iron clean by wiping off debris with a damp sponge.

- When soldering, heat the connection, not the solder. After the connection is hot, touch the solder to the connection, without removing the soldering iron, and allow the heated connection to melt the solder. Allow the solder to flow through and around the connection before removing the solder and the soldering iron.

- Allow a soldered connection to cool before moving. This will prevent damage to the connection.

- To prevent painful burns or the potential for a fire, never leave a soldering iron unattended when it is "on."

There are two major types of circuit boards onto which you can solder components when assembling a permanent circuit. These are the perforated circuit board (perf board) and the printed circuit (PC) board (Figure 7-56).

**7-56.** The perforated (perf board) circuit board (left) and printed (PC) circuit board (right).

A ***perforated board (perf board)*** is a nonconductive board with a regular pattern of holes (perforations) drilled through it. Component leads and short wires (called jumper wires) are placed through these holes and soldered together to form a permanent circuit. Perf boards are useful for constructing simple to moderately complex circuits.

A ***printed circuit (PC) board,*** like a perf board, is made of a nonconducting material and has a regular pattern of holes drilled through it. But, in addition, the PC board has copper traces on one (or occasionally both) side of the board that act as connecting wires between components. This makes circuit assembly quicker, easier, and neater.

Two types of PC boards are commonly available. Universal PC boards have a generalized pattern of copper traces and can be used to assemble a variety of circuits. A custom PC board is designed for use in assembling a specific circuit.

## WIRE WRAPPING

*Wire wrapping* is a permanent circuit assembly technique that does not involve soldering. A wire wrapped circuit is made by tightly wrapping a thin wire around a square post. The edges of the post bite into the wire, making a connection that is both mechanically and electrically sound. The components in a wire wrapped circuit are placed in special sockets with attached leads. To connect the component into the circuit, these leads are wrapped around the binding posts. Wire wrapping is primarily used to assemble circuits containing several integrated circuits.

# SUMMARY

The operation and use of non-semiconductor components, such as resistors, potentiometers, photo resistors, thermistors, capacitors, and inductors are important in many agricultural activities. The principles of capacitance and inductance are a part of these activities.

Basic operating theory of semiconductors is important in understanding electronics. Elements having four valence electrons are doped with other elements to produce both p-type and n-type semiconductor materials. Different types of semiconductor components, such as diodes and transistors, are used in various ways.

Integrated circuits (ICs) are important in the modern electronics industry. Analog ICs respond to or produce continuous electrical signals and are used in instrumentation and control circuits. Digital ICs only respond to two voltage levels and are widely used in computer circuits.

The ability to both interpret and produce schematic drawings is essential in understanding electronics. Knowing various circuit assembly methods, such as breadboarding, soldering, and wire wrapping, is especially important in agriculture.

# REVIEW QUESTIONS

1. Define "electronics" and identify five different agricultural machines or processes that rely on electronics.

2. Determine the resistance rating and the tolerance for the resistor shown below.

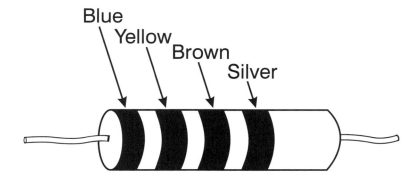

3. An electronic component with a maximum forward current ($I_F$) rating of 75 mA is to be powered by a 6 volt battery. What size series resistor should be used to limit current flow through the component to a safe level? (Note: Assume the resistance of the electronic component is .10 ohm.)

4. Describe the construction of a capacitor. Explain the effects of adding a capacitor to a DC circuit and to an AC circuit.

5. Define inductance. Explain the effects of adding an inductor to a DC circuit and to an AC circuit.

6. Describe the process of producing p-type and n-type silicon crystals.

7. Define "anode" and "cathode."

8. List three different types of diodes, draw the schematic symbol for each, and describe a typical use for each.

9. Describe the physical construction of npn and pnp bipolar transistors.

10. What is the primary difference in the operation of a bipolar transistor and a field-effect transistor?

11. Describe the two classes of thyristors and explain how they differ in construction and in use.

12. Define the term "integrated circuit" and describe the two major categories of integrated circuits.

13. Explain the difference between a pictorial drawing of a circuit and a schematic drawing.

14. Describe three common methods of assembling electronic circuits.

# APPLYING THE CONCEPTS

1. Construct the light intensity metering circuit shown below. Use the device to determine the relative light intensity at various locations, as directed by your instructor. Also, explain the basis for the operation of this circuit.

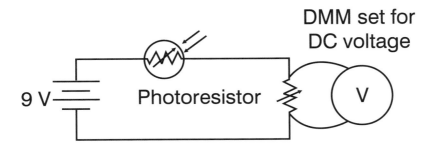

2. Construct the same circuit as in #1, except replace the photoresistor with a thermistor. Use this device to measure the relative temperature of various locations and/or objects. Explain the basis for the operation of this circuit.

3. Construct the circuit shown below. Close the switch and then open it, observing the light. Describe what happens and explain why it happens. If one is available, replace the light with a small piezoelectric buzzer, and repeat this activity.

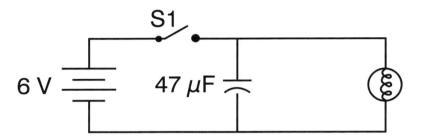

4. Construct both of the circuits shown below. Record the voltmeter reading for each, and explain your results.

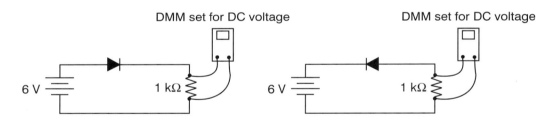

5. Construct the circuit shown in Figure 7-31, using a 6 volt zener diode. Size the series resistor to limit current flow through the zener diode to a safe level (use Ohm's Law). Use a variable voltage (0-15V) DC power source to vary the source voltage between 0 and 15 volts in 3 volt increments. At each setting, read and record the voltage at the meter. Explain your results in a written or oral report.

6. Construct the circuit shown on the left in Figure 7-42, using a 6 volt battery as the power source and a 6.3 volt lamp as the load. Size the series resistor to limit SCR gate current ($I_{GT}$) to below the maximum specified level. Test the assembled circuit. Depressing the NO switch should cause the lamp to glow. Depressing the NC switch should cause the lamp to go off. Explain the operation of the circuit.

# 8

# HOW INTERNAL COMBUSTION ENGINES OPERATE

The agricultural industry depends on efficient sources of power to produce food, fiber, horticultural, and forestry products. Power is used to mow grass, pump water, plow land, harvest crops, process foods, and transport products.

Power comes from many sources and is used by many different kinds of devices. The development and use of power has been a cornerstone for the advancement of agriculture.

Considerable investment has been made in sources of power. Tractors and implements use internal combustion engines. Knowing how engines operate helps use them efficiently.

8-1. Internal combustion engines are used to power agricultural equipment and machinery, such as the combine shown here.

# OBJECTIVES

This chapter provides information about the basic principles of engine operation. After completing this chapter, you will:

1. Provide three basic descriptions for internal combustion engines.

2. Describe the four events of the internal combustion engine cycle.

3. Explain the operation of the four-stroke cycle internal combustion engine.

4. Explain the operation of the two-stroke cycle internal combustion engine.

5. Compare four- and two-stroke cycle engines.

6. Compare spark-ignition and compression-ignition engines.

7. Describe internal combustion engine systems.

8. Classify internal combustion engines.

9. Describe the first and second laws of thermodynamics as related to engine operation.

10. Describe Boyle's Law and how it relates to engine operation.

11. Describe the Law of Charles and Gay-Lussac and how it relates to engine operation.

**T E R M S**

battery ignition system
bottom dead center (BDC)
BTU (British Thermal Unit)
Boyle's Law
combustion
compression
compression ignition engine
compression ratio
cycle
engine
engine displacement
engine timing
exhaust
firing order
governor
ignition timing
intake
internal combustion engine
Law of Charles and
    Gay-Lussac
lubrication system
magneto ignition system
motor
power
scavenging
spark ignition engine
stroke
thermodynamics
top dead center (TDC)

# AGRICULTURAL POWER

Agriculture has been a function of society for about ten thousand years. Prior to developing agriculture, we existed as hunters and gatherers. From the beginning, agriculture involved hand labor and the use of tools and power.

The first tools were operated by hand—sticks to punch holes in the soil to plant seeds. Technological developments resulted in new power sources that decreased physical labor and increased crop production.

**8-2. A tractor from about four decades ago (left) and a current model (right).**

Alternative power sources were developed. Animal, wind, and water power performed tasks. These have now mostly been replaced by the internal combustion engine.

The internal combustion engine was not developed exclusively for agriculture. Its initial development was more directly related to the transportation industry. The internal combustion engine was not the first form of combustion engine used by agriculture. The external combustion (steam) engine was used first. However the relative advantages of the internal combustion engine led to its predominance in agriculture.

To be a knowledgeable and an effective user of agricultural power, it is necessary to understand the basic principles that allow internal combustion engines to operate and function.

8-3. A large engine (left) used to power machinery and a small engine on a log splitter (right).

# THE ENGINE

Engines are described in three ways: power production, combustion, and internal processes.

## POWER PRODUCTION

An *engine* is a device or machine that can produce power on its own—independent of an external source of energy. An engine has an energy source (fuel) and converts the fuel to useable power. The power produced is usually in the form of mechanical power.

How is an engine different from a motor? Generally, a *motor* is considered to be a device or machine that produces power from the energy supplied by an external source. For example, an electric motor takes the electrical power produced somewhere else, like a generator, and then converts it to mechanical power.

## COMBUSTION

*Combustion* is the chemical process of oxidation that produces heat. The combustion process requires three things: fuel, air (oxygen) and heat. A more technical definition of combustion is the rapid oxidation of carbon, hydrogen, and carbohydrates. An internal combustion engine uses the process of rapid combustion to operate. Sufficient heat must be produced from the combustion process to produce useable power.

A basic formula for the combustion of carbon is:

Carbon + Oxygen → Carbon dioxide + Heat

$$C + O_2 \rightarrow CO_2 + Heat$$

Carbon is combined with a molecule of oxygen, which produces carbon dioxide and heat energy. Heat energy is measured as BTUs (US system) and joules (SI system). A ***BTU (British Thermal Unit)*** is the unit of heat needed to raise the temperature of 1 pound of water 1°F. The amount of heat produced per gram of carbon is 31 BTUs or 32.8 kiloJoules (kJ). One BTU is equal to 1055 joules or 1.055 kiloJoules. One kiloJoule is equal to 1000 joules.

The basic formula for the combustion of diesel fuel, where the cetane molecule ($C_{16}H_{34}$) represents the diesel fuel is:

Diesel fuel + Oxygen → Carbon dioxide + Water + Heat

$$C_{16}H_{34} + 24.5\ O_2 \rightarrow 16CO_2 + 17H_2O + Heat$$

The cetane molecule combines with oxygen molecules to produce carbon dioxide, water, and heat. One gallon of No. 2 diesel fuel (48 cetane)

**8-4. A diesel engine is often used to power large agricultural machinery.**

produces 138,750 BTUs of heat. In atmospheric conditions, the diesel fuel combustion process involves nitrogen from the air as a somewhat inert component of the combustion process.

## *INTERNAL PROCESSES*

Internal means that the combustion occurs in an enclosed chamber. The heat produced is converted to mechanical power. An ***internal combustion engine*** is a machine or device that is capable of converting heat energy into mechanical power. The mechanical power produced is usually in the form of a rotating force.

An external combustion engine uses combustion to produce power. The heat energy is transferred from combustion energy to external devices where it is converted to mechanical power. A steam engine is an example of an external combustion engine. The fuel is burned in a chamber, the heat energy is transferred to water, and the water is converted to steam. The energy of the boiling water produces power, by the expansion of gaseous water (steam), that is converted by the engine into mechanical power.

# ENGINE CYCLES

Internal combustion engines operate based upon the principle of a cycle, which is repeated over and over again. A ***cycle*** is considered to be a series of events that recur regularly.

Internal combustion engines operate based upon a series of events. These events must happen in a cycle and must occur in the same sequence. The four basic events of an internal combustion engine that uses gasoline as a fuel are:

1. *Intake*—the process of getting the fuel and air required for combustion into the combustion chamber.

2. *Compression*—the process of compressing the fuel and air mixture in the combustion chamber to increase the potential chemical energy of the heat from combustion.

3. *Power*—the result of converting the chemical potential energy to mechanical power by the rapid expansion of heated gases, which

are produced by the combustion of the compressed fuel and air mixture in the combustion chamber.

4. *Exhaust*—the process of removing spent products of combustion from the combustion chamber.

These four basic events make up an internal combustion engine cycle. They must occur in the proper sequence and at the proper time. **Engine timing** refers to the proper timing and sequencing of these events. Once a cycle has been completed, another cycle begins immediately. In a multiple-cylinder engine, each cylinder is going through the same series of events. However, the cycles are occurring in sequence to balance the engine operation. This sequence is commonly referred to as the **firing order**.

## PRINCIPLES OF OPERATION OF THE FOUR-STROKE CYCLE INTERNAL COMBUSTION ENGINE

The four-stroke cycle internal combustion engine is a type of piston, or reciprocating, engine. The piston moves up or down in the cylinder. This back and forth, linear motion is converted to circular or rotary motion by the crankshaft. The crankshaft works much the same way as a person

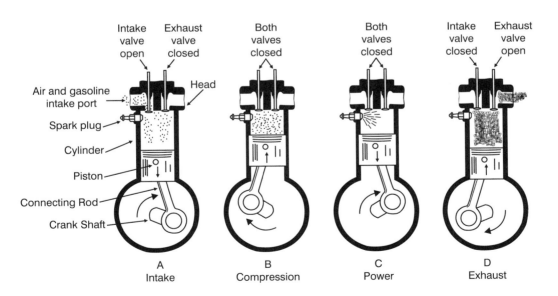

8-5. A four-stroke cycle internal combustion gasoline engine.

pedaling a bicycle. The up and down movement of the person's legs is converted to rotary movement of the bicycle wheels. The basic principles of operation of the four-stroke cycle engine should be clearly understood.

As the pistons move back and forth, the movement in one direction is called a *stroke*. When the piston reaches the top of its stroke or has minimized the volume of the combustion chamber, it is at ***top dead center (TDC)***. When the piston has reached the bottom of the stroke or has maximized the cylinder volume, this is ***bottom dead center (BDC)***. The four-stroke cycle engine uses four piston strokes to complete one engine cycle.

### Intake

The first stroke of the cycle is the intake stroke. The piston moves down increasing the volume of the combustion chamber. The stroke creates a partial vacuum in the combustion chamber that allows air (in a diesel engine) or air-fuel mixture (in a gasoline engine) to be pushed into the cylinder. The air (or air-fuel mixture) comes in through the intake system. The intake valve is open during the intake stroke. Once the piston reaches the end of the intake stroke, the intake valve closes and the intake stroke is completed.

### Compression

The second stroke is the compression stroke. The purpose of the compression stroke is to compress the contents of the combustion chamber. Diesel engines compress only air on the compression stroke. Gasoline engines compress an air-fuel mixture. The relative degree that the air and/or air-fuel mix is compressed is referred to as the ***compression ratio***. During the compression stroke, the engine valves, piston rings, cylinder wall, cylinder head, and head gasket must maintain a seal capable of holding in excess of 1,000 psi combustion pressure.

### Power

The third stroke of the cycle is the power stroke. As the piston reaches the TDC position, the air-fuel mixture in the combustion chamber is ignited. In a gasoline engine, the air-fuel mixture is ignited by an electrical spark from the spark plug. In a diesel engine, atomized diesel fuel injected into the combustion chamber is ignited due to the heat of the compressed air. The rapid combustion, or controlled explosion, forces the piston down. The power stroke converts the rapid expansion of combustion into linear mechanical energy. This action is result of the basic principles of thermodynamics. As with the compression stroke, both the intake and exhaust valves must remain closed and sealed tight during the power stroke.

### Exhaust

The fourth and final stroke of the cycle is the exhaust stroke. The purpose of the exhaust stroke is to remove the burned air-fuel mixture so a fresh charge of air and fuel can be brought into the combustion chamber. During the exhaust stroke, the exhaust valve opens and, as the piston moves up, the exhaust gases are forced out through the exhaust system. The process of removing the exhaust gases is called *scavenging*. For an engine to operate efficiently, the exhaust must be scavenged as completely as possible.

At the end of the exhaust stroke, the piston is at TDC, and a new engine cycle begins. It is important to keep in mind that a complete cycle of the four-stroke cycle engine happens in a very short period of time. As an example, if a single cylinder engine is operating at a speed of 3000 revolutions per minute (rpm), the engine is operating at 50 revolutions per second. Therefore, the engine is completing 25 cycles per second and each piston stroke is taking 1/100 of a second to complete.

## THE TWO-STROKE CYCLE
## INTERNAL COMBUSTION ENGINE

The two-stroke cycle internal combustion engine is also widely used in the agricultural industry. The two-stroke cycle engine is also a piston- or reciprocating-type internal combustion engine. It completes the same four engine cycle events as does the four-stroke cycle engine—intake, compression power, and exhaust. However, the two-stroke cycle engine completes these events in two piston strokes. Generally, the operation of the two-stroke cycle engine is somewhat more difficult to understand, because more than one engine cycle event is occurring at the same time.

The two-stroke cycle engine operates on the principle of using the movement of both ends of the piston to create compression and a partial vacuum. The top of the piston is used to operate and create the combustion

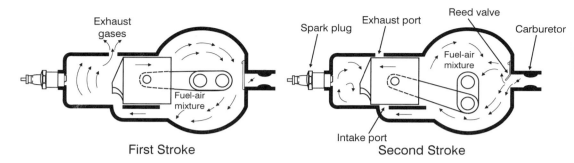

First Stroke                                             Second Stroke

**8-6. A two-stroke internal combustion engine.**

chamber in the cylinder. The bottom of the piston is used to draw the air-fuel mixture into the engine and force it into the combustion chamber.

There are several different designs of two-stroke cycle engines. To better understand the basic principles of operation, we will use one of the more basic designs.

The first stroke of the two-stroke cycle engine we will consider is the piston's movement downward—from TDC to BDC. Notice in the diagram that ignition occurred at TDC and the piston is being driven down. The combustion gases are expanding rapidly. Also, the piston on its way down passes the exhaust port opening in the cylinder wall. This allows the exhaust gases to be removed from the combustion chamber. In addition, the piston moves below the intake ports on the other side of the cylinder, opening the way for the air-fuel mixture to enter the combustion chamber. The air-fuel mixture is forced into the cylinder by the movement of the piston down into a sealed crankcase, which contains the air-fuel mixture. The movement of the air-fuel mixture across the cylinder helps to scavenge the exhaust from the combustion chamber.

The second stroke of the two-stroke cycle engine occurs as the piston changes direction and moves from BDC to TDC. Notice, as the piston moves up, it closes the intake and exhaust ports. This allows the piston to compress the air-fuel mixture for combustion. Also note, that as the piston moves up, a partial vacuum occurs in the crankcase. This allows the air-fuel mixture to enter the crankcase through a type of one-way directional valve. Reed valves are a common type of one-way valve found on two-stroke cycle engines. Once the piston reaches TDC, the air-fuel mixture is ignited and the piston is forced down. The one-way valves in the crankcase then close trapping the air-fuel mixture in the crankcase. At this point, one two-stroke cycle has been completed and the process is repeated.

Two-stroke cycle engines are commonly used in agriculture for small engine applications. However, two-stroke cycle engines can also be rather large. Also, most two-stroke cycle engines used in agriculture operate on gasoline; however, two-stroke cycle diesel engines are available.

## COMPARING FOUR- AND TWO-STROKE CYCLE ENGINES

The four-stroke and two-stroke cycle internal combustion engines have specific characteristics that allow both to be practical for different applications in agriculture. Figure 8-7 provides an overview of some of the basic characteristics of each.

Generally, the four-stroke cycle engine operates more quietly, is heavier, has a longer life, and is cleaner burning than a two-stroke cycle engine. However, the two-stroke cycle engine is lighter, can be operated in a wider range of positions, has fewer moving parts, and is more applicable to smaller jobs.

**8-7. Characteristics of four-stroke and two-stroke cycle engines.**

| Two-Stroke Cycle Engines | Four-Stroke Cycle Engines |
|---|---|
| Lighter weight | Heavier weight |
| Operates in many positions | Operates in limited positions |
| Higher power to weight ratio | Lower power to weight ratio |
| Engine oil usually mixed with fuel | Engine oil in a reservoir |
| Louder operation | Quieter operation |
| Higher engine speeds | Slower engine speeds |
| More vibration | Smoother operation |
| Rough idling operation | Smoother Idling operation |

## ROTARY INTERNAL COMBUSTION ENGINES

Piston- or reciprocating-type engines are the most common type used in agriculture. Rotary-type engines are found in other applications, such as the transportation industry. The turbine engine is an example of a rotary engine and a specific example is the jet engine. Another type of rotary engine is the rotary-cycle internal combustion engine or Wankel engine. This engine uses an internal rotor, which turns inside the engine housing. Rotary engines also complete the same basic engine cycle of intake, compression, power, and exhaust as do piston-type engines.

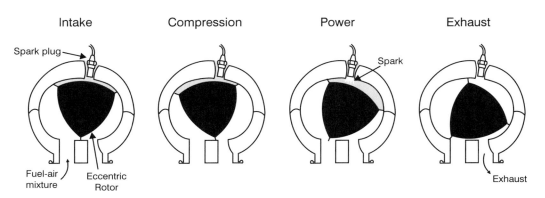

**8-8. A rotary internal combustion engine.**

Radial piston engines should not be confused with rotary engines. Radial piston engines use pistons that are located around an axis. The pistons move in a back and forth motion as with other piston type engines. Some aircraft engines are radial piston engines. In agriculture, some crop dusting airplanes use radial piston engines.

# FUEL SOURCES: COMPARING GASOLINE AND DIESEL ENGINES

Gasoline and diesel powered internal combustion engines are widely use in agriculture. Both gasoline and diesel engines can be found as single and multiple cylinder engines. Gasoline or diesel powered engines can be either two- or four-stroke cycle engines. However, two-stroke cycle diesel engines are somewhat uncommon in agriculture. A comparison of gasoline and diesel powered engines is presented in Figure 8-9.

Gasoline, or spark-ignition, engines are easier to start (especially in cold conditions), better accelerating, and generally operate at higher speeds (rpm) than diesel engines. Diesel, or compression-ignition, engines are more fuel efficient, have a longer life, are heavier, and are designed for "lugging" power and for larger jobs. Therefore, as an agriculturalist, you need to understand how both gasoline and diesel engines operate, and how to maintain them.

| Spark Ignition (Otto Cycle) Engines | Compression Ignition (Diesel Cycle) Engines |
| --- | --- |
| Lighter weight components | Heavier weight components |
| Lower compression ratios | Higher compression ratios |
| Easier starting | More difficult starting |
| Lower fuel efficiency | Higher fuel efficiency |
| Quicker speed acceleration | Slower speed acceleration |
| Higher engine speeds | Slower engine speeds |
| Lower engine torque | Higher engine torque |

**8-9. A comparison of spark ignition and compression ignition engines.**

# ENGINE SYSTEMS

Internal combustion engines are complex machines that perform a series of different events simultaneously in a relatively short period of time. An engine can be described as a technological system. It operates based upon several principles of the physical sciences and uses a series of operating systems to produce mechanical power. Each of these engine systems performs its own tasks, however all of the systems must be synchronized for the engine to perform properly. If one system performs poorly, or fails, then all the other engine systems will be affected. Many times when one system begins to operate poorly, another system will have to work harder for the engine to operate. Some engine systems are so vital to proper engine operation that if they fail, the engine will stop running immediately. For an engine to operate at its full potential, all of its systems must operate at their full potential.

## COMPRESSION SYSTEM

The primary purpose of this system is to efficiently compress the air to increase the potential energy resulting from the combustion of the fuel. The compression system of the conventional internal combustion engine uses pistons that move up and down in a cylinder. The piston and cylinder must form a leak-proof combustion chamber for the engine to operate. The air tightness of the combustion chamber is a major design feature for internal combustion engines. If the compression system loses compression, the engine will not operate properly.

8-10. An example of internal combustion engine systems.

## INTAKE SYSTEM

The purpose of the air intake system is to allow clean air to efficiently enter the combustion chamber. Air is composed of approximately 20 to 25 percent oxygen. Oxygen is required for combustion. The air intake system cleans dirt particles from the air without causing a significant restriction to the free flow of the air, which would decrease engine power output.

## FUEL SYSTEMS

The fuel system is designed to deliver clean fuel to the combustion chamber and meter the amount of fuel necessary for efficient operation. The fuel needs to be delivered at the correct time and in the best proportion with the air for the engine to operate properly. There are a variety of fuel systems and components to meet the needs of different kinds of engines, fuels, and applications. However, all fuel systems operate based upon the same basic principles.

## EXHAUST SYSTEMS

The exhaust system performs the task of removing the burned gases from the combustion chamber. The exhaust system also helps with engine noise reduction and heat transfer. In recent years the exhaust system has been designed to help control engine emissions, which could damage the environment.

## COOLING SYSTEMS

Engine cooling systems are designed to manage the heat produced by the combustion of the air and fuel. Every engine has an optimal operating temperature. The task of the cooling system is to allow the engine to reach the optimal temperature and then maintain this temperature under varying conditions.

There are two basic kinds of cooling systems: liquid cooling and air direct cooling. The liquid cooling system uses a liquid to transfer heat from the engine components. The air direct system transfers the heat from the engine components directly to the surrounding air. Both cooling systems require clean air to operate efficiently. These cooling systems operate based upon the basic principles of heat transfer.

## IGNITION SYSTEMS

Ignition systems are designed to ignite the air and fuel mixture in the combustion chamber. Spark ignition engines use an electrical spark to ignite the air and fuel mixture. Compression ignition engines use the heat of compression to ignite the air-fuel mixture. Whereas spark ignition engines have an ignition system, generally, compression ignition engines do not. However, compression ignition engines may use starting aids, such as glow plugs.

Spark ignition systems create an electrical spark in the combustion chamber at the end of the compression stroke. With correct ***ignition timing***, the ignition spark occurs at the precise moment to insure the most complete and efficient combustion of the air-fuel mixture. The electrical spark may be generated from a magnetic field created by magnets. This system is called a ***magneto ignition system***. A ***battery ignition system*** uses the energy from a battery or charging system to create the spark. If the battery is not kept charged during operation, the ignition system will eventually fail. That is why a battery charging system is needed to recharge the battery. Since batteries can only store direct current (DC) electricity, battery ignition systems operate as DC electrical systems. Ignition systems may also operate as electronic ignition systems. Solid state ignition systems are examples of electronic ignition systems. These systems are being used on newer ignition systems.

## LUBRICATION SYSTEMS

Internal combustion engines need lubricants to keep engine parts operating smoothly. The engine uses a *lubrication system* to keep the engine parts lubricated to reduce friction, remove heat, keep engine parts clean, and provide tight seals on various engine parts to keep dirt out, and compression pressure in. The lubrication system is designed to maintain the optimum amount of engine oil lubricant on various parts. A system of passageways, filters, pump(s), reservoirs, and coolers are often used in modern internal combustion engines. Even small engines have lubrication systems, though they may not be as complex as the systems used on larger engines.

## GOVERNING SYSTEMS

Many internal combustion engines used in agriculture include a governing system to maintain the operating speed of the engine. The *governor* keeps the engine operating at the same speed under varying loads by increasing or decreasing the amount of fuel supplied to the engine. If the load on the engine increases, the governing system will increase the fuel to keep pace. As the load decreases, the governing system will decrease the amount of fuel. Governing systems may be mechanical, pneumatic, or electronic systems.

## STARTING SYSTEMS

All internal combustion engines require some type of system to start. Some small engines use a manual operation system, such a recoil rope starter, which the operator pulls. Most larger engines use an electrical starting system, which uses an electrical motor to start the engine. A few engines use other starting systems, such as another internal combustion engine, sometimes called a "pony motor" or compressed air.

## OTHER INTERNAL COMBUSTION ENGINE SYSTEMS

There may be other internal combustion engine systems, which you may come in contact with. These systems often complement the other systems of the engine. An example is an exhaust gas recirculation system. This system helps the engine to operate more cleanly, putting less pollution in the atmosphere. Another example would be the turbocharger system, which uses the exhaust gases to drive an air pump or turbine which increases the amount of air flowing through the intake system.

# CLASSIFICATIONS OF INTERNAL COMBUSTION ENGINES

There are many ways by which we classify or describe internal combustion engines. Some classifications are basic; others may be somewhat technical or more difficult to describe.

## NUMBER OF PISTON STROKES PER CYCLE

For many years, internal combustion engines have been classified as either "two-stroke" or "four-stroke." As previously described, this method of classification refers to the number of piston strokes required to complete the engine cycle.

8-11. A two-stroke engine (left) and a four-stroke engine (right).

8-12. A small engine (left) has less than 25 horsepower. A large engine (right) has 25 or more horesepower.

## ENGINE POWER

A common way to classify or describe internal combustion engines is by the amount of power the engine is capable of producing. When classifying engines by power output, a common classification is to consider those producing less than 25 horsepower as small engines. Those producing 25 or more horsepower are considered large engines.

## NUMBER OF CYLINDERS

Another way to describe engines is by the number of cylinders. The internal combustion engine cylinder is the round tube in which the sealed piston travels back and forth. Single-cylinder engines have only one cylinder, while multi-cylinder engines may have 2, 3, 4, 5, 6, 8, or more cylinders.

8-13. A single cylinder engine (left) and a multiple cylinder engine (right).

## ENGINE DISPLACEMENT

Another method of describing internal combustion engines is to refer to the displacement of the engine. The term ***engine displacement*** describes the total swept volume of the engine cylinders as the pistons complete one stroke. Engine displacement is expressed as either cubic inches or cubic centimeters. The equation for calculating engine displacement is shown in Formula 8-1.

$$ED = \frac{\pi(B^2)}{4}(S)(N)$$   **Formula 8-1.**

where,

$\quad$ ED $=$ Engine Displacement

$\quad\quad \pi = 3.1416$

$\quad\quad$ B $=$ Bore of cylinder

$\quad\quad$ S $=$ Stroke

$\quad\quad$ N $=$ Number of cylinders

As an example, assume that a single cylinder engine has the following measurements:

$\quad$ 4" Bore (cylinder diameter)

$\quad$ 4" Stroke (length of piston travel or stroke)

The engine displacement is calculated as follows:

$$ED = \frac{\pi(B^2)}{4}(S)(N)$$

$$= \frac{3.14(4^2)}{4}(4)(1)$$

$$= 50.2 \text{ in}^3$$

Piston displacement is the swept volume in a cylinder during one stroke of the piston. In the above example, the engine displacement and piston displacement are equal.

**298**

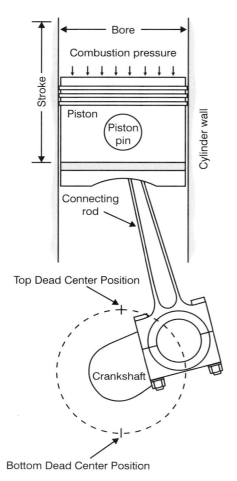

**8-14. The bore and stroke of a single engine cylinder.**

# CYLINDER ARRANGEMENT

Internal combustion engines are also classified by their cylinder arrangements. There are two common cylinder arrangements found on multi-cylinder internal combustion engines. In-line means all of the cylinders are arranged in a straight line. A V engine means the cylinders are arranged into banks that form a "V" configuration. A 90-degree, "V" engine indicates that the two banks of cylinders form a 90-degree angle and they operate off of the same crankshaft.

There are other cylinder arrangements for multi-cylinder engines. Radial cylinder arrangements are found on some multi-cylinder engines used in special applications, such as crop dusting aircraft. Flat cylinder arrangement refers to the cylinders being perpendicular, or flat, in relation to the surface of the earth. While not very common, a few multi-cylinder engines used in agriculture are flat.

Single cylinder engines are classified based upon the position of the crankshaft in relationship to the surface of the earth, either vertical or horizonal. A vertical crankshaft single cylinder engine means the crankshaft is straight up and down in relation to the surface of the earth. A hori-

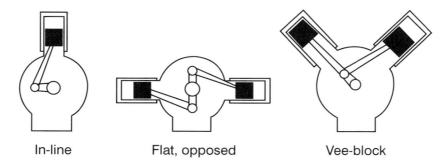

**8-15. Cylinder arrangements found on internal combustion engines.**

zonal crankshaft single cylinder engine means the crankshaft is perpendicular to the surface of the earth. Both are very common in four-stroke cycle single cylinder engines used in agriculture. Two-stroke cycle engines can be designed to be used in a variety of positions, so this classification is only used in reference to four-stroke cycle engines.

## FUEL IGNITION AND COMBUSTION

Internal combustion engines are also classified by the type of fuel used and the way in which the fuel is ignited. Engines are described as being gasoline powered, diesel powered, or by some other type of fuel. Engineers and mechanics will refer to engines as being Otto-cycle engines or Diesel-cycle engines. Both of these types of engines were developed in Germany in the latter part of the nineteenth century and named for their respective inventors. The Otto-cycle engine is also commonly called a spark ignition engine. A *spark ignition engine* uses an electrical spark to ignite the fuel. The air-fuel mixture is drawn into the combustion chamber, compressed and then ignited by an electrical spark. Gasoline engines are considered spark ignition. The Diesel-cycle engine is commonly called a *compression ignition engine*. Many engines used in agriculture are classified as compression ignition. The heat generated from the compression of the air in the combustion chamber produces enough heat for the fuel to burn. In Diesel-cycle engines, only air enters the combustion chamber on the intake stroke, the air is compressed, which heats the air, and fuel is injected into the combustion chamber where the air and fuel mixture ignites due to the heat of compression.

# THERMODYNAMICS

Internal combustion engines operate because the air-fuel mixture is burned in a controlled manner. The chemical energy is converted to mechanical energy. This conversion is based upon the principles of thermodynamics.

*Thermodynamics* is the field of physics dealing with the mechanical action or movement of heat. The fuels used to operate internal combustion engines have the chemical properties to produce a great deal of heat. Internal combustion engines are designed to convert as much of that heat as possible into useable mechanical energy.

The first law of thermodynamics states that "Energy cannot be created or destroyed, but may be converted from one form to another, as from work into heat. However, the total energy in the universe is constant." The first law of thermodynamics is the same as the law of conservation of energy. According to this first law of thermodynamics, the energy level in a closed system remains constant, but the forms in which it appears change. All of the energy in the air-fuel mixture must be accounted for. Some is converted to mechanical energy for work, some is used by the engine to run, and most of the energy is lost as heat.

The second law of thermodynamics states that "heat cannot be converted completely into work." Basically, this law means that internal combustion engines lose energy as the transfer of heat to the surrounding air. The more heat loss, the less efficient the engine.

The second law of thermodynamics can be expressed as the equation:

$$Q_1 = Q_2 + W$$    | **Formula 8-2.** |

where,

$Q_1$ = heat input
$Q_2$ = heat output
$W$ = work done

The heat from the combustion process is used either to produce work or is lost as heat energy.

# PRINCIPLES OF ENGINE OPERATION—BOYLE'S LAW

In 1662, English scientist Robert Boyle discovered that the pressure a gas exerts can be increased by reducing its volume while holding the temperature constant. According to **Boyle's Law**, when a volume of a gas is decreased, the gas molecules bombard the container walls more frequently. This bombardment increases the pressure. In the engine cylinder, as the piston moves towards TDC of the compression stroke, the volume gets smaller and the pressure increases. The cylinder pressure may be 300 to 500 pounds per square inch (psi). The volume of a gas is inversely proportional to the pressure applied to the gas. Boyle's Law is expressed by the formula:

$$P_1 \times V_1 = P_2 \times V_2$$    | **Formula 8-3.** |

where:

$P_1$ = original pressure of a gas
$V_1$ = original volume of a gas
$P_2$ = pressure of a gas under new condition
$V_2$ = volume of a gas under new condition

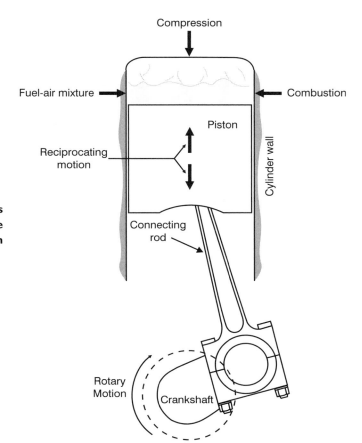

**8-16. The air and fuel mixture is compressed, increasing the pressure in the cylinder of an internal combustion engine.**

As an example, if an engine has a compression ratio of 10:1, the volume of the combustion chamber when the piston is at BDC is ten times greater then the volume of the combustion chamber when the piston is at TDC. If the air pressure in the 100 cubic inch volume cylinder is 15 psi at BDC and the air in the cylinder is compressed to a volume of 10 cubic inches at TDC, the pressure would rise to 150 psi.

$$P_1 \times V_1 = P_2 \times V_2$$
$$P_2 = (P_1 \times V_1) / V_2$$
$$P_2 = (15 \text{ psi} \times 100 \text{ in}^3) / 10 \text{ in}^3$$
$$P_2 = 150 \text{ psi}$$

Boyle's Law is the basic principle that explains how internal combustion engines operate and produce power. The air and fuel mixture is compressed, increasing the pressure. When the air and fuel mixture is ignited, the piston is forced down on the power stroke, increasing the volume of the combustion chamber.

# PRINCIPLES OF
# ENGINE OPERATION—LAW OF
# CHARLES AND GAY-LUSSAC

As gas is heated, the pressure will increase. If the pressure is held constant, the volume of the gas will increase. All gases undergo approximately the same change in volume with the same change in temperature. This discovery was made independently by two scientists, Jacques Charles and Joseph Gay-Lussac. This is known as the *Law of Charles and Gay-Lussac*. Using absolute temperature, the law states that the volume of a gas varies directly with its absolute temperature, provided the pressure remains the same. Absolute temperature is based upon absolute zero temperature, which is –273 degrees Celsius (or 0 degrees Kelvin).

The Law of Charles and Gay-Lussac is expressed by the formula:

$$V_I / V_F = T_I / T_F \qquad \boxed{\textbf{Formula 8-4.}}$$

where,

   $V_I$ = initial volume
   $V_F$ = final volume
   $T_I$ = initial absolute temperature
   $T_F$ = final absolute temperature

At higher temperatures, the gas molecules are moving faster and, on average, are farther apart from one another. Therefore, the gas will take up more space.

This law allows for the internal combustion engine to develop power. As the air and fuel mixture is rapidly expanding from the heat of combustion, the gases are expanding, pushing the piston down during the power stroke.

# SUMMARY

Internal combustion engines are used to produce mechanical power. These engines convert chemical energy into mechanical power. Internal combustion engines perform four basic events—intake, compression, combustion, and exhaust.

Many different kinds of engines are used in agriculture. Engines are described and classified by the ways they operate and produce power.

Engines use a series of operating systems that work together. Each system is designed to perform certain tasks. However, all systems must work together for the engine to operate properly. Internal combustion engines are complex technological machines that require maintenance to work efficiently.

Internal combustion engines operate upon basic physical science principles. These include the principles of thermodynamics, the basic gas properties, and the principles of chemical combustion.

# REVIEW QUESTIONS

1. What are three basic descriptions for internal combustion engines?

2. Define combustion and explain the basic formula for the combustion of carbon.

3. What are the four events of the internal combustion engine cycle?

4. How does a four-stroke cycle internal combustion engine operate?

5. How does a two-stroke cycle internal combustion engine operate?

6. What are some differences between four-and two-stroke cycle internal combustion engines?

7. What are the major differences between gasoline and diesel engines?

8. What are the functions of the internal combustion engine systems?

9. How can you classify kinds of internal combustion engines?

10. How do the first and second laws of thermodynamics relate to engine operation?

11. What is Boyle's Law and how does it relate to engine operation?

12. What is the Law of Charles and Gay-Lussac and how does it relate to engine operation?

# APPLYING THE CONCEPTS

1. Create a list of the various engines found on a farm, agribusiness, or school facility. Set up a system of classification of the engines on such characteristics as engine size, number of cylinders, two-and four-stroke cycle engine, and diesel or gasoline engine.

2. Make a classification list of engines based upon their use. Based upon your observations, which classes of engines are used for which purposes?

3. Make a comparison of engine systems found on the engines used at a farm, agribusiness, or school. Create a checklist of all the possible engine systems. For each engine indicate and describe the engine systems. Do all of the engines have the same systems? How do the engine systems differ?

4. Use the measurements of a cylinder bore and piston stroke to determine engine displacement. Use a small engine cylinder block, or an engine manual to get the measurements. Describe several ways you could increase or decrease engine displacement.

# 9

# DETERMINING ENGINE POWER AND EFFICIENCY

All aspects of agriculture rely on the efficient use of resources. Agricultural power units and internal combustion engines in particular have evolved based upon the principles of power and efficiency. The basic function of internal combustion engines in agriculture is to produce usable power. To understand how an engine produces power, the concept of power and how it is measured should be understood.

The terms used to describe the operation and maintenance of engines are technical. These terms have meanings unique to internal combustion engines. Most technical terms were derived from the basic physical sciences.

9-1. Internal combustion engines used in mechanical technology have evolved based upon the design and utilization of the principles of power and efficiency.

# OBJECTIVES

This chapter is designed to help you understand how engines generate power and operate efficiently. After completing this chapter, you will:

1. Describe force, work, and energy and how they relate to engine operation.

2. Describe torque and how engine torque is measured.

3. Describe how to measure engine speed.

4. Describe types of power applications used in agriculture.

5. Describe and calculate engine power measurements.

6. Describe the concept of efficiency.

7. Describe and determine mechanical efficiencies.

8. Describe and determine volumetric efficiencies.

9. Describe and determine thermal efficiencies.

10. Describe and determine engine fuel efficiencies.

11. Determine engine horsepower.

12. Interpret reported engine power data.

**TERMS**

absorption dynamometer
drawbar power
energy
force
friction power ($P_f$)
horsepower
indicated power ($P_i$)
intercooler
International System (SI)
kinetic energy
mass
mechanical efficiency
metric system
potential energy
power
power-take-off
PTO power
speed
supercharger
tachometer
thermal efficiency
torque
turbocharger
United States Customary System (US)
volumetric efficiency
work

# USING UNITS OF MEASURE

Before studying basic internal combustion engine operating principles and characteristics, the units used need to be understood. Manufacturers and engineers present engine specifications and performance data in two different measurement systems. They may use either system, or both at the same time. The first system used in the United States is referred to as the **United States Customary System (US)**. This system is gradually being replaced by the **International System (SI)** of units. The SI system is also called the **metric system**. The SI system is recognized as the international standard. For our purposes, we will use both systems, as you need to be familiar with both. (See Table 9-1.)

## *FORCE*

To develop power, there needs to be a force that exerts energy. A technical definition of a **force** is energy that is exerted by one source upon another body with the tendency to change the action of the body being acted upon. As an example, if a child (the source) pushes a toy (exerts a force upon a body), the toy moves (tends to change) from one place to another (the action).

Another example would be to lift a small engine and place it on a work table. The weight, called the **mass**, of the engine is 50 pounds. Therefore, you must exert a force of 50 pounds to lift the engine. In this example, weight, as mass, refers to the force you must exert to lift the engine.

A somewhat confusing principle is that while the engine is setting on the table, it has a weight (mass) of 50 pounds exerted by gravity on the table. The table must exert a force of 50 pounds away from the direction of gravity

**9-2. An example of force—a small engine (50 lbs) on a work table.**

## Table 9-1
## Conversion Factors for U.S. Customary to Metric (SI) Units

| Quantity | U.S. Customary Unit | Symbol | Multiply By | To Obtain Metric (SI) | Symbol |
|---|---|---|---|---|---|
| **Length** | Inches | in | 25.4 | Millimeters | mm |
| | Inches | in | 2.54 | Centimeters | cm |
| | Inches | in | 0.02540 | Meters | m |
| | Feet | ft | 0.30481 | Meters | m |
| | Yards | yd | 0.9144 | Meters | m |
| | Miles | mi | 1.6093 | Kilometers | km |
| **Area** | Square inches | $in^2$ | 0.000645 | Square meters | $m^2$ |
| | Square feet | $ft^2$ | 0.0929 | Square meters | $m^2$ |
| | Acres | | 4046.8 | Square meters | $m^2$ |
| | Acres | | 0.4047 | Hectares | ha |
| **Force** | Pounds-force | lbf | 4.4482 | Newtons | N |
| | Pounds-force | lbf | 0.004482 | Kilonewtons | kN |
| **Torque** | Pounds-feet | lb-ft | 1.3558 | Newton-meters | N-m |
| | Pounds-inches | lb-in | 0.112985 | Newton-meters | N-m |
| **Mass** (Weight) | Pounds | lb | 0.4536 | Kilograms | kg |
| | Ounces | oz | 28.3495 | Grams | g |
| **Pressure** | Pounds-force per square inches | $lbf/in^2$ | 6.8948 | Kilopascals | kPa |
| | Pounds-force per square feet | $lbf/ft^2$ | 0.04788 | Kilopascals | kPa |
| **Velocity** | Feet per second | ft/s | 0.3048 | Meters/second | m/s |
| | Feet per minute | ft/min | 0.00508 | Meters/second | m/s |
| | Miles per hour | mi/h | 0.4470 | Meters/second | m/s |
| | Miles per hour | mi/h | 1.6093 | Kilometers/hour | km/h |
| **Flow, Volume** | Ounces | oz | 29.574 | Milliliters | mL |
| | Pints | pt | 0.004732 | Cubic meters | $m^3$ |
| | Gallons | gal | 0.003785 | Cubic meters | $m^3$ |
| | Pounds per acre | lb/acre | 1.121 | Kilograms/hectare | kg/ha |
| | Gallons per acre | gal/acre | 9.354 | Liters/hectare | L/ha |
| | Gallons per hour | gal/h | 3.7854 | Liters/hour | L/h |
| | Bushels (USA) | bu | 0.03524 | Cubic meters | $m^3$ |
| | Bushels per acre | bu/acre | 0.087 | Cubic meters/hectare | $m^3$ha |
| **Rate** | Horsepower-hours per gallon | hp•/gal | 0.197 | Kilowatt-hours/liter | kW•h/dL |
| | Pounds per horsepower-hour | lb/hp•h | 0.6083 | Kilograms/kilowatt-hour | kg/kW•h |
| **Power** | Horsepower | hp | 0.7457 | Kilowatts | kW |
| **Temperature** | Fahrenheit | °F | $\left(\dfrac{t°F-32}{1.8}\right)$ | Celsius | °C |

to support the engine. Otherwise, the engine will fall toward the earth until it finds a surface that will counterbalance its weight.

Force is expressed as a single dimension unit, usually pounds (US system) or kilograms (SI system). It is considered single dimensional because it is not moving. Once it is moving, the force will have two dimensions.

## WORK

*Work* is the movement of a force through a distance. This is where we add a second dimension. When you lift a small engine and put it on the table, you are performing work. If you lifted the 50-pound (force) engine 3 feet (distance), you performed 150 foot-pounds of work. Work can be described as having two dimensions—force and distance.

W = F × D    | **Formula 9-1.** |

where,

W = Work, in foot-pounds
F = Force, in pounds
D = Distance, in feet

In the example:

Work = 50 pounds × 3 feet
Work = 150 foot-pounds

## ENERGY

In a very traditional definition, *energy* is described as the capacity to produce an effect or to do work. This definition includes two key concepts.

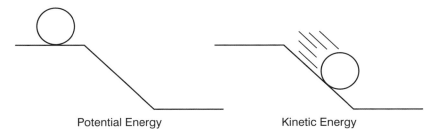

Potential Energy          Kinetic Energy

**9-3. Energy of position, potential (left), and energy in motion, kinetic (right).**

First, capacity, which means that energy can be stored. A large boulder on the top of a mountain has capacity. If allowed to roll down the mountain, it could produce an effect. This implies that the energy will be transferred from one system to another. A barn in the path of the boulder may stop the boulder from rolling down the mountain. The energy will then be transferred to the barn. If the boulder has enough energy, it will flatten the barn and lose some of its energy as it slows.

Energy appears in many forms. The most common forms in agriculture are mechanical, electrical, and chemical. This chapter will deal with the principles of mechanical energy. Mechanical energy is either energy in motion, called **kinetic energy**, or the energy of position, called **potential energy**. The boulder on the top of the mountain has potential energy. As the boulder rolls down the mountain, it has kinetic energy. The fuel of an internal combustion engine has potential energy. Once the engine is running, and producing motion, the engine is producing mechanical kinetic energy.

# TORQUE

Internal combustion engines produce mechanical energy. The mechanical energy produced is in the form of rotary energy at the engine crankshaft. Pistons move in a linear (back and forth) motion but the crankshaft converts the linear motion of the pistons to rotary motion. Engines perform work as a rotary or turning force. The physical quality that causes a device, such as a drive shaft, to rotate around a point is called torque. A technical definition of **torque** is a force that tends to produce or modify rotation about an axis. It is a measure of the product of a force times the perpendicular distance (radius) from the axis of rotation to the line of action of the force.

One way to understand the concept of torque is to use a torque wrench. The torque wrench is designed to measure the amount of twisting force, or torque, to tighten a nut or bolt. Torque wrenches come in a variety of sizes, and usually measure torque in pound-feet, pound-inches, or Newton-meters.

$$To = F \times D$$
| Formula 9-2. |
|---|

where,

  To = Torque, lb.-ft (Newton-meters)

   F = Force, lbs. (Newtons)

   D = Distance, ft. (meters)

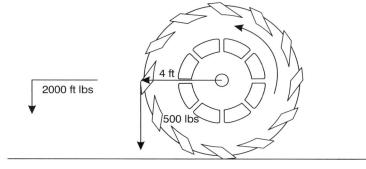

**9-4. A large wheel with a radius of 4 feet is turning and produces a force of 500 pounds.**

Consider Figure 9-4 where a large wheel with a radius of 4 feet is turning and produces a force of 500 pounds. The torque is:

Torque = 500 pounds × 4 feet
Torque = 2000 lb-ft

Notice that torque has the same two dimensions as work. Torque is a measure of turning or rotary work. For clarity, foot-pound force (ft-lbf) is used as the U.S. unit and joules (J) as the SI unit to express work. Pounds force-feet (lbf-ft) is used as the U.S. unit and Newton-meter (N-m) as the SI unit for expressing torque. Just as one unit of foot-pound force is equal to one unit of pound force-foot, one unit of joule is equal to one unit of Newton-meter.

## ENGINE TORQUE

Internal combustion engines are designed to perform work by converting chemical energy into mechanical energy. The linear movement of the pistons is converted to the turning, or rotary, movement of the crankshaft. Torque is the measure of the engine's rotary output. We express engine torque as the number of "foot pounds" the engine will produce at a specific engine speed. For example, an engine may produce 120 foot-pounds of torque at 1800 revolutions per minute (rpm) of the crankshaft. The metric unit commonly used for engine torque is the Newton-meter. Many engine manufacturers now provide both units in the engine specifications.

# VELOCITY AND SPEED

*Speed* is the rate at which a body moves. Speed is based upon two dimensions, distance and time. For our purposes, the terms speed and velocity have the same meaning.

9-5. This pto dynamometer measures speed in revolutions per minute as one of the variables required to determine horsepower output.

Most of us are familiar with using miles per hour to express the speed of a motor vehicle. Speed is presented as a distance divided by time.

Speed = distance / time        | **Formula 9-3.** |

If you traveled 120 miles in 2 hours, your average speed would be 60 miles/hour.

Engine speed is expressed in terms of the number of revolutions of the crankshaft for each minute of operation. The unit of measurement is

9-6. A tachometer in the instrument panel of this tractor measures the crankshaft speed.

revolution/minute, or rpm. A ***tachometer*** is a device used to measure the speed of a rotating shaft. An engine tachometer is used to measure engine, or crankshaft speed.

## RELATIONSHIP BETWEEN SPEED, DISTANCE, AND TIME

As a unit of measurement, speed is different from work or torque in that it is an indirect relationship between the two dimensions. A direct relationship between two dimensions means that as either or both of the dimensions increase the resulting work or force also increases. In a direct relationship, the two dimensions are multiplied to derive the measure. Torque is directly related to both the force and the distance or radius.

In an inverse or indirect relationship, one dimension, in this case speed, is divided by the other dimension, time. Therefore, as time increases to travel the same distance, speed decreases. However, if a vehicle travels a greater distance in the same amount of time, speed would increase. Speed is directly related to distance, and inversely related to time.

# POWER

***Power*** is defined as the rate of performing work. Power can be determined by the equation:

$$P = \frac{F \times D}{t}$$

| Formula 9-4. |

where,

$P$ = Power, ft-lbs/min or ft-lbs/sec
$F$ = Force, in lbs
$D$ = Distance, in ft.
$t$ = time, in minutes or seconds

For example, a force of 200 pounds, lifted 50 feet in 10 seconds, is equal to 1000 ft-lb/second of power. Note, velocity or speed is part of the power equation. Go back to the speed equivalent equation (Formula 9-3):

Speed = distance / time

By substituting speed into the power equation for (distance) / (time), we can develop a second equation for power:

Power = force × speed　　　**Formula 9-5.**

## INTERNAL COMBUSTION ENGINE POWER

Power is used to indicate the rate at which work is being performed. We commonly measure power as either ft-lb / min in the US system or watts in the SI system.

In the United States, engine power is usually stated as horsepower. The term **horsepower** was derived from the amount of work a horse could perform in one minute. The unit of power, based upon how much work a horse could do, was first suggested by John Savery. When James Watt was working on the development of the steam engine, he was often asked by mine operators, "If I buy one of your engines, how many horses will it replace?" Watt took Savery's idea and harnessed work horses to a load. He determined that one horse could travel at a rate of 2½ miles per hour while steadily developing 150 foot-pounds of force for several hours. By calculation, this can be converted to 33,000 foot-pounds per minutes, or 550 foot-pounds per second. This became the standard for one horsepower. The basic horsepower formula is given below.

$$Hp = \frac{F \times D}{t \times 33,000}$$　　**Formula 9-6.**

where,

Hp = horsepower
F = Force, lbs
D = Distance, ft
t = Time, minutes
33,000 = a constant

Horsepower is still used to describe engine power. Also, since an engine can produce a relatively large number of watts, the kilowatt is used to describe engine power in the SI system. One kilowatt is equal to 1000 watts. For conversion, these equations can be used:

1 Horsepower (Hp) = 746 watts (W)　　**Formula 9-7.**

1 Horsepower (Hp) = 0.746 Kilowatts (kW)　　**Formula 9-8.**

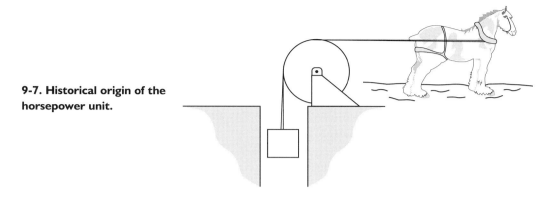

**9-7. Historical origin of the horsepower unit.**

A smaller engine can do the same amount of work as a larger engine, however, it will take a longer period of time. You can plow a field faster with a 100-horsepower tractor than with a 25-horsepower tractor. However, the larger engine may not necessarily be the most efficient for the job. Or, running a smaller engine at maximum power may not be the most efficient operation of the engine.

# TYPES OF POWER

Agricultural machines driven by internal combustion engines produce and utilize several basic types of power. The basic types of power are drawbar pulling, power-take-off (PTO), hydraulic, and electrical.

*Drawbar power* is linear power as machines are pushed or pulled by power produced by the engine and delivered through the drive wheels. A good example is an agricultural tractor pulling a planter. This type of power is called drawbar power (DBP) and is measured as either horsepower (US) or kilowatts (SI).

Rotary or twisting power is delivered by a tractor *power-take-off* (PTO) shaft. Many different kinds of attachments are mounted to PTO shafts. Power is transferred from the engine to the attachment or implement. The resulting rotary power can be used to power machines that grind feed, mow grass, pump water, and perform many other operations. The rotary power may also be converted to hydraulic or electrical energy. This type of power is called *PTO power* and is also measured as either horsepower or kilowatts.

*Indicated power* ($P_i$) is the theoretical power an engine is capable of producing. It is a product of the cylinder pressure, engine displacement, and engine speed. Indicated power can be calculated based upon the pressure produced in the combustion chamber.

Indicated Power = (cylinder pressure) × (cylinder volume) × (engine speed)

or

$P_i = pcyl \times V \times n$ | **Formula 9-9.** |

where,

$P_i$ = indicated engine power
pcyl = cylinder pressure
V = total engine cylinder volumes
n = engine speed

By converting and substituting units, the following formula is used for four-stroke cycle engines:

$P_i = (pcyl \times V \times n) / 792,000$ | **Formula 9-10.** |

where,

$P_i$ = indicated engine horsepower (Hp)
pcyl = average (mean) cylinder pressure in pound per square inch (psi)
V = total engine cylinder volumes in cubic inches (cu.in.)
n = engine speed in revolutions per minute (rpm)

As an example, if an engine is operating at 2100 rpms, the displacement is 268 cubic inches (4.39 liters), and has a mean (average) cylinder pressure of 120 psi (840 kPa). The indicated horsepower is:

$P_i = (pcyl \times V \times n) / 792,000$
$P_i = (120 \text{ psi} \times 268 \text{ cu.in.} \times 2100 \text{ rpm}) / 792,000$
$P_i = 85.3$ horsepower.

Indicated power is a product of the cylinder pressure, engine displacement, and engine speed. There are only three ways to increase engine power—increase the cylinder pressure, increase engine displacement, or increase engine speed.

The power, which is actually delivered from the engine crankshaft, is called the brake horsepower ($P_b$). The brake horsepower is numerically smaller than the indicated power due to friction between the various engine components or parts. The numerical difference between the indicated power and the brake power of an engine is called *friction power* (**$P_f$**).

# MEASURING POWER

The device used to measure engine power is called an ***absorption dynamometer***. An absorption dynamometer has the ability to load the engine and absorb the power being produced. The term dynamometer is derived from the terms dynamo, which means power, and meter, which means measurement gage.

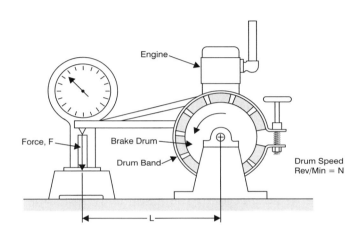

**9-8. A prony brake dynamometer connected to an engine crankshaft for measuring brake power.**

A prony brake is a type of simple absorption dynamometer. This type of dynamometer uses a friction wheel that is attached to the engine output shaft. Some type of braking device is used to create friction between the friction wheel and the torque arm of the dynamometer. As the engine operates the prony brake, turning the friction wheel, the braking device transfers the force to the torque arm. By measuring the force produced (pounds, kilograms) and the length of the arm (feet, meters), and the speed (rpm) of the brakedrum, the brake horsepower (bhp) of the engine can be calculated.

U.S. Brake Power (bhp) = [Force (lbs.) × length (feet)
$\qquad$ × Revolution per minute(rpm)] / 5252

| Formula 9-11. |
| --- |

SI Brake Power (kW) = [force (N) × length (meters)
$\qquad$ × (rpm)] / 9549

| Formula 9-12. |
| --- |

As an example, an engine that produces 60 pounds of force (267N) on a dynamometer with a 2-foot ( .61 meters) arm, turning at 1800 revolutions per minute, would produce 41.7 brake horsepower (30.7kW).

U.S. Brake Power (bhp) = [Force (lbs.) × length (feet)
                                         × Revolution per minute (rpm)] / 5252
U.S. Brake Power (bhp) = [60 lbs. × 2 feet × 1800 rpms] / 5252
U.S. Brake Power (bhp) = 41.1 Bhp


SI Brake Power (kW) = [force (N) × length (meters) × (rpm)] / 9549
SI Brake Power (kW) = [267 N × 0.61 meters × 1800 rpm] / 9549
SI Brake Power (kW) = 30.7 kW


The prony brake is limited in use to small engines for short periods because of the amount of heat produced by the friction wheel.

A common type of dynamometer used in agriculture is the power take-off (PTO) dynamometer. This dynamometer is attached to the PTO shaft of the tractor or power unit. The dynamometer is capable of providing varying loads on the engine through the PTO shaft. There are two basic kinds of PTO dynamometers, either electrical resistance or hydraulic resistance. The electrical resistance type makes the engine produce electrical power by creating an electrical load. The hydraulic type PTO dynamometer makes the engine pump some type of fluid, usually water or hydraulic fluid.

The use of a PTO dynamometer redefines the equations for determining engine power. By substituting the amount of torque produced by the engine, we are able to use the following equations.

U.S. Power take-off power (PTOhp) = [Torque (lbs.ft)
                                         × Revolution per minute (rpm)] / 5252


SI Power take-off power (kW) = [Torque (N-m) × (rpm)] / 9549


As an example, an engine producing 120 lbs.ft of torque while running at a speed of 1800 revolutions per minute, would be producing how much power?

Using US units of measurement,

_____BHp = (120 lb-ft × 1800 rpms) / 5252

or,

41.1 BHp

Using the SI system,

_____Brake Power (kW) = [162.8 N-m × 1800 rpm ] / 9549

or,

30.7 Kilowatts of power.

Note: One N-m = 1.357 × lbf-ft of torque

These equations can be very useful for matching the power requirements of machines with the power produced by internal combustion engines.

## THE CONCEPT OF EFFICIENCY

What is meant by efficiency? Why is engine efficiency important? In planning a travel route, the shortest and easiest route is taken. This makes efficient use of resources. Some of the resources conserved by being more efficient are time, money, fuel, and the environment. Examples of efficiencies commonly used for agricultural equipment and machinery are time, fuel, and material.

To demonstrate efficiency, consider mowing a lawn with a small, push-type mower. The first thing needed is an accurate record of your activities. If the total time on the job was 1 hour and 35 minutes, how efficient was the work? How much time was spent mowing versus not mowing?

Of the time spent, 1 hour 15 minutes was mowing and 20 minutes was in mower preparation and resting. To determine efficiency, divide the time spent mowing by the total time.

Percent efficiency = (working time) / (total time) (100)

Mowing Percent Efficiency = (75 minutes) / (95 minutes) (100)

Mowing Percent Efficiency = 79%

This exercise calculates efficiency based upon time, as a percentage. Time is one of several resources used in calculating efficiencies. Some of the others are material efficiencies. These are based on the amount or capacity of the machine to handle materials. Also, fuel efficiencies are commonly used to determine the relative efficiencies of engines.

# MECHANICAL EFFICIENCY

*Mechanical efficiency* is the ratio of actual power delivered by a machine divided by the total power produced. The mechanical efficiency of a machine is determined by the amount of power used to operate the machine. Much of the power lost as a machine operates is due to friction. The same is true for internal combustion engines. Power used to operate the mechanical components of the engine is lost. For example, some of the engine's power may be used to operate the oil pump, alternator, and fan. However, these examples use a relatively small amount of power. If an engine were to overheat, or not be lubricated properly, then losses due to friction could become large enough to actually stop the engine.

To determine the mechanical efficiency of an internal combustion engine, the brake or flywheel power is divided by the indicated engine power. The difference between the brake power and indicated power is called the friction power. Stated in other terms, friction power is the engine power that is not converted to brake power. The mechanical efficiency of an engine can be calculated using Formula 9-13.

$$Eff_{mech} = P_b / P_i \qquad \boxed{\textbf{Formula 9-13.}}$$

where,

$Eff_{mech}$ = Mechanical Efficiency,
$P_b$ = Brake engine power, and
$P_i$ = indicated power.

As an example, if an engine has an indicated power of 100 horsepower, and it was determined using a dynamometer that the engine produces 90 horsepower at rated engine speed, the mechanical efficiency of the engine can be calculated to be .90 (or 90%).

$Eff_{mech} = P_b / P_i$
$Eff_{mech} = 90 \text{ hp} / 100 \text{ hp}$
$Eff_{mech} = .90$

Note: This can be expressed as 90 percent efficient. Multiply the efficiency value by 100 to convert to a percentage

Friction power is determined by subtracting brake engine power from the indicated engine power. The equation is:

$P_f = P_i - P_b$ | **Formula 9-14.** |

where,

    $P_f$ = Friction power,
    $P_i$ = indicated power, and
    $P_b$ = Brake engine power.

Using our previous example, the friction horsepower is determined by:

$P_f = P_i - P_b$
$P_f = 100 \text{ hp} - 90 \text{ hp}$
$P_f = 10 \text{ hp}$

The concepts of mechanical efficiency and friction power losses are very useful when considering adding attachments and accessories. Power is lost as engines are expected to do more. Operating a hydraulic pump or air-conditioning pump when not needed decreases the mechanical efficiency of the engine.

# VOLUMETRIC EFFICIENCY

Volumetric efficiency is a measure of the air-pumping ability of an engine. It is the ratio of actual air-handling capacity divided by theoretical air-handling capacity. As an engine operates, it cannot completely fill the cylinder with air during the intake stroke. The incoming air enters through the intake valve port, which is a relatively small passage. The size of the intake valve is limited due to the size and shape of the combustion chamber. Therefore, some restriction to incoming air flow occurs. Also, the engine cannot completely hold all of the air as some will leak out of the combustion chamber.

The formula for volumetric efficiency is:

$Eff_{vol} = V_{air} / V$ | **Formula 9-15.** |

where,

  $Eff_{vol}$ = Volumetric Efficiency
    $V_{air}$ = Volume of the air that enters the combustion chamber.
      $V$ = Theoretical or calculated volume of the combustion chamber at BDC.

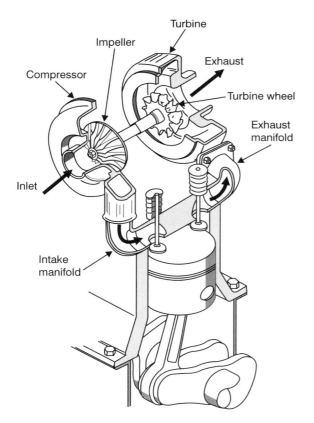

**9-9. An engine equipped with a pump to increase the air pressure which increases the volumetric efficiency of the engine.**

The volumetric efficiency of a naturally aspirated diesel engine is approximately 0.85, or 85 percent. Naturally aspirated engines are sometimes called normally aspirated engines. A naturally aspirated engine is not equipped with a pump or device to increase the air pressure. The naturally aspirated engine operates at atmospheric pressure. A naturally aspirated engine will always have a volumetric efficiency of less than 100 percent. You can increase the air handling capacity of a naturally aspirated engine by increasing the engine cylinder displacement or the engine speed. However, these increases may not increase the volumetric efficiency of the engine, and may actually decrease efficiency.

Internal combustion engines may be equipped with devices to increase the volumetric efficiency of the engine, and, therefore, increase the potential power output. There are three devices commonly used to increase volumetric efficiency: turbochargers, superchargers, and intercoolers. Turbochargers and superchargers are types of air pumps. A *turbocharger* is a turbine-type air pump driven by the engine's exhaust gases. A *supercharger* is a mechanically driven air pump. Superchargers are usually driven by a belt or chain-drive system on the engine—the engine itself drives the supercharger. An *intercooler* is a device that cools the incoming air to the engine making the air more dense. Turbochargers and intercoolers are used on some diesel-powered agricultural equipment. Turbochargers tend to heat the intake air. The temperature of the compressed air may be several hundred degrees Fahrenheit. An intercooler is basically a heat exchanger that cools the heated intake air. The cooler intake air is more dense. Therefore, more molecules of oxygen will enter the combustion chamber, increasing the volumetric efficiency of the engine. An intercooler has a significant impact upon the volumetric efficiency of an engine when used with a turbocharger. The volumetric efficiency of a turbo charged engine should be greater than 100 percent.

# THERMAL EFFICIENCY

*Thermal efficiency* is a measure of how well the engine is utilizing the potential energy in the fuel. The fuel in an engine is burned to provide thermal energy. An engine does not use all of the heat produced from the fuel to produce usable power. Much of the energy produced is removed, as heat, by the cooling and exhaust systems. Thermal efficiency is the ratio of the indicated power of the engine and the equivalent power of the fuel. Thermal efficiency is calculated by the formula:

$$\text{Eff}_{\text{therm}} = P_i / P_{\text{fe}}$$ | **Formula 9-16.** |

where,

$\text{Eff}_{\text{therm}}$ = Thermal Efficiency
$P_i$ = indicated power
$P_{\text{fe}}$ = Fuel equivalent power

To use this equation, the fuel equivalent power needs to be known. A variation of the equation can be used to determine thermal efficiency based upon the actual power produced and the fuel consumed by the engine.

$$\text{Eff}_{\text{therm}} = ( P \times \text{constant}) / ( FC \times HV)$$ | **Formula 9-17.** |

where,

$\text{Eff}_{\text{therm}}$ = thermal efficiency,
$P$ = power produced, (US use horsepower, SI use kilowatts),
constant = a factor (US use 2545, SI use 3600),
$FC$ = fuel consumption (US use gallons per hour, SI use kilogram per hour)
$HV$ = heat value of the fuel (US use BTU/gal, SI use k/kg)

The heat value of fuel is expressed as the number of British Thermal Units (BTU) per gallon for the US system of measurement. For the SI system of measurement the number of kiloJoules in a kilogram of fuel (kJ/kg) is used. An estimate of the heat value of regular gasoline is 145,000 BTU/gallon (47,600 kJ/kg) and an estimate of the heat value of a No. 2 diesel fuel (48 cetane) is 138,750 BTU/gallon (45,500 kJ/kg).

An example is a tractor that produced 86.62 PTO horsepower (64.56 kW) at rated engine speed. For this tractor, the engine crankshaft speed was 2100 revolutions per minute. The tractor used fuel at the rate of 5.521 gallons per hour (17.765 kg/hr). The fuel used was No. 2 diesel fuel, rated number 48 cetane. To determine the thermal efficiency of the tractor, substitute the values in the thermal efficiency equation.

Using US units of measurement:

$\text{Eff}_{therm}$ = (P × constant) / ( FC × HV)
$\text{Eff}_{therm}$ = (86.62 Hp × 2545) / ( 5.521gal/hr × 138,750 BTU/gal)
$\text{Eff}_{therm}$ = .288, or 28.8 percent

Using SI units of measurement:

$\text{Eff}_{therm}$ = (P × constant) / ( FC × HV)
$\text{Eff}_{therm}$ = (64.59 kW × 3600) / (17.765 kg/hr × 45,500 kj/kg)
$\text{Eff}_{therm}$ = .288, or 28.8 percent

This tractor has a thermal efficiency of 28.8 percent based on the amount of PTO power it produced during an actual test.

Internal combustion engines are not very thermally efficient, as much power is lost through heat loss. Diesel engines are considered the most thermally efficient type of internal combustion engine. A well-designed diesel engine will achieve an optimal thermal efficiency of about 40 percent under the best operating conditions.

# FUEL EFFICIENCY

Fuel efficiencies are a practical application of thermal efficiencies. Engine fuel efficiencies are determined as a ratio of fuel consumption to power output. A common measure of fuel efficiency of motor vehicles is miles per gallon, or kilometers per liter. This is commonly called fuel economy. Agricultural equipment also use measures of fuel efficiency. The most common measure for agricultural engines is the power-hours per volume of fuel. The US system uses horsepower-hours per gallon (Hp-hr/gal) and the SI unit is kilowatts-hour per liter (kW-hr/L). Another measure of fuel efficiency is the ratio of fuel consumption to a measure of actual performance. Examples of this measure of fuel efficiency are gallons per hour, gallons per acre, and gallons per ton of material handled.

A motor vehicle, which uses 15 gallons of fuel to travel 300 miles, has a fuel efficiency or fuel economy of 20 miles per gallon. Using SI measures, a motor vehicle, which uses 58 liters of fuel to travel 500 kilometers, has a fuel efficiency of 8.6 kilometers per liter.

The equation for fuel efficiency is:

$Eff_{fuel}$ = (Power × Time) / Amount of fuel $\qquad$ | **Formula 9-18.** |

US units: Hp-hr/gal = (horsepower × hours) / Gallons of fuel
SI units: kW-hr/L = (kilowatts × hours) / Liters of fuel used

Measures of fuel efficiency are very useful and practical as one factor to consider when selecting internal combustion engines.

## INTERNAL COMBUSTION ENGINE POWER EFFICIENCY

An internal combustion engine operates because it can produce more power than it takes to operate the engine. This "excess" power is used to perform work. However, internal combustion engines lose power because there are some inefficiencies. Efficiency ratios indicate the amount of power available and the amount lost through heat, friction, or other losses. The most practical measure for agricultural equipment is the power-hours per volume of fuel.

# DETERMINING USABLE ENGINE POWER

The most useful measures of engine power for agricultural equipment, especially tractors, are power-take-off (PTO) power and drawbar power. Tests of the tractor engine alone are seldom of practical value. PTO and drawbar power are more useful measurements.

The PTO equation is:

PTO power = (T × N) / constant $\qquad$ | **Formula 9-19.** |

where,

PTO power = the horsepower or kilowatts produced at the PTO shaft,
$\qquad$ T = PTO shaft torque, lb-ft (N-m)
$\qquad$ N = shaft speed in revolutions per minute, and
$\quad$ constant = 5252 (9549)

As an example, a tractor producing a PTO torque of 200 lb-ft (271N-m) at a PTO speed of 540 revolutions per minute (rpm) would be producing how much PTO power? First, determine the horsepower using US units.

PTO power = (T × N) / constant
PTO power = (200 ft.lbsf. × 540 rpms) / 5252
PTO power = 20.6 horsepower

Next, use SI units to determine the kilowatts:

PTO power = (T × N) / constant
PTO power = (271 N-m × 540) / 9549
PTO power = 15.3 kW

Drawbar power is the power available at the drawbar for pulling implements or other loads. The drawbar power equation is:

DBP = (F × S) / constant        |  **Formula 9-20.**  |

    where,

    DBP = Drawbar power in horsepower or kilowatts,
        F = force pulled, lbs (kN),
        S = speed, miles per hour (km/hr), and
constant = 375 (3.6).

As an example, a tractor pulling a force of 2000 pounds (8.90 kN) at a speed of 4.0 miles per hour (6.44 km/hr) would be producing how much drawbar power?

For this example, drawbar power would be determined for US units as:

DBP = (F × S) / constant
DBP = (2000 pounds of force × 4.0 miles per hour) / 375
DBP = 21.3 horsepower

The same example using SI units would determine:

DBP = (F × S) / constant
DBP = (8.90 kN × 6.44 km/hr) / 3.6
DBP = 15.9 kilowatts

## *Estimating Usable Power*

A rather simple method of estimating usable tractor power has been devised by Wendell Bowers, an agricultural engineer at Oklahoma State University. This method uses a factor of 0.86 each time power is transferred from one location (or tractive condition) to another. Since usable power decreases each time it is transferred, the power decreases as the location of use moves farther away from the engine itself. The system starts with the maximum rated engine horsepower, which is available from the manufacturer.

The Bowers method of estimating available power can be illustrated using the following example. Assume that the tractor has a 120 hp (89.5kW) engine.

1. maximum engine power = 120 Hp (89.5 kW)

2. maximum PTO power = 120 Hp (89.5 kW) × 0.86 = 103.2 Hp (77.0 kW)

3. maximum drawbar power on concrete = 103.2 Hp (77.0 kW) × 0.86 = 88.8 Hp (66.2 kW)

4. maximum drawbar power on firm soil = 88.8 Hp (66.2 kW) × 0.86 = 76.4 Hp (56.9 kW)

5. usable drawbar power on firm soil = 76.4 Hp (56.9 kW) × 0.86 = 65.7 Hp (48.9 kW)

6. usable drawbar power on tilled soil = 65.7 Hp (48.9 kW) × 0.86 = 56.5 Hp (42.1 kW)

7. usable drawbar power on soft soil = 56.5 Hp (42.1 kW) × 0.86 = 48.6 Hp (36.3 kW)

This method is simple and provides a reasonable estimate of usable tractor power. The system is not designed to replace actual test information, but rather to provide an estimate if test information is not available.

# INTERPRETING REPORTED ENGINE POWER DATA

Engine data are reported using several sources. Manufacturers report their own data and independent data are reported by testing laboratories.

| | |
|---|---|
| **Tractor Model** | 2955 Dsl (4 whl dr) |
| Transmission | 16 speed w/Hi-Lo |
| **Engine** | |
| Bore and stroke ................... in | 4.19 x 4.33 |
| Number of cylinders ................. | 6 |
| Displacement ....................cu in | 359 |
| Rated RPM ......................... | 2300 |
| Compression ratio .................. | 17.8 to 1 |
| **Chassis** | Front |
| Type | Whl assist |
| Tires: number, size, ply ........front | 2; 13.6-28; 8 |
| ........................rear | 2; 18.4-38; 8 |
| Weight as tested...............lbs | 11150 |
| **PTO Performance** | |
| Max power @ rated eng RPM ......... | 86.22@2300 |
| PTO RPM ....................... | 1058 |
| Fuel: Gal/hr .................. | 5.017 |
| Hp.hr/gal .................. | 17.18 |
| Max power @ std PTO RPM ......... | 85.54 |
| Eng RPM .................... | 2173 |
| Fuel: Gal/hr................. | 4.913 |
| Hp.hr/gal .................. | 17.41 |
| **Drawbar Performance** | |
| Max Hp (short term) @ mph ........ | 74.20@5.42 |
| 100% load (2 hrs)...........HP@mph | 72.99@5.42 |
| Fuel: Gal/hr ............... | 4.924 |
| Hp.hr/gal ................. | 14.82 |
| 75% load (10 hrs) ..........HP@mph | 58.50@5.70 |
| Fuel: Gal/hr............... | 4.242 |
| Hp.hr/gal ................. | 13.79 |
| 50% load (2 hrs) ...........HP@mph | 39.61@5.83 |
| Fuel: Gal/hr............... | 3.405 |
| Hp.hr/gal ................. | 11.64 |
| 50% load (2 hrs) ...........HP@mph | 39.66@5.83 |
| Reduced eng RPM ............ | 1609 |
| Fuel: Gal/hr ............... | 2.767 |
| Hp.hr/gal ................. | 14.33 |
| Max pull .............lbs@mph | 9971@2.44 |
| % slip of drivers ............ | 14.94 |
| Lugging ability—% of increase of | |
| pull at 80% rated RPM ......... | 24 |
| **Sound Level** | |
| At operator's ear ............... | w/cab |
| 100% load................dB(A) | 77.5 |
| 75% load................dB(A) | 77.0 |
| 50% load................dB(A) | 76.0 |
| 50% ld: Rd RPM...........dB(A) | 72.5 |
| Bystander................dB(A) | .... |

**9-10. A sample tractor test data report.**

Nebraska established a law that requires that all tractors sold in the state be tested by an outside laboratory, so Nebraska established a tractor testing laboratory. In recent years, as much of the tractor manufacturing industry has shifted overseas, the Nebraska law was changed to recognize tests conducted by either the Nebraska tractor testing laboratory or by the Organization for Economic Cooperation and Development (OECD) located in Europe.

Basically, these tests determine engine power production and efficiencies under standardized test conditions. Tractor power is reported as both drawbar and PTO power. Both US and SI units are presented. Fuel efficiencies are calculated and reported. The tests are performed under varying load conditions.

Reviewers should compare tests for different tractors. Consider the rated engine performances and compare them not only to other tractors but also to the data reported by the manufacturers. It is interesting to observe that data from the same manufacturer varies from tractor to tractor. Several models of tractors from one manufacturer may use, and often do use, the same engine size based on engine displacement. However, these engines may have different power outputs and fuel efficiencies as the engines have different operating systems and characteristics, such as turbochargers.

# SUMMARY

Internal combustion engines operate to convert chemical energy to mechanical energy to produce power and perform work. Engine power is expressed as units of horsepower or kilowatts.

Engine efficiencies provide measures of the engine outputs compared with the engine inputs. Engines are designed to operate as mechanically, thermally, volumetrically, and fuel efficiently as possible based on the operating conditions and characteristics of the engine.

# REVIEW QUESTIONS

1. Define force, work, and energy and describe how they relate to engine operation.
2. What is torque and how can you measure engine torque?

3. How is engine speed measured?
4. What are the different types of power applications used in agriculture?
5. Define and give the formulas for power, horsepower, and brake horsepower.
6. What is efficiency?
7. What is mechanical efficiency?
8. How do you calculate volumetric efficiencies?
9. What is thermal efficiency and how you determine engine thermal efficiencies?
10. How can you determine engine fuel efficiencies?
11. How can you to determine engine horsepower ratings?

# APPLYING THE CONCEPTS

1. Set a board on a slope in order to roll several different size balls down the slope. Observe the action of the different size and weight of various balls as the roll down the slope. What will cause the balls to stop rolling? Write down you observations and conclusions.

2. Use a torque wrench to help understand the concept of torque. Place a bolt in a vise, and use the torque wrench to try and turn the bolt. Be sure not to exceed the capacity of the torque wrench. What happens as you apply more torque? What happens with different size bolts? List several applications where you would need to use a torque wrench.

3. Calculate the speed of several moving objects. You can use a set course such as a measured course of 100 feet to measure the speed of a runner, bicycle, garden tractor, or other object. You can measure the speed of rotation of a shaft by counting the number of revolutions per minute.

4. Make power requirement measurements for some activities you can do. You can measure the amount of force it takes to push a lawnmower, and determine the speed you mow the grass. You can determine how much power you need to ride a bicycle for given distance. You will need to know how much work is being done, and how fast you are doing it. You may be able to make measurements for power equipment. You can use a small tractor to pull a sled or wagon. If you can, determine the amount of work being done and how fast you are doing it.

5. You can also calculate the relative efficiencies you can perform tasks. You can see how fast and accurately people can perform a task. For example, you could get several people to mow the same size area with a mower and see who gets done quicker, who uses less fuel, and who has the best looking area. Which type of efficiencies are the best for this example? What are other examples where you can measure efficiencies?

# 10

# ENGINE PRIMARY SYSTEM COMPONENTS AND FUNCTIONS

The primary system components of the internal combustion engine are those directly involved in creating compression and producing power. The compression system is designed to compress the air, increasing the energy produced by the combustion of the fuel. The rapidly expanding combustion energy is converted to mechanical power.

The compression system uses pistons that move up and down in a cylinder. The piston, cylinder, and cylinder head must form a leak-proof combustion chamber for the engine to operate efficiently. The seal of the combustion chamber is a major design feature for internal combustion engines. The pistons must operate smoothly and with a minimum power requirement. If an engine loses too much compression or requires too much power to operate, then it will not operate efficiently.

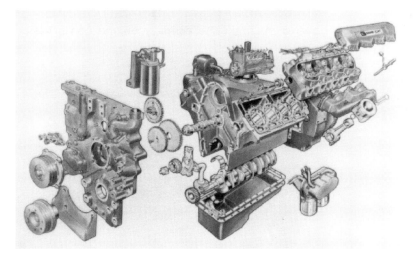

10-1. A cutaway view of a typical V-8 diesel engine. (Courtesy, Caterpillar Tractor Co.)

331

# OBJECTIVES

This chapter covers the components of the primary system of an engine and their functions. After completing this chapter, you will:

1. Explain the three basic systems of an internal combustion engine.

2. Determine engine compression ratios and describe the differences between gasoline and diesel engine compression ratios.

3. Measure engine compression.

4. Describe engine cylinder blocks, cylinder heads, crankshaft assemblies, piston components, and piston rings.

5. Describe the operation of an engine valve assembly.

6. Describe the functions of the engine camshaft.

7. Explain how an engine firing order operates for multiple cylinder engines.

8. Describe how to maintain the primary engine compression system.

**TERMS**

accessory system
compression gage
compression ring
crankshaft throw
cylinder block
cylinder leakage test
dome
duration
firing order
flat head
lands
lobe profile
main journal
oil ring
operating system
overhead valve cylinder heads
piston
piston blow-by
primary system
scavenging
skirt
sleeves
valve clearance
valve face

# INTERNAL COMBUSTION ENGINE SYSTEMS AND COMPONENTS

The internal combustion engine is a series of operating systems that work together to make the engine run. Each system performs its own series of tasks and is composed of different parts or components. The systems must work together. Engine troubleshooting and maintenance practices are based on engine systems. To understand how engines operate, it is beneficial to study individual engine systems. The functions of individual engine components are also easier to describe and understand when considered as parts of a system.

Engine systems can be divided into the primary system, operating systems, and accessory systems. The *primary system* is the system that creates the engine compression and converts the energy of combustion to mechanical energy. For our purposes, the primary engine system will be considered the same as the compression system. The *operating systems* are those systems that perform the other engine operating functions. The engine will not operate without the operating systems. For example, an engine electrical system is an operating system. Sometimes, operating systems are called auxiliary systems. *Accessory systems* are those systems that are not necessary for engine operation. An example of an accessory system is a power steering system.

This chapter will deal with the functions and components of the engine's primary system. The primary system functions to create compression and produce power.

## COMPRESSION RATIO

Compression ratio (CR) is the ratio of the total volume (TV) of the combustion chamber when the piston is at BDC (bottom dead center) to the volume of the combustion chamber when the piston is at TDC (top dead center). The volume of the combustion chamber when the piston is at TDC is called the clearance volume (ClV). The compression ratio of an engine can be calculated using Formula 10-1.

Compression ratio = total volume divided by clearance volume,

or

$$CR = \frac{TV}{ClV}$$   | **Formula 10-1.** |

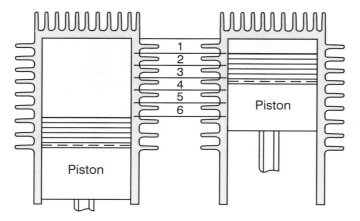

10-2. An engine with 6 to 1 compression ratio.

where,

CR is the compression ratio,

TV is the total volume, and

CIV is the clearance volume.

The total cylinder volume (TV) is determined by adding the piston displacement volume and the clearance volume. Therefore, the compression ratio can also be calculated by Formula 10-2.

$$CR = \frac{PdV + CIV}{CIV}$$     **Formula 10-2.**

where,

CR is the compression ratio,

PdV is the piston displacement volume, and

CIV is the clearance volume.

## GASOLINE ENGINE COMPRESSION RATIOS

Compression ratios vary based upon engine design and applications. Small gasoline-powered engines have compression ratios of about 6.0:1. The ratio is stated as "a compression ratio of six to one." This means that six volumes are compressed into one volume during the compression stroke. Large gasoline-powered engines have compression ratios of about 9.0:1. However, these compression ratios can be higher. As compression ratios increase, the engine requires higher octane gasoline to operate properly. Higher compression ratio gasoline engines tend to "ping" or "knock" when operating on lower-octane gasoline.

## DIESEL ENGINE COMPRESSION RATIOS

Diesel engines require even higher compression ratios then gasoline engines. Diesel engine compression ratios may range from 16:1 to 24:1. Diesel engine compression ratios have increased as engine technologies have become more advanced. Compression ratios of from 18:1 to 21:1 are commonly used on diesel powered agricultural equipment. Diesel engine cylinder pressures of 600 pounds per square inch (psi) may be produced by these higher compression engines. These increased cylinder pressures require very sturdy internal engine components.

Generally, as we increase the compression ratio and cylinder pressures in the combustion chamber, we increase the power and fuel efficiencies of the engine. As with many concepts and principles in the physical sciences, there are tradeoffs for the gains. Higher compression ratios create greater internal engine pressures, which put greater strain on internal engine components. Higher compression engines tend to be more costly to build and repair. Therefore, proper maintenance and operation of high compression engines are extremely important.

# TESTING ENGINE COMPRESSION

The compression of an internal combustion engine can be measured by performing compression tests. A ***compression gage*** is used to determine

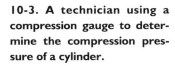

10-3. A technician using a compression gauge to determine the compression pressure of a cylinder.

compression pressure. The engine manufacturer will specify a recommended compression pressure and indicate the proper procedure to follow for checking compression. The procedures and compression gages for checking the compression in gasoline and diesel engines are usually different.

## USING COMPRESSION GAGES

A common procedure for checking the compression of a gasoline engine is to first remove all spark plugs. Install the compression gage in a spark plug port and allow the starter to turn the crankshaft. This is commonly called "cranking" or "turning over" the engine. The compression gage will register the amount of pressure the cylinder is producing. This is usually given as pounds per square inch (psi). Be sure to measure the pressure in each cylinder following the same procedure. Some manufacturers do not recommend using a compression gage on small engines, especially, those started manually. Always compare the compression readings to the manufacturer's specifications.

Cylinder pressures of between 150 psi and 200 psi are common for gasoline engines. If low readings are found, a common procedure is to add a tablespoon of engine oil (SAE 30 is often used) to each cylinder and take another reading. The engine oil will temporarily help to seal around the piston rings. If an increase in cylinder pressure is then found, the test indicates worn piston rings, cylinder wall, or both. If the cylinder pressure remains low, then the problem is more likely to be with the valves, head gasket, or a damaged piston.

Diesel engines create much higher cylinder pressures then gasoline engines. Therefore, the compression tests usually require different compression gages and procedures. Some diesel engine manufacturers use a procedure similar to the one for a gasoline engine. However, some manufacturers recommend removing each diesel injection nozzle one-at-a-time, installing a diesel engine compression gage, and measuring the cylinder pressures while the engine is running. You then have to reinstall that nozzle, remove the next nozzle, install the gage, and restart the engine. As you can see, testing diesel engine compression can be more involved than testing gasoline engines, and requires more experience and know-how.

Compression test results should be interpreted using the manufacturer's recommendations. The pressure readings for all cylinders should be about the same. There should be a difference of no more then 10 percent between the highest and the lowest cylinders. Generally, low cylinder pressure readings indicate possible problems associated with the pistons, piston rings, head, head gasket, valves, or worn cylinders.

## CYLINDER LEAKAGE TESTS

Another form of a compression test is the ***cylinder leakage test.*** A cylinder leakage tester is used to perform the test. The tester is attached to the cylinder port and compressed air is forced into the cylinder with the piston at top dead center (TDC) of the compression stroke. When the cylinder is pressurized, the tester indicates the percentage of leakage. Generally, if the leakage is more than 20 percent, the cylinder leakage is considered too high. The key to interpreting a leakage test that indicates too much pressure leakage is to determine where the air is going. For example, if the air is going to an adjacent cylinder, a leaking, or "blown," head gasket would be a probable cause. A leaking head gasket could also cause air bubbles in a liquid cooling system. Excessive air leaking into the crankcase would suggest leakage past the piston rings. Air pressure leaking past the intake valve would be forced back through the intake systems, and leaking air beyond the exhaust valve would allow air to come out of the exhaust system. In any case, excessive cylinder pressure leakage suggests some problem in the compression system.

Compression tests are excellent tools for determining the operating condition of the primary compression system of an engine. A compression test, along with a dynamometer test, is an excellent method of identifying engine problems.

# MAJOR ENGINE PARTS

## ENGINE CYLINDER BLOCK

The internal combustion engine ***cylinder block*** houses the cylinders and crankshaft. It serves as a frame for attaching other engine components and systems. Generally, the engine block and cylinder block are the same thing. However, some engines use an engine block and attach the cylinders to the block. Engine blocks are usually made from cast iron or cast aluminum. The various mounting surfaces are machined on the engine block. Many small air-cooled engines have the cooling fins cast with the

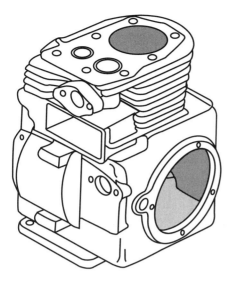

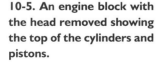

10-4. A cylinder block for a small engine.

aluminum block. Liquid cooled engines are cast with coolant passageways and then machined to specifications.

The cylinders can be machined directly in the engine block. This is very common for small gasoline engines. Some engines use cylinders that are inserted in the block. These removable cylinders are called *sleeves*. Sleeves allow different alloys to be used for the cylinder. They also allow the cylinder to be reconditioned without "reboring" the cylinder. Many diesel engines used in agriculture have sleeves. There are two basic types of sleeves—wet and dry. Wet sleeves are designed to contact the engine coolant directly. They tend to be thicker than dry sleeves and require seals to keep the coolant from contaminating the engine oil. Dry sleeves are fitted in a machined cylinder but are not in direct contact with the coolant. They tend to be thinner than wet sleeves. Removal and installation of sleeves require special cylinder sleeve tools.

Some engines use an engine block that houses just the crankshaft. Removable individual cylinders are attached to the crankcase block. Several air cooled engine designs use this method. The individual cylinders allow for better air flow and cooling.

Internal combustion engine blocks can be very costly to repair. Often, it is less expensive to install a new "short" block. A short block is a new,

10-5. An engine block with the head removed showing the top of the cylinders and pistons.

or rebuilt, engine block, with a new crankshaft, pistons, rings, bearings, and other primary compression components installed. Sometimes, the cylinder heads are also included and mounted on the block. When the heads are included, this is called a "long" block.

Careful consideration should be given to deciding whether to repair the old block or trade the old block for a short or long block. Cylinders can be re-bored by an engine machine shop and refitted with new pistons. Cylinder sleeves are designed to be replaced when worn, rather then re-bored. Replacing worn cylinder sleeves requires special tools and must be completed according to the manufacturer's recommendations. If the engine cylinders meet the manufacturer's measurement specifications, they can sometimes be cleaned, or de-glazed. Be sure to check the manufacturer's recommendations, as many engine manufacturers do not recommend using a de-glazing tool on certain types of cylinders, especially some aluminum cylinders.

## CYLINDER HEAD ASSEMBLY

The cylinder head is used to seal or "cap" the top of the cylinder and forms the top of the combustion chamber. Cylinder heads are usually made of cast aluminum or cast iron. On some small engines, the cast aluminum cylinder head has cooling fins. Air from the small engine flywheel is directed by the engine shroud over the cylinder head for cooling. This type of cylinder head is called a *flat head* as it does not house the engine valves.

On larger engines, the cylinder head not only forms the top of the combustion chamber and seals the cylinders, it also supports the valve assembly. These cylinder heads house the intake and exhaust valves and

10-6. A typical bare cylinder head. Top view (upper photo) and bottom view (lower photo).

are called **overhead valve cylinder heads**. Some of these cylinder heads also house the camshaft. This is often the configuration for an overhead camshaft assembly. Most of the overhead valve and overhead camshaft types of cylinder heads also have liquid coolant passages to help cool the cylinder head components.

Almost all internal combustion engines use a cylinder head gasket to provide a seal between the cylinder head and the cylinder block. A few engine designs use a series of seals instead of a head gasket. It is recommended that any time the cylinder head is removed a new head gasket be installed. Because many head gasket seals were compressed when the gasket was first installed, they will generally not create a good seal if reinstalled.

The cylinder head is attached to the cylinder block by head bolts. Cylinder head bolts are always tightened to a recommended torque specification. Head bolts should always be tightened in the proper sequence or rotation. When tightening cylinder head bolts, always follow the manufacturer's recommendations. Using lubricants or "anti-seize" compounds on the head bolts may be recommended. Some manufacturers recommend using a step procedure, where each head bolt is tightened to a specific torque level and then each is torqued to a higher level. A manufacturer may recommend several levels or steps in the head bolt torquing sequence.

The removal and installation of cylinder heads can be performed if you have some basic tools and a good repair manual for the engine. However, cylinder heads are difficult to repair. Generally, cylinder heads should be taken to an engine machine shop to determine what service they need and for repairs. Cylinder heads should be checked to see if they fit well on the cylinder block. Follow recommended procedures. Usually, you can make basic checks with feeler gages. The heads should be cleaned and checked for cracks. Specialized equipment is needed to accurately check for cracks in the cylinder head.

Installing cylinder heads is a very critical engine reassembly step. Follow the manufacturer's recommendations. Always use the proper head gasket and correct installation process. Often, engine failures are caused by improper installation of the cylinder head.

## ENGINE CRANKSHAFT ASSEMBLY

The engine crankshaft converts the linear (back and forth) motion of the piston to a rotary or circular movement. The piston is connected to the crankshaft by the connecting rod. The connecting rod is attached to the piston by a piston pin or wrist pin. The connecting rod is attached

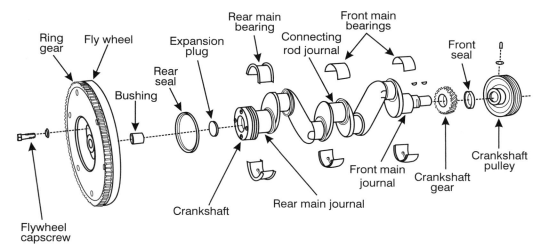

**10-7. Engine crankshaft assembly components.**

to the crankshaft at the connecting rod journal. Journals are the surfaces that rotate or spin in the bearings.

Crankshafts rotate in the engine block on the main bearings. The surfaces of the crankshaft, where the main bearings contact the crankshaft, are called the **main journals**. The connecting rods attach to the connecting rod journals on the crankshaft. The distance from the center line of the crankshaft to the end of the connecting rod journal is called the **crankshaft throw.** As the crankshaft turns by the action of the pistons, the crankshaft throw converts the linear force to crankshaft torque. The length of the crankshaft throw is one-half of the length of the piston stroke.

## Crankshaft Torque and Piston Speed

As you increase piston stroke, you have the potential to increase engine torque. The increased crankshaft throw helps to increase torque. Increasing the piston stroke, coupled with increasing the compression ratio, would be beneficial for increasing engine torque and, therefore, increasing engine power. The question then becomes, "As we increase piston stroke and crankshaft throw, what other factors in the engine are also being changed?"

One important consideration is the relative speed of the piston as we increase piston stroke. Let's consider a four-stroke cycle engine operating at 3600 crankshaft revolutions per minute (rpm). The engine is operating at a speed of 60 revolutions per second. Since there are two piston strokes for each engine crankshaft rotation, that represents 120 piston stokes per second.

In our example, let's assume the engine has a piston stroke of 3 inches. Therefore, the average piston speed would be 360 inches per second, or 30 feet of piston travel per second. Keep in mind that this is an average piston travel speed. To illustrate further, if you were to go outside and throw a softball straight up in the air, the ball would travel straight up, slow down, stop for a brief moment, start back down, and then you would catch it. The piston traveling back and forth must do the same stopping and starting of movement. When the piston gets to both TDC and BDC, it must stop and change its movement to the opposite direction. Therefore, piston speed is not constant, rather, its movement pattern is more like a wave—going back and forth. The piston moves fastest when it is traveling in the middle of a stroke. If we were to double the piston stroke, and keep the engine crankshaft speed at 3600 rpms, we would double the average piston speed. In the previous example, if we increase the piston stroke from 3 inches to 6 inches, we would increase the average piston speed to 60 feet per second. The increased average piston speed tends to increase the stresses on the internal engine components. This is why engines with longer strokes or higher compression ratios tend to operate at slower engine speeds. Furthermore, if you were designing an engine to operate at very high speeds, you would need to consider designing an engine with a shorter piston stroke.

### Engine Flywheel

A flywheel is attached to one end of the crankshaft. Some engines have a harmonic balance attached to the other end. The purpose of the engine flywheel is to provide smooth engine operation. The flywheel helps to smooth out the pulses of the power strokes. An engine crankshaft does not operate at a smooth, even speed of rotation. The crankshaft actually spins in a pulsating motion as the engine power strokes are being produced. This helps to explain why the more cylinders an engine has, generally, the smoother it operates. A four-cylinder, four-stroke cycle engine is producing a power stroke every 180 degrees of crankshaft rotation. An eight-cylinder, four-stroke cycle engine produces a power stroke every 90 degrees of crankshaft rotation. The heavier the flywheel, the smoother the engine operation. However, a heavier flywheel will use more engine power to operate. Engineers design the flywheel to provide smooth operation with a minimum loss of power.

## Crankshaft Bearing

The crankshaft bearings and journals require lubrication by the engine oil. The clearances between the crankshaft journals and bearings are very small, usually less than a couple of thousandths of an inch. Most crankshafts use plain bearings, which can be replaced. However, some engines, mostly two-stroke cycle engines, may use needle bearings for the crankshaft or connecting rod bearings. Some manufacturers also use ball or roller bearings for the main crankshaft bearings. All bearings require adequate and constant lubrication.

Crankshafts can be refitted, new bearings installed, and repaired. You should only perform work on an engine crankshaft when you have the proper tools and equipment, the manufacturer's repair recommendations, and considerable know-how or expert help. The crankshaft bearing journals should be measured and checked according to the manufacturer's specification whenever the crankshaft is removed. The clearance between the crankshaft journals and bearings is a critical engine specification and should only be performed with very accurate micrometers or similar measurement devices. Crankshaft end-play refers to freedom of the crankshaft to move from end to end in the engine block. This specification is also very critical and should be checked whenever any work is being performed on a crankshaft.

The replacement of crankshaft bearings should be performed accurately and according to the manufacturer's recommendations. Improperly installed crankshaft bearings, or ones that were not properly fitted, will cause very severe engine damage in a relatively short period. Crankshaft bearings should always be tightened to the recommended torque specification. It is a good practice to pre-lubricate crankshaft bearings when installing or reinstalling them. Most manufacturers will recommend using an engine preassembly lubricant on the bearings.

## Straightening Crankshafts

Small engine crankshafts, especially those found on lawnmowers, can become bent from striking hard objects. The removal and installation of a small engine crankshaft can be performed if you have the recommended tools and a manufacturer's repair manual. However, the straightening of a bent crankshaft requires special equipment and should only be done by an authorized repair shop. It may be more economical to replace the crankshaft, or even the entire engine than to straighten the crankshaft.

## PISTON ASSEMBLY COMPONENTS

The *piston* is the engine component that slides back and forth in the engine cylinder. The main function of the piston is to convert the heat energy from the combustion process to linear motion. The piston is a very accurately manufactured component. It must slide freely in the cylinder under varying conditions. The piston must be designed to withstand very hot temperatures and be able to move freely in the cylinder as it heats up. Cylinder combustion temperatures may exceed 4500 degrees (°F). The piston must also be designed to withstand the forces of compression and combustion pressures. Pistons are usually machined from lightweight alloys. The piston surfaces between the ring grooves are called *lands*. The bottom of the piston is called the *skirt* and the top of the piston is called the piston head or *dome*.

The top of a piston can be one of three general shapes: flat, concave, or convex. The top of a piston is called the piston dome or piston head. Flat pistons are very common for internal combustion engines used in agriculture. Some compression ignition engines use a depression, or concave-shaped piston head to allow for higher compression ratios. These types of pistons allow for flat cylinder heads, and therefore, can be used to decrease combustion chamber volume and increase compression ratios.

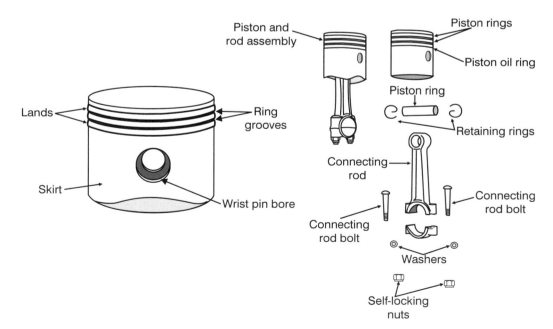

10-8. Components of a piston and connecting rod assembly.

Domed or convex piston tops are used in some engines to increase compression ratios by decreasing the volume of the combustion chamber.

## Piston Rings

Pistons are fitted with piston rings to help seal the combustion chamber and control lubrication between the cylinder wall and the piston. Pistons may have two, three, or even four piston rings. The piston rings generally are fitted near the top of the piston. The rings fit in the piston ring grooves. The top piston rings are called **compression rings**. These piston rings help prevent the loss of compression during the compression stroke and prevent the loss of combustion pressure during the power stroke. Most engines will have two or more compression rings. The lower rings are called **oil rings**. These rings are designed to control the amount of oil on the cylinder walls. A small amount of oil is needed to lubricate and seal the piston rings and the cylinder walls. A common piston ring assembly is to have two compression rings and one oil ring. However, this varies depending on the design of the engine. Some two-stroke cycle engines only have compression rings.

Piston rings are usually made of alloys and are easy to break. Always handle piston rings with care and use ring expanders and compressors to properly install piston rings. Be sure to install piston rings in their proper groove and position. Most piston rings have a top and bottom, which must be correctly installed. Some oil rings are actually made of several different parts and need to be put together very carefully. Always check and follow the manufacturer's recommendations and use the proper tools.

The movement of combustion gases past the rings is called **piston blow-by**. As the oil rings wear, they tend to allow too much oil to coat

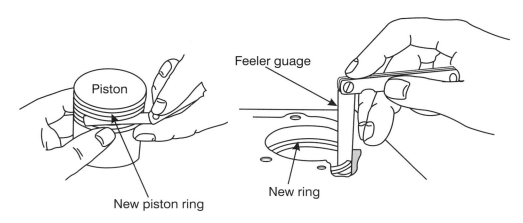

Piston

New piston ring

Feeler guage

New ring

**10-9. Checking piston ring grooves (left) and piston ring gap (right).**

the cylinder walls and increase engine oil consumption. Excessive oil in the combustion chamber will tend to foul spark plugs on a spark ignition engine and increase carbon buildup on all types of engines.

### Piston and Ring Measurements

In addition to visual inspection, there are three basic measurements used to check the condition of pistons and rings. To check the condition of the rings, measure the ring end gap, which is the space between the ring ends when the ring is placed in the cylinder. The ring end gap is critical to allow for the expansion of the ring as it heats. Too little ring end gap will cause the ring to put too much pressure on the cylinder wall and probably break the ring and score the cylinder wall. As the ring wears, the ring end gap will increase. Eventually, too much ring end gap will cause significant losses of compression and combustion pressure, thus, decreasing the power and efficiency of the engine.

Two sets of measurements should be made to check the condition of a piston. First, use a micrometer to measure the piston at locations indicated by the engine service manual. To determine if excessive wear has occurred, check the obtained measurements against the service manual specifications. The second piston measurement is ring groove side clearance, which is the distance between a new compression ring and the piston lands. The rings need some room to move; however, too much ring side clearance causes loss of compression. If the ring groove clearance is greater than the service manual specification, the piston is worn and should be replaced.

Pistons can be cleaned and refitted with new piston rings, provided the pistons meet or exceed manufacturers' specifications. Be very careful when cleaning piston ring grooves and piston domes or heads. Even the smallest scratches may lead to premature failure. Generally, pistons are not repaired. New pistons are usually a better choice than attempting to repair damaged pistons. Pistons with worn grooves, damaged heads, scratched sides, or worn skirts are better replaced than refitted.

# ENGINE VALVE ASSEMBLY OPERATION

The internal combustion engine valve train assembly is one of the most critical systems in the engine. The valve assembly works along with the pistons and engine cylinder and block assembly to perform compression, and complete the internal combustion engine events. Engine valves can be arranged in several different configurations. The valves may be housed

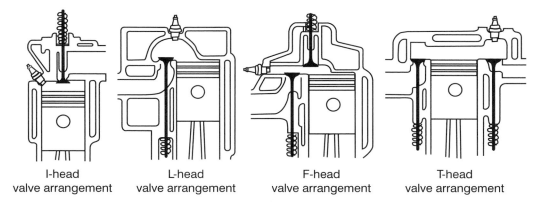

|  I-head  |  L-head  |  F-head  |  T-head  |
| valve arrangement | valve arrangement | valve arrangement | valve arrangement |

**10-10. Four engine valve arrangements.**

in the block, parallel to the cylinder. This is common on some small engines and is called an "L-head" engine. On most larger engines, the valves will be housed in the cylinder head. In this configuration, the valves are located directly above the cylinder and the engine. This engine is called an overhead valve engine.

The basic components of the valve assembly are the intake and exhaust valves, the valve springs and spring retainers, the valve seats, the valve guides, the camshaft, and valve pushrods. Their basic functions are:

- intake valves open and seal the intake ports;
- exhaust valves open and seal the exhaust ports;
- valve springs close the valves and hold the valves closed;
- valve seats seal the valve against the ports;
- spring retainers hold the springs on the end of the valves;
- valve guides support the valve stem as the valve moves back and forth;
- camshafts open and close the valves; and
- pushrods transfer the rotating movement of the camshaft to the linear movement of the valves.

Engine valves operate in very hot conditions and under high cylinder pressures. If a four-stroke cycle engine is operating at 3600 crankshaft revolutions per minute, each valve is opening and closing 30 times each second. The temperatures at the head of an exhaust valve can reach up to 1200°F. The intake valve is subjected to the heat of combustion and then a blast of cold air during each intake stroke.

Engine valves have two basic parts—the valve head and the valve stem. The surface of the valve head seals against the valve seat. The valve surface

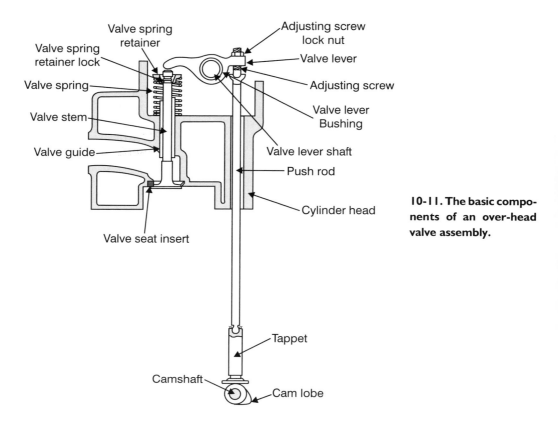

10-11. The basic components of an over-head valve assembly.

is called the **valve face**. The valve margin is the edge of the valve head. The valve neck is the part of the valve stem that is in the valve guide (see Figure 10-12).

## RE-CONDITIONING ENGINE VALVES

Engine valves can be cleaned and refitted in an engine. Usually, this involves removing the valve and grinding the valve face and seat. This type of repair requires special equipment and considerable know-how. Valve face and seat angles are very precise and must be re-conditioned properly. Engine machine shops are usually your best choice for repairing valves and cylinder heads. When installing new valves, it is recommended that a machine shop do the work. The valve guides and seats may need to be refitted or replaced. Some small engine valves can be refitted with relatively simple specialized equipment. Some manufacturers recommend lapping valves. This is a process of using a valve lapping compound, which is an abrasive type paste, to resurface the valve face and seat to match. Be sure to check the manufacturer's recommendations as many do not recommend lapping valves and seats.

## VALVE TIMING

The ports are passageways in and out of the combustion chamber. The basic function of the valves is to open and close these ports at the right time and for the right length of time. The intake port allows the air and fuel mixture to enter the combustion chamber of an Otto cycle—a spark ignition engine— during the intake stroke. The intake port on a Diesel cycle engine—a compression ignition engine—allows only air to enter the combustion chamber during the intake stroke. A typical valve timing pattern is for the intake valve to open 10 degrees of crankshaft rotation before top dead center. Also, the intake valve stays open beyond BDC, and actually closes as the piston is going up on the compression stroke. The intake valve will be completely closed at about 50 degrees of crankshaft rotation past BDC. Note that the intake valve actually is open 240 degrees of crankshaft rotation for a typical four-stroke cycle engine.

The exhaust port allows the burned combustion gases to escape from the combustion chamber during the exhaust stroke. The basic purpose of the exhaust valve is to open and close the exhaust port. The removal of exhaust gases is called *scavenging*. The more efficiently an engine can remove exhaust gases, the

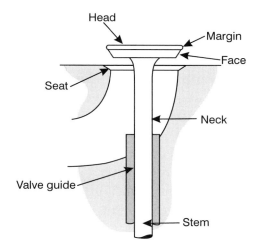

**10-12. Parts of an engine valve.**

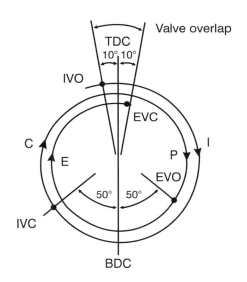

C = Compression
E = Exhaust
P = Power
I = Intake
IVO = Intake valve opens
IVC = Intake valve closes
EVO = Exhaust valve opens
EVC = Exhaust valve closes

**10-13. Valve timing spiral showing typical valve timing.**

more efficiently it will be able to get air and fuel in the engine on the next intake stroke. Generally, on a typical four-stroke cycle valve timing pattern, the exhaust valve is open the same number of degrees of crankshaft rotation as the intake valve. The exhaust valve will start to open at about 50 degrees of crankshaft rotation before BDC of the power stroke. The exhaust valve will remain open until about 10 degrees past TDC of the exhaust stroke. The total number of degrees an exhaust valve is open is also 240 degrees. Valve overlap is the time that both the intake and exhaust valves are slightly open. For a typical engine, it is about 20 degrees of crankshaft rotation. This knowledge and understanding of how the four-stroke cycle engine operates is very beneficial when attempting to determine if an engine is properly timed.

## VALVE SPRINGS

The valve spring serves the important function of holding the valve face tightly against the valve seat. The valve spring also holds the tappets or cam followers tightly against the cam lobes as the camshaft is opening and closing the valves. Most engines use only one valve spring for each valve, however, some engines use two springs, one inside of another, for each valve. Generally, valve spring failure is rare unless the engine has been subjected to severe operating conditions. An engine that has been allowed to operate too hot, too fast, or without adequate lubrication may experience valve spring failure. Valve springs may simply wear out from use, however, they usually will last as long as the valves. Valve springs can be tested for compression strength and spring free length according to the manufacturer's recommendations. It is generally a good practice to replace the valve springs when the valves are being replaced.

# ENGINE CAMSHAFT
# OPERATION AND DESIGN

The purpose of the camshaft is to open and close the engine valves. The camshaft is a rotating shaft having lobes that create the movement needed to open and close the valves. There will usually be one lobe for each valve. The camshaft is housed either in the block or on top of the cylinder head. Most internal combustion engines use only one camshaft, however some larger engines may use two. The camshaft is driven, or rotated, by the crankshaft. On a four-stroke cycle engine, the camshaft will always turn at one half of the speed of the crankshaft. Camshafts can be driven by gear assemblies, chain and sprocket assemblies, or belt assemblies. These are called timing gears, timing chains, and timing belts, respectively.

## CAMSHAFTS FOR FLAT HEAD ENGINES

Camshafts that are housed in the engine block use some form of pushrod to transfer the shape of the camshaft lobes into the up and down movement of the valves. A common design of small engines, where the valves are also housed in the block, is to use relatively short pushrods, sometimes called tappets, to open and closes the valves. One end of the tappet rides on the camshaft lobe and the other end comes in contact with the end of the valve stem.

## CAMSHAFTS FOR OVERHEAD VALVE ENGINES

In another camshaft configuration, the camshaft is housed in the engine block and the engine has overhead valves. A cam follower, sometimes called a lifter, "rides" on the cam lobe as the camshaft rotates. The lifter may be a solid lifter, made of solid metal, or a hydraulic lifter. Hydraulic lifters are filled with engine oil to create smoother and quieter valve operation. The use of hydraulic lifters reduces the need for valve clearance adjustment. A pushrod transfers the movement of the cam follower or lifter to a rocker arm. The rocker arm then opens and closes the valves. When the camshaft is housed on the cylinder head, this is called an overhead camshaft. Overhead camshafts reduce the need for many valve assembly parts needed in in-block camshaft designs. Most engines currently use the in-block camshaft design.

## CAMSHAFT DESIGN

Camshafts can be designed for different engine operations. The actual shape of the camshaft lobes can be designed for different engine applications. By changing the shape of the camshaft lobes in an engine, you can significantly change the operating characteristics of the engine. Some basic camshaft terms are lift, duration, and slope. Lift is the relative height of the lobe and this creates the relative amount of valve opening. ***Duration*** refers to the length of time the valve is open based upon the number of degrees of crankshaft rotation. *Lobe profile* determines the relative time that it takes the lobe to fully open and then fully close the valve. The lobe profile can be ground to shapes which open and close the valves quicker or more gradually.

Camshafts can be refitted and reinstalled in an engine. However, many times it is more economical to replace the camshaft. Also, camshaft bearings can be replaced when they become worn. Replacing camshaft bearings is similar to replacing crankshaft bearings on most engines. Be sure to replace the camshaft and all bearings based upon the manufacturer's recommendations.

## VALVE CLEARANCE

*Valve clearance* refers to the gap between the tappet and the valve. This gap is necessary to maintain valve timing and to allow the valve to seal against the valve seat as the valve heats and expands during operation. When checking or adjusting valve clearance, always consult the manufacturer's service recommendations. Generally valve clearances for solid lifters or tappets are measured with a flat thickness gage. Some manufacturers recommend checking the valve clearances while the engine is cold, sometimes referred to as a "cold" setting. Other manufacturers recommend that the clearance be checked and set while the engine is running. This is sometimes called a "hot" setting. Hydraulic lifters are often set initially while the engine is not running and then set again while the engine is running. Also, many times the intake and exhaust valves have different settings. Exhaust valves tend to get hotter than intake valves and, therefore, some manufacturers recommend a larger exhaust valve clearance. When

10-14. Adjusting valve clearance.

checking and adjusting valve clearances while the engine is not running, be sure to position the camshaft lobes in the proper position. Some manufacturers will recommend setting the intake and exhaust valves at TDC of the compression stroke. Others may specify that the clearances be set at specific camshaft positions for each valve. When checking and adjusting valve clearances, always follow the manufacturer's recommended procedures.

# DETERMINING
# THE ENGINE FIRING ORDER

Internal combustion engines operate based upon a series of events. The proper sequence of engine operations is critical for the engine to run. *Firing order* refers to the order in which the cylinders complete a power stroke. For the engine to operate smoothly, the firing order must be evenly spaced.

A good example is to visualize a four-cylinder, four-stroke cycle engine. This engine requires two 360° crankshaft revolutions to complete one engine cycle. This represents 720 degrees of crankshaft rotation. Therefore, the engine needs to start a power stroke every 180 degrees of crankshaft rotation (720°/4cyl.). Since there are four cylinders and four different strokes, every 180 degrees of crankshaft rotation one of the cylinders is doing the intake stroke, one the compression stroke, one the power stroke, and one the exhaust stroke. This sequence balances the engine operation.

Now, for this same engine consider that two pistons are going up and two are going down at the same time. Also, when two pistons are at TDC, then the other two pistons are at BDC. If you consider the crankshaft design, two crankshaft throws would be opposite of the other two crankshaft throws, or 180 degrees offset. On most four cylinder engines the number 1 and 4 pistons move together, and the number 2 and 3 pistons move together. This helps to balance the engine operation and reduce vibration. Pistons are generally numbered in the relative position from the front of the engine (radiator end) to the back (flywheel end). Therefore, a common four-cylinder firing order is 1, 2, 4, and 3. However, a 1, 3, 4, and 2 firing order would also be possible.

As an extension of this exercise, consider a six-cylinder, four-stroke cycle, in-line engine. The engine would need to start a power stroke every 120 degrees of crankshaft rotation (720°/6 cyl.). Therefore, the cylinders are divided into three pairs. To help with the design of the crankshaft and balance engine operation, we would pair number 1 and 6, 2 and 5, and 3 and 4 pistons. These pairs move together, but are on opposite strokes. For example, when the number 1 piston is moving down on the power stroke, the number 6 piston is moving down on the intake stroke. Therefore, a common firing order for this type of engine would be: 1, 5, 3, 6, 2, and 4. Note that once the firing order of the first half of the cylinders is set, the rest of the firing order is determined.

The firing order for other types of engines can be determined by consulting the manufacturer's service information. The concept of firing order is fundamental to servicing and maintaining engines. If you can visualize and comprehend this fundamental concept, you will be able to understand repair and maintenance practices more clearly.

# MAINTAINING THE PRIMARY ENGINE COMPRESSION SYSTEM

The key to proper maintenance of the internal combustion engine compression system is to properly maintain the other engine operating systems. The cooling and lubrication systems are designed to protect the engine's internal parts. If you maintain the operating systems according the manufacturer's recommendations, the engine primary system components should last for many hours of use. Be sure to not allow engines to operate under severe conditions, such as when the engine is overheated. Be sure to use the recommended lubricants, and follow a regular maintenance schedule.

Some manufacturers recommend regular service and testing of engine components. Examples include checking valve clearances and performing periodic compression tests. Generally, a well maintained and properly operated engine will last well beyond the manufacturer's expectations. Studies of agricultural equipment have indicated that the life expectancy of farm tractors has approximately doubled in the last thirty years. Well maintained farm tractors operate from 3000 to 4000 hours before requiring service work. Such work would include removing and reconditioning the cylinder head for example. Today, modern engines operate from 6000 to 8000 hours before needing major service. New technologies in engine design and maintenance have greatly increased the life expectancy of the internal combustion engines used in agriculture.

# SUMMARY

The primary system engine components of the internal combustion engine are those components that are directly involved in creating compression and producing power. The compression system of the internal combustion engine is designed to efficiently compress the air (or air-fuel mixture) to increase the potential energy of the combustion of the fuel and then allow the rapidly expanding combustion energy to be converted to mechanical power.

The compression system of conventional internal combustion engines uses pistons that move up and down, linear movement, in a cylinder. The primary system components are the cylinder block, crankshaft, pistons, cylinder head, valve assembly, camshaft, and related components. These components are designed to operate under varying conditions for a long period of time.

The internal combustion engine operates as the operating systems work together to convert chemical energy into useable mechanical energy. All of the components must be properly maintained in order to perform as they were designed.

# REVIEW QUESTIONS

1. What is engine compression ratio and how is it calculated?

2. What are the differences between gasoline and diesel engine compression ratios?

3. How do you measure engine compression?

4. What are engine cylinder blocks, cylinder heads, and crankshaft assemblies?

5. What the basic engine piston components?

6. How do you measure pistons and piston rings?

7. What are the basic components of an engine valve assembly?

8. What are the functions of the engine camshaft?

9. What determines the engine firing order for multiple cylinder engines?

10. What are some basic practices for maintaining the primary engine compression system?

# APPLYING THE CONCEPTS

1. Compare several engines on a farm, agribusiness, or school facility to determine the different kinds of engine blocks, cylinder arrangements, and cylinder heads. Make an inventory of what you found. What general observations can you make about the primary engine systems of the engines you observed?

2. Check the compression of an engine. Be sure to check the repair manual for recommendations. Some small engines can be checked by turning the flywheel by hand and determining the "rebound". Use a compression gage to check compression of larger engines. Can you estimate the compression ratio of the engine?

3. Remove the cylinder head and head gasket from a small, single-cylinder engine. Rotate the engine flywheel and observe the action of the piston and valves. Identify each engine stroke (intake, compression, power, and exhaust) and describe what happens during each stroke. Turn the engine flywheel until the piston is TDC at the beginning of the intake stroke. Place a reference mark (with chalk or a marker) on the engine flywheel at the 12:00 position. Turn the flywheel to operate the engine through one complete 4-stroke cycle. Develop a valve timing diagram for the engine based on your observations.

4. Remove and install the head and head gasket of a small engine. Be sure to use a torque wrench to tighten the head bolts in the proper sequence. Write down an outline of the recommended procedure from the repair manual.

5. Check the crankshaft journal and bearing wear on a small engine. Also check crankshaft endplay according to the specifications. What are the recommended crankshaft bearing and journal specifications? Why do you think the specifications of crankshafts are so important for long engine life?

6. Properly remove, measure and install piston rings on a engine piston. You can also learn to use a ring compressor to install the piston in the cylinder. Be sure to read and outline the procedure from the manufacturer for installing the piston and piston rings.

7. Check valve clearances and specifications. A small engine is good learning tool. You can learn to properly remove and install the engine valves. Be sure to check the valve specifications according to the manufacturer's recommendations.

# 11

# UNDERSTANDING AND MAINTAINING AUXILIARY SYSTEMS

An internal combustion engine operates based on a number of systems—intake, fuel, exhaust, cooling, ignition, lubrication, starting, governing—that perform critical engine functions. These systems work together to allow the engine to run efficiently and produce usable mechanical power.

The internal combustion engine operates from a centralized engine block. The engine block houses the primary engine components that create compression and convert chemical energy to mechanical energy.

This chapter presents the operating principles, major components, and general maintenance procedures for internal combustion engine operating systems.

11-1. The four-cylinder engine in this pickup truck has a series of auxiliary systems that work together to allow the engine to run efficiently.

# OBJECTIVES

This chapter covers the fundamentals of internal combustion engine systems. Upon completing the chapter, you will:

1. Describe how an internal combustion engine intake system operates, including the operation of engine turbochargers, superchargers, and intercoolers.

2. Explain how different engine fuel systems operate and the characteristics of engine fuels.

3. Describe the components and functions of exhaust systems.

4. Explain how engine cooling systems manage engine heat and distinguish between air direct and liquid cooling systems.

5. Describe the basic principles of operation of different ignition systems.

6. Explain the operation of the internal combustion engine lubrication system and characteristics of engine lubricants.

7. Describe the operation and components of engine starting systems.

8. Explain the functions of the engine speed governing system.

## TERMS

air intake system
battery-type ignition system
boost
carburetor
cetane number
conduction
convection
cranking amperage
engine coolant
engine cooling system
exhaust system
fuel system
governing system
hydrocarbon fuel
hydrodynamic lubrication
hydrostatic lubrication
ignition system
intercooler
lubrication system
magneto-type ignition system
octane number
radiation
refining
saturated hydrocarbon fuel
starting system
supercharger
turbocharger
vacuum gage
viscosity
waste gate

# INTAKE SYSTEM

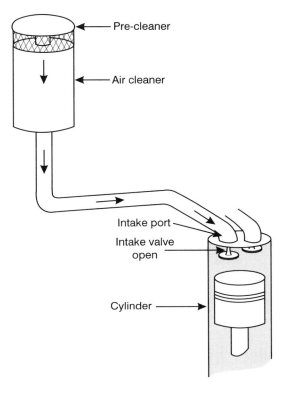

The *air intake system* allows clean air to enter the combustion chamber. The air intake system is designed to clean dirt particles from the air without causing severe restrictions to the free flow air. Too much air restriction would decrease engine power output.

The air intake of the internal combustion engine operates during the intake event of the engine cycle. The four-stroke cycle engine most clearly demonstrates the operation of the intake system. This system is represented in Figure 11-2. As the piston travels down, the intake valve is open, and air is pushed through the intake system and into the combustion chamber by atmospheric pressure.

**11-2. The operation of a basic engine intake system.**

The general value of atmospheric pressure at sea level is 14.7 psi (pounds per square inch). As engines operate at higher altitudes, the amount of atmospheric pressure decreases. This is why many manufacturers of agricultural equipment have operating specifications for higher altitude environments. At higher altitudes, the air is less dense and, therefore, internal combustion engines get less air on which to operate.

Restrictions in the intake system decrease the volumetric efficiency of the engine. As air cleaners become clogged with dirt, the volumetric efficiency of the engine decreases. If you were to remove the air cleaner, the volumetric efficiency of the engine would increase. But, the life expectancy of the engine would be shortened because of abrasion from grit. For this reason, never operate an engine with the air cleaner removed.

A basic intake system has these components:

**Precleaner:** removes larger particles and debris from the incoming air.

**Air cleaner:** removes fine particles from the air.

**Intake manifold:** carries air (or air-fuel mixture) to the individual cylinders of a multicylinder engine.

**Intake valve:** opens and closes the intake port, controlling air movement into and out of the combustion chamber.

**Intake port:** intake passage into the cylinder.

## TESTING THE INTAKE SYSTEM

A *vacuum gage* is a tool used to test the intake system. The vacuum gage is attached to a vacuum line from the intake manifold. Using a reference chart, possible problems can be determined, such as leaking gaskets, a damaged intake valve, or incorrect engine timing. A vacuum gage is also a very useful tool for determining engine performance—the efficiency of operation and fuel usage.

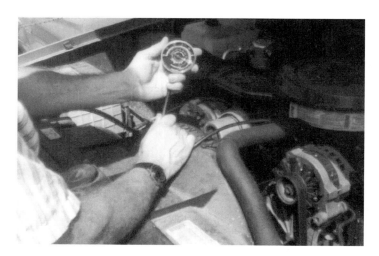

11-3. A vacuum gage being used to test an intake system.

## TURBOCHARGERS, SUPERCHARGERS, AND INTERCOOLERS

An engine *turbocharger* is a turbine-driven air compressor pump. The turbocharger turbine is driven by the exhaust gases of the engine. As the hot exhaust is forced from the cylinders, it pushes against the turbine fins, causing the turbine to spin. The turbine is directly connected to another turbine with the fins pointed in the opposite direction—toward the intake valve. The exhaust turbine spins the intake turbine, which

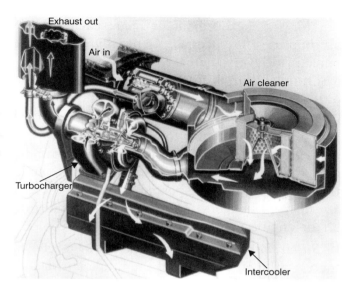

Exhaust out

Air in

Air cleaner

**11-4. A turbocharged system including an intercooler used on a diesel engine.**

Turbocharger

Intercooler

forces air into the combustion chamber during the intake stroke. Both gasoline and diesel engines may have turbochargers. However, in the agricultural industry, diesel engines are the most common type of turbocharged engines.

The increased intake air pressure created by a turbocharger is called **boost**. Most turbochargers limit the maximum amount of boost produced. A device that controls the boost pressure is a **waste gate**. The term is derived from the action of the waste gate—diverting the excess air pressure. Turbochargers can spin at over ten thousand revolutions per minute. Because of this speed, turbochargers require constant lubrication. Some manufacturers recommend specific oils for turbocharged engines. Also, some manufacturers recommend specific cool down periods. This will ensure that the turbocharger has cooled before shutting the engine off. Some manufacturers also specify certain practices when starting turbocharged engines after the engine oil has been changed. One such recommendation is to turn the engine over, while not allowing the engine to start, for 15 seconds to ensure that oil has reached the turbocharger. Many turbocharged engines require shorter periodic maintenance intervals than naturally aspirated engines. The key point is to check and follow all recommendations for turbocharged engines, as they may differ from those for naturally aspirated engines.

One of the main benefits of turbocharged engines is that they do not decrease in engine power output as the altitude changes as much as naturally aspirated engines do. Most engine performance tests are carried out (or standardized) at or near sea level. As the altitude increases, the air becomes less dense. Generally, engine output decreases by 2 to 3 percent for every increase of one thousand feet in altitude. A turbocharged engine's output decreases less than 1 percent for each thousand feet of altitude change. At altitudes higher than 5000 feet above sea level, this can be a good reason to use turbocharged engines.

Turbochargers tend to increase the temperature of the intake air. The air temperature may increase to several hundred degrees Fahrenheit. This decreases the density of the air. An intercooler can be used to decrease the temperature of the heated intake air, increasing its density. *Intercoolers* are heat exchangers. They cool the heated intake air either by circulating air or engine coolant through the intercooler.

*Superchargers* are mechanically or electrically driven air pumps, which increase the air pressure of the intake air. Usually, superchargers are driven by a belt or chain. Superchargers are not very common on agricultural engines.

## Types of Air Cleaners

Three basic types of air cleaners are used on internal combustion engines: dry element, oil foam, and oil bath. The dry element air cleaner has become the most common type used on agricultural engines. It is found on all types and sizes of engines. The filters are easy to maintain and effectively remove small particles from the air.

The oil foam air filter is used extensively on small engines. The filter is saturated with a small amount of engine oil. The air is drawn through the filter and the dirt particles are collected by the oil. Oil foam filters require periodic maintenance and tend to disintegrate if not properly maintained. A common maintenance interval for the small engine oil foam filter is to clean and re-oil every 25 hours of operation. Some manufacturers use a thin oil foam filter to cover and help keep dry element air cleaners clean.

The oil bath air cleaner has a bowl, or reservoir, of engine oil on the bottom. The air travels down through the center of the filter and goes back up through the outer diameter passageway. The air flows through the oil bowl causing the oil to coat the filtering fiber material. Dirt particles are trapped by the oil film on the fibers and settle to the bottom of the bowl as the oil flows up and down the filter. Oil bath filters require frequent periodic checks to ensure proper operation.

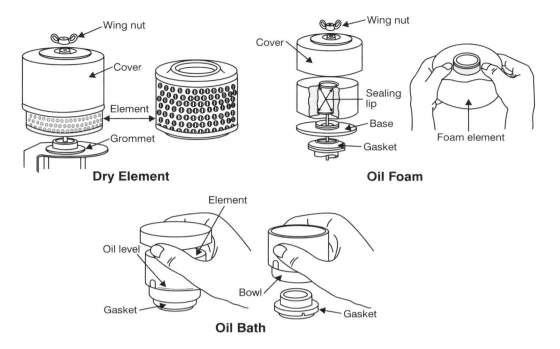

11-5. Three different types of air cleaners.

## GENERAL MAINTENANCE PRINCIPLES FOR INTAKE SYSTEMS

All intake systems require periodic preventive maintenance. The manufacturer's recommendations should always be followed. Use the best quality filters, cleaners, and oils. Never operate an engine without the proper air cleaners installed. Check on a regular basis for intake system leaks and worn hoses and gaskets. When servicing intake systems and their components, be sure to work in a clean environment. Do not use gasoline to clean air filters. Gasoline will damage most types of filters, is not a good cleaning solvent, and is very dangerous to work with.

# FUEL SYSTEMS

The *fuel system* is designed to deliver clean fuel to the combustion chamber and meter the correct amount needed for efficient operation. The fuel must be delivered at the correct time and in the correct proportion with air for the engine to operate properly. There are a variety of fuel systems and components to meet the needs of different kinds of engines, fuels, and applications. However, all fuel systems operate on the same basic principles.

Engines operate most efficiently at an optimum air-to-fuel ratio. The ratio of 15 parts of air to 1 part of fuel, by weight, is considered the optimal ratio. The actual air-to-fuel ratio for an engine is about 13.5: 1. This means that not all of the fuel is being burned efficiently to produce power. The air-to-fuel ratio is based upon the thermal and volumetric efficiencies of the engine. Based upon the volume, it takes about 9,000 gallons of air to burn 1 gallon of fuel. Keeping an engine properly tuned and maintained will increase the fuel efficiency.

## TYPES OF FUEL SYSTEMS

There are two basic types of internal combustion engine fuel systems: carburetor and injection. Carburetor systems use a carburetor to meter the fuel and mix the fuel with the intake air. Injection systems inject the fuel into either the intake system or directly into the combustion chamber.

## TYPES OF FUELS

Internal combustion engines can run on a variety of fuels. The two most common are gasoline and diesel. Gasoline is the predominant fuel for spark ignition engines and diesel fuel is the predominant fuel for compression ignition engines. However, internal combustion engines can also run on propane, natural gas, alcohol, kerosene, and other fuels. A common characteristic of all of these is they are **hydrocarbon fuels**. The chemical composition of these fuels is based upon hydrogen and carbon.

| Fuel | Carbon Content of Compounds | Uses | Hydrocarbon | Molecular Formula | HR Octane Number |
|------|------|------|------|------|------|
| Natural gas | $C_1$-$C_4$ | Industrial and home fuel | n-Butane | $C_4H_{10}$ | 93.6 |
| Propane | $C_3H_8$ | Bottled fuel gas | n-Pentane | $C_5H_{12}$ | 61.7 |
| Butane | $C_4H_{10}$ | Bottled fuel gas | 2-Methylbutane | $C_5H_{12}$ | 92.6 |
| Gasoline | $C_5$-$C_{12}$ | Motor fuel | n-Hexane | $C_6H_{14}$ | 24.8 |
| Kerosene | $C_{12}$-$C_{16}$ | Jet fuel, domestic heating | n-Heptane | $C_7H_{16}$ | 0.0 |
| Fuel oil | $C_{20}$-$C_{18}$ | Diesel fuel, industrial fuel | Methybenzene (Toulene) | $C_7H_8$ | 103.2 |
| | | | 2,2,4-Trimethylpentane (Isooctane) | $C_8H_{18}$ | 100.0 |
| | | | Isopropylbenzene | $C_9H_{12}$ | 113.0 |

**11-6. Hydrocarbons and uses.**

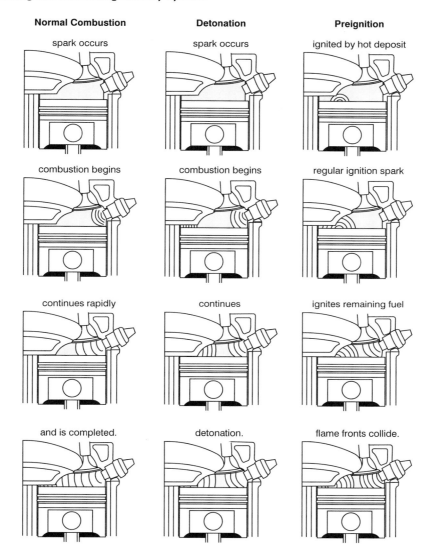

| Normal Combustion | Detonation | Preignition |
|---|---|---|
| spark occurs | spark occurs | ignited by hot deposit |
| combustion begins | combustion begins | regular ignition spark |
| continues rapidly | continues | ignites remaining fuel |
| and is completed. | detonation. | flame fronts collide. |

11-7. A comparison of preignition and denotation.

Gasoline and diesel fuel are considered to be ***saturated hydrocarbon fuels***. In complete combustion, they form carbon dioxide and water and produce large amounts of heat energy. They are refined petroleum products. Gasoline chemical compounds have between 5 and 12 carbon atoms. Diesel fuel compounds have between 15 and 18 carbon atoms.

Alcohols are made of compounds called hydrocarbon derivatives. While there are many different kinds of alcohols, methyl and ethyl are the most

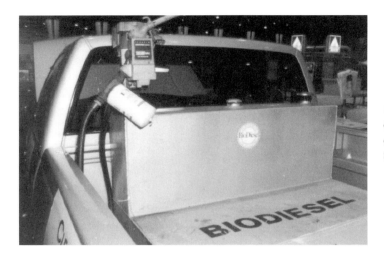

11-8. This pickup truck is equipped to operate on bio-diesel fuel. (Courtesy, Jasper S. Lee)

common kinds used for fuels. Ethyl alcohol, or ethanol, $CH_3CH_2OH$, is the most common type of alcohol. Ethanol is also called grain alcohol. Grain alcohol is often produced by fermenting sugars from grains and other agricultural products. Methyl alcohol, or methanol, $CH_3OH$ is also called wood alcohol and is poisonous. Both of these types of alcohol can be used to run internal combustion engines. Ethanol is generally the more common, more compatible, and most readily available fuel alcohol.

## RATING FUELS

The *octane number* is a rating of the burning quality of gasoline. The higher the octane number, the slower and smoother the gasoline burns. A lower octane gasoline will burn faster. An engine will "knock" if too low of an octane fuel is used. The engine knock is caused by an explosion of gasoline as it burns across the combustion chamber. The higher the compression ratio of a gasoline powered engine, the higher the octane level of gasoline needed.

There are two methods for determining the octane rating of gasoline. One method is called the research method. The letter R is used to indicate research method octane ratings. The research method is based upon the chemical composition of the gasoline. Isoocatane ($C_8H_{18}$) and heptane ($C_7H_{16}$) are used to determine the R octane value. Isoocatane has been assigned a value of 100 and heptane a value of 0. Therefore, a mixture of 90 percent isooctane and 10 percent heptane would have a R octane value of 90. The second method for determining the octane rating of a gasoline is called the motor method. The letter M is used to designate the motor method octane rating. This method is based upon testing the gasoline mixtures in test engines to determine the relative octane level. To avoid confusion and get a more practical octane rating, the R and M octane ratings are averaged for gasoline mixtures. The formula (R + M)/2 is used the get the "pump" octane rating.

| Engine Compression Ratio | Octane Number Required |
|---|---|
| 5:1 | 73 |
| 6:1 | 81 |
| 7:1 | 87 |
| 8:1 | 91 |
| 9:1 | 95 |
| 10:1 | 98 |
| 11:1 | 100 |
| 12:1 | 102 |

11-9. Octane number and compression ratio.

Fuel additives can be used to increase the octane rating of gasoline. Tetraethyl lead $(C_2H_5)_4Pb$ was used for many years to increase the octane rating of gasoline. However, because of the pollution and health hazards associated with lead, it is no longer legal to use this compound in gasoline. Aromatic hydrocarbon compounds are now used as fuel additives. These compounds tend to burn slower than the other hydrocarbon compounds in gasoline. An example of an aromatic hydrocarbon is toluene $(C_6H_5CH_3)$.

Diesel fuel is rated by the cetane number. Cetane is a hydrocarbon $(C_{16}H_{34})$ found in petroleum. The **cetane number** is the percentage of cetane by volume in the mixture, which indicates the ignition quality of a diesel fuel. Most diesel engines used in agriculture have a recommended minimum cetane number for the diesel fuel. A minimum cetane number of 40 is common. Many diesel fuels used in agriculture have a cetane rating between 45 and 50.

There are also two basic kinds of diesel fuel, number 1 and number 2. No. 1 diesel fuel is used in cold weather conditions and No. 2 is used in warm weather conditions. Be sure to use the recommended diesel fuel based on the type of operating conditions.

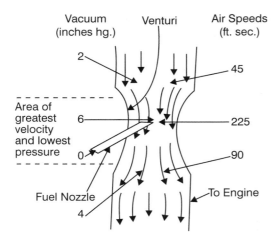

11-10. **A venturi is a restricted air passage in a carburetor.**

# CARBURETOR FUEL SYSTEMS

Carburetors have been used for many years on all kinds of engines. They work best for those fuels that vaporize easily, such as gasoline. The carburetor is placed in the intake system between the air cleaner and the intake port. The purpose of the *carburetor* is to meter the correct amount of fuel, mix the fuel with the intake air, and atomize the fuel. The carburetor operates on basic principles of air movement. A carburetor contains a venturi, or restricted air passage, that reduces the diameter of the intake port. As the air is pushed through the venturi, it speeds up, and the pressure decreases. The air goes from a larger-diameter area, through a smaller-diameter area, and then into a larger-diameter area again. Once the air moves back into a larger-diameter area, it slows down. The carburetor is designed to "bleed" fuel into the moving air in the low-pressure area. Actually, the surrounding air pressure pushes the fuel into the intake due to the low pressure as the air speeds through the venturi.

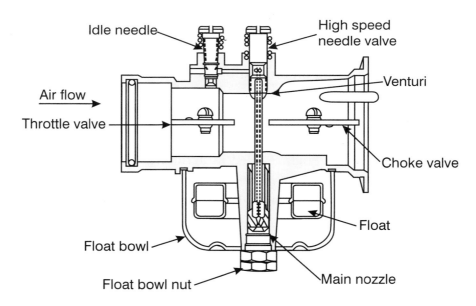

11-11. **Parts of a carburetor.**

Carburetors are still used on many gasoline-powered small engines. However, large gasoline-powered engines are now fueled by injection systems. Carburetors are not as efficient as the modern fuel injection systems.

## INJECTION FUEL SYSTEMS

Injection fuel systems inject the fuel into the combustion chamber or into the intake manifold. All diesel engines and most large gasoline engines use fuel injection systems. There are two basic types of fuel injection systems: mechanical and electronic. Mechanical fuel injection systems use mechanical-type pumps to inject high-pressure fuel into the combustion chamber. Electronic fuel injection systems use electrically operated injectors to inject the fuel into either the combustion chamber or the intake manifold. Some fuel injection systems use a mechanical-type system that is controlled by electrical sensors and controls.

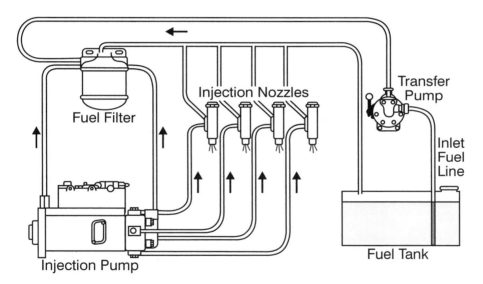

11-12. A diesel fuel-injection system.

Most diesel fuel systems use mechanical fuel injection. The diesel fuel is injected directly into the combustion chamber at the proper time for ignition. One kind of system uses injection nozzles. A low-pressure pump transfers the diesel fuel from the tank, through the filters and lines, to the injection pump. An injection pump directs high-pressure diesel fuel to each cylinder. These pumps can produce injection pressures of 2500 psi to 3000 psi. The injection pump can be controlled mechanically or electronically. This kind of fuel injection system is widely used on agricultural equipment.

Another kind of mechanical fuel injection system uses individual injectors for each cylinder. These injectors are driven usually by a camshaft. The injectors deliver diesel fuel into the combustion chamber as the fuel injection camshaft rotates. This system is used on some large diesel engines.

Gasoline engines can also have fuel injection systems. These are usually electronic type systems. The electronic injectors can deliver the fuel into the intake manifold, the intake ports, or the combustion chamber. The injectors operate by a magnetic pulse. An air-flow sensor or valve will determine the amount of air entering the engine and then determine the length of time the injectors deliver fuel. The more fuel needed, the longer the injector delivers fuel. Some engines have what appears to be a carburetor, but it actually uses electronic fuel injectors instead of the venturi air pressure. Electronic fuel injection systems will work with many different types of fuels. Furthermore, because they are more efficient than carburetors, electronic fuel injectors are becoming more and more widely used.

**11-13. An electronic fuel-injection system.**

## GENERAL PRINCIPLES OF FUEL SYSTEM MAINTENANCE

The first general principle of fuel system maintenance is to use clean, quality fuels. Be sure to use the type of fuel recommended by the equipment manufacturer. Second, keep the fuel filters properly maintained. Third, follow off-season fuel management practices. This is very important when the equipment may sit idle for several months, such as lawn care equipment. Fourth, only make fuel system adjustments according to the recommendations of the service manual. Do not guess at proper fuel system adjustments.

# EXHAUST SYSTEMS

The *exhaust system* removes the exhaust gases and particles from the combustion chamber. The exhaust system also helps to manage engine noise and heat transfer. Exhaust systems are one of the simplest engine systems.

The basic exhaust system has these components:

**Exhaust valve:** opens and closes the exhaust system passage.

**Exhaust port:** passage that the exhaust gases flow through. Several passages together are called an exhaust manifold.

**Exhaust manifold:** collects exhaust gases from individual cylinders.

**Exhaust pipe:** tube that connects the exhaust manifold to the muffler.

Note: Not all engines will have an exhaust pipe. On some engines, the muffler will mount directly onto the exhaust manifold.

**Muffler:** a sound deadening device used to quiet engine operation. Also eliminates (or reduces) sparks in exhaust gases.

## *EXHAUST SYSTEM OPERATION*

The exhaust system is designed to allow the exhaust gases and particles from the combustion process to freely exit the combustion chamber during the exhaust

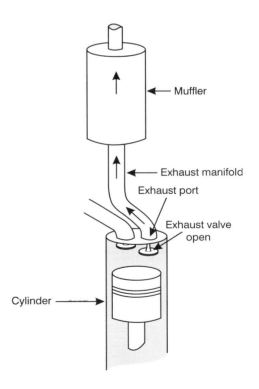

11-14. The basic operation and parts of an exhaust system.

stroke. If an exhaust system becomes restricted, the combustion chamber cannot efficiently take in a new charge of air and fuel during the intake stroke.

A restricted exhaust system will create back pressure. This will decrease the volumetric efficiency of the engine. If too much back pressure is created, the engine cannot clear the exhaust from the combustion chamber and, therefore, not as much air can enter. Exhaust systems are designed to fit the operating characteristics of the agricultural machine. For example, some exhaust systems on lawnmowers are designed to send the exhaust under the mower. Other exhaust systems send the exhaust toward the side, rear, or over the top of the machine. Do not re-route or re-design exhaust systems without full consideration of changes in system back pressure and where the exhaust is being routed. A freer-flowing exhaust system will increase volumetric efficiency, however, other problems may occur.

## EXHAUST SYSTEM MAINTENANCE

The exhaust system is fairly easy to maintain. As with all engine systems, be sure to check the manufacturer's recommendations. However, many manufacturers will not include exhaust system maintenance procedures because the system is so basic.

Always check to make sure the exhaust system does not have any leaks. Leaking exhaust fumes can be very dangerous, especially in confined areas. Also, make periodic checks to ensure that the exhaust system is not clogged. Many agricultural machines are stored outside, so be sure that the exhaust system does not allow rain, dust, dirt, or snow to enter the engine. Do not operate an engine when the exhaust system components have been removed—the exhaust system is designed to remove heat from the engine. An incomplete exhaust system could result in overheating and seriously damage the engine.

# COOLING SYSTEMS

The *engine cooling system* is designed to manage the heat produced by the combustion of the air and fuel. Every engine has an optimum operating temperature. The task of the cooling system is to allow the engine to reach the optimum temperature and then maintain this temperature under varying conditions.

The operation of the cooling system affects the thermal efficiency and life of the engine. Engines operating at too low temperature will not efficiently burn the fuel. Engines operating at too high temperature will increase the stresses on the internal engine parts.

There are two basic kinds of cooling systems: liquid coolant and air direct. The liquid coolant cooling system uses a liquid to transfer heat from the engine components to the surrounding air. The air direct cooling system transfers the heat of the engine components directly to the surrounding air. Both cooling systems require clean air to operate efficiently. These cooling systems operate on the basic principles of heat transfer.

## HEAT TRANSFER—CONDUCTION, CONVECTION, AND RADIATION

Not all of the heat produced by the combustion process is used by the engine to produce mechanical power. Actually, even a very efficient engine only uses about one-third of the heat energy produced to provide mechanical power. The other two-thirds of the heat energy is removed by the cooling, lubrication, and exhaust systems.

If you put a metal spoon in a hot cup of coffee, you will notice that the handle of the spoon will heat up and may become too hot to touch. The spoon conducts the heat of the hot coffee up the spoon handle. This is called conduction. **Conduction** is the transfer of heat through the interaction of molecules or atoms without the conducting material itself being moved. Metals are generally considered to be good heat conductors. However, some metals are much better conductors than others. Silver, copper, and aluminum are considered to be very good heat conductors,

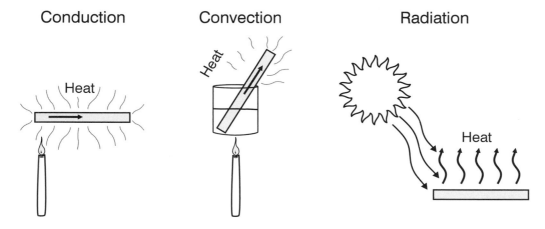

11-15. Three types of heat transfer.

while iron and steel alloys are considered good conductors. We use metals in engines to transfer heat.

Now, if you stir the coffee, or take the spoon out of the coffee and wave it in the air, the spoon will cool down. This is an example of convection. **Convection** is the process that causes the mixing of the warmer and cooler regions of the liquid or gas. Generally, both liquids and gases are poor conductors of heat. Good heat transfer results when a liquid or gas has movement or circulation. Liquids and gases will move by the differences in temperature. However, if the area of contact of a liquid or gas is increased, convection heat transfer improves. Internal combustion engines rely on convection for cooling. All engines use air to remove the heat from combustion. Air-cooled engines use fins to increase surface area and to improve the effectiveness of the heat transfer process. Liquid-cooled engines use a liquid to transfer heat from the engine parts, and then the radiator uses air to cool the liquid. Both the air and the liquid coolants are moved across the engine components to aid the cooling process.

The third type of heat transfer is radiation. **Radiation** is the energy given off by a material in the form of electromagnetic waves. All materials, including solids, liquids, and gases, radiate energy if their temperature is above absolute zero. A good example of radiation heat transfer is what occurs in a parked truck or car outside on a sunny day with the windows rolled up. The interior of the vehicle will heat up from the radiant energy

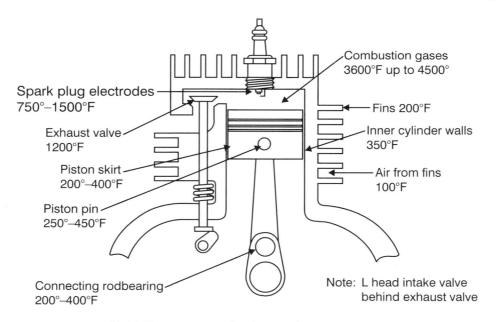

Spark plug electrodes
750°–1500°F

Combustion gases
3600°F up to 4500°

Fins 200°F

Exhaust valve
1200°F

Inner cylinder walls
350°F

Piston skirt
200°–400°F

Air from fins
100°F

Piston pin
250°–450°F

Connecting rodbearing
200°–400°F

Note:  L head intake valve
behind exhaust valve

**11-16. Temperatures of various engine components.**

from the sun even when the outside, or ambient, temperature is cold. A rough surface radiates better than a polished surface. Also, a black surface radiates better than a white surface. Experiments indicate that good radiators of heat are also good absorbers of heat. This helps to explain why engine blocks, cylinder heads, and manifolds are usually rough cast and not polished smooth. Furthermore, the process of radiation heat transfer also helps us to understand why engine radiators are usually painted black.

## LIQUID COOLING SYSTEMS

Liquid cooling systems use liquids to transfer heat from the engine components to the surrounding air. The liquid is called the ***engine coolant.*** To help the heat transfer process, engine coolants are designed to lower the freezing point in the winter and increase the boiling point during summer. The engine coolant is commonly called "antifreeze". However, antifreeze is only one part of the liquid coolant; the other part is water.

The liquid coolant is circulated through the engine block. As the coolant contacts internal engine surfaces, heat is transferred to the coolant. The coolant is then circulated through the radiator, where the heat is transferred

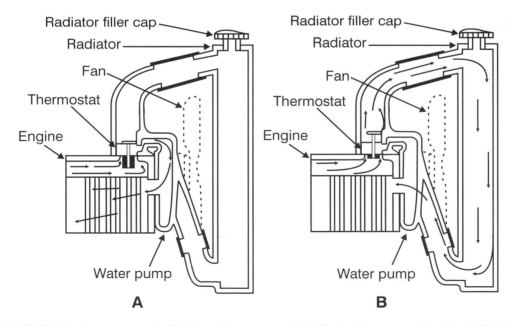

**11-17. The basic structure of a liquid cooling system with (A) the thermostat closed and (B) the thermostat open.**

to the surrounding air. The cooling system is designed to maintain a constant, optimal operating temperature.

## Liquid Cooling System Components

The liquid cooling system of an internal combustion engine operates as a pressurized, closed circulation system. The liquid coolant circulates around the engine components and through the radiator where the heat is removed by the surrounding air.

The basic liquid cooling system has these components:

**Coolant:** liquid used to transfer heat from the engine to the surrounding air.

**Radiator:** heat transfer device, through which the coolant and the surrounding air flow.

**Water jacket:** passageways in the engine through which the coolant flows.

**Water pump:** mechanical device that forces the coolant to flow through the cooling system.

**Thermostat:** flow control valve that remains closed restricting the coolant flow until the coolant reaches a desired temperature, at which point the valve opens to allow the coolant to flow through the radiator.

**Radiator cap:** pressure control valve that allows the cooling system to maintain an optimum operating pressure.

**Fan:** used to force air through the radiator, can be driven electrically or mechanically by the engine.

**Fan belt:** used on some engines to drive the water pump and mechanical fan.

**Temperature gage:** indicates the temperature of the engine coolant. A temperature gage is not used on all cooling systems.

## Engine Liquid Coolant

The liquid used to cool an engine is called the engine coolant. The engine coolant circulates through the engine to transfer heat. The coolant helps to heat a cold engine, and cool a hot engine. The coolant needs to have several specific properties. First, the coolant must remain a liquid at very low temperatures—not freeze. Second, the coolant must not readily evaporate under operating conditions. Third, the coolant must not corrode the engine. Fourth, the coolant must transfer heat.

The most common engine coolant is a mixture of water and ethylene glycol. Other additives are used in engine coolants to prevent rust and corrosion. We commonly use the term "antifreeze" for ethylene glycol. However, a mixture of ethylene glycol does more than just lower the freezing temperature. A good engine coolant will have a low freezing temperature, a high boiling temperature, will not corrode engine parts, and will improve heat transfer. Ethylene glycol is a kind of alcohol. The chemical formula for ethylene glycol is $C_2H_6O_2$. When we mix ethylene glycol and water, we form a solution. The chemical properties of the solution change its freezing and boiling temperatures. These properties are dependent upon the proportion of the chemicals in the solution. Water freezes at 32°F, and ethylene glycol freezes at –9°F. However, if we mix a

**Antifreeze Chart**

| Cooling System Capacity Quarts (Liters) | Full Strength "Permanent" Antifreeze Required — Quarts | | | | | | | | | |
|---|---|---|---|---|---|---|---|---|---|---|
| | 4 °F (°C) | 5 °F (°C) | 6 °F (°C) | 7 °F (°C) | 8 °F (°C) | 9 °F (°C) | 10 °F (°C) | 11 °F (°C) | 12 °F (°C) | 13 °F (°C) |
| 5 ( 4.7) | | | | | | | | | | |
| 6 ( 5.7) | | | | | | | | | | |
| 7 ( 6.6) | -54° (-47.5°) | | | | | | | | | |
| 8 ( 7.6) | -34° (-36.5°) | -69° (-56.0°) | | | | | | | | |
| 9 ( 8.5) | -21° (-29.5°) | -50° (-45.5°) | | | | | | | | |
| 10 ( 9.5) | -12° (-24.5°) | -34° (-36.5°) | -62° (-52.0°) | | | | | | | |
| 11 (10.4) | -6° (-21.0°) | -23° (-31.0°) | -47° (-44.0°) | | | | | | | |
| 12 (11.4) | 0° (-17.5°) | -15° (-26.0°) | -34° (-36.5°) | -57° (-49.5) | | | | | | |
| 13 (12.3) | 3° (-16.0°) | -9° (-23.0°) | -25° (-31.5°) | -45° (-43.0°) | -66° (-55.5°) | | | | | |
| 14 (13.2) | 6° (-14.5°) | -5° (-20.5°) | -18° (-28.0°) | -34° (-36.5°) | -54° (-47.5°) | | | | | |
| 15 (14.2) | 8° (-13.5°) | 0° (-17.5°) | -12° (-24.5°) | -26° (-32.0°) | -43° (-41.5°) | -62° (-52.0°) | | | | |
| 16 (15.1) | 10° (-12.0°) | 2° (-16.5°) | -8° (-22.0°) | -19° (-28.5°) | -34° (-36.5°) | -52° (-46.5°) | | | | |
| 17 (16.1) | 12° (-11.0°) | 5° (-15.0°) | -4° (-20.0°) | -14° (-25.5°) | -27° (-33.0°) | -42° (-41.0°) | -58° (-50.0°) | | | |
| 18 (17.0) | 14° (-14.0°) | 7° (-14.0°) | 0° (-17.5°) | -10° (-23.5°) | -21° (-29.5°) | -34° (-36.5°) | -50° (-45.5°) | -65° (-54.0°) | | |
| 19 (18.0) | 15° (- 9.5°) | 9° (-13.0°) | 2° (-16.5°) | - 7° (-22.0°) | -16° (-26.5°) | -28° (-33.5°) | -42° (-41.0°) | -56° (-49.0°) | | |
| 20 (18.9) | 16° (- 9.0°) | 10° (-12.0°) | 4° (-15.5°) | - 3° (-19.5°) | -12° (-24.5°) | -22° (-30.0°) | -34° (-35.5°) | -48° (-44.5°) | -62° (-52.0°) | |
| 21 (19.9) | 17° (- 8.5°) | 12° (-11.0°) | 6° (-14.5°) | 0° (-17.0°) | - 9° (-23.0°) | -17° (-27.0°) | -28° (-33.5°) | -41° (-40.5°) | -54° (-47.5°) | -68° (-55.5°) |
| 22 (20.8) | 18° (- 8.0°) | 13° (-10.5°) | 8° (-13.5°) | 2° (-16.5°) | - 6° (-21.0°) | -14° (-25.5°) | -23° (-31.0°) | -34° (-36.5°) | -47° (-44.0°) | -59° (-50.5°) |
| 23 (21.8) | 19° (- 7.0°) | 14° (-10.0°) | 9° (-13.0°) | 4° (-15.5°) | - 3° (-19.5°) | -10° (-23.5°) | -19° (-28.5°) | -29° (-34.0°) | -40° (-40.0°) | -52° (-46.5°) |
| 24 (22.7) | | 15° (- 9.5°) | 10° (- 12.0) | 15° (-15.0) | 0° (-17.0°) | - 8° (-22.0°) | -15° (-26.0°) | -24° (-31.0°) | -34° (-36.5°) | -46° (-43.5°) |

11-18. A typical antifreeze chart for mixing water and ethylene glycol.

solution of ½ ethylene glycol and ½ water, by volume, the freezing point of the solution is about −34°F. This also increases the boiling point of the coolant solution. Therefore, a mixture of water and ethylene glycol makes a good engine liquid coolant.

Engine coolants are called "permanent". This means that the coolant should be used in the engine during the entire year. Many years ago, antifreeze would be drained during the summer. Modern engine coolants should be used all year. However, engine coolants should be drained and replaced periodically according to the equipment manufacturer's recommendations. Most manufacturers recommend that the liquid cooling system be drained/flushed and the coolant replaced every one or two years. This will ensure the effectiveness of the additives in the coolant and clean the system as well.

## AIR DIRECT COOLING SYSTEMS

Air direct cooling systems use the outside air to cool the engine. Air is directly blown or forced across the engine parts to remove the heat. This method of cooling is very common for small engines used in agriculture.

The air direct cooling system is simple with a few basic parts:

**Fins:** used to increase the surface area in contact with the air so that engine heat can be transferred more efficiently.

11-19. An air cooling system on a typical small engine.

**Shroud:** engine cover that directs the cooling air across the engine fins.

**Fan:** used to force the cooling air through the engine cooling system. The fan is usually cast as part of the engine flywheel.

**Precleaner:** used to clean the air for the cooling system—usually a metal screen.

## GENERAL PRINCIPLES FOR MAINTAINING COOLING SYSTEMS

The engine cooling system is one of the most critical engine systems. Many engine problems and failures can be traced to cooling system failure. Be sure to follow the equipment manufacturer's recommendations for your specific engine. All cooling systems work better when they are kept clean. Dirt acts as an insulator and reduces the effective transfer of engine heat. All cooling systems rely on air movement to cool the system. Any restrictions in air movement through a cooling system will reduce the efficiency of the system.

# IGNITION SYSTEMS

The *ignition system* starts the combustion of the air and fuel mixture. There are two kinds of ignition systems—compression ignition and spark ignition. Compression ignition systems use the heat produced by compressing the air in the combustion chamber to ignite the air and fuel mixture. Spark ignition systems produce an electrical spark in the combustion chamber that ignites the air fuel mixture. Gasoline fuel engines use spark ignition systems and diesel fuel engines use compression ignition systems.

## COMPRESSION IGNITION SYSTEMS

Compression ignition systems are considered part of the compression system of the engine. There are no unique parts in a compression ignition system. The temperature needed to burn the air and fuel mixture is provided by heat during the compression stroke or cycle. Many compression ignition engines use starting aids. These components are presented as part of the starting system.

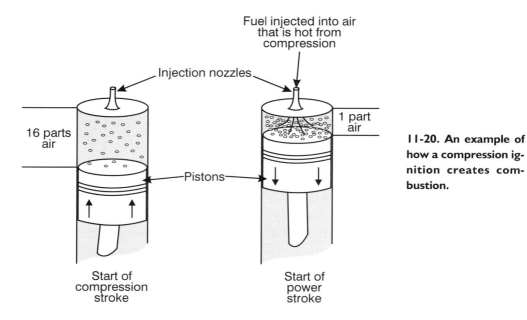

11-20. An example of how a compression ignition creates combustion.

Start of compression stroke

Start of power stroke

## SPARK IGNITION SYSTEMS

Spark ignition systems use a high voltage electrical spark to ignite the compressed air and fuel mixture in the combustion chamber. The ignition system must create a spark with enough voltage to jump the gap of the spark plug and ignite the fuel. Spark ignition systems are of either the magneto-type or of the battery-type.

### Magneto-Type Ignition Systems

*Magneto-type ignition systems* use magnets and a coil and armature to generate the electrical energy for the ignition spark. Magneto ignition systems have two separate electrical circuits—the primary and the secondary circuit. The function of the primary circuit is to generate low-voltage electricity. The function of the secondary circuit is to step-up the voltage to a level sufficient to cause a strong spark at the spark plug.

Several different types of magneto ignition systems are found on small gasoline engines. These include the breaker-type, electronic breakerless, and capacitor discharge ignition systems.

A *breaker-type* magneto system is shown in Figure 11-21. The flywheel magnet, mechanical breaker points, condenser, and the primary coil winding make up the primary circuit. The secondary circuit is composed of the secondary coil winding, spark plug, and spark plug wire.

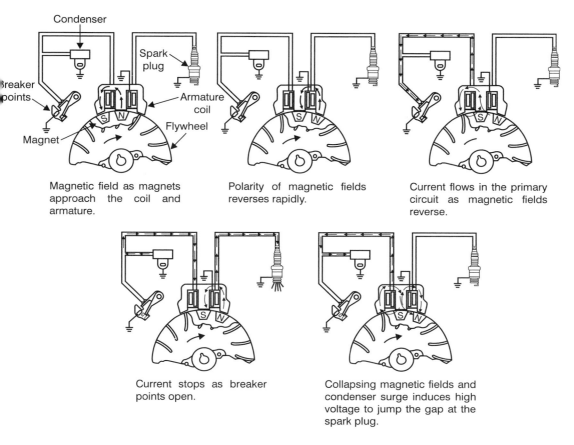

Magnetic field as magnets approach the coil and armature.

Polarity of magnetic fields reverses rapidly.

Current flows in the primary circuit as magnetic fields reverse.

Current stops as breaker points open.

Collapsing magnetic fields and condenser surge induces high voltage to jump the gap at the spark plug.

**11-21. A breaker-type magneto ignition system.**

The flywheel magnet creates a magnetic field which cuts across the armature and coil assembly as the flywheel rotates, inducing voltage into the primary circuit. Current flow in the primary ignition circuit causes a magnetic field to build up around the coil's primary winding. The opening of the breaker points opens the primary ignition circuit, causing current flow to stop. Since no current is flowing in the primary circuit, the magnetic field surrounding the coil's primary winding collapses. This collapsing magnetic field cuts across the coil's secondary winding, inducing voltage into the coil secondary.

The secondary coil winding consists of many times more turns of copper wire than the primary winding. As the collapsing magnetic field cuts across the secondary winding, the voltage is ***stepped-up*** (increased) by a factor equal to the ratio of secondary to primary coil windings. This process produces the high voltage necessary to cause a strong ignition spark across the spark plug gap.

An *electronic breakerless* magneto ignition operates in the same way as a breaker-type system, except that solid-state electronic components (instead of breaker points) are used to open and close the primary circuit. These components are usually contained in a sealed package, called an *ignition module,* and cannot be serviced. If the module fails, it is simply replaced with a new one.

The *capacitor discharge* ignition system is the most common magneto-type ignition system used on small engines. The primary components include: a capacitor; charging and trigger flywheel magnets; charging, trigger, and ignition coils; a rectifier bridge; a silicon control rectifier, or SCR; and spark plug and spark plug wire.

An ignition cycle begins when the charging magnet rotates beside the charging coil assembly, inducing voltage into the charging coil. The induced voltage passes through the diodes of the rectifier bridge, and is stored in the capacitor. The SCR, a solid state electronic switch, is temporarily in a nonconducting state and prevents the capacitor from discharging to the ignition coil.

As the trigger flywheel magnet aligns with the trigger coil, a voltage is induced into the trigger coil. Current flow from the trigger coil to the SCR's gate terminal switches the SCR to a conducting state. The rapid build-up of the magnetic field around the primary winding induces a voltage in the ignition coil's secondary winding. Since the secondary winding consists of many more turns of wire than the primary winding (approximately a 300:1 ratio), the voltage is increased sufficiently to cause the spark to jump the gap at the spark plug. This process repeats as long as the engine operates.

## Battery-Type Ignition Systems

*Battery-type ignition systems* use the energy from a battery and/or alternator to create the ignition spark. These systems work similarly to magneto systems. A low voltage electrical flow is provided to the primary circuit. The primary circuit is opened by a switch. The low voltage primary circuit collapses onto the secondary winding. The voltage is increased by the proportion of windings. The electrical energy is delivered to the spark plug through the secondary winding. This occurs once the voltage is high enough to jump the spark plug gap and the resistance of the combustion chamber pressure.

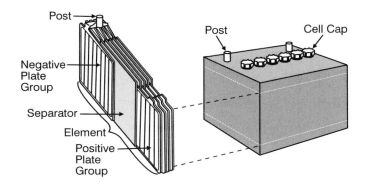

11-22. A storage battery is made of cells and plates. Plates are kept apart by porous separators. This allows the lead plates and sulfuric acid solution to convert chemical energy to electrical energy.

The basic components of a battery ignition system are:

**Battery:** provides the source for the electrical energy.

**Coil:** creates the electrical current for the spark.

**Condenser:** electrical storage device.

**Spark plug:** creates the ignition spark in the combustion chamber.

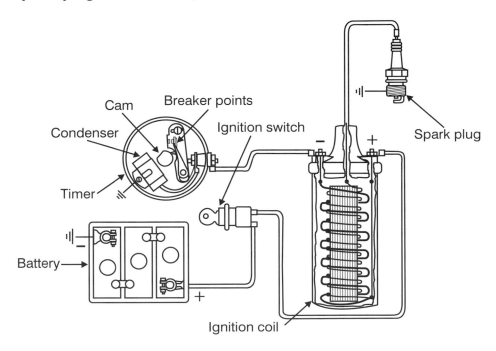

11-23. Breaker point-type battery ignition system and its basic components.

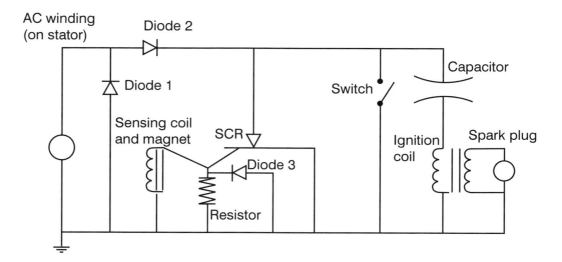

11-24. **A schematic diagram of a solid state ignition system.**

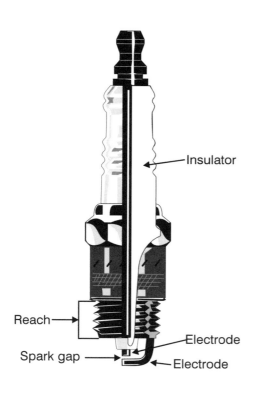

11-25. **The parts of a typical spark plug used in an engine.**

**Primary circuit or wiring:** low voltage electrical circuit of the ignition system.

**Secondary circuit or wiring:** high voltage electrical circuit of the ignition system.

**Magnetic pickup:** sensor that opens and closes the primary circuit and times the creation of the ignition spark.

## SPARK PLUGS

One of the most important parts of the spark ignition system is the spark plug. On some spark ignition engines, the spark plug is the only ignition system component that requires regular maintenance. There are many different kinds of spark plugs. You should recognize that while many spark plugs will fit in an engine, only one may actually be the correct type.

Spark plugs vary according to their reach, heat range, and operating characteristics. Some plugs are designed to run hotter than others. These spark plugs will have less insulation on the center electrode. Also, some spark plugs are designed to extend further into the combustion chamber. Putting a spark plug with too much extension or reach into an engine may cause serious damage. You should always use the recommended spark plug.

## GENERAL PRINCIPLES OF
## IGNITION SYSTEM MAINTENANCE

The ignition system has changed over the years from one of the most maintained engine systems to one that requires less maintenance. Part of this is due to the replacement of mechanical ignition points with electronic sensors. Individual ignition system components have actually decreased in number. Electronic ignition systems last longer and are more reliable. A key principle of good maintenance is to keep the parts clean and in good condition. Electronic parts are damaged by temperature extremes—hot and cold. Electrical systems should be kept clean; however, water and some solvents can damage ignition parts. Be sure to follow the maintenance recommendations and keep all the components in very good working condition.

# LUBRICATION SYSTEMS

The *lubrication system* is a critical internal combustion engine operating system. An engine operating even for just a few seconds without proper lubrication may have significant damage. An engine that is not properly lubricated will have a very short operating life and could fail immediately. Failure of the lubrication system usually means very extensive and expensive engine repairs.

The lubrication system has several basic functions. A primary function is to keep internal engine components coated with oil to reduce friction. A second function is to help cool the engine. The engine oil helps to remove heat. The engine coolant system operates at temperatures from about 160°F to about 225°F. The lubrication system usually operates at slightly higher temperatures from about 200°F to about 250°F. The lubrication system also helps to seal the internal components of the engine. The engine oil forms a seal around moving parts, such as between the piston rings and cylinder wall. A fourth basic function is to clean the internal engine components.

## TYPES OF LUBRICATION SYSTEMS

There are two basic types of lubrication systems, circulating and pressure feed. The circulating type is the basic lubrication system. Circulating systems rely on the principle of hydrodynamic lubrication. *Hydrodynamic lubrication* occurs when moving or sliding surfaces "pull" the engine oil between the surfaces by adhesion of the oil to the engine parts. Circulating splash is a type of lubrication system where the engine oil is splashed around the engine crankcase. Mechanical devices are used to splash the engine oil around. One kind of device is a camshaft or crankshaft-driven splash wheel that "slings" the oil around. Another circulating device is a rod attached to the connecting rod. This rod "dips" in the engine oil and

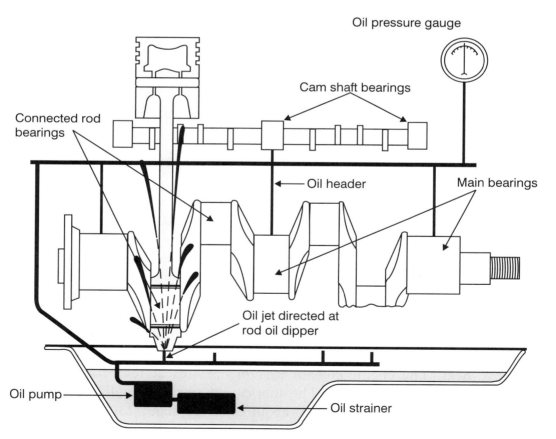

11-26. A full-pressure lubrication system.

splashes it around the crankcase. This device is sometimes called an oil dipper.

Circulating contact is another type of circulating lubrication system. Many two-stroke engines use this system. The engine oil is mixed with the gasoline. As the fuel mixture moves through the engine crankcase, droplets of oil are left on the engine parts. By the action of hydrodynamic lubrication, the droplets move on the sliding contact surfaces to lubricate them.

The pressure feed lubrication system uses a pump to circulate the engine oil to the engine internal components. This is called ***hydrostatic lubrication***. Rather then relying upon adhesion only, an external source generates fluid pressure to keep the engine oil between moving parts. There are several different configurations of pressure feed systems. Most large internal combustion engines use a pressure feed type lubrication system. However, many engines use a combination of circulating and pressure feed systems, relying upon the principles of hydrodynamics and hydrostatics to keep the internal components clean, cool, sealed, and to reduce friction.

## LUBRICATION SYSTEM COMPONENTS

There are many different configurations of engine lubrication systems. The components found in the basic force feed lubrication system of an internal combustion engine are:

**Oil filter:** removes dirt particles from the oil.

**Pressure regulator:** maintains the operating pressure of the lubrication system, usually a pressure relief type valve.

**Sump:** a reservoir for the engine oil, usually directly under the cylinder block and called the oil pan.

**Galleries:** the passages through which oil flows.

**Oil pump:** usually a mechanically driven pump that circulates the engine oil through the engine.

**Oil cooler:** heat transfer device used on some engines to cool the engine oil. Oil coolers are used on some engines.

**11-27. Reading an engine oil dipstick.**

# ENGINE OIL

Engine oils are complex fluids. Because of the relative importance of the lubrication system and engine oil in the internal combustion engine, equipment manufacturers and oil companies continue to work to make better engine lubricants.

There are three basic classes of engine lubricants or oils: mineral oils, synthetic oils, and organic oils. Mineral oils are the most common. Mineral oils are refined from crude petroleum. *Refining* means the impurities, or what we do not want, are taken out. Various substances are then added to the refined oil to make engine oil. Synthetic oils are created or "synthesized." Most synthetic oils are created from petroleum. Synthetic oils are not as widely used as mineral oils. However, as technology increases the need for better engine lubricants, synthetic oils will increase in usage. Synthetic oils generally have better lubricating, cooling, cleaning, and sealing properties than mineral oils, but are more expensive. Organic oils are produced from organic materials, such as soybeans, rather then from petroleum. These engine oils are not widely used.

Basic terms used in discussing engine oils include:

**Additive** — a chemical compound added to a lubricant to enhance the characteristics and properties of the lubricant.

**Anti-foam** — an additive that prevents bubbles of air from forming in oil.

**Anti-oxidant** — an additive that reduces the tendency of oil to oxidize or thicken.

**API class** — the American Petroleum Institute classification of oils based on standard performance tests.

**Detergent** — an additive that coats internal engine surfaces to prevent contaminants from sticking to the surfaces. Detergents neutralize acids and prevent carbon buildup.

**Dispersant** — an additive that surrounds contaminant molecules, keeping them from sticking together and suspending them in the oil until it is changed. This helps to reduce engine sludge buildup.

**Hydrocarbons** — a general term for organic compounds that have only carbon and hydrogen in the molecule.

**Pour point** — the lowest temperature at which an oil will flow.

**SAE grade** — the Society of Automotive Engineers designations for the viscosity ranges of crankcase and gear lubricants.

**Surfactant** — an additive that reduces the surface tension of a liquid.

**Synthetic oil** — lubricant produced synthetically, rather than by extraction and refinement.

**Viscosity** — the measure of a liquid's resistance to flow.

**Viscosity index** — the measurement range of the viscosity of oils. The higher the viscosity index number, the greater the resistance to flow—the thicker the oil.

## ENGINE OIL CLASSES AND VISCOSITY GRADES

The proper selection of engine oils is based upon the original equipment manufacturer's recommendations. Always select the recommended class and grade of engine oil. The classes of engine oil are established by the American Petroleum Institute (API). The classification is based upon the type of engine and the operating conditions. The classification uses a system of letters to identify engine oils. A "C" class of oil is for compression ignition engines, such as diesel fuel powered engines. An "S" class of oil is designed for spark ignition engines. A particular oil may have both a "C" and an "S" classification.

As engine technology advances, more advanced oils are required. Thus, in addition to the "S" classification, a second letter is added to indicate the engine model years in which the oil can be used. The "higher" the second letter of the classification for S oils, the more technologically advanced the lubricant. For example, SE oil is intended for use in automobile engines manufactured from 1972 until 1979. SG oil is intended for use in automobile engines beginning with the 1989 model year. The key point to remember is to use the class of oil that is recommended for your engine. As new oils become available, check with the manufacturer to see if these can be used in the older engines. As a general rule, the newer S oils can be used in older engines, but the older S oils should not be used in newer engines.

The classification of the C engine oils is based on the operating conditions of the engines. For example, a CD oil has been available for a number of years as a severe duty use oil, and it is still recommended for many new diesel engines.

Engine oil grades are established by the Society of Automotive Engineers (SAE), based on the *viscosity,* or flow rate of the engine oil. Higher viscosity grades flow slower than lower viscosity grades. As engines operate under varying conditions, the manufacturer may recommend using a different viscosity of oil to maintain proper lubrication. Heavier oils, those with a higher viscosity index, will not flow as well under cold operating conditions.

There are two basic types of engine oil grades, single viscosity oils and multiple viscosity oils. The single viscosity oils are developed based on a single viscosity range. A multiple viscosity oil meets several different viscosity flow ranges. A single viscosity 30 SAE oil means that oil has a viscosity flow number of 30 when the oil is at a temperature of 212°F (100°C). A multiple viscosity 5W – 30 SAE oil has a viscosity flow number of 5 at a temperature of 32°F (0°C) and a viscosity number of 30 at a temperature of 212°F (100°C).

Synthetic oils are available in both C and S classes and in both single and multiple viscosity grades. As new engine and oil technologies are developed, synthetic oils will come into greater use. The other classes and grades of refined oil will be unable to meet the newer standards.

## GENERAL PRINCIPLES OF LUBRICATION SYSTEM MAINTENANCE

The basic principles of lubrication system maintenance are to use the recommended engine oil and change the engine oil and filters at the interval recommended by the manufacturer. Also, engine oil level should be checked on a regular basis, with oil being added if necessary. Just a few minutes of inadequate lubrication will severely damage or destroy an engine.

# STARTING SYSTEMS

The purpose of the *starting system* is to turn the engine crankshaft until the engine starts. The starting system is designed to operate for a relatively short period of time (usually 30 seconds or less). There are two basic types of engine starting systems—manual and powered.

Manually operated starting systems are common on small engines. The engine is started by manually turning the engine crankshaft. The most common method is to use a rewind rope starter. This system uses a spring

11-28. A manual rewind small engine starting system.

to rewind the rope after it has been pulled out to start the engine. Another type of manual starter is a windup spring starter. This starting system uses a mechanical spring that is wound tight with a mechanical crank and then released to start the engine. Many older engines used a hand crank, which was attached to the end of the crankshaft, and the operator turned the crank to start the engine.

Larger engines use some type of powered starting system to turn the engine crankshaft. The most common type of powered starter is the electric starter. In this system the starter motor converts electrical power (from the battery) into mechanical power at the starter motor. The electric starter motor turns the engine flywheel by a gear drive to crank the engine.

Some engines, especially very large ones, use another, smaller engine to turn the engine crankshaft for starting purposes. The starting engines are sometimes called "pony" motors.

Components of an electrical starting system (Figure 11-29) include:

**Battery:** stores chemicals that produce electricity to power the starting system.

**Starter switch:** opens and closes the starting circuit.

**Battery cables:** conduct electricity to the starter and back to the battery.

**Solenoid:** an electro-magnetic switch that closes and opens the circuit to the starter motor.

**Ring gear:** a gear with external teeth attached to the engine flywheel. The gear drive from the starter motor meshes with the ring gear to turn the flywheel and crankshaft.

**Bendix type drive:** a term for the mechanism that engages the starter motor driver gear with the driven ring gear and disengages the starter drive once the engine has started to run.

**Starter motor:** the electric motor that converts electrical energy to mechanical torque for starting the engine.

## ELECTRICAL STARTING SYSTEM OPERATION

The electrical starting system converts stored chemical energy from the battery to electrical energy and then to mechanical energy. This turns the crankshaft and starts the engine. When you operate the starter switch (button or key), you close the electrical circuit to the starter solenoid. The starter solenoid is an electro-magnetic switch that closes the electrical circuit between the battery and the starter motor. The solenoid works by creating a magnetic field, which causes a piston to move in the solenoid, closing the contact between the battery and the starter motor. Once the starter motor begins to turn, the gear on the starter motor must engage the ring gear on the flywheel. Also, once the engine has started, the gears must disengage to prevent damage to the starter motor. One device used to engage (and disengage) these gears is a Bendix type drive.

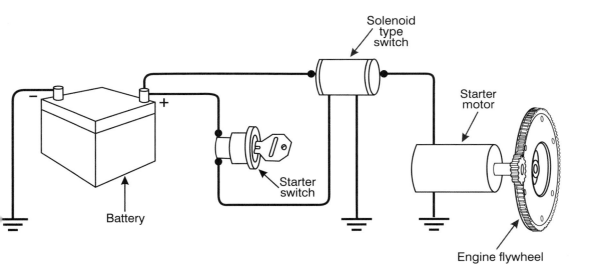

**11-29. How a basic electrical starting system operates and its parts.**

Starting an internal combustion engine requires a considerable amount of electrical power. We rate the electrical energy required as ***cranking amperage***. When selecting a battery, make sure that it can provide enough amperage to start the engine. Starter motors are designed to operate for a short period of time. Prolonged operation may overheat the starter motor. This could damage the starter motor and the starting circuit. A common recommendation is to operate the starter motor for less than thirty seconds. Allow the starter motor to cool for one to two minutes, before trying to start again. This also helps to prevent damage to the battery. Diesel engine starting systems usually require heavier starter motors and larger batteries because of the higher cylinder pressures.

## STARTING AIDS

Some engines are designed to start using starting aides. Glow plugs are examples of starting aides commonly used on diesel engines. The glow plugs quickly heat up in the combustion chamber allowing the diesel fuel to ignite more readily. In some engines, glow plugs are placed in the intake manifold.

Another type of starting aid is a starting fluid. Starting fluids are very volatile gases packaged in pressurized cans. Some manufacturers install mounting brackets on the intake manifolds for starting fluid cans. Be very careful when handling starting fluids. They are very dangerous and extremely flammable. Also, check with the engine manufacturer to see if starting fluid may be used. Many engines can be damaged by excessive use of starting fluids.

Another engine starting aid is an engine heater. They are very common in colder climates. Engine heaters are usually electrical heaters that plug into alternating current electrical circuits. Some heat the engine coolant, others heat the engine oil. As with any starting aid, follow the manufacturer's recommendations. Overuse of engine heaters may damage the engine coolant or oil.

# ENGINE SPEED
# GOVERNING SYSTEM

The primary function of the **governing system** is to maintain a constant engine speed under varying load conditions. The governing system is designed to maximize the operating efficiency of the engine. Its basic function is to control fuel flow to the engine.

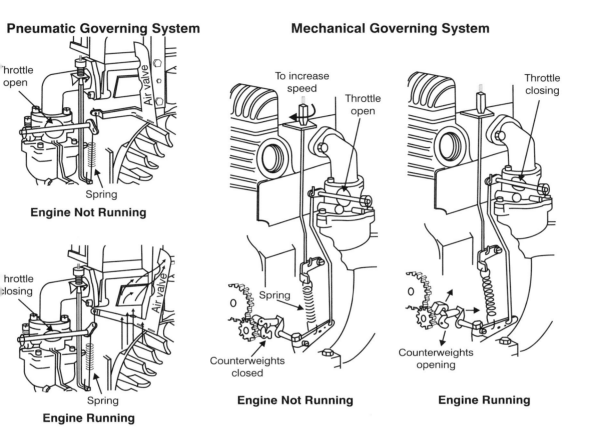

11-30. A pneumatic governing system (left) and a mechanical governing system (right).

There are three basic types of internal combustion engine governing systems. The pneumatic governor uses air, usually from the fins on the flywheel, to control the throttle position. This system is still used on some small engines. The air vane is attached to the throttle plate and a spring. The spring keeps tension on the air vane to open the throttle setting. As the engine speed slows, less air is forced to the air vane. With less air pressure to hold the air vane open, the spring pulls the throttle open. This action allows more fuel into the engine and increases engine speed. As the engine speeds, more air pushes against the air vane, closing the throttle plate, slowing the engine speed as the throttle plate closes.

A second type of engine speed governor is the mechanical governor. This system uses the speed of rotation of a series of weights to maintain engine speed. The position of the governor weights is controlled by centrifugal force. The mechanical system works much the same as the pneumatic system. Rather than using air to control speed, the engine uses spinning weights. The faster the weights spin, the further they extend, and through a mechanical connection, the amount of fuel to the combustion chamber is decreased. As the weights spin slower, they control the linkage mechanism to allow more fuel to be supplied to the engine. Diesel, as well as gasoline powered engines, may use mechanical type governor systems.

Many modern engines now use electronic governors to control engine speed. An electronic sensor determines changes in engine speed and then a control mechanism adjusts the amount of fuel supplied to the engine. Electronic governors are becoming more common on newer engines.

Engine governor systems do not require much maintenance. Regular maintenance of the other engine systems will usually ensure proper operation of the governor system. Periodic checks should be made to determine if the engine is operating at the proper speeds. The technical specifications of an engine will often provide data concerning the amount of response for the governor system.

Failure of a speed governing system can usually be traced to one of two broad causes: Either a particular part has failed, or the system is improperly maintained or installed. Examples include the improper arrangement of the air vane and throttle linkages, worn or broken centrifugal weights in the governor or incorrect setting of the engine speed. Be sure to follow the manufacturer's recommendations for maintaining and adjusting the engine speed governing system.

# SUMMARY

Each of the internal combustion engine systems has a very important role in making the engine run. Properly maintain all systems and follow recommended practices. The engine will run only as long as each system is operating properly. The failure of one system can lead to inefficient operation and possible engine failure.

The operation of internal combustion engine systems is easier to understand if the system is broken down to the basic parts. Following recommended general maintenance practices will allow engine systems to operate efficiently for long periods of time. An engine runs well because all the engine systems are operating properly and working together.

# REVIEW QUESTIONS

1. What are the basic components of the internal combustion engine intake system?

2. What are the advantages of engine turbochargers, superchargers, and intercoolers?

3. How do carburetor and injection engine fuel systems differ?

4. What are the characteristics of different engine fuels?

5. What are the components and functions of a basic exhaust system?

6. How does the cooling system manage heat produced by the engine?

7. How do air-direct and liquid cooling systems operate?

8. What are the basic principles of operation of magneto-type and battery-type ignition systems?

9. What are the basic principles of operation of an internal combustion engine lubrication system?

10. How are engine lubricants classified?

11. What are the basic components and operating principles of engine starting systems?

12. What are the functions of the engine speed governing system?

# APPLYING THE CONCEPTS

1. Determine the different types of air cleaners used on the agricultural equipment on a farm, golf course, or at an agribusiness. Make a listing and compare the types of air cleaners to the types of engines.

2. Conduct an experiment using different mixtures of antifreeze and water, and determine their relative freezing temperatures.

3. Collect information about different fuels available in your community. Compare the costs and operating characteristics. Are special fuel mixtures used in your community for environmental and/or climatic conditions?

4. Conduct an experiment to determine the heat transfer characteristics of different materials.

5. Collect an engine oil sample and have it analyzed through a local equipment dealer or engine lubricant supplier.

6. Determine the operation and components of engine starting systems found on different kinds of agricultural equipment.

7. Service one or more systems on an engine. Work under the direction of a teacher or engine service technician. The system(s) serviced depends on the type of engine. In general, the following systems or system parts are usually easy to service: air filtration, oil filtration and lubricating system, fuel filtration, and battery. Refer to the manual for the engine for details on the procedures to follow.

# 12

# PRACTICING PREVENTIVE MAINTENANCE

Internal combustion engines operate as a series of systems working together to produce mechanical power from the combustion of air and fuel. For the engine to operate efficiently, each system must do its job. This chapter presents preventive maintenance practices for general agricultural equipment and internal combustion engines.

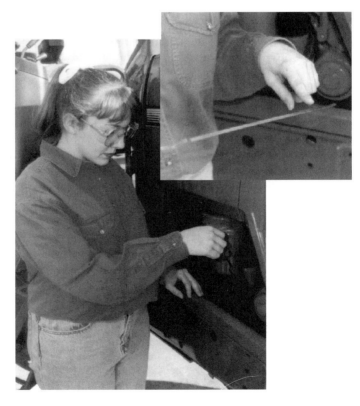

12-1. Engines should be regularly checked to see that the crankcase oil level is okay or if oil is needed. (Courtesy, Jasper S. Lee)

# OBJECTIVES

This chapter covers routine preventive maintenance for internal combustion engines. After completing the chapter, you will:

| T |
| E |
| R |
| M |
| S |

bleed
compression system
coolant hydrometer
condenser
dwell
fuel combustion meter
hour meter
maintenance interval
odometer
pressure tester
preventive maintenance

1. Explain preventive maintenance and list practices applicable for all machines and equipment.

2. Establish maintenance schedules based on hours or miles of operation.

3. Explain recommended safety practices to follow when maintaining equipment.

4. Test the air intake system of an internal combustion engine.

5. Check and maintain a precleaner, a dry element air cleaner, an oil foam filter, an oil bath air filter, and a turbocharger.

6. Determine the general condition of the compression system.

7. Check and maintain various fuel delivery systems.

8. Define and correct common problems associated with the exhaust system.

9. Identify and recommend any service requirement of the cooling system.

10. Check and diagnose an ignition system for problems.

11. Determine whether the lubrication system is functioning properly.

12. Define and service the different types of starting systems.

# WHAT IS PREVENTIVE MAINTENANCE?

There are two fundamental keys to managing agricultural equipment. First, operate equipment as it is designed to be operated. Second, maintain equipment in good operating condition. *Preventive maintenance* is performing periodic practices to keep equipment in good working condition. The term "preventive" means trying to prevent costly repairs and downtime.

**12-2. Some engines have a maintenance schedule decal on them to help the operator with preventive maintenance.**

Preventive maintenance practices include such things as changing fluids, cleaning components, and replacing filters. Remember, if one of the systems is not operating properly, the other systems will be affected. System failure will eventually lead to engine failure.

Preventive maintenance also involves minimizing human error—someone fails to do something or they do something wrong. Often, agricultural machines fail to operate properly because of an operator's or technician's error. While preventive maintenance does not eliminate human error, it helps reduce the risk of mistakes by performing and keeping accurate records of routine maintenance.

# GENERAL PREVENTIVE MAINTENANCE PRACTICES

Properly maintaining agricultural equipment requires not only that you develop the necessary skills, but that you also develop the practices of quality management. Preventive maintenance is doing the job right, not just doing it.

The following general preventive maintenance practices are applicable to all machines and equipment, not just internal combustion engines.

1. Read the operator's manual. Know the equipment with which you are working.

2. Know the history of the equipment you are maintaining. If you are not the primary operator, find the operation history of the equipment from those who do operate it. If possible, it is a good idea to actually observe the equipment as it is being used.

3. Follow the manufacturer's recommendations. Manufacturers take great pride in the machines they manufacture and they want customers to continue to use their products. Therefore, manufacturers provide recommended preventive maintenance practices, which will allow the equipment to last a reasonable lifetime.

4. Be clean. Agricultural equipment operates under many different conditions. The internal components of internal combustion engines are particularly susceptible to problems caused by dirt. Always perform preventive maintenance practices under the cleanest conditions possible.

5. Use quality materials as recommended by the manufacturer. Select only fluids, filters, and other products that meet or exceed manufacturer's recommendations.

6. Use the recommended amounts. More is not necessarily better when it comes to preventive maintenance. Too much lubricant in a gearbox may be just as harmful as not enough. Always double-check the amounts according to recommendations.

7. Keep accurate records. This practice is just as important as any other preventive maintenance practice. Some modern agricultural machines are even equipped with computers, which keep track of preventive maintenance schedules.

**12-3. Computers can be used to keep accurate records on individual pieces of equipment.**

8. Use common sense. This practice will save you as much time and effort as any of the others. Do not be afraid to ask questions and check the manual. For example, if the old filter and the new filter do not look the same, recheck the filters. Human error is still a major cause of equipment failures.

9. Be safe. Protect not only yourself, but also your family, other workers, and the environment.

## MAINTENANCE INTERVALS

Agricultural equipment operators and technicians should always follow the manufacturer's recommendations for proper maintenance and service intervals. *Maintenance intervals* will either be based upon how much the machine has been used or the length of time the machine has been in service. Modern machines and equipment are sometimes equipped with sensors, which indicate when service should be performed.

Machine usage is usually measured by the number of hours of operation. Many machines are equipped with *hour meters*, which keep track of the time the machine is operated. A manufacturer will provide a series of service maintenance recommendations for selected intervals. For example, a small-engine manufacturer may specify the engine oil be changed every 25 hours of operation. Hours are commonly used on agricultural equipment to determine service intervals. The number of miles operated is commonly used for motor vehicles, such as farm trucks. Motor vehicles are usually equipped with *odometers*, which keep a running total of the miles (kilometers) traveled. If motor vehicles are operated for long periods while

**12-4. An hour meter (left) or an odometer (right) are two means of measuring maintenance intervals.**

stationary, this should be allowed for when determining recommended service intervals.

Agricultural equipment manufacturers often have more than one recommended service interval. Examples are a regular service interval and a severe service interval. The owner or operator must decide which type of interval best suits the operation of the machine. Examples of severe conditions include temperature extremes, lots of starting and stopping, and very dusty conditions. Consult the operator's manual or local service representative if unsure whether the equipment would qualify for severe operating conditions.

Manufacturers install sensors on equipment to indicate when particular systems or components need to be serviced. Some manufacturers may not recommend any maintenance be performed until the sensor indicates that service is needed. Modern equipment may be equipped with computers, which monitor the equipment as it operates. Heat, vibration, and pressure sensors are used to indicate possible operating conditions that may cause problems. Also, monitoring computers installed on machines keep track of when services were performed and inform the operator of when future scheduled maintenance should be performed. There are several computer software packages which can assist agricultural producers in keeping equipment records. However, a computer spreadsheet may be adequate for tracking periodic maintenance.

Some manufacturers also provide recommendations based upon the season of the year. For example, they may recommend service be performed every six months—in the spring and fall of the year. To achieve the maximum potential from your equipment, follow the type of scheduled periodic maintenance that represents the first interval. As an example, if an engine manufacturer recommends an oil change every 100 hours or at least every six months of operation, then change the engine oil at whichever interval comes first. If this engine has been operated for 80 hours and six months, change the oil at six months.

# WORKING SAFELY

When performing any kind of work on agricultural machinery and equipment, always follow recommended safety practices.

1. Follow the safety practices in the service and operator's manuals.

2. Learn to recognize safety emblems and warning signs used on agricultural machines.

3. Wear protective eyewear, clothing, and footwear.

4. Support all machines and engines safely. Always use jackstands, engine stands, and other designed supports when working on raised or dismantled equipment.

5. Handle all fuels and other flammable materials safely.

6. Operate internal combustion engines only in well-ventilated areas.

7. Park machines safely. Use wheel blocks and lower implements and attachments before working on them.

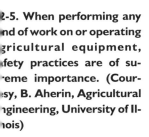

2-5. When performing any nd of work on or operating gricultural equipment, fety practices are of su-reme importance. (Cour-sy, B. Aherin, Agricultural ngineering, University of Il-ois)

8. Work in a well-lighted and ventilated work area.

9. Keep the floor clean and free of obstacles and fluids.

10. Handle all batteries safely. Liquid-cell batteries produce hydrogen gas, which is very explosive.

11. Keep fire extinguishers and smoke detectors in the work area.

12. Use caution in working on high pressure systems, such as pressurized cooling and hydraulic systems.

13. Use protective hearing devices when working on or near running engines.

14. Dispose of used fluids in a safe manner to protect people, animals, and the environment.

# MAINTAINING THE INTAKE SYSTEM

The purpose of the air intake system is to clean dirt and other particles from the air and bring it into the combustion chamber. This should occur without severe restrictions to the free flow of the air, which would decrease engine output.

## TESTING THE INTAKE SYSTEM

The intake system can be tested using a vacuum gage. To test an internal combustion engine, follow this basic procedure.

1. Connect the vacuum gage to the intake manifold.

2. Allow the engine to run for a few minutes to warm up.

3. Record the gage reading with the engine operating at fast-idle speed.

4. Compare the observed gage reading with the manufacturer's technical specifications.

5. Inspect the intake system for possible restrictions, leaks, and other diagnosed problems.

This general procedure will work for both diesel and gasoline-powered engines. However, diesel-engine intake systems are usually easier to troubleshoot then gasoline engines.

## MAINTAINING PRECLEANERS

The precleaner may be a device as simple as a screen on a small engine. Larger engines often use a precleaner that has a collection bowl. The precleaner should be checked on a daily basis. A common manufacturer recommendation is to check the precleaner every ten hours of use. Do not operate an engine with the precleaner removed; this may cause the air cleaner to fail prematurely.

## MAINTAINING DRY ELEMENT AIR CLEANERS

Dry element air cleaners are easy to maintain. Check the operator's manual for proper procedures and recommendations. Some manufacturers install air intake sensors to monitor filter conditions. They do not recommend inspecting or servicing the dry element air cleaner until the sensor indicates that service is needed. The use of the sensor decreases the possibility of getting dirt in the intake system, which may occur when removing, inspecting, and reinstalling the filter. Here are some general procedures for servicing dry element air cleaners.

1. Always remove the filters carefully, so as not to get dirt in the intake system.

2. Visually inspect the dry element air cleaner, with an inspection light, for any holes. If any holes are found, regardless of how small, discard the filter and replace it with a new one.

3. Since some manufacturers do not recommend cleaning their filters, verify proper procedures.

4. If the filter can be washed, use only the recommended type of detergent. Cleaning solvents, such as parts cleaner solvent, are seldom recommended for dry element filters. Provide adequate time for drying filters.

5. If a filter is difficult to clean, replace it.

6. If the manufacturer recommends using compressed air to clean a filter, care should be taken. Usually, air should be blown only from the inside of the filter out and the air pressure should be limited to less than 30 psi. If you are not sure, then do not use compressed air for cleaning.

7. If air directional fins are used to direct the incoming air, be sure the fins are in good condition and properly installed. This helps to clean particles from the air by centrifugal force.

8. Make sure that all gaskets are in good condition.

## MAINTAINING OIL FOAM FILTERS

Many of the practices for the dry element type air cleaners apply to servicing and maintaining oil foam air cleaners. In addition, for oil foam filters follow these practices.

1. Clean the filter properly and, as with other filters, use the proper cleaning agent (usually soapy water).

2. Allow the oil foam filter to dry properly. Some manufacturers recommend allowing the filter to dry overnight.

3. Use the proper type and amount of oil for the filter. Most manufacturers recommend using the same type of oil as is recommended for the engine. However, some manufacturers do recommend specific air filter oils. This oil may come in a bottle, spray can, or tube.

4. If the air cleaner shows any signs of deterioration, it should be replaced.

5. Install the filter properly and check the condition of all gaskets.

## MAINTAINING THE OIL BATH AIR FILTER

Maintenance for the oil bath filter consists of cleaning the bowl and changing the oil according to the manufacturer's recommendations. If being operated under dirty conditions, the oil bath filter should be checked regularly. Common manufacturer's recommendations for servicing oil bath air cleaners are every 50 or 100 hours of normal use.

## MAINTAINING TURBOCHARGERS

Turbochargers are lubricated by the engine's pressure feed lubrication system. Several checks should be made on a daily basis for the following conditions.

1. Possible leaks of engine oil.

2. Excessive smoke (if detected during the acceleration of a diesel engine, may indicate a failing turbocharger).

3. Excessive noise (may indicate that the bearings are failing).

4. Excessive vibration (may indicate failing internal components).

**12-6. A crack in the hose connecting the turbocharger to the air cleaner will permit airborne abrasives to enter the engine and cause rapid wear. Engine failure may occur in a short time.**

# COMPRESSION SYSTEM

The purpose of the *compression system* is to efficiently compress the air to increase the energy of the combustion of the fuel in conventional internal combustion engines. It uses pistons, which move up and down—linear movement—in a cylinder. The piston and cylinder must form a leak-proof combustion chamber for the engine to operate efficiently. The air-tightness of the combustion chamber is a major design feature. Also, the compression system must operate smoothly and with a minimum power requirement. If the compression system loses too much compression or requires too much power to operate, then the engine will not operate properly.

There are several basic checks to determine the general condition of the compression system.

1. Compression tests are an excellent tool and can be an excellent preventive maintenance practice.

12-7. A compression pressure gage.

2. Perform a dynamometer test of engine performance. This test will also indicate the relative condition of the compression system. The compression system has a direct impact upon engine horsepower output.

3. Make daily checks of engine oil consumption. An engine will burn oil if the compression system allows excess oil to enter the combustion chamber by the piston rings, valve guides, or another worn or broken part.

4. Perform regular recommended checks and adjustments of engine valve clearances. Valve clearance should be checked and set about every 500 hours of operation. Hydraulic-type operated valves do not need to be checked as frequently as solid-type valve systems. Be sure to check the manufacturer's recommended service interval and follow the proper procedure.

5. Determine whether or not the engine requires regular re-torquing of the cylinder head bolts—most manufacturers do not recommend changing the torque of cylinder head bolts and disturbing the cylinder head gasket seal.

12-8. If a cylinder head does not have the proper torque, the engine may lose compression.

# MAINTAINING FUEL SYSTEMS

The fuel system is designed to deliver clean fuel to the combustion chamber and to meter the amount of fuel for efficient operation. The fuel needs to be delivered at the correct time and in best proportion with the air for the engine to operate properly. There are a variety of fuel systems and components to meet the needs of different kinds of engines, fuels, and applications. There are some basic practices for maintaining fuel systems and the fuel-handling area.

1. Use clean, fresh fuel.
2. Properly store and handle all fuels.
3. Use the correct fuel.
4. Keep the work area clean.
5. Follow general safety practices.

## SERVICING FUEL FILTERS

There are many different kinds of fuel filters used on engines. Some small engines use a simple screen to filter out dirt. Many diesel engines use several filters to ensure that the fuel is clean and will not clog the injection nozzles or damage the injection pump. Fuel systems can be very dangerous to work on because of the possibility of fires and explosions. The work area should be clean and a fire extinguisher should be easily accessible. In addition to following the manufacturer's recommendations, there are some general guidelines for servicing fuel filters.

1. Some engines are equipped with a sediment bowl and fuel strainers. These should be visually checked daily—every 10 hours of

12-9. A glass bowl fuel filter separates water from fuel by collecting water at the bottom.

use. To clean, shut the fuel supply off, remove, and clean with a recommended parts cleaning solvent. **Do not use gasoline.** Be sure to check the condition of the sediment bowl or strainer gasket.

2. Fuel filters should be changed according to the preventive maintenance schedule. A common schedule for a diesel engine is to replace fuel filters every 500 hours of operation, or at least once a year.

3. Some engines have multiple fuel filters. This is very common on diesel engines. Be sure to replace all fuel filters when servicing the system.

4. Be sure the area around the fuel filter is clean. Always work on and service fuel systems in a clean work area.

5. Be sure to shut the fuel supply off at the tank. Do not leave fuel filters off of an engine for long periods.

6. Make sure you have the correct replacement filter(s) and the proper gaskets.

7. Be sure to bleed the fuel filters and the fuel system. To *bleed* is to remove air from the system. Most fuel systems will have bleed screws or vents, which may be loosened. Some engines have a pump, sometimes called a priming or hand pump, to help bleed air out of the system.

8. Check the system for leaks. Operate the engine for a few minutes, and then check again for possible leaks.

## SERVICING CARBURETORS

Carburetors are still used on many small engines. Larger engines now use fuel injection systems instead of carburetors. Carburetors require regular maintenance and periodic replacement of gaskets, diaphragms, and other internal parts. Here are some basic guidelines for maintaining carburetors.

1. Service the other fuel system parts, such as fuel filters, before making carburetor adjustments.

2. Make sure you are working in a safe, clean area with a fire extinguisher nearby.

3. Service carburetors whenever other major engine repairs are done. If a carburetor has been removed, adjust the carburetor settings.

4. Once a year, check, and, if necessary, adjust the operating speed of the engine.

5. Whenever a carburetor is taken apart and cleaned, install a new set of gaskets and possibly some other parts. A carburetor overhaul kit will provide the necessary parts, seals, and gaskets.

6. When reinstalling or adjusting a carburetor, the manufacturer will recommend initial settings. These settings will allow you to get the engine started and then you can make the final running adjustments.

7. You can make most small engine adjustments by observing the sound and smoothness of the engine operation. A common technique is to observe changes in engine speeds as you lean and enrich the fuel settings and then set the fuel mixture in the middle.

8. Some engine manufacturers recommend using a *fuel combustion meter* which measures the air and fuel ratio. It can be used to set a carburetor to the settings that produce the least amount of unburned hydrocarbons.

9. Make daily checks around carburetors for possible fuel leaks. If you smell gasoline while an engine is operating, inspect the engine immediately for possible fuel leaks.

12-10. Manufacturers recommend initial settings when reinstalling or adjusting a carburetor. (Courtesy, Jasper S. Lee)

## SERVICING DIESEL FUEL INJECTION SYSTEMS

Fuel injection systems are used on both gasoline and diesel engines. These systems will last a long time if they are properly maintained. The preventive maintenance practices for gasoline and diesel fuel injection systems are similar. As with all engine systems, check the recommendations in the operator's and service manuals.

1. Always use clean fuel.
2. Replace the filters and drain sediment or water collection bowls as recommended.
3. Visually inspect the fuel injection system every day (10 hours of use).
4. If you install new filters or replace any parts, make sure you have bled all air from the system.
5. If you suspect a fuel system problem, a dynamometer test with a fuel flow meter can indicate possible causes.
6. Diesel engine smoke can indicate possible problems. White smoke indicates incomplete combustion. A cold engine or low compression can produce white smoke. Blue-colored exhaust usually will indicate oil combustion. Heavy black smoke indicates incomplete combustion usually from over-fueling or too much fuel or restricted air intake.
7. Injection nozzles can be removed from the engine and tested with a nozzle tester. If service is needed, nozzles should be taken to a diesel engine repair shop. Do not remove the nozzles unless you have good reason to do so.

If a fuel injection system is well maintained, it should last the lifetime of the engine. If you replace the fuel filters and use good quality fuel, the system should not need any other repairs or service for many years. Keep in mind that a diesel fuel injection system can be very expensive and time consuming to repair.

When testing or servicing diesel fuel injection systems be extremely careful and follow all applicable safety precautions. Be aware that fuel under high pressure can cause severe injuries.

# MAINTAINING EXHAUST SYSTEMS

The exhaust system performs the task of removing burnt gases and particles from the combustion chamber. The exhaust system also helps to manage engine noise and heat transfer. In recent years, the exhaust system has also been designed to help control engine emissions, which could damage the environment. The exhaust system just as important as the other systems for efficient engine operation. Some general practices for testing exhaust systems are:

1. Make periodic checks for exhaust leaks. Discolored parts and excessive noise may indicate exhaust leaks. By carefully restricting the exhaust system, you can observe possible leaks by the sound produced.

2. A vacuum gage attached to the intake manifold, which drops steadily as the engine idles, may indicate a restricted exhaust system.

3. A compression test may indicate a leaking exhaust valve.

4. Gas bubbles in the liquid cooling system may also indicate a leaking exhaust system.

12-11. Cleaning the exhaust ports in a 2-cycle engine is part of its maintenance.

## MAINTAINING COOLING SYSTEMS

Engine cooling systems are designed to manage the heat produced by the combustion of the air and fuel. Every engine has an optimum operating temperature. The task of the cooling system is to allow the engine to reach the optimum temperature and then maintain this temperature under varying operating conditions.

The two basic kinds of cooling systems are: liquid coolant and air direct. The liquid coolant cooling system uses a liquid to transfer heat from the engine components to the surrounding air. The air direct cooling system transfers the heat of the engine components directly to the surrounding air. Both cooling systems require clean air to operate efficiently. These cooling systems operate on the basic principles of heat transfer.

## GENERAL PRINCIPLES FOR MAINTAINING COOLING SYSTEMS

The engine cooling system is one of the most critical engine systems, requiring periodic checks and maintenance. Many engine problems and failures can be traced to cooling system failure. Be sure to follow the equipment manufacturer's recommendations for your specific engine. All cooling systems work better when they are kept clean. Dirt acts as an insulator and reduces the effective transfer of the engine heat. All cooling systems also rely upon the movement of air to cool the system. Any restrictions in the air movement through a cooling system will reduce the cooling efficiency of the system.

**12-12. Proper belt tension and condition is important if the engine's waterpump is to operate properly.**

## MAINTAINING LIQUID COOLING SYSTEM

There are some basic, general maintenance recommendations for liquid cooling systems.

1. Always perform regular, periodic cooling system checks. Most agricultural equipment manufacturers recommend daily (every 10 hours of operation) visual checks of the engine cooling system. Check hoses and belts for leaks and cracks.

2. Maintain the proper coolant level in the system.

3. Keep the system clean.

4. Change the coolant according to the manufacturer's recommendations, usually every one or two years.

5. Use the recommended coolant, usually a mixture of 50 percent ethylene glycol type antifreeze and 50 percent water.

6. Perform regular checks of the cooling system for leaks. A ***pressure tester*** is used to pressurize the liquid cooling system to check for leakage.

7. Use a ***coolant hydrometer*** to regularly check the specific gravity of the coolant. This determines the proportion of antifreeze and water. Some coolant may have evaporated or too much antifreeze or water may have been added.

8. If the system uses an electrical fan, make sure the fan is operating properly. Electrical fans are usually operated by an electrical sensor, which determines when the engine is warmed up. Usually, these sensors can be checked with an ohmmeter for the recommended resistance—when the sensor is cool. When the sensor warms up, it will close the circuit and the fan will come on. There should be little or no electrical resistance when the sensor is at normal operating temperature. However, not all sensors work in this manner, so be sure to follow the manufacturer's recommended procedure.

9. If the cooling system uses a mechanical fan, usually operated by a belt, you should check the fan belt tension. The manufacturer will recommend the amount of deflection of the belt between two points, usually pulleys, as you push on the belt. A common example is 1/4 inch of deflection when you pull a spring scale with a force of 10 pounds between two pulleys 1 foot apart.

10. Some manufacturers recommend periodic pH tests of the coolant. Certain acids are very corrosive to some engine components, particularly some alloys and plastics.

11. The cooling system should be drained and flushed whenever you change the coolant. Follow the manufacturer's recommendations. Most manufacturers will specify using a recommended cooling system cleaner and flushing the system. If the cleaner is a caustic-type acid cleaner, the system must be flushed thoroughly. Properly dispose of flushed coolant fluids.

12. Some large engines are equipped with a coolant filter-conditioning element. Replace this element as recommended by the manufacturer.

## TESTING THE LIQUID COOLING SYSTEM

There are several basic checks to determine the condition of the cooling system. These checks reveal any existing or potential problems.

First, perform a system pressure check. A pressure tester, which is available at most agricultural or automotive tool supply stores, will be needed. The tester pressurizes the system so you can check for leaks. The pressure on the gage should remain constant, which indicates that the system does not leak. Be sure not to pressurize the system beyond listed specifications, as this may cause leaks.

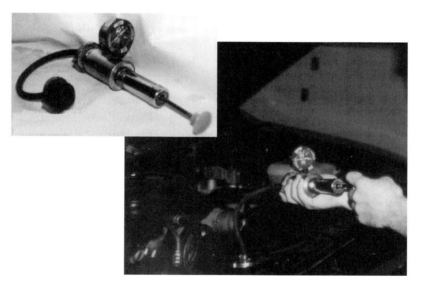

12-13. A pressure tester is used to pressurize the liquid cooling system to check for leaks.

Second, use the same tester to test the radiator cap. The radiator cap maintains the cooling system pressure. The cap should not leak and should open at the rated pressure.

Third, test the cooling system thermostat. In normal operation, the thermostat stays closed, limiting the circulation of the coolant, until the coolant reaches operating temperature. Once the engine coolant reaches operating temperature, the thermostat opens and allows the coolant to circulate through the radiator to transfer heat. The coolant temperature of an engine warming up should slowly increase until it reaches the rated temperature of the thermostat. Then the thermostat should maintain this rated temperature level. To test a thermostat, remove it from the cooling system and check the opening temperature. The opening temperature should be stamped on the thermostat. Hang the thermostat from a string in a container of water containing a thermometer. Heat the water, stirring it as it heats. The thermostat should open at the rated opening temperature. A general rule is that the thermostat should open within 10 degrees (either above or below) of its rated temperature. Otherwise, the thermostat should be replaced.

## MAINTAINING AIR DIRECT COOLING SYSTEMS

The air direct cooling system works very well, as long as the system remains clean and the basic components are in good working condition. Observe the following basic principles for maintaining an air cooling system:

1. Keep the cooling system clean. Dirt can easily clog the air passages and prevent proper cooling of the engine.

2. Make sure that the precleaner, usually a screen, is in place and working properly.

3. Do not operate air cooled engines in a confined space where the engine is not able to circulate air freely.

4. Make sure the fan is operating properly and can move the air freely.

5. Keep all engine shields and shrouds in place to allow for the proper circulation of the cooling air.

12-14. The cooling fins need to be clean in an air direct cooling system.

As with all engine systems, be sure to follow the engine manufacturer's service recommendations. All manufacturers will suggest periodic inspections of the cooling system.

# IGNITION SYSTEMS

The purpose of the ignition system is to provide the spark for a spark ignition type internal combustion engine. Some small engines still use a mechanical type breaker point ignition system. However, most modern engines use a solid state or electronic ignition system. These systems use a magnetic sensor to time the spark. The use of solid state or electronic ignition systems has greatly decreased the amount of preventive maintenance required for spark ignition systems.

## *GENERAL MAINTENANCE PRACTICES*

There are several maintenance practices that apply to all types of ignition systems. The following practices will help prevent possible problems and diagnose existing problems:

1. Most ignition systems will require a series of ignition tests. Small engines use simple devices called spark testers. If the tester indicates a good spark, only general maintenance should be performed.

2. Maintain a fully charged battery on battery-type ignition systems.

3. Check the condition of all wires and connections. A voltmeter and an ohmmeter can be used to test ignition circuitry. The high-voltage secondary circuit leads or wires should be replaced on a regular maintenance schedule. These wires tend to crack and create possible voltage leaks as they get older.

4. Replace spark plugs and set gaps as recommended.

5. Keep the ignition system clean. Be careful when cleaning ignition systems as water and other fluids may damage ignition parts.

6. Most electronic components can be damaged by temperature extremes. Do not expose electronic parts to high-temperature steam cleaners and other extreme heat sources.

7. Systems that use mechanical ignition contacts, or breaker points, should be adjusted and replaced according to recommendations.

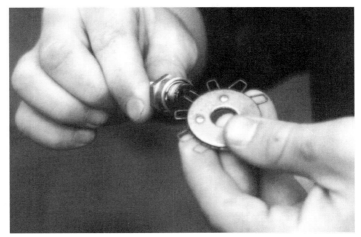

12-15. **Proper replacement spark plugs and their gap settings are listed in the operator's manual. Here, the gap is being set with a plug gap tool.**

Ignition points are set either with a flat feeler gage or by using a dwell reading. *Dwell* is the number of degrees of crankshaft rotation that the ignition points are closed.

8. Some ignition systems use a **condenser,** which is a type of electrical capacitor or storage unit. Generally condensers do not wear out, but they may become damaged. As a general recommendation, if you install new ignition points, you should also install a new ignition condenser.

# LUBRICATION SYSTEMS

Proper maintenance of the internal combustion engine lubrication system is critical for the engine to run properly. Lubrication systems require periodic checks and regular preventive maintenance. The following general practices are suggested for all lubrication systems:

1. Check the engine oil level daily, or every 10 hours of operation.
2. Change the engine oil and filters according to the manufacturer's recommendations.
3. Always use the recommended engine oil, including the recommended class and grade.
4. Maintain a clean work area, tools, and supplies.
5. Safely dispose of used engine oil and filters.
6. Be safe and follow all safety practices.

## GENERAL PROCEDURE FOR CHANGING ENGINE OIL AND FILTERS

The engine oil should be changed regularly. A common recommendation for small engines is to change the oil every 10 to 25 hours of normal use. For large engines, change the engine oil every 100 hours of normal use. Engines used under severe operating conditions should have more frequent service intervals. If the engine is equipped with an oil filter, it should be changed every time the oil is changed.

12-16. Motor oils vary in viscosity and other properties. Viscosity is the internal friction of a fluid.

A general procedure for changing the oil and filter.

1. Assemble the tools and materials. You will probably need: the recommended amount of oil and a new filter, an oil drain pan, some clean shop-type cloths, wrenches to remove the drain plug and filter.

2. Be sure the machine or engine is in a safe, level working position.

3. Operate the engine until the oil is warmed up—warm to the touch when you remove the dipstick.

4. Shut off the engine and remove the drain plug. Be sure to catch all of the draining oil so it can be safely recycled.

5. Allow the oil to drain for several minutes.

6. Clean dirt from the oil filter area and remove the filter. Often, it is difficult to catch the oil as it drains from the filter.

7. Install a new filter. Be sure the filter gasket is oiled and properly installed. Most spin-on filters should be hand-tightened only. Do not over tighten!

8. Fill the crankcase with the recommended amount of oil. Never overfill.

9. Start the engine and operate for about two minutes. If equipped with an oil pressure gage, be sure the system has correct operating pressure.

10. Check the engine for leaks.

11. After shutting the engine off, and waiting several minutes, check the engine oil level and fill to the recommended level if necessary.

This general procedure may vary from one type of engine to another. Always check the service or operator's manual for the recommended procedure. If the engine is equipped with either a turbocharger or an oil cooler, the procedure may be somewhat different.

## TESTING LUBRICATION SYSTEM PRESSURE

Periodic checks of engines that have a pressure-type lubrication system should be made to determine if the system is operating at the recommended pressure. Some systems are equipped with oil pressure gages. If so, check and make sure the gage is operating properly. Some engines have an oil pressure sensing light. The light works from an oil pressure sensor. Check the operation of the sensor by checking the electrical resistance of the sending unit. If major work is done on an engine, such as reconditioning the cylinder head or installing new piston rings, the engine oil pressure should be checked.

12-17. An oil pressure gauge shows the pressure of the lubrication system when the engine is running.

The following is a general procedure for checking the engine lubrication system pressure.

1. If the engine is equipped with an oil pressure gage, it should read in the normal range. Always observe the gage when operating the engine. If the reading is outside the normal operating range, stop the engine immediately.

2. If the engine is not equipped with a gage, or you think the gage is not working properly, you can install a gage in the system. Remove the pressure sensor and install the gage with the proper fittings.

Watch this gage while the engine is operating at a fast idle speed. If the engine begins to knock, vibrate, or is not operating smoothly, shut the engine off immediately and check the engine oil.

3. After the engine has warmed up to operating temperature, record the oil pressure. Compare this reading with the engine specifications.

4. A lack of oil pressure is a very serious engine problem. It may be caused by a lack of oil, a broken oil pump, a major internal oil leak, a broken oil pressure regulator, or a broken drive mechanism on the oil pump.

5. A low oil pressure reading may indicate (1) the engine does not have enough oil, (2) the wrong kind of oil was used, (3) the pressure regulator is not working correctly, (4) the oil pump is worn, or (5) the gage is not working.

6. Oil pressure that is too high is also a problem. Some possible causes are (1) a broken pressure gage, (2) a broken or out of adjustment pressure regulator, or (3) the engine oil is of the wrong viscosity.

7. It is possible on some engines to adjust the engine oil pressure regulator or valve. If a gage, pump, or regulator is defective, it is recommended the defective part be replaced.

# STARTING SYSTEMS

Starting systems require regular preventive maintenance. The failure of an engine to start is frustrating and may cause economic losses. Practicing preventive maintenance will keep starting systems in good working condition.

## MAINTAINING MECHANICAL STARTING SYSTEMS

Several different kinds of mechanical starting systems are found on engines. Some systems use a rewind starter rope, some use a wind up type crank, or another type of mechanical device. Mechanical starting systems are used on small engines. These systems generally require some periodic maintenance.

Here are a few suggestions for maintaining mechanical starting systems.

1. Keep the starting system clean.
2. Regularly check the condition of the starting rope and rope handle.

3. Mechanical starters usually use a spring to recoil the starter. These springs can become fatigued and either lose their strength or break. Replace the spring if it breaks or can no longer recoil the rope. The spring is not difficult to install if you follow the recommendations.

4. Lubricate mechanical starting systems only if recommenced to do so. Some manufacturers do not recommend the use of any oil or grease. The lubricant may collect dirt and jam or "freeze" the starter mechanism or starter clutch.

## MAINTAINING AND TESTING ELECTRICAL STARTING SYSTEMS

Electrical starting systems use the electrical energy from a battery to turn the engine crankshaft and allow the engine to start running. The starting system has two basic circuits, one to carry the electrical

12-18. The condition of the starting rope and handle should be checked regularly on small engines.

current to the starter motor, and another controlled by a starter switch that opens and closes the starter circuit. Several basic system checks can be made by using a voltmeter and an ohmmeter, as follows:

1. Test the voltage of the battery. Most engine starting systems use a liquid-cell battery, but some small engines use a dry-cell battery. Check the voltage according to the battery rating.

2. Batteries can be tested for the amount of load or cranking amperage they can produce. This test requires a load tester. Most agricultural and automotive stores, which sell batteries, will test your battery for a small fee or at no cost.

3. Check the starting system wiring for corrosion and bad connections. An ohmmeter can check the condition of electrical connections. Little or no resistance should be measured across the connections.

4. The ohmmeter can also be used to check the operating condition of the starter switch, the starter solenoid, and the circuit wiring.

5. Keep the starting system circuit and battery clean and protected from corrosion.

## *SERVICING BATTERIES*

Batteries must be in good working condition. Some batteries are sealed and cannot be serviced. However, many batteries used in agriculture and industry allow access to the electrolyte and can be serviced. The following are some guidelines for servicing batteries:

1. Check the battery electrolyte level every 50 hours of use.

2. Fill the battery with clean distilled water only, be sure not to overfill.

3. A battery can be cleaned with a solution of baking soda and water. Clean the battery at least every 250 hours of use. Be sure to dry the battery and rinse the surrounding area.

4. When you clean the battery, also clean (with a wire-brush battery cleaner) the cable clamps and the battery terminals.

5. When you reinstall the battery cables, apply a light coat of battery protectant grease or petroleum jelly to inhibit corrosion.

6. If a battery needs to be recharged, use a slow charge rate (less than 10 percent of the battery ampere-hour rating) over an extended period. Expect from 12 to 24 hours of slow charging to recharge a battery.

7. Use a battery hydrometer to check the electrolyte condition. The hydrometer indicates the specific gravity. There should not be more

12-19. Batteries must be serviced and kept in good working condition if they are to work when you need them.

than a 0.050 specific gravity reading difference between any two cells. A fully charged battery will have a reading of from 1.260 to 1.270. A battery reading less then 1.140 is very discharged.

8. A battery load test will indicate the electrical storage capacity of the battery. This requires a current transducer. An agricultural or automotive battery supply store will usually load test batteries for you.

Always wear splash-proof eye protection and work in well-ventilated areas when servicing liquid-cell, acid-type batteries.

# SUMMARY

Internal combustion engines require regular preventive maintenance. Follow the recommended preventive practices for the various engines and agricultural implements. Machines that are well maintained will perform better, last longer, operate more efficiently, cost less to operate, and retain their value. Always read the operator's and service manuals before operating or servicing equipment. A few minutes of regular preventive maintenance and visual checks can prevent costly repairs and the loss of valuable work time.

Be sure to work in a safe, clean area. Use good quality products and the proper filters, lubricants, fuels, cleaning solvents, and other materials. The life expectancy of a machine is directly related to how well it is cared for and operated. The life expectancy of a machine is directly related to how well you maintain the machine, as well as how well you operate it.

# REVIEW QUESTIONS

1. What is preventive maintenance?

2. What are the general preventive maintenance practices applicable for all machinery and equipment?

3. What are maintenance intervals and how do we measure them?

4. What are the recommended safety practices in performing preventive maintenance?

5. What are the basic procedures for performing a vacuum test on an intake system?

6. How do you service dry element and oil foam type air cleaners?

7. What are the basic checks for testing the compression of an engine?

8. What are the basic guidelines for servicing fuel filters?

9. What are the basic guidelines for servicing carburetors?

10. What are the general practices for maintaining diesel fuel injection nozzles?

11. What are the basic tests for the exhaust system?

12. How do you maintain and test a liquid cooling system?

13. What are the general practices for maintaining an ignition system?

14. How do you maintain mechanical starting systems?

# APPLYING THE CONCEPTS

1. Using an operator's manual, outline a preventive maintenance schedule for a small engine or a larger engine operating agricultural equipment.

2. Perform the maintenance practices on an air intake system of an engine according to the operator's manual.

3. What are the basic procedures for performing a vacuum test on an intake system and servicing the air cleaner?

4. Perform the basic checks for testing the compression of an engine.

5. Service the fuel system of an engine, including servicing the fuel filters.

6. Repair a small engine carburetor by the basic guidelines and using a carburetor repair kit.

7. If you have the testing equipment, perform a test of a diesel fuel injection nozzle.

8. Perform basic tests on an exhaust system.

9. Perform a test on a liquid cooling system on an engine.

10. Test the ignition system of a small engine and perform the general practices for maintaining the ignition system.

11. Using the operator's manual or a repair manual, maintain a rope mechanical starting system by replacing the rope and/or spring.

# 13

# USING THE PRINCIPLES OF HYDRAULICS

Much of the "muscle" required in modern agricultural production and processing is supplied by hydraulics. Most tractors, combines, and many agricultural field machines (disc harrows, chisel plows, field cultivators, etc.) rely on hydraulics in some way. Also, hydraulic actuators (motors and cylinders) are found on much of the machinery used in processing agricultural products.

If you have ever driven a tractor (or automobile) equipped with power brakes or power steering, you have used hydraulics. If you have ever raised a load using a floor jack, you have likely used hydraulics. The applications of hydraulics are almost limitless.

Since hydraulics is so widely used in agriculture (and other areas of life), a basic understanding of this area of technology is needed. The many uses of hydraulics in the agricultural industry and in everyday life are amazing!

13-1. Field equipment uses hydraulics to supply the muscle in modern agricultural production.

# OBJECTIVES

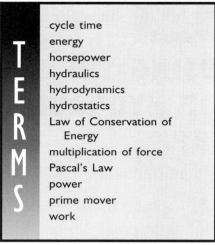

cycle time
energy
horsepower
hydraulics
hydrodynamics
hydrostatics
Law of Conservation of
Energy
multiplication of force
Pascal's Law
power
prime mover
work

This chapter covers the important principles of hydraulics. After completing this chapter, you will:

1. Describe hydraulics and the two major operating systems.

2. Describe the advantages and disadvantages of hydraulics as a method of power transmission.

3. Explain Pascal's Law.

4. Describe the mathematical relationship between force, pressure, and area in a hydraulic system.

5. Calculate the cycle time for a hydraulic cylinder.

6. Describe how the Law of Conservation of Energy relates to the operation of a hydraulic system.

7. Determine both the mechanical and fluid horsepower output of a specific hydraulic system.

# HYDRAULICS: DEFINITION AND OPERATING SYSTEMS

*Hydraulics* is the branch of physics dealing with the mechanical properties and practical applications of liquids in motion. The applications of hydraulics can be grouped into two major operating systems: hydrodynamics and hydrostatics.

## HYDRODYNAMICS

*Hydrodynamics* is the use of liquids at high flow and low pressure to perform work. If you have ever rafted down a river or stream, you have made use of hydrodynamics. You used the energy of the flowing water to move you and your raft through a distance (downstream).

The old-fashioned gristmill operates because of hydrodynamics. The energy of the stream's moving water turns the mill wheel. The mill wheel transmits this rotating force to machinery inside the mill, which grinds grain into meal.

Hydrodynamic power transmission is not often used in modern agriculture. For that reason, hydrostatics is most important.

**13-2. Hydrodynamics powers this water wheel.**

## HYDROSTATICS

*Hydrostatics* is the use of liquids at high pressure and low flow to perform work. When compared to the water in a flowing river or stream, the oil in a tractor's hydraulic system moves at a very slow rate; however, the oil is under a much greater pressure.

For example, less than a gallon of oil flow may be required to raise a heavy load using a tractor's hydraulic lift. Although the speed (flow rate) of the oil is relatively slow, the oil may be under a pressure of approximately 2750 psi (pounds per square inch). A tractor hydraulic lift is a good application of hydrostatics: liquid under low speed and high pressure being used to perform work. In the remainder of this chapter, hydraulics refers to hydrostatics.

Hydraulic systems transmit power; they do not create power. Hydraulic systems require an outside source of power to operate. This outside power source is called the *prime mover*.

A good example is a tractor. The hydraulic pump that moves the fluid is powered by the tractor's engine. Without the power supplied to the pump by the engine, the hydraulic system would not function. Therefore, the tractor's engine serves as the prime mover for the tractor hydraulic system.

13-3. This wheel on an irrigation system is turned by a hydraulic motor. (Courtesy, Jasper S. Lee)

# ADVANTAGES AND DISADVANTAGES OF HYDRAULICS

The fact that hydraulics is so widely used in the agricultural industry indicates that it has many advantages. Yet, despite these advantages, some disadvantages do exist.

## ADVANTAGES

Hydraulic power transmission has several advantages over mechanical power transmission (belts and pulleys, drive shafts, etc.). These include:

*Increased Flexibility*—Unlike mechanical drive components, hydraulic hoses (and even tubing) can be routed around obstructions. Since the drive and driven components in a hydraulic system do not have to be aligned, machines that are more simple and compact can be designed and constructed.

*Infinitely Variable Speed*—The speed at which a hydraulic system operates is determined by the volume of fluid moved by the hydraulic pump per unit of time (per second or minute). The speed at which a hydraulic cylinder or pump operates can be infinitely varied by controlling the flow rate of the pump.

*Multiplication of Force*—Using hydraulics, a small input force can be multiplied to create a larger output force. While multiplication of force can be achieved with a mechanical power transmission system, the use of hydraulics makes this process much more simple.

*Reduced Wear*—Less metal-to-metal contact occurs in a hydraulic power transmission system (as compared to a mechanical system). Also, the hydraulic fluid lubricates the moving components. Thus, less wear occurs in a hydraulic system.

*Increased Automation Potential*—Hydraulic operations can be easily automated using sensing devices and controls that react to pressure, temperature, electrical current, or the position of one or more components. Sensors and controls can also be used to automatically sequence operations containing two or more events.

*Decreased Equipment Damage*—Almost all hydraulic systems contain one or more pressure relief valves. These valves help prevent equipment damage by diverting oil flow back to the reservoir when fluid pressure reaches a specific critical level. Once the pressure relief valve opens, fluid flow to actuators stops until pressure falls below the pressure relief valve setting. Thus, if a hydraulic system becomes overloaded, the pressure relief valve will prevent damage to the system.

*Reversibility*—Hydraulic systems can be designed so that cylinders and motors may be reversed, or operate in either direction.

## DISADVANTAGES

Despite the many advantages, hydraulic power transmission does have some disadvantages. Three primary disadvantages are described.

**Use of High Pressures**—Hydraulic systems operate under very high pressures. These high pressures require heavy tubing and hoses, tight joints, and careful maintenance.

**Need for Cleanliness**—Because of the high pressures and close tolerances under which hydraulic components operate, they can be easily damaged by dirt, rust, or corrosion. Thus, cleanliness is essential to the long life and effective operation of a hydraulic system.

**Safety Hazards**—Again, because hydraulic systems operate under high pressure, they pose unique safety hazards. For example, a pinhole sized puncture in a hydraulic hose can release fluid under sufficient pressure to puncture the skin, causing severe injury. Always wear eye protection and protective clothing when checking for pinhole leaks. Do not attempt to locate the leak by feeling the hose with your hands; instead, use a piece of wood or cardboard. See a doctor immediately if hydraulic fluid is injected into your body.

# BASIC PRINCIPLES OF HYDRAULICS

In 1653, a French scientist named Blaise Pascal formulated the fundamental law that explains the operation of hydraulic equipment. The law, which became known as *Pascal's Law*, states that:

> Pressure applied to a confined fluid is transmitted undiminished in all directions, acts with equal force on equal areas, and acts at right angles to the walls of the container.

Pascal's Law can be illustrated using the container of liquid shown in Figure 13-4. A 10-lb force applied to the stopper (having an area of 1 in$^2$) will result in a pressure of 10 lbs per in$^2$ (10 psi) being exerted by the fluid (10 lbs ÷ 1 in$^2$ = 10 psi). This pressure will be transmitted undiminished in all directions and will act at right angles to the walls of the container.

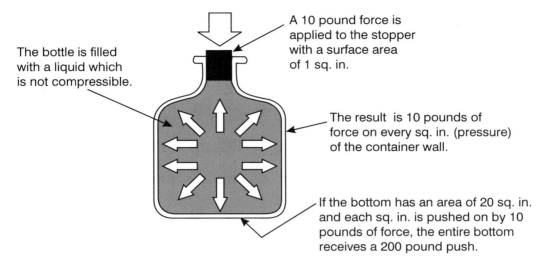

The bottle is filled with a liquid which is not compressible.

A 10 pound force is applied to the stopper with a surface area of 1 sq. in.

The result is 10 pounds of force on every sq. in. (pressure) of the container wall.

If the bottom has an area of 20 sq. in. and each sq. in. is pushed on by 10 pounds of force, the entire bottom receives a 200 pound push.

**13-4. A simple application of Pascal's Law.**

According to Pascal's Law, the pressure applied to an enclosed fluid acts with equal force on equal areas, so each 1 in² of container surface will receive 10 lbs of applied force. If the bottom of the container has a surface area of 20 in², the 10-lb force applied to the stopper will result in a total of 200 lbs of force being exerted against the bottom of the container (10 psi × 20 in² = 200 lbs force).

# MULTIPLICATION OF FORCE IN A HYDRAULIC SYSTEM

Hydraulic systems are generally used to produce a multiplication of force. *Multiplication of force* means that the hydraulic system takes a small input force and transforms it into a larger output force. In the previous example, the 10-lb force applied to the stopper produced a 200-lb force against the bottom of the container. Thus, multiplication of force occurred—a small input force produced a larger output force.

## *FORCE, PRESSURE, AND AREA RELATIONSHIPS*

In a hydraulic system, a definite relationship exists between the output force developed, the pressure of the fluid, and the area of the moveable surface against which the fluid operates. Formula 13-1 summarizes this relationship.

F = P × A          | Formula 13-1 |

  where,

      F = Output force (lbs.)
      P = Fluid pressure (psi)
      A = Area of output cylinder (in²)

13-5. A hydraulic system is used to illustrate the F = P × A equation.

In this hydraulic system (Figure 13-5), the 10-lb force applied to the 1 in² input piston will create a fluid pressure of 10 psi (10 lbs ÷ 1 in² = 10 psi). This pressure will be applied against the 10 in² area of the output piston. Inserting these values into Formula 13-1 shows that 10 lbs of force applied to the small piston generates 100 lbs of output force at the large piston.

F = P × A
F = 10 psi × 10 in²
F = 100 lbs

Formula 13-1 can also be rearranged to solve for pressure or area if values for the other two system variables are known. Using Figure 13-5 as an example, the output force is 100 lbs and the area of the output piston is 10 in². The system pressure is easily determined by rearranging Formula 13-1 and inserting known values.

$$F = P \times A$$
or

$$P = \frac{F}{A}$$

$$P = \frac{100 \text{ lbs}}{10 \text{ in}^2}$$

$$P = 10 \text{ psi}$$

The calculated pressure value of 10 psi is equal to the value in the original example.

Assume that values are known for output force and system pressure in Figure 13-5. The output piston area can be determined by rearranging Formula 13-1. Insert the known values and solve for the area of the piston.

$$F = P \times A$$
or

$$A = \frac{F}{P}$$

$$A = \frac{100 \text{ lbs}}{10 \text{ psi}}$$

$$A = 10 \text{ in}^2$$

The calculated piston area of 10 in² is the same as the value given in the original example.

The force-pressure-area formula is an indispensable aid in working with hydraulics. The formula has many uses. Many people find it easier to remember the formula (and the different ways of rearranging it) when it is written as a "pie" formula.

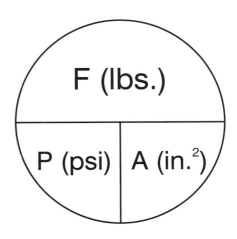

**13-6.** The pie formula for the relationship between force, pressure, and area.

To use the pie formula, simply cover the unknown variable and perform the mathematical operation implied. For example, if you want to solve for force, cover the "F" and multiply pressure (P) times area (A) as indicated. If you want to solve for area, cover the "A" and divide pressure (P) into force (F). Lastly, if you want to solve for pressure, cover the "P" and divide area (A) into force (F).

# CALCULATING THE CYCLE TIME OF A HYDRAULIC SYSTEM

The *cycle time* for a hydraulic application is the amount of time required for one complete set of operations to occur. For example, if 16 seconds is required to fully extend a hydraulic cylinder and 12 seconds to fully retract the cylinder, then the system has a cycle time of 28 seconds (16 sec/extend + 12 sec/retract).

The speed with which a hydraulic cylinder extends and/or retracts is a function of the volume of the cylinder (in³) and the flow rate (gallons per minute) of the hydraulic fluid. To better understand this relationship, calculate the cycle time for the cylinder illustrated in Figure 13-7.

Cycle time is the amount of time required for a cylinder to completely extend and retract because hydraulic fluid is pumped into the cylinder. Therefore, if we know how much fluid (in³) is required to extend and retract a cylinder and how fast (gpm) the fluid is delivered, we can calculate the time required to complete one cycle. In this example, assume that the system hydraulic pump delivers fluid at the rate of 22 gpm.

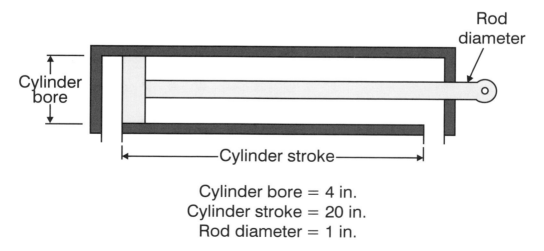

Cylinder bore = 4 in.
Cylinder stroke = 20 in.
Rod diameter = 1 in.

13-7. An example of a hydraulic cylinder.

**Step 1.** Calculate the amount (gallons) of hydraulic fluid required to fully extend the cylinder.

   A. Determine the area (in$^2$ of the cylinder piston).

   A = πr²

where,

   A = area
   π = 3.1416
   r = radius of cylinder piston

   A = πr²
   A = 3.1416 × (4/2)²
   A = 3.1416 × 4
   A = 12.57 in²

   B. Determine the volume (in$^3$) of the cylinder, which must be filled with hydraulic fluid to fully extend the cylinder.

   V = piston cylinder area × length of piston stroke
   V = 12.57 in² × 20 in
   V = 251.4 in³

   C. Determine the amount (gal.) of hydraulic fluid required to fully extend the cylinder using the following formula:

$$\text{Hydraulic fluid required (gal.)} = \frac{\text{Volume}}{231 \text{ in}^3}$$

where,

   volume = in³ area to be filled by hydraulic fluid (from Step 1B)
   231 in³ = volume of 1 gallon of fluid

$$\text{Hydraulic fluid required (gal.)} = \frac{251.4 \text{ in}^3}{231 \text{ in}^3}$$
$$= 1.09 \text{ gal.}$$

**Step 2.** Calculate the amount (gallons) of hydraulic fluid required to retract the hydraulic cylinder.

   A1. Determine the area (in$^2$) of the cylinder piston.

$A = \pi r^2$

$A = 3.1416 \times (4/2)^2$

$A = 12.57$ in²

A2. Determine the area (in²) of the cylinder rod.

$A = \pi r^2$

$A = 3.1416 (1/2)^2$

$A = 0.79$ in²

A3. Determine the "effective" area ($A_e$) of the cylinder piston.

$A_e$ = Area of cylinder piston − Area of cylinder rod

$A_e$ = 12.57 in² − 0.79 in²

$A_e$ = 11.78 in²

B. Determine the volume (in³) of the cylinder, which must be filled with hydraulic fluid to fully retract the cylinder.

V = piston cylinder area x length of piston stroke

V = 11.78 in² × 20 in

V = 235.6 in³

C. Determine the amount (gal.) of hydraulic fluid required to fully retract the hydraulic cylinder.

$$\text{Hydraulic fluid required (gal.)} = \frac{\text{Volume}}{231 \text{ in}^3}$$

$$= \frac{235.6 \text{ in}^3}{231 \text{ in}^3}$$

$$= 1.02 \text{ gal.}$$

**Step 3.** Determine the total cycle time required to extend and retract the cylinder.

A. Determine total gallons required per cycle.

Total Gal/Cycle = Gal to extend + Gal to retract

= 1.09 gal + 1.02 gal

= 2.11 gal.

B. Determine total cycle time

$$\text{Total cycle time} = \frac{\text{Total Gal / Cycle}}{\text{Pump Capacity (gpm)}} \times 60 \text{ sec / min}$$

$$= \frac{2.11 \text{ gal}}{22 \text{ gpm}} \times 60 \text{ sec / min}$$

$$= .096 \times 60 \text{ sec/min}$$

$$= 5.75 \text{ seconds}$$

Based on these calculations, the cylinder will complete one full cycle in 5.75 seconds. The time required to complete one full cycle is determined by two factors: (a) the volume of hydraulic oil that must be pumped and (b) the flow rate of the system hydraulic pump.

# CONSERVATION OF ENERGY IN HYDRAULIC SYSTEMS

One major advantage of hydraulic power transmission is the ability to use a small input force to produce a large output force. This multiplication of force may

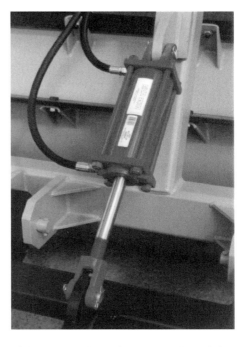

13-8. Hydraulic cylinder showing piping and connection to an earth-moving blade. (Courtesy, Jasper S. Lee)

seem to be an example of "getting something for nothing." This is not the case. A tradeoff occurs when a hydraulic system produces a multiplication of force. In order to understand this tradeoff, the concepts of work and energy are important.

## WORK

In the physical sciences, **work** is the movement of a force through a distance. Work is measured in foot-pounds (ft-lbs) and can be calculated using Formula 13-2.

$$W = F \times D$$ 
| Formula 13-2 |
| --- |

where,

  W = work (ft-lbs)
  F = force (lbs)
  D = distance (ft)

To better understand work, let's solve a couple of example problems. First, assume that a 100-lb weight (force) is lifted a distance of 10 ft. By inserting known values into Formula 13-2, we determine that 1000 ft-lbs of work has been done. These calculations are shown.

$$W = F \times D$$

$$W = 100\text{-lbs} \times 10\text{-ft}$$

$$W = 1000 \text{ ft-lbs}$$

Next, assume the same 100-lb weight is pulled the same distance of 10 ft. In this case, since the earth's surface supports the load's weight, assume that only 45 lbs of force is required to move the 100-lb weight. Again, by inserting our known values into Formula 13-2, we determine that 450 ft-lbs of work has been done in this example. These calculations are shown.

$$W = F \times D$$

$$W = 45\text{-lbs} \times 10\text{-ft}$$

$$W = 450 \text{ ft-lbs}$$

Review the two example problems. First, notice that the force value used in calculating work is always the value of the force that causes the movement. In the first example, since the weight was lifted, the force required was equal to the weight of the object being lifted. But, in the second example, since the weight was pulled, only the force actually used to move the load was considered in calculating the amount of work done. Again, when calculating work, consider only the magnitude of the force used to produce the movement.

The second important point is that no work is done unless movement occurs regardless of the amount of force applied. Any number multiplied by zero is equal to zero. Therefore, if distance equals zero, work will also equal zero.

## ENERGY

Energy is one of the central concepts of science and technology. Stated quite simply, *energy* is the capacity to do work.

Energy comes in many forms. For example, a gallon of gasoline contains chemical energy that can be used to power an engine that does work. Light from the Sun contains radiant energy that can be converted to electricity by a solar cell. This electricity can then be used to power a motor or other device that does work. Also, a tightly wound spring contains mechanical energy that can be used to do work as the spring uncoils.

### Law of Conservation of Energy

The *Law of Conservation of Energy* states that energy may be changed from one form to another, but it cannot be either created or destroyed. Thus, the total amount of energy in a system never changes.

What does the Law of Conservation of Energy mean as far as understanding the multiplication of force in a hydraulic system? Since energy is the capacity to do work, the law means that we cannot get more work out of a hydraulic system than is put into the system.

Since work is equal to force times distance (Formula 13-2), the product of input force multiplied by input distance must be equal to the product of output force multiplied by output distance (assuming 100 percent efficiency). This is shown in Formula 13-3.

$$F_i \times D_i = F_o \times D_o$$    | Formula 13-3 |

where,

$F_i$ = input force (lbs)
$D_i$ = input distance (ft)
$F_o$ = output force (lbs)
$D_o$ = output distance (ft)

Assume that a hydraulic system is capable of developing 1000 lbs of output force with an input force of 100 lbs. Use Formula 13-3 to determine how far the 100-lb input force must move to move the 1000-lb output force a distance of 1 ft. By inserting known values into the formula and solving the problem algebraically, we find that the input force must move a distance of 10 ft to move the 1000-lb force a distance of 1 ft.

The necessary calculations are shown.

$$F_i \times D_i = F_o \times D_o$$

$$100 \text{ lbs.} \times D_i = 1000 \text{ lbs} \times 1 \text{ ft}$$

$$\frac{100 \text{ lbs.} \times D_i}{100 \text{ lbs}} = \frac{1000 \text{ lbs} \times 1 \text{ ft}}{100 \text{ lbs}}$$

$$D_i = 10 \times 1 \text{ ft}$$

$$D_i = 10 \text{ ft}$$

In hydraulics there is no such thing as getting something for free. When an input force is multiplied (to produce a larger output force) the input force must be moved a proportionally greater distance. Thus, work output from a hydraulic system can never be more than the work put into the system. In fact, since hydraulic systems are not 100 percent efficient, more work must go into the system than is gotten out of it. (This is because some of the work into the system is used to overcome friction and produces no productive, usable output. This energy is lost as heat.)

# HORSEPOWER IN A HYDRAULIC SYSTEM

Power and horsepower are often associated with work. Both are important concepts.

## POWER

*Power* is defined as the rate of doing work. More power is required if a certain amount of work must be done in a shorter period. Conversely, less power is required if this same amount of work can be done over a longer period of time. Power is expressed in foot-pounds per minute (ft-lbs / minute) and can be calculated using Formula 13-4.

$$P = \frac{W}{T}$$ | **Formula 13-4** |

where,

$P$ = power (ft-lbs per minute)
$W$ = work (ft-lbs)
$T$ = time (minutes)

To illustrate the use of Formula 13-4, calculate the power required to move a 1000-lb force a distance of 100 ft in five minutes.

$$P = \frac{W}{T} \quad \text{or} \quad P = \frac{\text{Force} \times \text{Distance}}{T}$$

$$P = \frac{1000 \text{ lbs} \times 100 \text{ ft}}{5 \text{ minutes}}$$

$$P = 20,000 \text{ ft-lbs per minute}$$

## HORSEPOWER

Although power can be expressed as ft-lbs per minute, few people use this unit when discussing power. In the United States power is usually measured and discussed in terms of *horsepower*.

## Basic Horsepower Formula

One horsepower is defined as the ability to do 33,000 ft-lbs of work in one minute. Formula 13-5 presents the basic formula for calculating horsepower.

$$hp = \frac{F \times D}{T \times 33,000}$$
                     **Formula 13-5**

where,

$hp$ = horsepower
$F$ = force (lbs)
$D$ = distance (ft)
$T$ = time (min)
$33,000$ = a constant (based on 33,000 ft-lbs / min)

Earlier the amount of power (ft-lbs / min) required to move a 1000-lb force a distance of 100 ft in five minutes was calculated. This example can be used to calculate the horsepower required. As shown, by substituting values into Formula 13-5, 0.61 hp is required to do the work in the specified period.

$$hp = \frac{F \times D}{T \times 33,000}$$

$$hp = \frac{1000 \text{ lbs} \times 100 \text{ ft}}{5 \text{ min} \times 33,000}$$

$$hp = .61$$

## Fluid Horsepower Formula

Formula 13-5 is the basic definitional formula for horsepower. However, in some situations, when working with a hydraulic system, it may not be possible to measure the variables (force and distance) necessary to calculate horsepower using this formula. Because of this, the basic horsepower formula can be modified to allow calculation of the horsepower developed by a hydraulic system using the variables of fluid pressure (psi) and flow rate (gpm). This formula, called the fluid horsepower formula, is given as Formula 13-6.

$$FHP = \frac{P \times Q}{1714}$$

| **Formula 13-6** |
| --- |

where,

FHP = fluid horsepower
P = pressure (psi)
Q = flow rate (gpm)
1714 = a constant

Use Formula 13-6 to determine the maximum horsepower that can be produced by a tractor hydraulic system having a 28 gpm pump (flow rate) and a maximum system pressure setting of 2250 psi. Inserting our known values into Formula 13-6, we find that this tractor can develop a maximum fluid horsepower (FHP) of 36.8 hp. The necessary calculations are shown.

$$FHP = \frac{P \times Q}{1714}$$

$$FHP = \frac{2250 \text{ psi} \times 28 \text{ gpm}}{1714}$$

$$FHP = 36.8$$

# SUMMARY

Hydraulics is the branch of physics concerned with the use of fluids in motion. The two hydraulics operating systems are hydrodynamics and hydrostatics. There are both advantages and disadvantages of hydraulic power transmission.

Pascal's Law is the basis for hydraulics (hydrostatics) and explains how force can be multiplied in a hydraulic system. The relationship between force, pressure, and area in a hydraulic system is important.

Cycle time refers to the amount of time required for a hydraulic system to complete one full sequence of operations. In this chapter, you learned the two factors (volume and flow rate) that determine the required cycle time for a system. You also learned how to calculate cycle time, given necessary system specifications.

A hydraulic system transmits force from one location to another. In the process, it can increase the magnitude of the force. However, the Law of Conservation of Energy tells us that a hydraulic system cannot deliver more power than is put into the system. In other words, when a hydraulic system increases the magnitude of an output force, there is a proportional decrease in the distance the output force moves.

Hydraulic systems transmit force to accomplish work. Power is the rate at which work is done. Horsepower is the unit of power commonly used in the United States. The horsepower output of a hydraulic system is easily calculated.

# REVIEW QUESTIONS

1. Define "hydraulics" and explain the difference between "hydrodynamics" and "hydrostatics."

2. Describe a specific situation where hydraulic power transmission would be clearly superior to mechanical power transmission. Explain why hydraulics would be the best power transmission system for the situation you described.

3. Explain Pascal's Law in your own words.

4. Describe the mathematical relationship between force, pressure, and area in a hydraulic system.

5. Describe the two factors that determine the cycle of time for a hydraulic cylinder.

6. According to the Law of Conservation of Energy, what trade-off is involved when a hydraulic system produces a mechanical advantage of force?

7. Define "horsepower" and list the variables that must be known (or measured) in order to calculate the fluid horsepower output of a hydraulic system.

# APPLYING THE CONCEPTS

1. Develop a list of machines and devices that use hydraulics to transmit power. Discuss why these items use hydraulic rather than mechanical power transmission.

2. Examine the illustration below, and answer the questions that follow.

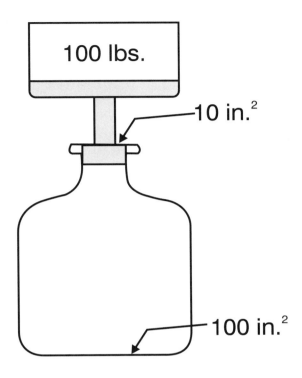

100 lbs.

$-10$ in.$^2$

$-100$ in.$^2$

   A. What is the pressure (psi) on the fluid in the container?

   B. How much force will be applied against the bottom of the container?

3. Assume that the hydraulic cylinder shown below is connected to a hydraulic system that operates at a maximum system pressure of 2500 psi. Also assume that the flow rate of the system's hydraulic pump is 2.9 gallons per minute (gpm). Answer the following questions.

Extend

Retract

Cylinder bore = 6 in.
Cylinder stroke = 30 in.
Rod diameter = 1.75 in.

A.  At maximum system pressure, how many pounds of force will the cylinder develop when extending? When retracting?

B.  What is the cylinder's cycle time when the hydraulic pump is operating at its maximum flow rate?

C.  What is the maximum fluid horsepower output of this hydraulic system?

4.  Secure one large syringe and one small syringe (without needles). Remove the plunger from the small syringe. Join the needle-ends of the syringes together with a length of clear plastic tubing. Fill the syringes and tubing with water. Replace the small plunger in the syringe. Hold one syringe in each hand and depress both plungers with equal force. What happens? Why?

5.  Disassemble a small hydraulic jack, being careful to collect the hydraulic fluid in a pan or other container. Measure the diameter of the jack's input (small) plunger and output (large) plunger. Determine the jack's theoretical multiplication of force (due to hydraulics) by dividing the diameter of the output plunger by the diameter of the input plunger. What is this ratio? In addition to the multiplication of force due to hydraulics, does a mechanical multiplication of force also occur with this jack? If so, how?

# 14

# HYDRAULIC SYSTEM COMPONENTS AND FUNCTIONS

A hydraulic system is just that — a system. A system is made of two or more components that work together to accomplish a specific task (or tasks). A common example of a system is the human circulatory system. The circulatory system is composed of various components (heart, veins, arteries, etc.) that work together to circulate blood throughout the body. Successful performance of this task requires each component to perform in a satisfactory manner.

Like your circulatory system, a hydraulic system is composed of various components. Each of these components must perform its function(s) effectively if the system is to perform its intended task(s). The components of hydraulic systems and how these contribute to the overall operation of the hydraulic system are important in understanding how the systems work.

14-1. The loader on this tractor is a system of components that work together to accomplish a specific task.

# OBJECTIVES

This chapter covers the components and their functions in a hydraulic system. After completing this chapter, you will:

1. List the primary components of a hydraulic system and explain the function(s) of each component.

2. Describe the construction and basic operating principles of gear, vane, and piston hydraulic pumps.

3. Describe and identify directional control valves based on position, port, and way characteristics.

4. Describe the operation of open, closed, and tandem centered hydraulic systems.

5. Describe and identify various types of hydraulic cylinders and motors.

6. Identify common hydraulic schematic symbols and interpret hydraulic system schematics.

**TERMS**

axial piston pump
balanced vane pump
compound pressure relief
   valve
connector
cracking pressure
differential cylinder
direct acting pressure relief
   valve
filter
fixed displacement pump
full-flow pressure
hydraulic actuator
hydraulic cylinder
hydraulic motor
linear actuator
non-differential cylinder
non-positive displacement
piping
port
position
positive displacement
pressure override
radial piston pump
ram
rotary actuator
schematic symbol
strainer
unbalanced vane pump
unloading valve
variable displacement pump
way

# HYDRAULIC SYSTEM COMPONENTS

Each component of a hydraulic system contributes to the operation of the total system. The hydraulic system illustrated in Figure 14-2 shows the major components: reservoir, strainer and filter, pump, pressure gauge, pressure relief valve, directional control valve, actuator, and piping and connectors. In order for this system to operate, a prime mover (not shown) would also be required.

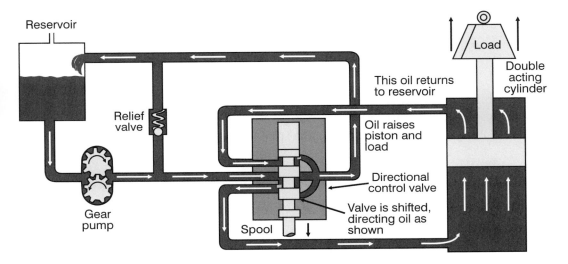

14-2. The major components of a hydraulic system.

## *RESERVOIR*

The reservoir supplies oil to the hydraulic pump and stores oil that returns after passing through the hydraulic circuit. The oil cools in an over-sized reservoir or in an oil-cooler before being sent back through the circuit.

Generally, an over-sized reservoir must be two to three times as large as the capacity of the pump (rated in gallons per minute, gpm) for this method to be effective. This limits the practicality of using this cooling method on mobile equipment where weight and size are limiting factors.

Oil-coolers are used when it is not practical to cool the oil using a reservoir. In a liquid oil-cooler, hydraulic oil and coolant flow through separate passageways in the oil-cooler. The hydraulic oil gives off heat to

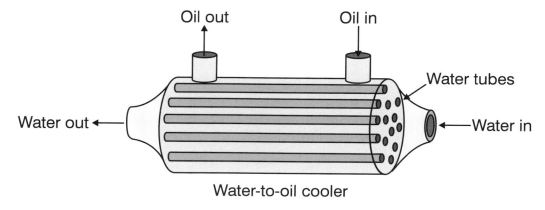

14-3. A typical oil-cooler.

the coolant. In turn, the coolant dissipates the absorbed heat to the atmosphere. Oil-to-air oil-coolers are also available.

The actual design of a hydraulic reservoir will depend on the particular application. For example, in a tractor, the hydraulic reservoir is generally

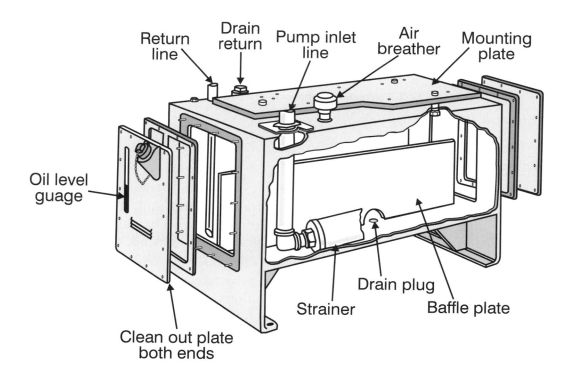

14-4. A reservoir for a piece of stationary hydraulic equipment.

the sealed case that contains the tractor's transmission and differential. However, on a piece of stationary hydraulic machinery, such as a hydraulic press, a separate reservoir will usually be provided.

## STRAINERS AND FILTERS

Hydraulic oil is kept clean primarily by strainers and filters. Each performs similar functions in cleaning the oil.

A *strainer* directs the hydraulic oil in a straight line through the strainer element, which is usually made of one or more fine mesh screens attached to a metal core. As the oil passes through the strainer, particles larger than the screen openings are retained on the screen. Generally, strainers remove particles larger than 40 microns, which is the lower limit of visibility to the human eye. (Note: One micron is equal to 39 millionths of an inch, or .000039 inch.)

A *filter* directs the hydraulic oil in a round-about path through one or more layers of a porous element that may trap particles as small as one micron. Thus, filters remove the smaller particles from the hydraulic oil, while strainers remove the larger particles.

Because of their construction and operation, filters generally cause greater pressure losses in a hydraulic system than do strainers. For this reason, filters are usually placed in the return (or low pressure) side of the hydraulic circuit so they do not restrict oil flow to the hydraulic pump. Strainers offer less resistance to flow loss and are generally used on the supply (inlet) side of the circuit.

In addition to trapping particles mechanically, some strainers and filters use magnets to collect extremely small metallic particles from the hydraulic system. Hydraulic systems have very close tolerances and even tiny bits of trash will cause failure.

14-5. A typical hydraulic filter. (Note the 10 micron filter rating.)

## *PUMP*

The hydraulic pump is the "heart" of a hydraulic system. The pump uses mechanical power (supplied by the system's prime mover) to cause hydraulic oil to flow through the circuit. The function of a pump is to change mechanical power to fluid power.

A hydraulic pump does not produce pressure. Pressure is produced when the hydraulic fluid encounters a resistance to flow. This resistance may be caused by a closed hydraulic system valve or by a load that is to be moved.

Pumps used in agricultural hydraulics are *positive displacement* pumps. A positive displacement pump delivers (or displaces) the same volume of oil per cycle, regardless of the pressure at the pump outlet. This is in contrast to *non-positive displacement* pumps, where the delivery rate decreases as the outlet pressure increases.

A pump can also be classified as either a *fixed displacement pump* or a *variable displacement pump*. The volume of the pumping chamber in a fixed displacement pump cannot be increased or decreased while the pump is in operation. Thus, the pump delivers (or displaces) the same amount of oil during each cycle. Conversely, the volume of the pumping chamber in a variable displacement pump can be increased or decreased while the pump is in operation. Thus, the amount of oil delivered during each pump cycle can be varied. Both fixed and variable displacement pumps are used in agricultural hydraulics.

Three types of hydraulic pumps are commonly used in agricultural applications. They are the gear pump, the vane pump, and the piston pump. The basic construction and operating characteristics of each of these pump types will be discussed in the following sections.

### *Gear Pumps*

A gear pump causes fluid to flow by carrying the fluid between the teeth of two meshed gears. The meshed gears are enclosed in a metal housing containing the inlet and outlet ports.

Figure 14-6 shows how a gear pump produces fluid flow. As the gear teeth nearest the inlet port unmesh, a vacuum (low pressure area) is produced in the inlet side of the pump. This vacuum causes hydraulic fluid from the reservoir to enter the pump. Meanwhile, the fluid trapped between the gear teeth is delivered to the outlet side of the pump. Since, for all practical purposes, hydraulic fluid is incompressible, the fluid must displace an equal amount of fluid already in the outlet side of the pump. This displacement causes fluid to flow through the hydraulic circuit.

Gear pumps are usually fixed displacement pumps. This means that the same amount (volume) of fluid is delivered to the outlet side of the pump during each pump revolution. Thus, the only way to pump more oil per unit of time is to increase the speed at which the pump turns.

Several variations of the basic gear pump design are used in agricultural hydraulics. These include the external gear pump (shown in Figure 14-6), the internal gear pump, the lobe pump, and the geroter pump. These last three design variations are shown in Figure 14-7. Despite differences in their design, these pumps operate in the same basic fashion.

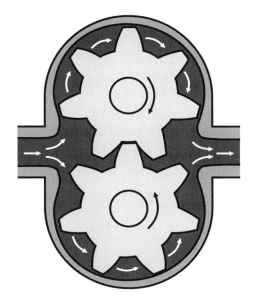

**14-6. A typical gear pump.**

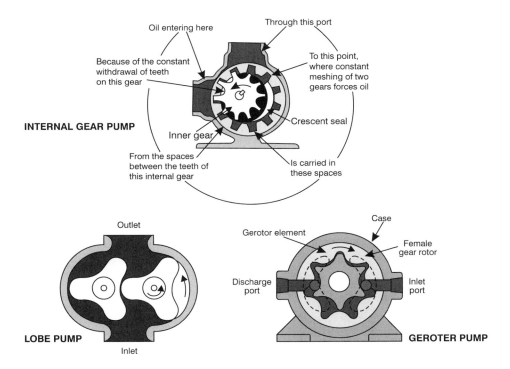

**14-7. A lobe pump (left), an internal gear pump (center), and a geroter pump (right).**

## Vane Pumps

A cutaway drawing of a typical vane pump is shown in Figure 14-8. The slotted rotor is connected to the drive shaft and turns inside the cam ring. The vanes are fitted in and turn with the rotor. Because of centrifugal force and oil pressure under the vanes, the tips of the vanes ride against the inner surface of the cam ring. As the rotor turns, the vanes travel past the pump's inlet and outlet ports.

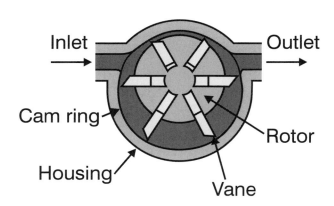

14-8. A cutaway of a typical vane pump.

As the vanes travel past the inlet port, the shape of the cam ring allows the vanes to move away from the rotor, expanding the volume of the area between the vanes and the cam ring. This expanding volume creates a low pressure area that causes hydraulic oil to flow into the pump. This oil is trapped between the rotating vanes and the cam ring. As the rotor reaches the outlet port, the shape of the cam ring pushes the vanes back into the rotor, decreasing the volume at the outlet port. This decreased volume forces the oil to displace oil, causing it to flow through the hydraulic circuit.

The vane pump illustrated in Figure 14-8 is an ***unbalanced vane pump.*** The pump is said to be unbalanced because the oil pressure on the outlet side of the pump is much higher than the oil pressure on the inlet side of the pump. This unbalanced condition results in heavy force being applied against the pump's rotor and bearings. Unbalanced vane pumps are variable displacement pumps. The pump's displacement can be changed by moving the cam ring to increase or decrease the size of the pumping chamber.

A ***balanced vane pump*** uses two sets of inlet and outlet ports to balance the pressure load. The two outlet ports are located 180 degrees apart, so pressure forces on the rotor cancel each other out, preventing excessive side-loading on the rotor shaft and bearings. Balanced vane pumps are of the fixed displacement type.

## Piston Pumps

A piston pump is composed of two sub-assemblies—a stationary sub-assembly and a rotating sub-assembly. The stationary sub-assembly is composed of the inlet and outlet ports and the valve plate. The rotating sub-assembly is composed of the cylinder block and bore, pistons, shoe plate, swash plate, and drive shaft.

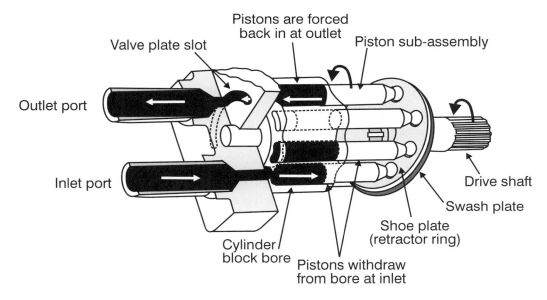

**14-9. A typical axial piston pump. (Piston pumps deliver higher pressure than other types of pumps.)**

The operation of a piston pump is quite simple. Power supplied to the drive shaft causes the rotating sub-assembly to turn. Because of the angle of the shoe and swash plates, the pistons move away from the stationary sub-assembly as the pistons align with the inlet port. This movement produces a low pressure area in the bore, which draws oil into the pump. Once the pistons are no longer in alignment with the inlet port, the oil is trapped in the bore. As the pistons continue to turn, the angle of the shoe and swash plates causes the piston to move back toward the stationary sub-assembly, increasing the pressure on the trapped oil. Once the pistons align with the outlet port, the pressurized fluid escapes the pump and is forced through the hydraulic circuit.

A piston pump can be of either the fixed or variable displacement type, depending on how the pump is built. If the angle of the swash plate is

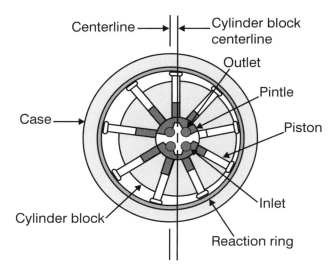

**14-10. A radial piston pump.**

not adjustable, the effective stroke of the pistons will be constant. Therefore, the pump will have a fixed displacement. Conversely, if the angle of the swash plate can be adjusted, the effective stroke of the pistons can be changed. Therefore, the pump will have a variable displacement.

The type of piston pump illustrated in Figure 14-9 is called an **axial piston pump.** This is because the pistons are parallel to the drive shaft. Compare this arrangement to the **radial piston pump** shown in Figure 14-10. In the radial piston pump, the pistons are arranged perpendicular to the drive shaft. Despite the difference in the arrangement of the pistons, both pumps work similarly.

## PRIME MOVER

For a pump to operate, the pump must receive an input of power from some external source. This external power source is called the hydraulic system's prime mover. In a stationary hydraulic machine, the prime mover would likely be an electric motor. For a mobile hydraulic application such as a tractor, the prime mover would be a gasoline or diesel engine.

Regardless of type, the prime mover must deliver enough horsepower to operate the hydraulic pump under all likely load conditions. In addition, the prime mover should have some degree of reserve capacity to accommodate unexpected, momentary overloads.

## PRESSURE GAUGE

A pressure gauge shows the pressure being produced in a hydraulic system. This is necessary on equipment where system pressure must be adjusted or changed manually.

The Bourdoin tube pressure gauge is commonly used in hydraulic systems. In the Bourdoin tube gauge, a sealed tube is formed into an arc. When pressure is applied to the inlet port opening, the tube tends to straighten, causing the connected linkage to move. This movement of the linkage causes the pointer to rotate over the face of the calibrated dial indicating system pressure.

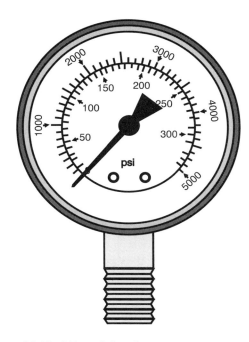

14-11. A Bourdoin tube pressure gauge.

## PRESSURE RELIEF VALVE

The pressure relief valve limits the pressure in the hydraulic system to some preset maximum level. The pressure relief valve is located between the pump outlet and the reservoir. When system pressure reaches the relief valve setting, the valve opens, diverting some or all of the pump's output back to the reservoir. This protects the hydraulic system components from possible damage from overloads. Additionally, since Force = Pressure × Area, the system's pressure relief setting effectively limits the output force available from a hydraulic system (assuming the area against which the fluid acts remains constant).

The two primary types of pressure relief valves commonly used in hydraulic equipment are the direct acting relief valve and the compound relief valve.

### Direct Acting Relief Valve

A *direct acting pressure relief valve* has inlet and outlet ports separated by a spring-loaded check ball. As long as the force produced by the oil pressure acting against the exposed area of the check ball is less than the force exerted by the spring, the check ball will remain seated. Thus, there will be no way for the hydraulic oil to flow through the pressure relief valve and back to the reservoir. However, if system pressure rises to the relief valve setting, the force exerted by the fluid will be sufficient to push the check ball off its seat, allowing the oil to flow through the pressure relief valve and back to the reservoir.

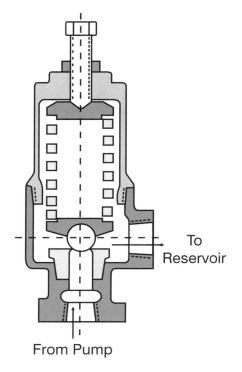

**14-12. A direct acting pressure relief valve.**

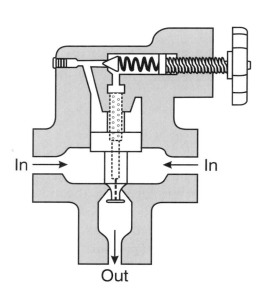

**14-13. A compound pressure relief valve.**

The pressure at which a relief valve first begins to open and divert oil flow is called *cracking pressure*. The pressure required to fully open the relief valve is called *full-flow pressure*, since, at this pressure, maximum flow occurs. The difference between full-flow pressure and cracking pressure is often called *pressure override*.

In some applications, a fairly high pressure override value may not be particularly bad. However, the oil flowing through the pressure relief valve consumes energy from the prime mover without doing productive work. Thus, the oil flow through a pressure relief valve represents wasted energy. The larger the relief valve's pressure override, the greater the amount of wasted energy.

## Compound Pressure Relief Valve

A *compound pressure relief valve* (Figure 14-13) operates in two stages. The pilot stage (in the upper valve body) contains the pressure limiting valve, which is a poppet held against its seat by an adjustable spring. When on its seat, the poppet valve closes the passageway through the pilot stage from the pump to the reservoir. The lower valve body contains the port connections. A balanced piston, also located in the lower valve body, is responsible for full flow diversion of the hydraulic oil back to the reservoir under overload conditions.

The balanced piston has a hole drilled through it. During non-overload conditions (Figure 14-14), this hole allows the hydraulic oil to exert equal pressure on the upper and lower piston surfaces.

Since the pressure exerted on the upper and lower piston surfaces is the same, the light duty spring is able to keep the valve on its seat, closing off the passageway to the reservoir.

During a pressure overload (Figure 14-15), the oil pressure in the upper valve body is sufficient to overcome the spring pressure on the poppet valve and lift the valve body off its seat. This allows oil in the upper valve body to flow to the reservoir. Since oil in the upper valve body can now flow to the reservoir, the oil pressure in the upper valve body decreases while the oil pressure in the lower valve body remains relatively constant. This pressure imbalance causes the balanced piston to move upward, opening the full flow port between the pump and the reservoir. Thus, the output of the pump can now be unloaded back to the reservoir through the lower valve body.

Because compound pressure relief valves operate in two stages, they operate with significantly smaller pressure overrides than do direct acting relief valves. This results in the increased hydraulic system operating efficiency required in many applications.

## DIRECTIONAL CONTROL VALVE

The directional control valve controls the operation of hydraulic system actuators (cylinders, motors, etc.) by directing the flow of fluid in the hydraulic

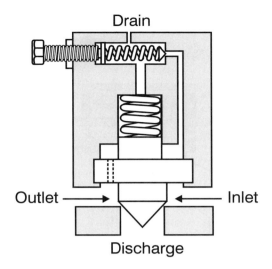

14-14. The balanced piston has a hole drilled through it to allow hydraulic oil to exert equal pressure on the upper and lower piston surfaces during non-overload conditions.

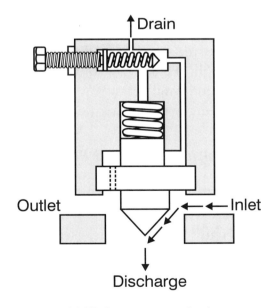

14-15. A pressure overload.

system. The directional control valve accomplishes this task by opening and closing internal ports between the pump, reservoir and the system

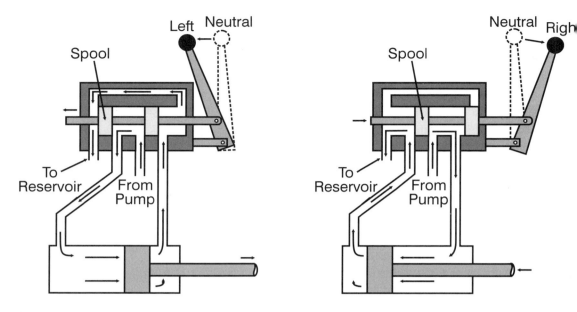

14-16. A directional control valve extending a hydraulic cylinder (left) and retracting a hydraulic cylinder (right).

actuator(s) through the movement of the valving element (usually a sliding spool). Figure 14-16 illustrates how a simple directional control valve extends and retracts a hydraulic cylinder. (Note how the movement of the sliding spool opens and closes the internal ports to control fluid flow.)

## Position, Way and Port

Three terms are widely used to describe directional control valves. These terms are position, way and port. The directional control valve shown in Figure 14-17 will be used to illustrate these terms.

14-17. A directional control valve illustrating position, way and port.

*Position,* as applied to a directional control valve, refers to the number of locations within the valve body that the valving element can assume in directing the flow of hydraulic fluid. In Figure 14-17, the directional control valve's sliding spool can occupy only three positions (left, center, and right). Thus, the valve is a three-position directional control valve.

*Way,* in a directional control valve, refers to the number of paths for oil to flow through the directional control valve, including reverse flow. One-way, two-way, three-way and four-way directional control valves may be used on agricultural equipment. The directional control valve in Figure 14-17 is a four-way valve because four oil flow paths (including reverse flow) are provided.

A *port* is a plumbing connection that allows oil to flow in and/or out of the directional control valve. The directional control valve in Figure 14-17 has four port connections. Therefore, the valve is a four-port directional control valve.

In describing a directional control valve, it is important to indicate the number of positions, ways, and ports. Thus, the directional control valve in Figure 14-17 would be described as a three-position, four-way, four-port directional control valve. This type of directional control valve is widely used in agricultural tractors to control both the hydraulic lift and remote hydraulic applications.

## Open, Closed, and Tandem Center Hydraulic Systems

In a three-position directional control valve, the center position is considered to be the neutral position, since the pump is not connected to the actuators when the spool (or other valving device) is centered. Tractor hydraulic systems are often classified as open-center, closed-center, or tandem-center, depending on how the ports to the pump, reservoir, and load(s) are connected when the directional control valve is in the neutral (center) position.

**Open-Center Hydraulic Systems.** In an open-center hydraulic system, the directional control valve's pump and reservoir ports are connected when the valve is in the center position. This connection of the pump and reservoir ports allows the output of the pump to unload to the reservoir when the directional control valve is in the neutral position. In addition, the load ports can discharge to the reservoir when the valving device is in the center position. Thus, a hydraulic cylinder under load would not

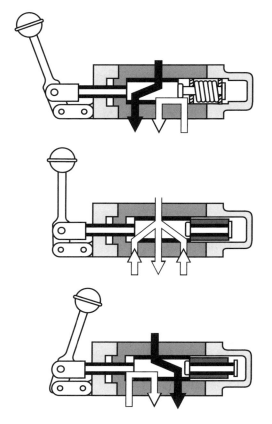

14-18. A three-position, open-center directional control valve in the left, center, and right positions.

hold its position when the directional control valve is shifted to the center position.

An open-center hydraulic system will have constant fluid flow from the pump to the reservoir when the directional control valve is in the center position. Also, when the directional control valve is in the neutral position, fluid pressure will drop to a minimum value since the fluid has a low resistance back to the reservoir. Because of this pressure drop, open-center hydraulic systems experience a response delay when the control valve is shifted from the neutral position, since the hydraulic system must be brought back to working pressure before work can be accomplished. This response delay is undesirable in many agricultural applications, especially with tractors.

Figure 14-18 shows that the load ports are open to the reservoir when the directional control valve is in the neutral position. Since this is the case, a hydraulic cylinder under load would not hold its position with the directional control valve in the center position. This is a disadvantage in many agricultural applications.

Open-center hydraulic systems were once widely used in agricultural tractors. However, as a greater demand for rapid-response hydraulic power (power brakes, power steering, remote hydraulics) became more common, open-center systems were largely replaced by closed-center and tandem-center hydraulic systems.

**Closed-Center Hydraulic Systems.** In a closed-center hydraulic system, all ports in the directional control valve are blocked when the valving device is in the center position.

Closed-center hydraulic systems maintain hydraulic pressure when in the neutral position. Because fluid pressure is maintained, the system actuator(s) respond almost immediately when the directional control valve is shifted. Also, since the load ports are blocked in the center position, a hydraulic cylinder controlled by a closed-center directional control valve will hold its position when the valve is centered. (Safety Warning: Never work under a load held in place only by a hydraulic cylinder. If a leak should develop, the load would fall, causing serious injury.)

In a closed-center system, hydraulic fluid cannot flow through the directional control valve and back to the reservoir when the valve is in the neutral

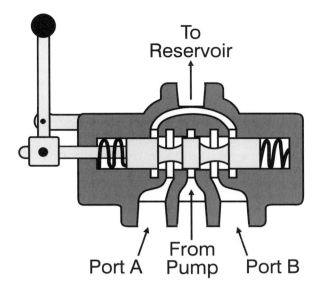

14-19. A three-position, closed-center directional control valve in the center position.

position. If a fixed displacement pump is used in a closed-center system, a special type of valve (called an ***unloading valve***) is often used to divert the pump output back to the reservoir when the valving device is in the center position.

If a variable displacement pump is used in a closed-center system, no special provision for unloading the pump output is necessary. The pump stops pumping when the directional control valve is in the center position.

**Tandem-Center Hydraulic Systems.** Tandem-center directional control valves combine the best features of open- and closed-center systems. Like the open-center valve, the pump and reservoir ports of a tandem-center directional control valve are connected when the valving device is in the center position. Thus, a fixed displacement pump may be used in a tandem-center system without the need for an unloading valve.

A tandem-center directional control valve blocks the load ports when the valving device is in the center position, as does a closed-center valve. Thus, cylinder loads may be supported when the directional control valve is in the neutral position.

## Manual and Automatic Operation of Directional Control Valves

Directional control valves may be actuated either manually or automatically. A manually actuated directional control valve requires a human operator to physically move a device (lever, pedal, etc.) to operate the valve.

An automatically actuated directional control valve operates in response to one or more control mechanisms that do not require human action. An automatic directional control valve may be actuated hydraulically (by pilot pressure), pneumatically (by air pressure), or electrically (by solenoids or servo-drives receiving input from an electronic controller). The ability to control hydraulic system operation either manually or automatically (or by a combination of the two methods) is a major advantage of hydraulic power transmission systems.

# HYDRAULIC ACTUATORS

A *hydraulic actuator* converts fluid energy into mechanical energy. The two primary types found on agricultural equipment are the *hydraulic cylinder* and the *hydraulic motor.*

## Hydraulic Cylinders

A hydraulic cylinder is a *linear actuator.* This means that the output of a cylinder occurs in a straight-line manner, as the cylinder extends or retracts.

Cylinders can be classified as either single- or double-acting. Double-acting cylinders can be further classified as either differential or non-differential.

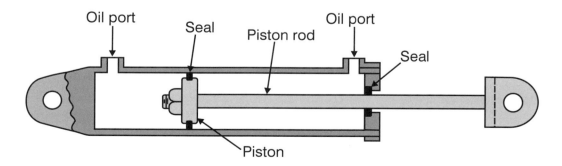

14-20. The primary parts of a typical cylinder.

**Single-acting Cylinders.** A special type of single-acting cylinder, called a ***ram***, is shown in Figure 14-21. The cylinder has only one port for the flow of hydraulic fluid.

When pressurized fluid from the pump is directed into the single-acting cylinder (through the port), the fluid acts against the moveable piston and causes the cylinder rod to extend, applying force to the attached load. Once extended, there is no provision for retracting the rod hydraulically (thus, the term, single-acting cylinder). With a single-acting cylinder, an external force must be used to cause the cylinder to retract. This force is normally supplied by the weight of the load just lifted or by a

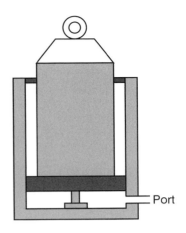

**14-21. A ram cylinder.**

heavy-duty spring. Hydraulic jacks and bearing presses are two common equipment items that use single-acting cylinders.

**Double-acting Cylinders.** The operation of a double-acting cylinder is shown in Figure 14-22. Notice that two ports are provided for the flow of oil. When oil from the pump flows through the bottom port (Figure 14-22 left), the cylinder rod extends, lifting the load and causing oil in the top of the cylinder to return to the reservoir. When the pump forces oil through the top port (Figure 14-22 right), the cylinder rod retracts and oil in the

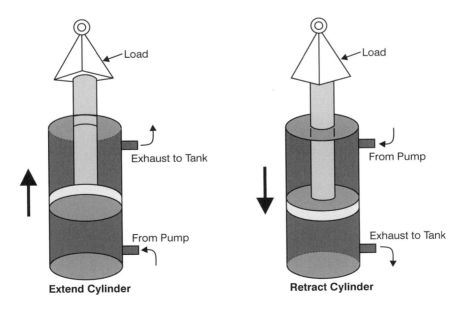

**14-22. A double-acting cylinder.**

bottom of the cylinder is returned to the reservoir. Thus, in a double-acting cylinder, the cylinder rod (and the attached load) can be both extended and retracted hydraulically.

The double-acting cylinder shown in Figure 14-22 can be further classified as a double-acting, ***differential cylinder.*** Notice, during extension (Figure 14-22 left), the pressurized oil can work against the full area of the piston. However, during retraction (Figure 14-22 right), oil pressure cannot work against the full area of the piston, since the cylinder rod occupies part of this area.

In a hydraulic system, force is the product of pressure multiplied by area (F = P × A). Since the available piston surface is greater during extension than during retraction, the largest output force will be developed as the cylinder rod extends (assuming pressure remains constant). However, since cylinder speed is determined by the flow rate of the oil and the volume of the cylinder to be filled, a differential cylinder will retract faster than it will extend (assuming a constant rate of oil flow).

Figure 14-23 shows a double-acting, ***non-differential cylinder.*** Notice, each side of the piston is fitted with a cylinder rod. As one cylinder rod extends, the other rod retracts. Since the working area on each side of the piston is the same, the double-acting, non-differential cylinder will develop the same output force and speed regardless of the direction of movement.

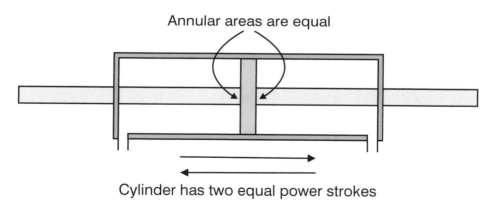

Annular areas are equal

Cylinder has two equal power strokes

14-23. A double-acting, non-differential cylinder.

## Hydraulic Motors

A hydraulic motor is a ***rotary actuator***. This means that it produces a rotating output force.

**14-24. A typical gear-type hydraulic motor.**

Hydraulic motors are very similar in construction to hydraulic pumps. But, instead of using an input force to push fluid as does the pump, a hydraulic motor is pushed by the incoming fluid and delivers a rotating output force or torque. Thus, while hydraulic pumps and motors are built much the same, they serve opposite functions.

Several types of hydraulic motors are available. Gear, vane, and piston hydraulic motors are commonly used in agricultural applications.

## PIPING AND CONNECTORS

*Piping* is the general term for the fluid conducting lines that connect the various components in the hydraulic system. For both safety and efficiency, hydraulic piping must withstand extremely high fluid pressures. Steel pipe, steel tubing, and flexible rubber hose are the three primary types of piping used in hydraulic systems.

Seamless steel pipe is widely used in industrial hydraulic equipment because of its low cost and high durability. Steel tubing is more expensive than pipe, but tubing can be bent, reducing the number of joints that must be installed in a hydraulic system plumbed with tubing. Flexible hose is used in hydraulic systems where the lines must move, such as the ones that serve the remote cylinder on a wheel-type disk.

A *connector* is used to join one piece of hydraulic piping to another piece of piping or to a hydraulic component, such as a cylinder or a directional control valve. Different types of connectors are used with each type of piping. Pipe fittings are used with steel pipe, tube fittings are used with steel tubing, and hose fittings are used with flexible rubber hose. Like the piping itself, connectors must withstand extremely high pressures without leaking or otherwise failing.

# HYDRAULIC SYSTEM SCHEMATICS

Hydraulic systems (or even individual components) are usually represented using schematic symbols. A *schematic symbol* is a form of visual
shorthand that conveys essential information in a standard, graphical
format. Standard hydraulic schematic symbols are presented in Appendix
B of this book.

Figure 14-25 is a schematic drawing of a hydraulic motor circuit. The
individual components of the circuit are the vented reservoir; filter; electric
motor (used as the prime mover); fixed displacement pump; fixed compound
pressure relief valve; two-position, one-way, two-port, closed-center, manually operated directional control valve; fixed displacement hydraulic motor;
and assorted hydraulic hoses and connectors.

In addition to identifying the individual components of the hydraulic
system, the circuit schematic shows how the system operates. In the circuit
shown in Figure 14-25, the hydraulic motor will rotate when the directional
control valve is shifted to the right and will not rotate when the directional
control valve is shifted to the left. When the directional control valve is
in the left position, the fixed volume pump will discharge to the reservoir
through the pressure relief valve.

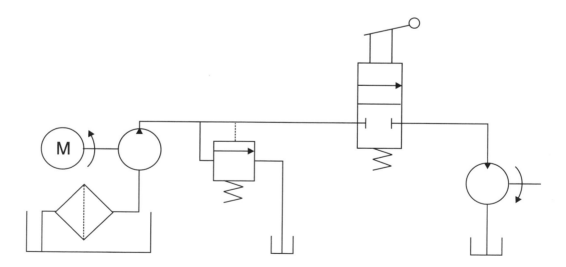

14-25. A schematic drawing of a hydraulic cylinder circuit.

# SUMMARY

The individual components that make up an operational hydraulic system allow it to perform efficiently. Reservoirs, filters and strainers, pumps, prime movers, pressure relief valves, directional control valves, hydraulic cylinders, and hydraulic motors are the major components. When the proper fluid is used, a hydraulic system can perform useful work.

Hydraulic systems can be shown pictorially or with schematics. Pictoral representations uses photographs or line art resembling the component. Schematics uses symbols that convey information in a standard graphical form.

# REVIEW QUESTIONS

1. List the primary components of a hydraulic system and explain the function(s) of each components.

2. Explain the operation of gear, vane, and piston pumps. For each type, tell if it is a fixed or variable displacement pump.

3. Define the terms position, port, and way as used to describe a directional control valve.

4. Describe the operating characteristics of open, closed, and tandem center hydraulic systems.

5. List two types of hydraulic actuators.

6. Explain why schematic symbols are used to represent hydraulic components and systems.

# APPLYING THE CONCEPTS

1. Secure the operator's manual for a tractor with which you are familiar. Locate the following hydraulic system specifications (if available).

    Type of system (open, closed, or tandem center)

    Pump type (gear, vane, or piston)

Pump capacity (gpm) at rated speed (rpm)

Pressure relief valve setting (psi)

Number of integral hydraulic cylinders and motors

Number of remote cylinder ports

Maximum hydraulic lift capacity (lbs)

Fluid capacity of system (gallons or quarts)

2. Examine a piece of agricultural (or other) equipment that uses hydraulic power transmission. Identify each major hydraulic system component. Be as specific as possible in identifying each component.

3. Obtain a selection of used gear, vane, and piston hydraulic pumps from a local machinery dealership or repair shop. Disassemble each type of pump, making note of the parts of each type of pump. Sketch the principal working parts of each pump and explain how each type pumps fluid.

4. Examine the hydraulic circuit schematic below and answer each of the following questions.

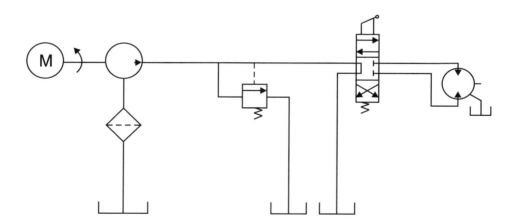

A. List each of the components of this system. Include all available details about each component.

B. Describe the operation of this hydraulic system.

C. Is this an open, closed, or tandem center hydraulic system? How do you know?

5. Obtain catalogs and/or other product literature from various hydraulic component manufacturers. (If possible, conduct an Internet search to locate manufacturers' product literature.) Study the various types of components available and their features, specifications, and potential uses.

# 15

# DESIGNING A HYDRAULIC SYSTEM

Careful planning is needed to have a hydraulic system that can do the job. Inadequate or poorly designed systems fail to provide the needed power. Money is lost when equipment fails or responds slowly.

Good systems must be designed and field-tested. Sometimes a design that appears good may not do what is needed. Field testing is needed. Build a prototype (sample or trial) version and try it out under actual conditions. If it works well, the design has been successful. If it doesn't, improvements in the design are needed. A knowledge of design helps in selecting a system.

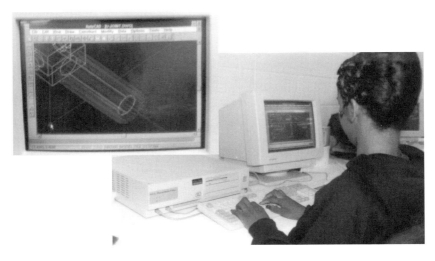

15-1. Computers using Auto CAD software are often used for design in mechanical technology. (Courtesy, Jasper S. Lee)

# OBJECTIVES

This chapter covers the fundamentals in designing a hydraulic system. After completing this chapter, you will:

1. Describe and apply the steps of the design process.

2. Develop system output objectives and operating parameters and describe how these serve as the basis for system design.

**TERMS**

conductor
interactive process
Occupational Safety and
    Health Administration
    (OSHA)
reservoir
system objective
system operating parameter

3. Design a hydraulic system that will satisfy the specified output objectives and operating parameters.

4. Correctly size and select major components for a hydraulic system.

5. Describe how to ensure compliance with applicable safety standards.

# DESIGN STEPS

The design of a hydraulic system requires several distinct steps:

1. Determine and specify system output objectives.
2. Specify system operating parameters.
3. Design the hydraulic circuit.
4. Size and select the hydraulic system components.
5. Assemble the system.
6. Monitor and analyze system performance.
7. Check the system and machine to ensure safe operation and compliance with all applicable safety standards.

These steps are not necessarily completed in the order listed. A system designer may be considering two or more of these steps at the same time. A decision at one step may require a change in decisions made during one or more previous steps. Designing any system is an ***interactive process.*** Current decisions may require altering previous decisions, while, at the same time, changing the basis for future decisions. This is one of the factors that makes system design both challenging and interesting.

A log (wood) splitter is a good example to use in studying hydraulic system design. Figure 15-2 shows a log splitter of the type used in this example.

15-2. A hydraulic log splitter.

# DESIGNING THE HYDRAULIC SYSTEM FOR A LOG SPLITTER

In designing the hydraulic system for the log splitter, follow the steps outlined in the previous section.

## DETERMINE AND SPECIFY SYSTEM OUTPUT OBJECTIVES

The function of a log splitter is to split wood. However, as a system objective, this statement is not particularly helpful. A *system objective* is a statement that describes the desired output of the log splitter in measurable terms. To that end, use the following statement as the system objective for designing the log splitter hydraulic system.

> System objective: The log splitter hydraulic system will horizontally extend and retract a splitting wedge (mounted on the end of the cylinder rod) a distance of 24 inches. The hydraulic system will be capable of developing an output force of 30,000 lbs at the splitting wedge.

## SPECIFY SYSTEM OPERATING PARAMETERS

*System operating parameters* specify the conditions under which the system objectives will be met. The two conditions of most interest are (a) maximum system operating pressure and (b) approximate cycle time.

### Maximum Operating Pressure

Specifying system operating pressure involves a trade-off. Since force is equal to pressure times area ($F = P \times A$), specifying a higher pressure will allow use of a smaller diameter cylinder to produce the specified output force. On the other hand, a higher pressure setting will require the system prime mover to be of greater horsepower. In addition, higher pressures may result in increased safety hazards.

A maximum operating pressure of 2500 psi is a fairly standard value. Fixed, 2500 psi pressure relief valves are available from a variety of vendors.

### Approximate Cycle Time

This is an important system parameter from the standpoint of operating the log splitter. The cycle time (period of time required for the cylinder to fully extend and retract) should be long enough to allow safe operation, yet short enough to allow efficient use of operator time.

Cycle time is determined by the total volume of the cylinder and the flow rate (gpm) of the hydraulic pump. With a wood splitter, a range of 10- to 20-seconds is an acceptable cycle time. Once cylinder size and pump capacity have been tentatively selected, the actual cycle time can be calculated. If the calculated cycle time falls within the specified range, the cylinder and pump will be acceptable. If the calculated cycle time falls outside of the specified range, the pump and/or cylinder selections need to be changed.

To this point, the (1) system output objectives and (2) the system operating parameters under which these objectives must be met have been specified. These objectives and parameters are summarized.

> The log splitter hydraulic system will horizontally extend and retract a splitting wedge (mounted on the end of the cylinder rod) a distance of 24 inches with an output force of 30,000 lbs at a maximum system pressure of 2500 psi. The hydraulic system will complete one cycle in a time period of not less than 10 seconds or more than 20 seconds.

## DESIGN THE HYDRAULIC CIRCUIT

The basic requirements for the log splitter hydraulic circuit are relatively simple. Under the manual control of the operator, the hydraulic circuit must extend and retract a hydraulic cylinder with a specified output force within a specified time period. The hydraulic circuit shown in schematic form in Figure 15-3 will accomplish this task.

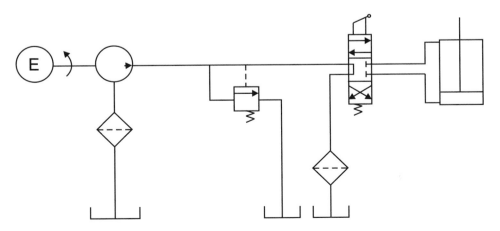

**15-3. Schematic of the hydraulic circuit for a log splitter.**

The hydraulic circuit contains a reservoir, filters and strainers, pump, prime mover, pressure relief valve, directional control valve, hydraulic cylinder, and the necessary plumbing lines and fixtures. Many of these will be described in detail during the process of selecting and sizing the system components.

## SIZE AND SELECT HYDRAULIC SYSTEM COMPONENTS

System design almost always starts at the output end of the system (in this case the cylinder) and works back to the input end (prime mover). Thus, the first task is to select the hydraulic cylinder for our log splitter.

### Selecting the Hydraulic Cylinder

The cylinder must have a stroke of 24 inches and deliver a force of 30,000 lbs when operating at 2500 psi. Since the cylinder must both extend and retract hydraulically, a double-acting cylinder will be needed. The cylinder does not need to develop the same force (or speed) when extending and retracting, so a differential cylinder will work. Thus, a double-acting, differential hydraulic cylinder will be selected for the log splitter.

Now that the type of hydraulic cylinder needed is known, cylinder size should be determined. Formula 15-1 can be used to determine cylinder diameter when required output force and maximum system pressure are known.

$$db = \sqrt{\frac{4F}{pi \times P}}$$

$$\boxed{\textbf{Formula 15-1}}$$

where,

$\quad$ db = diameter of cylinder bore (inches)

$\quad$ F = required output force (lbs)

$\quad$ pi = 3.1416

$\quad$ P = maximum operating pressure (psi)

$\quad$ 4 = a constant

By inserting known system values into Formula 15-1, a cylinder having a 3.9 in diameter bore will be required. These calculations are shown.

$$db = \sqrt{\frac{4F}{pi \times P}}$$

$$db = \sqrt{\frac{(4) \times (30{,}000 \text{ lbs})}{3.1416 \times 2{,}500 \text{ psi}}}$$

$$db = 3.9 \text{ in}$$

Since 3.9 inches is not a standard size cylinder, select a slightly larger cylinder (4.0 inch bore) for the log splitter. Since a 4.0 inch cylinder has an area of 12.6 in² (as compared to an area of 11.9 in² for a 3.9 inch cylinder), the output capacity of our log splitter will increase from 30,000 lbs to 31,500 lbs (2500 psi × 12.6 in² = 31,500 lbs). Thus, using the 4.0-in cylinder will give our log splitter a reserve capacity of approximately 5 percent.

A final factor to consider in selecting a hydraulic cylinder is to determine the minimum recommended diameter cylinder rod that can be used. The minimum size requirement is influenced by: (a) the strength of the rod material, (b) the force applied to the rod in compression, (c) the method of mounting the cylinder and of supporting the rod, and (d) the cylinder's stroke. Other calculations determined that the hydraulic cylinder must have a 2-inch diameter rod.

Based on these considerations and calculations, the hydraulic cylinder required for the log splitter can be specified. The cylinder must be a 4-inch, double-acting, differential cylinder with a 2-inch rod and a 24-inch stroke.

### Selecting the Hydraulic Pump

Due to its availability, low cost, and rugged operating characteristics, a fixed displacement, external gear pump will be selected for the log splitter. The pump must be rated for use at an operating pressure of 2500 psi and an rpm to be determined later. After the pump type is known, determine the required pump capacity (gpm) based on the 10- to 20-second cycle time specified earlier.

Cycle time is determined by pump capacity and cylinder volume (in³). The first step in selecting pump capacity is to determine the total volume of oil that must be pumped to complete one cycle. Based on the calculations, the pump must deliver 529 in³ of hydraulic fluid to complete one cycle.

Total volume per cycle (in$^3$) = Extension volume + Retraction volume

$$\text{Volume / cycle (in}^3) = \left[ \left( (\text{pi}) \left( \frac{\text{cyl dia}}{2} \right)^2 (\text{stroke}) \right) \right]$$

$$+ \left[ \left( (\text{pi}) \left( \frac{\text{cyl dia}}{2} \right)^2 \right) - \left( (\text{pi}) \left( \frac{\text{rod dia}}{2} \right)^2 \right) (\text{stroke}) \right]$$

$$= 301.7 \text{ in}^3 + 226.2 \text{ in}^3$$

$$= 529.9 \text{ in}^3$$

Since one gallon of fluid is equal to 231 in³, the pump must deliver approximately 2.3 gallons of hydraulic fluid to cause the cylinder to complete one cycle (529.9 in³ / 231 in³ = 2.29 gal). If a cycle time of 20 seconds is selected, a pump capable of completing three cycles per minute (60 sec per min / 3 cycles per minute = 20 sec) will be needed. Since 2.3 gallons of fluid must be pumped per cycle, a pump capacity of 6.9 gpm (2.3 gal per cycle × 3 cycles per minute) should be used.

For purposes of this example, assume that a fixed gear pump with a capacity of 7 gpm at a speed of 3000 rpm is used. Also, assume that the pump is rated at 3250 psi.

### Selecting the Prime Mover

The function of the prime mover is to supply the input energy necessary to power the hydraulic system. Electric motors or internal combustion engines are generally used as hydraulic system prime movers, depending on the specific application. If the log splitter will be used in remote locations without electrical service, an air-cooled gasoline engine will be selected as the prime mover.

To calculate the required size (horsepower) of the prime mover, first determine the fluid horsepower output produced by the hydraulic pump. This can be calculated based on available information using the fluid horsepower formula.

$$\text{Fhp} = \frac{P \times Q}{1714}$$

where,

Fhp = pump output (fluid horsepower)  
P = system operating pressure (psi)  
Q = pump flow rate (gpm)

By inserting known values into this formula, the pump is found to produce 10.2 fluid horsepower (Fhp). The necessary calculations are shown.

$$Fhp = \frac{P \times Q}{1714}$$

$$= \frac{2500 \text{ psi} \times 7 \text{ gpm}}{1714}$$

$$= 10.2 \text{ Fhp}$$

Unfortunately, mechanical systems, such as a pump, do not operate at 100 percent efficiency. This means that more power must be put into the system than we get out of the system. Thus, the prime mover must put more power into the pump than the pump outputs. The question now becomes, "How much more do we have to put in than we get out?"

Assume that the pump operates at an efficiency of 87.5 percent. This means that for every one unit of power put in it, the pump outputs .875 units of power. Based on this assumption, an 11.7-hp engine is required. These calculations follow.

$$\text{Required Input HP} = \frac{\text{Pump Fhp}}{\text{Pump efficiency}}$$

$$= \frac{10.2 \text{ Fhp}}{.875}$$

$$= 11.7 \text{ Hp}$$

Based on these calculations, an air-cooled gasoline engine with a rated output of 12 horsepower at a speed of 3000 rpm has been selected for use on the log splitter.

## Selecting the Reservoir

A *reservoir* is where the hydraulic fluid (oil) is stored. Reservoirs are sized to be large enough to supply the necessary volume of oil required by the system while, at the same time, allowing some oil to remain in the reservoir for cooling. As a general rule, the minimum capacity of a reservoir should be two times the pump output (gpm) or two times the circuit volume, whichever is greatest. To get the size of reservoir, determine both values and select the larger of the two.

First, size the reservoir based on pump capacity. Since the pump is rated at 7.0 gpm, the first figure would be 14.0 gallons (7.0 gal × 2 = 14.0 gal).

15-4. A hydraulic system control valve. (Courtesy, Jasper S. Lee)

Next, estimate the circuit volume for the hydraulic system. From previous calculations, we know that our cylinder has an extension volume of 301.7 in², or 1.3 gallons. For lack of specific information, assume the volume of the rest of the circuit plumbing is equal to the cylinder extension volume. Thus, the total circuit volume is estimated to be 2.6 gal (2 × 1.3 gal = 2.6 gal). Based on estimated circuit volume requirements, a 5.2 gallon reservoir is required (2.6 gal × 2 = 5.2 gal).

Since the size of the reservoir is based on the largest of these two calculated values, select a 14.0-gal reservoir (or the next largest available).

### Selecting the Directional Control Valve

The directional control valve should allow the cylinder to manually extend. For convenience, the valve spool should hold in the return position until the cylinder is fully retracted, then automatically return to the neutral position. Since a fixed displacement gear pump was selected, the directional control valve should be either an open or tandem center valve. This will allow pump output to return to the reservoir under low pressure when the directional control valve is in the neutral position.

To satisfy these requirements, select a 3-position, 4-port, tandem center directional control valve. For cylinder extension, the spool valve will be manually operated with a spring return to the center position. For cylinder retraction, the spool valve will be manually activated with a detent to hold the valve in position until the cylinder is retracted. Once the cylinder is retracted, a pressure operated kickout will automatically return the spool valve to the center position. Finally, the directional control valve will be selected to meet or exceed the pressure and flow rate requirements of the hydraulic system.

## Selecting the Pressure Relief Valve

Some directional control valves have built-in pressure relief mechanisms. Assuming that is not the case in this instance, the next task is to specify a separate pressure relief valve for our hydraulic system.

Several factors enter into our selection of the pressure relief valve. Since the selected directional control valve is of the tandem center type, the only time the pressure relief valve will operate is when the system is overloaded. During a majority of operating time, the system pressure should be well below the relief valve's cracking pressure. In addition, there is no reason to vary the relief valve pressure setting from the specified value of 2500 psi. Finally, the pressure relief valve must have a flow capacity equal to or greater than the pump's flow rate (7 gpm). Based on these factors, a direct acting pressure relief valve with a fixed pressure setting of 2500 psi and a minimum flow rate of 7 gpm will be specified.

## Selecting Conductors and Connectors

A **conductor** provides the path for fluid flow between system components. Connectors are used to join conductors to hydraulic components and/or other conductors. In selecting conductors and connectors, two factors are critical. First, these components must convey required rates of fluid through the system with a minimum of friction loss. Second, conductors and connectors must withstand high operating pressures and adverse conditions without leaking.

As a general rule, flow velocity through intake lines should be less than 5 feet per second (fps); for pressure lines, velocity should be less than 20 fps. Using these two standards and Formula 15-2, calculate the minimum required area for our intake and pressure conductors.

$$\text{Area (in.}^2) = \frac{\text{Flow Rate (gpm)} \times 0.3208}{\text{Fluid velocity (fps)}}$$

| Formula 15-2 |
| --- |

First, calculate the required area for the intake conductor. Since a 7 gpm pump was selected, use this as the flow rate for calculations. To provide a margin of safety, size the conductors for a 3.5 fps flow rate (remember, the 5 fps is the maximum for the intake side of our system). By inserting these values into Formula 15-2, it is found that the intake conductor must have an area of .64-in². These calculations follow.

$$\text{Area (in.}^2) = \frac{\text{Flow Rate (gpm)} \times 0.3208}{\text{Fluid velocity (fps)}}$$

$$= \frac{7 \text{ gpm} \times 0.3208}{3.5 \text{ fps}}$$

$$= .64\text{-in.}^2$$

Since hydraulic conductors are sized by inside diameter (i.d.) rather than area, we must calculate the diameter of a circle having an area of .64-in². Since the area of a circle is calculated as the product of pi times the square of the circle's radius and the diameter of a circle is equal to twice the radius, calculate the i.d. of the .64-in² circle, as shown below.

$$\text{ID} = 2 \times \sqrt{\frac{A}{\pi}}$$

$$= 2 \times \sqrt{\frac{.64\text{-in}^2}{3.1416}}$$

$$= .90\text{-in.}$$

Thus, a connector having a minimum inside diameter of .90-in will be selected for the intake side of the hydraulic system.

Repeat this same process to select the required minimum i.d. of the connectors on the pressure side of the system. Assume fluid velocity will be limited to 15 fps, determine that the pressure-side conductors must have a minimum area of 15-in². These calculations follow.

$$\text{Area (in.}^2) = \frac{\text{Flow Rate (gpm)} \times 0.3208}{\text{Fluid velocity (fps)}}$$

$$= \frac{7 \text{ gpm} \times 0.3208}{15 \text{ fps}}$$

$$= .15\text{-in}^2$$

By converting area to diameter, it is determined that the pressure-side conductors must have a minimum inside diameter of .44-in. These calculations follow.

$$ID = 2 \times \sqrt{\frac{A}{\pi}}$$

$$= 2 \times \sqrt{\frac{.15 \text{-in.}^2}{3.1416}}$$

$$= .44 \text{-in.}$$

Assume that conductors made of steel tubing will be used on the log splitter. The final step in selecting conductors is to determine the minimum recommended wall thickness for the pressure side of the system. This is a two-part process. First, the initial wall thickness is calculated. This initial wall thickness value is then multiplied by an appropriate safety factor to determine the final wall thickness value.

Formula 15-3 shows how the initial wall thickness value is calculated.

$$WT_1 = \frac{(\text{p max}) \times (ID)}{2 \times TS} \qquad \boxed{\textbf{Formula 15-3}}$$

where

$WT_1$ = initial wall thickness (in.)

p max = maximum system pressure (psi)

ID = inside diameter of tubing (in.)

TS = tensile strength of the tubing material (psi)

2 = a constant

Inserting known values into Formula 15-3 (along with an assumed tensile strength value of 60,000 psi), indicates an initial wall thickness value of .019-in. These calculations are shown.

$$WT_1 = \frac{(\text{p max}) \times (ID)}{2 \times TS}$$

$$= \frac{2500 \text{ psi} \times .44}{2 \times 60,000 \text{ psi}}$$

$$= .01 \text{-in.}$$

A safety factor of 4:1 is commonly used for hydraulic systems operating at pressures between 1000 and 2500 psi. Thus, by multiplying the initial wall thickness value by the recommended safety factor of 4:1, it is determined that the tubing for the pressure side of the log splitter must have a minimum wall thickness of .04-in. (.01 × 4).

### Selecting Filters and Strainers

There are three locations in a hydraulic circuit where strainers or filters are typically located. These locations are in the inlet line, the pressure line, or in a return line. Strainers or coarse filters are generally used at the inlet because using fine mesh filters would cause excessive pressure drop in the inlet line. Filters located in pressure lines can be much finer than those installed in inlet lines. However, these filters must be capable of withstanding system operating pressures. Return line filters can also remove extremely fine particles. Also, less stress is placed on return line filters since the fluid returning to the reservoir is under fairly low pressure.

For the hydraulic system on the splitter, select a 150-micron inlet line strainer and a 5 micron return line filter. Note that these are nominal ratings. This means that the strainer or filter will remove most of the particles in the fluid that are equal to or larger than the respective micron rating.

## ASSEMBLE THE SYSTEM

Once the log splitter has been designed and the hydraulic components have been selected and sized, the next step is to fabricate the splitter and assemble the hydraulic circuit. Assuming that detailed construction drawings and procedures have been developed to guide this process, the actual construction of the log splitter should be fairly simple. Attention to detail, safety, and quality work are the keys to success.

## MONITOR AND ANALYZE SYSTEM PERFORMANCE

After the log splitter has been constructed, it should be operated and monitored to determine if it complies with the original design specifications. In addition to qualitative (visual, auditory, etc.) evaluation of system performance, quantitative measures should also be made and evaluated. These quantitative measures include: (a) verification of maximum and typical operating pressures, (b) maximum force output at the splitting wedge, (c) actual load and no-load cycle times, and (d) load and no-load pump flow rates. If no design or construction errors exist, these measured values should meet or exceed the design specifications.

## ENSURE COMPLIANCE WITH ALL APPLICABLE SAFETY STANDARDS

The log splitter just designed has several potential hazards. These include burns (contact with the engine, muffler, or exhaust gasses), pinches (moving parts), crushing (between the wedge and stop plate), poisoning (injection of hydraulic fluid under the skin), etc. The purpose of safety standards is to eliminate or minimize potential hazards in the workplace.

The ***Occupational Safety and Health Administration*** (OSHA) of the US Department of Labor is responsible for formulating and enforcing safety standards in the workplace. It is the responsibility of any designer or builder to ensure compliance with all applicable safety standards (both OHSA standards and those established by specific industry organizations).

In addition to formal safety standards, common sense goes a long way in designing safe machines. For example, common sense dictates that the operator controls for the log splitter should be placed in a safe location (e.g., away from the engine exhaust and away from the splitting wedge). The automatic return-to-center feature of the directional control valve also enhances safety by returning the system to neutral if the control handle is released as the cylinder extends.

Adherence to all applicable safety standards coupled with a common sense approach to system design and construction should result in a project that gives safe, durable, and economical service. This is the overall goal of the design process.

# SUMMARY

Designing a hydraulic system begins with the specification of the desired system output and operating ranges. Next, a hydraulic circuit is designed that will accomplish these objectives. Then, the required system components must be selected and sized so as to meet the output objectives and operating parameters. Finally, the system is assembled, its performance is monitored and the machine is evaluated for compliance with applicable safety standards.

In this chapter, the process of designing a hydraulic system for a log splitter was described. This example was intended to provide an overview of the design process as applied to hydraulics. It was not the intent of this chapter to make you a hydraulic system designer. Rather, the purpose was to provide a level of understanding of the design process. Actual design work requires advanced education and training.

Understanding the basics of hydraulic system design is needed to better operate and service hydraulic systems. Perhaps you will want to gain the required education and training and become a design engineer specializing in agricultural hydraulics.

## REVIEW QUESTIONS

1. List and explain each of the steps in the design process.
2. Explain the difference between system output objectives and operating parameters.
3. Why does system design work usually begin at the output end of the system?
4. Assuming a maximum system pressure of 2750 psi, what size (diameter) cylinder would be required in order to lift a 20 ton object?
5. Assuming a hydraulic pump with a capacity of 8 gpm, what would be the cycle time for a 4-inch double-acting differential hydraulic cylinder with a 24-inch stroke? Assume that the cylinder rod has a diameter of 2 inches.
6. A hydraulic pump delivers 10 gpm at a pressure of 2250 psi. What is the fluid horsepower output of this pump?
7. Could a 10 horsepower air-cooled engine be used to power the pump in Question #6? Why or why not?
8. What are two general rules for sizing the hydraulic reservoir?
9. What are the maximum flow rates for the intake-side and pressure-side conductors in a hydraulic system?
10. Explain how to ensure that a hydraulic system complies with all applicable safety standards.

## APPLYING THE CONCEPTS

1. Obtain the hydraulic system specifications for a hydraulic log splitter (or other piece of hydraulic equipment). Perform the necessary calculations to check the advertised specifications (e.g. output force, cycle time, etc.).
2. Apply the steps of the design process to design a hydraulic system that will meet output objectives and operating parameters established by your instructor. Present your work as a technical report including the following components: title page—include the project title, your name, class, and date; design criteria—brief description of the system designed as well as system output objectives and operating parameters; hydraulic circuit schematic; hydraulic component selection (include all formulas and calculations); bill of materials and estimated construction costs; and references.

# 16

# PLANNING FOR CONSTRUCTION AND MAINTENANCE

Before construction or repair work is undertaken, a definite plan should be developed. This plan is not only the drawings or sketches needed to complete the project, but, also, all the other activities that should precede actual construction or repair work. An adequate plan will reduce cost, save valuable time, improve the quality of finished product, and justify the need for the construction or repair project.

New planning and construction technologies are being used in agriculture and related areas. Computers, power tools, and materials are changing how construction is done.

16-1. Planning is required to have these pre-made trusses manufactured and delivered to the job site at the proper time. (Courtesy, John Childs, Illinois)

491

# OBJECTIVES

This chapter covers the basics of planning construction projects. Upon completion of the chapter, you will:

1. Describe the importance of planning for construction activities.

2. List the steps in planning for construction activities.

3. Explain the differences between a sketch and a drawing.

4. Identify isometric, oblique, and orthographic drawings and sketches.

5. Identify and correctly use the nine major line types used in mechanical drafting.

6. Identify and correctly use mechanical drafting equipment to produce scaled drawings.

7. Make scaled drawings using computer-assisted design (CAD) programs.

**TERMS**

bow instrument
compass
computer assisted design (CAD)
divider
drafting machine
drawing board
floor plan
grades of hardness
input device
isometric projection
mechanical drawing
oblique projection
orthographic projection
output device
pen plotter
protractor
scale
sketch
template
triangle
T-square

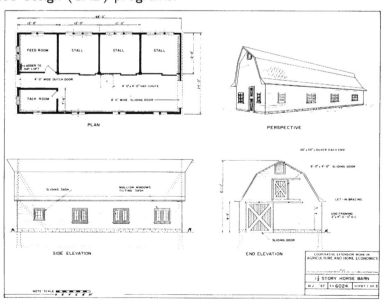

# PLANNING FOR
# CONSTRUCTION ACTIVITIES

Anyone who is considering the construction of an agricultural building needs to keep in mind certain principles. These principles will ensure that the building is useful and profitable to the agricultural enterprise. Look at each of these principles in detail.

## *GUIDING PRINCIPLES*

**Minimize unused space.** Strive to arrange the building so there is minimal unused space. In fact, in many instances the same space may be suitable for more than one use. The building should be planned so machines and people can move from one area to the other in circular patterns. By arranging traffic patterns in a circular format, backtracking and other types of unproductive movement can be prevented.

**Consider needed equipment and tools before construction.** Equipment and tools should be selected and locations determined before construction. Again, circular routes work best because they limit the amount of unproductive movement. Also, consider the use of drive-through paths of travel. Machinery buildings and other buildings can be used more efficiently when the necessity for backing up is limited. In addition, machinery buildings should be convenient to paths of travel. This will make storing machinery more convenient.

**Centralize related jobs.** Jobs that are related or that require similar equipment and tools should be centralized. One should be able to perform

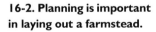
**16-2. Planning is important in laying out a farmstead.**

all machinery related activities in or near the machinery building. Everything related to grain storage should be located in one central location. By doing this, all tools and equipment related to the same aspect can be stored in one location.

**Utilize machines.** Buildings should be planned to take advantage of mechanization where possible. Using machines makes people more efficient and productive. Improving productivity can be accomplished if provisions are made for the bulk handling of agricultural materials.

## PLANNING STEPS

Keeping the above principles in mind, there are some essential preliminary planning steps that should occur before construction. The following steps are suggested:

**Decide the use of the building.** Obviously, there should be a clear, demonstrated need for a building before construction is considered. If one cannot justify the construction of a new building through increased profits, then the building should probably not be built.

**Decide where to locate the building.** Physical features, such as available water supply, electricity, sewage disposal, drainage, prevailing wind, and soil type should be considered in locating a building. Additionally, traffic patterns, location of other structures, and access to roadways should be addressed.

**Decide the size of the building needed.** The size of the building is dependent on several factors. Size of the enterprise to be housed, room for expansion, and economies of scale are all considerations.

**Decide the type of building needed.** Some buildings, such as those associated with dairies, are strictly one-use buildings. In most cases, once a milking parlor is built, that is the only enterprise that will ever be undertaken in that building. However, many modern facilities can be remodeled and used for other enterprises. Given this, it is wise to choose the types of buildings that make use of clear-span construction. These buildings are easily remodeled. Of course, there are other considerations in determining building type. Cost, appearance, and relationship to other buildings at the location should be considered.

16-3. A metal farm building has many potential uses.

**Decide on the kind of materials to be used.** There are many materials that can be used for the construction of agricultural buildings. Of course, one of the major determining factors in materials selection is cost. However, just because a particular material is inexpensive does not mean that it is right for a particular building. One must consider anticipated maintenance requirements, as well as expected useful life of the structure. Given these considerations, some of the more widely used materials are metal, lumber, poles, concrete, brick, and concrete block.

**Review plans and sketches of similar structures.** Anyone who is considering the construction of an agricultural building should make an attempt to visit and inspect as many similar buildings as possible. Visit with the owners of the buildings to determine how the structure is performing. Be alert to good and poor construction practices so you can make the appropriate decisions related to the structure you intend to build.

**Visit building materials suppliers.** Visiting with building material suppliers serves two purposes. First, the visit can acquaint the builder with new materials and construction practices. Second, the cost of construction can be determined.

**Consult with building experts.** Often, the Cooperative Extension Service will have recommended plans for agricultural buildings. Other experts, such as contractors, architects, and builders, should be consulted.

**Decide whether to construct or to hire contractor.** A major portion of the agricultural buildings built today are purchased structures from commercial building suppliers. The advantages to purchasing a building include time, efficiency, and expertise. However, if you have idle time during a quiet period of the production cycle, you may elect to construct your own building.

**Select plans.** If you have decided to purchase a building, plans will be available from the company. There are usually a few decisions that need to be made, such as door and window locations, etc. If, however, you are building the structure yourself, you will need to obtain plans. You may elect to produce sketches for relatively small or uncomplicated structures. However, architects or engineers may need to be involved in large or complicated buildings.

**Figure bill of materials and total cost of the building.** Building material suppliers will usually assist in determining the cost of the building. If a commercial contractor is used, you should obtain several bids. When considering bids, make decisions on more than just cost. Be concerned with the contractor's reputation, experience, and other factors.

16-4. Building material suppliers can usually assist in determining the cost of a structure. (Courtesy, Jasper S. Lee)

# SKETCHES AND DRAWINGS

## *SKETCHING*

A *sketch* is usually all that is needed for simple buildings and projects. In fact, sketches are often less intimidating and easier to work from than detailed drawings. Sketches are normally done in pencil and are not necessarily drawn to scale. However, the sketch should show the general shape

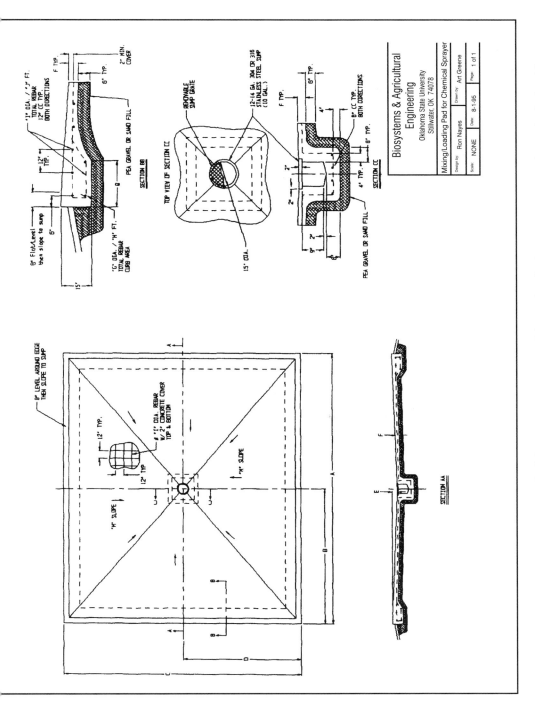

Biosystems & Agricultural
Engineering
Oklahoma State University
Stillwater, OK 74078

Mixing/Loading Pad for Chemical Sprayer

| Design by | Ron Nayes | Drawn by | Art Greene | Page: | 1 of 1 |
| Scale: | NONE | Date: | 8-1-95 | | |

16-5. Mechanical drawings show all of the component parts of the project in the proper perspective and relationship.

of the project and the arrangement of the various parts. All measurements should be clearly indicated. Multiple views of the project are desirable so the builder can more easily visualize the final desired appearance of the project. No project should ever be started without first obtaining or preparing at least a sketch of the project.

## DRAWING

*Mechanical drawings*, such as blue prints and construction drawings by architects and engineers, are carefully prepared and drawn accurately to scale. They show all of the component parts of the project in the proper perspective and relationship. Blueprints and construction drawings show a great many details through the use of standard lines, letters, and figures. Some architects and engineers use drawing instruments. Others use computer-assisted design (CAD) programs to produce blueprints and drawings.

An important characteristic of drawings is that they are drawn to *scale*. This means that even though the drawing may be considerably smaller than the project, the proportions represented are representative of the final project — all parts of the project are drawn to the same scale.

# ISOMETRIC, OBLIQUE AND ORTHOGRAPHIC PROJECTIONS

## ISOMETRIC PROJECTION

A drawing with an *isometric projection* depicts the object in a tilted position. This projection typically shows the top, front, and one side of the object. The primary distinguishing characteristic of this type of drawing concerns the vertical line and the two horizontal lines that form the near corner of the object. Each of the two horizontal lines must make a 60-degree angle with the vertical line.

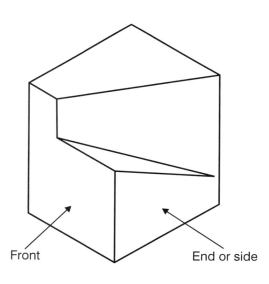

Front                    End or side

**16-6. An example of isometric projection.**

## OBLIQUE PROJECTION

*Oblique projections* are similar to isometric projections in that three sides of the object are shown. However, the angles formed at the near corner in an oblique projection are not equal. The near side of the object is drawn with 90-degree angles and to scale. This side typically represents the length of the object being drawn. The lines representing the width of the object are drawn at 60-degree angles to the vertical line. It is not unusual for lines representing the width of the object to be drawn at less than scale.

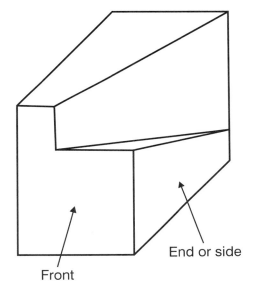

16-7. An example of oblique projection.

End or side

Front

## ORTHOGRAPHIC PROJECTION

Isometric and oblique projections are intended to simulate a three dimensional representation of an object. *Orthographic projections* typically show two or three sides of an object in separate drawings. These drawings are often called working drawings. The typical views of the object are the top, side, and end of the project.

Orthographic projections are often used in plans for agricultural buildings. These projections usually have all the necessary dimensions and materials needed to construct the building.

The top or overhead view is otherwise called the *floor plan*. Floor plans depict the general layout of the building. Floor plans include all horizontal dimensions, window and door locations, interior walls, stairwells, and locations for permanent equipment.

The front projection or front view shows the appearance of the building including the main entrance. This view shows horizontal and vertical dimensions, as well as types of building materials, and the placement of windows and doors. A similar view is that of the side projection or side view. If the back or other side of the building has special features, then additional drawings need to be made to depict the rear view and the other side view.

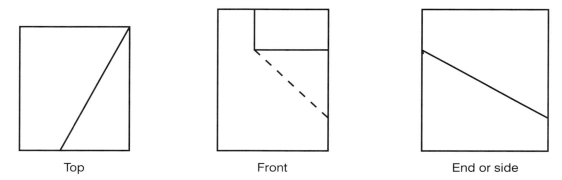

Top                    Front                    End or side

16-8. Orthographic projection typically shows two or three sides of an object in separate drawings.

# LINE TYPES USED IN MECHANICAL DRAWINGS

Although there are many variations of lines and symbols used in drawings, there are a few line types that are fairly standard in appearance in use. Many line types have specific meanings and uses. They are as follows:

**Border:** Border lines are very heavy, solid lines used to frame a drawing. They are typically drawn parallel to the drawing paper edges.

**Object:** Object lines are heavy, solid lines that show the visible edges of the object to be constructed. Object lines represent the form of the object.

**Hidden:** Medium-weight dashed lines are used to show the hidden edges of objects. These lines indicate the presence of unseen edges.

**Dimension:** Dimension lines are used to show the dimensions of objects. They are usually light, solid lines with arrowheads, which indicate the length, width, or height of an object.

**Extension:** Extension lines are light lines used to indicate the exact area specified by a dimension line.

**Break:** A break line is a solid, light line with zigzags. This line is used to indicate that the illustration stops, but the object being draw does not.

**Cutting Plane:** A cutting plane line is a very heavy line used to show the cutting plane, which is represented in a cross-section detail of a specific portion of a drawing.

**Center Line:** The center line is a long-short-long line used to show the center of an object. The object could be round or it could be used to indicate the center of rough openings for doors or windows.

**Leader:** The leader line is a solid line with an arrow, which is used to connect a explanatory note with a specific feature of an object.

| LINES | WEIGHT | USE | PENCIL NO. |
|---|---|---|---|
| BORDER | VERY HEAVY | TO FRAME A DRAWING | H |
| OBJECT | HEAVY | TO SHOW VISIBLE EDGES | 2 H |
| HIDDEN | MEDIUM | TO SHOW HIDDEN EDGES | 2 H |
| DIMENSION 0' 0" | LIGHT | DIMENSIONING | 3 H |
| EXTENSION | LIGHT | TO INDICATE THE EXTENT OF A MEASUREMENT GIVEN BY A DIMENSION LINE | 3 H |
| BREAK | HEAVY | SHORT BREAKS | 2 H |
| BREAK | LIGHT | LONG BREAKS | 2 H |
| CUTTING PLANE | VERY HEAVY | TO SHOW CUTTING PLANE | H |
| CENTER LINE | VERY LIGHT | TO SHOW CENTERS | 3 H |

16-9. Some lines, their thicknesses, and their uses are U.S. standard.

# DRAFTING EQUIPMENT FOR SCALED DRAWINGS

Certain instruments and materials are necessary for making scaled drawings. Unlike sketches, scaled drawings are required to show construction details as they relate to other parts of the object being drawn. Remember, scaled drawings also show specific dimensions and different views. When selecting equipment for scaled drawings, remember, drawing instruments need not be expensive. However, you should also know it is easier to produce high quality drawings with better equipment. Most of the equipment described in this section can be obtained from mail order houses, art supply, and office supply stores.

## DRAWING BOARD

The **drawing board** is essential for scaled drawings. The paper upon which the drawing will be made is attached to the board until the drawing is complete. In selecting a drawing board, look for one made from softwood and free from knots. Care should be taken to select a drawing board that will not warp and lose its shape. The size of the drawing board is dependent upon the size of drawing. A board 20" × 26" is suitable for drawings made on 17" × 22" paper. A smaller board, which will accommodate 8½" × 11" paper, is less expensive and easier to store when not in use. The primary concern when selecting a drawing board is to be sure that the edges are perfectly straight and that they are square to one another. This is important because a T-square must form a true right angle with the left and/or right edge(s) of the drawing board.

## T-SQUARE

A T-square is necessary for making scaled drawings. The **T-square** allows the person doing the drawing to use the left or right edge of the drawing board as a reference for drawing lines that parallel or are at right angles to the left or right edge of the drawing board. In combination with triangles, the T-square may be used to draw lines at specific angles. One should select a T-square that is long enough to extend completely across the drawing board.

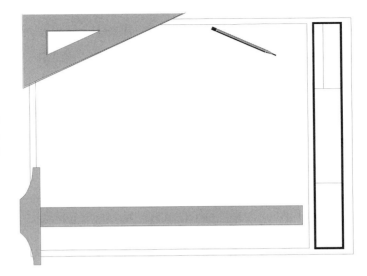

16-10. For scaled drawings made with a drawing board, one also needs a T-square and two plastic triangles.

## DRAFTING MACHINE

Drafting machines are made of metal or plastic. The typical *drafting machine* has an arm that can swivel about to allow lines to be drawn at specific angles. The drafting machine takes the place of the T-square and triangles. Normally, drafting machines are permanently attached to drafting tables and are used by draftsmen and architects.

## TRIANGLES

For scaled drawings made with a drawing board and T-square, one should also have two plastic *triangles*. The 45-degree triangle has two 45-degree angles and one 90-degree angle. The 45-degree triangle may be used to draw vertical lines and lines that are 45 degrees. The 30-degree × 60-degree triangle has one 30-degree angle, one 60-degree angle, and one 90-degree angle. It may be used for drawing lines that are vertical, 30 degrees, and 60 degrees. By using the two triangles in combination, angles that are 15 degrees and 75 degrees can also be drawn.

## SCALES

In scaled drawings, a *scale,* not a ruler, is used. Scales are marked to facilitate the proportional reduction of the object to be drawn. An architect's scale is often used in drawing agricultural projects. Architects' scales are marked so inches and fractions of an inch represent one foot. In addition to full scale, the most common scales on an architect's rule are $^1/_8$", $^1/_4$", $^3/_4$", 1" and 3", each representing one foot.

The Mechanical Engineer's Scale and the Civil Engineer's Scale may also be used. The Mechanical Engineer's Scale is used for smaller projects. Typically, the scales on the Mechanical Engineer's Scale has inches, or fractions of an inch, representing 1". The Civil Engineer's Scale is used for land maps. On this scale, inches are divided into 10ths, 20ths, 30ths, and so on, up to 100ths.

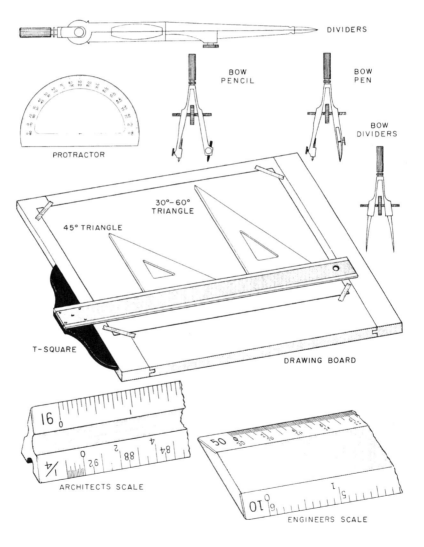

**16-11. Basic mechanical drawing equipment.**

# PROTRACTOR

Angles can be measured with a protractor. Protractors are divided into degrees. The ***protractor*** can be used to check the angles on an existing drawing or for drawing them in degrees that cannot be divided by 15. Triangles can be used in combination with the T-square to draw angles that are divisible by 15.

# PENCILS

Pencils for scaled drawings are available in 18 ***grades of hardness***. The grade mark can be found near the end of the pencil. Grades B, HB, and F are normally used for sketches, lettering, and freehand work. Harder grades, such as H, 2H, and 3H, are used for drawings. When extreme precision is desired, grades 4H through 9H should be used.

# COMPASSES, DIVIDERS, AND BOW INSTRUMENTS

Scaled drawings often call for circles, arcs, and ellipses. A ***compass*** may be used to draw these. Compasses vary greatly in cost and quality. Inexpensive varieties may be adequate for many applications. However, if one plans to do several drawings that call for a higher degree of accuracy, investing in quality instruments may be called for. Related to the compass are dividers and bow instruments. ***Dividers*** are used to transfer measurements and spacings from one drawing to another. ***Bow instruments*** are similar to a compass but are typically of a smaller size. The smaller size and more rigid construction greatly increases accuracy.

# ERASERS

For removing smudges and generally cleaning up the drawing, art gum erasers are useful. However, red rubber erasers are a better choice for removing pencil lines.

# TEMPLATES

There are many ***templates*** available for making letters and symbols. Lettering templates are use to label drawings. Symbol templates are available for drawing many needed symbols. Some are used for arrows, curves, and

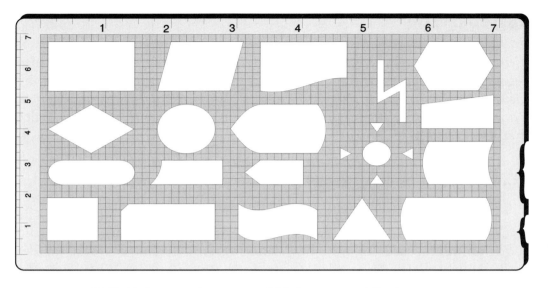

16-12. Various templates are available for very specialized purposes.

flow-charting. Others are available for very specialized purposes. For instance, there are templates specifically for drawing the symbols associated with electrical circuits and electronics.

# COMPUTER ASSISTED DESIGN

Drawing scaled drawings by hand is a very labor and time intensive activity. Many hours are spent drawing the details of structural designs

16-13. Personal computers are used to produce scaled drawings with Auto CAD (computer assisted design) application software. (Courtesy, Jasper S. Lee)

and plans. Computer applications in scaled drawings help the designer to produce drawings much faster and with reduced likelihood of making errors. Computer applications used to produce scaled drawings are referred to as ***computer assisted design*** or CAD. Other terms used include computer aided drafting, computer assisted drafting, or computer automated drafting.

## BENEFITS ASSOCIATED WITH CAD

One of the most important benefits realized through the use of CAD is speed. Designers are capable of producing more drawings in less time. CAD systems eliminate the need to hand draw lines and symbols. Computers are faster in drawing lines, circles, and complex objects. With a CAD system, the designer simply provides the end points for a line and selects a line thickness. The computer completes the line between the end points.

The "save," "copy," and "paste" capabilities of computers and CAD systems are big advantages when the speed of drawing is considered. The designer needs to draw an object only once. When hand drawing, the drawer must draw the same object numerous times. With CAD, once the object is drawn, the designer can simply copy and paste the object as many times as necessary.

The second benefit associated with CAD systems is quality. Lines drawn with a CAD system will be consistent throughout the drawing. When hand drawing with wooden pencils, the designer must make a conscious effort to maintain consistent line quality. With CAD, line quality is automatic.

Also related to quality is neatness. Smudges and smeared lines are a real problem with hand drawings. With CAD systems, smudges and smears are eliminated. With CAD systems, the designer can print a clean copy of the drawing at any time.

Legibility is a clear advantage with CAD. For instance, when hand drawing, the designer often will hand letter the drawing. With CAD, lettering remains consistent and legible throughout the drawing. The designer controls the lettering by selecting the size and style.

The third key to quality drawing is accuracy. To have a quality design, the drawing must be accurate. If a drawing is not accurate, problems can occur when construction of the object begins. The typical hand drawer can measure accurately to about a hundredth of an inch. Drawings with CAD systems can be possible to the nearest thousandths of an inch.

The fourth benefit associated with CAD systems is the ability to modify plans. It is rare that a plan does not have to be modified. With traditional hand drawing, modification is very time consuming—the designer may have to reproduce the entire plan by hand. CAD systems allow the designer to open the computer file containing the drawing and modify it on the spot. The designer can simply insert additional objects, move existing features, or remove unwanted features with a simple keystroke.

The final benefit associated with CAD systems is related to standardization. Standardization improves communication among designers and between designers and their clients. A designer may create a series of drawings, each following the same format. The consistency from drawing to drawing reduces confusion and helps the designer to better explain the drawings to other designers and to the clients.

## USING COMPUTER ASSISTED DESIGN SYSTEMS

CAD systems are used to increase the productivity of designers. The designer still must possess the skills and knowledge associated with traditional drawing. However, with CAD, the skill and knowledge of the designer in combination with the speed and efficiency of computers can produce improved quality and increased quantity of drawings.

Earlier in this chapter, the traditional tools of a designer were presented. Those tools included things like drawing boards, T-square, triangles, templates, pencils, erasers, and scales. With CAD systems, the tools include a computer, CAD software, computer monitor, input devices, and a printer.

The computer is used to electronically process the information that is input by the designer. CAD software consists of several programs that the computer uses to perform various functions. The software contains the instructions the computer needs to function and the commands needed to guide the designer in creating drawings.

The monitor allows the designer to view the drawing as work is progressing. Some monitors allow the designer to assign different colors to lines, circles, and other objects. Different colors may be used to help distinguish between different parts of the design. The designer may also chose to magnify portions of the drawing. The enlarged view results in greater detail.

*Input devices* allow the designer to enter information into the computer. Depending on the particular CAD system, these devices include a standard computer keyboard, mouse, and pen plotter. Some commands and any text can be input via the keyboard. The mouse can be used to enter commands and to designate the start and end point of a line. The *pen plotter* allows the designer to trace or draw an image on a flat surface. While the designer draws with the pen plotter, the image is transferred to the computer monitor.

16-14. Input devices for **CAD** software include a mouse and may include a pin plotter.

Output devices include printers and plotters. **Output devices** transfer the computerized information onto paper. To make a paper copy of the drawing, the designer sends the computer data concerning the drawing from the computer memory to the output device. The printer or plotter converts the information into images on the paper.

Compared to traditional drafting, a CAD system draws complex curves and lines of varying weights (thickness). The manipulation of objects on the display screen is possible. Shading and typing are automatic.

A drawing scale is no longer needed when the designer uses a CAD system. The CAD system automatically adds dimensions to the drawing. Also, the system will letter the drawing with the size and style of lettering specified by the designer.

# SUMMARY

Planning for construction activities is important in all phases of agriculture. A definite plan should be developed before any type of construction or repair work is undertaken. This plan consists of not only the drawings or sketches needed to complete the project but, also, all the other activities that should precede actual construction or repair work. An adequate plan will reduce cost, save valuable time, improve the quality of workmanship, and justify the need for the construction or repair project.

Traditional drawing techniques can be of use in planning for construction. A clear understanding of different views and the ability to effectively use drawing equipment can be useful.

Modern drawing techniques include the use of CAD systems. CAD systems allow the designer to produce higher quality drawings in a shorter amount of time. There are many additional advantages to using CAD systems.

# REVIEW QUESTIONS

1. Why is it important to consult with owners of buildings similar to one you are considering building?
2. What are the advantages of mechanical drawings over sketches?
3. How do mechanical drawings differ from sketches?
4. What is the difference between isometric, oblique, and orthographic projections?
5. List and describe the application of five different line types used in mechanical drawing.
6. Describe the use of 45-degree triangles and 30-degree × 60-degree triangles, include using them in combination.
7. Differentiate between architect, mechanical engineer, and civil engineer scales.
8. List and describe the benefits of CAD systems.
9. How does the ability to modify plans drawn with CAD systems differ from traditionally drawn plans?
10. List and describe the typical input devices for a CAD system.

# APPLYING THE CONCEPTS

1. Visit a building manufacturer who specializes in buildings for agriculture. Interview the builder to determine the cost of a specific building with various options. Prepare a paper which includes prices of the various options.
2. Obtain plans or blueprints for a small agricultural building. Visit a building supply store to determine the cost of the building.
3. Select a small wood or metal project which has been built in the agricultural mechanics laboratory. Sketch or draw isometric, oblique, and orthographic projections of the project.
4. Draw a floor plan for an agricultural building. You may use drafting equipment or CAD equipment to complete the drawing.

# 17

# FABRICATING METALS

Many machines and structures are made of metal. Metals are used because of unique physical properties. Some are easy to work with and serve as economical structural materials.

Metals are chemical elements easily distinguished from other elements because of their shiny appearance and reflection of light. Chemists have identified 81 metals, with many used in agriculture. Most metals do not exist in pure forms but as compounds. Elaborate mining and refining processes are used to convert them into useful materials.

Metals are used to fabricate machines and structures, design and improve existing equipment, and repair equipment and structures. Iron and steel—an iron alloy—are the most widely used metals. Aluminum, copper, and zinc are also used. Of course, everyone is familiar with the value of gold and silver and the dangers of lead and mercury.

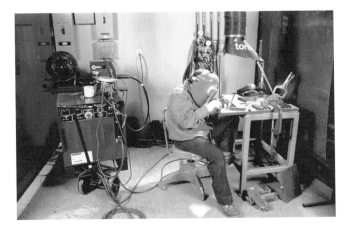

17-1. Welding is the process of joining materials by melting the metals, allowing them to flow together, and then returning the materials to a solid state. (Courtesy, American Welding Society)

**511**

# OBJECTIVES

This chapter provides an overview of metals fabrication in agriculture. After completing this chapter, you will:

1. Describe the kinds of metals used in agriculture.

2. Identify metals and describe their properties.

3. Explain cold metal fabrication processes.

4. Explain hot metal fabrication processes.

5. Perform cutting and welding processes.

**TERMS**

alloy
annealing
brazing
compression strength
corrosion resistance
cutting fluid
ductility
duty cycle
electrical conductivity
ferrous
galvanizing
hardening
hardness
heat treating
inert
machining
mechanical property
melting point
metal
metal inert gas welding (MIG)
metallurgy
non-ferrous
normalizing
physical property
points of carbon
puddle
slag
soldering
specific gravity
stress relieving
sweating
tempering
tensile strength
thermal conductivity
thread pitch
tinning
toughness
tungsten inert gas welding (TIG)
ultimate strength
welding
yield point

# METALS USED IN AGRICULTURE

The term, metal, is widely used and describes a variety of materials. From a scientific basis, a *metal* is a chemical element that has one or two electrons in the outer electron shell or orbit. These outer electrons are often called the valance electrons. If you look at the Periodic Table of the Elements, you will note that many of the elements are metals or described as being metallic.

## Periodic Table of the Elements

17-2. Periodic Table of the Elements.

Metals have a wide range of properties and uses. Generally, metals can be described as those materials that are made predominantly from one metallic chemical element. When a "metal" has two or more significant metallic elements, it is called an *alloy*. Common usage has produced a very broad definition of a metal. However, when we work with materials for fabrication, it is clearer to use technical terminology.

There are two basic classifications of metals and alloys used in agriculture—ferrous and non-ferrous. *Ferrous* means the primary element is iron (Fe). ***Non-ferrous*** metals are based upon metallic elements other than iron, such as aluminum and copper. Different metals have different properties and, therefore, different uses. Ferrous and alloy steels are common terms used to describe ferrous alloys made from iron and carbon. Carbon steel is made of iron and carbon. Other elements may be used in carbon steel, but in very small quantities. About 90 percent of all the steel produced and used is carbon steel. An alloy steel is a carbon steel with one or more additional metals added as alloying elements.

Wrought iron is the purest form of ferrous metal. It has less then 0.10 percent carbon. Wrought iron is not commonly used today.

Low carbon steel is widely used for structural materials. It is rolled and formed in common shapes, such as angle iron and structural beams. Low carbon steel has a carbon content between 0.10 and 0.30 percent. The carbon content is called ***points of carbon***. Low carbon steel is relatively easy to work with in both cold and hot metalworking processes. However, low carbon steel does not have enough carbon content to produce heat treating effects. The term mild steel generally refers to low carbon steel.

Medium carbon steel contains about 0.30 to 0.60 percent carbon. It can be heat treated and used for shafts, bolts, and tools.

High carbon steel is used for a large number of applications in agriculture. The carbon content is from .70 to 1.70 percent. Because of its high percentage of carbon, it is hard and resistant to wear. High carbon steel is somewhat difficult to work with. It is hard to drill, weld, and perform other metalworking processes. Tool steel is a common name for high carbon steel. To increase the strength and toughness of tools made from

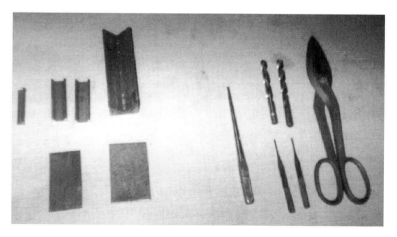

17-3. Low carbon steel is used for structural purposes and high carbon steel is used for many tools in agriculture.

high carbon steel, other elements may be added. Common tools made of high carbon steel are drill bits, taps, saw blades, and chisels.

Alloy steel is a carbon steel with one or more metallic elements added to change the properties. Some common alloying elements for steel are:

- Tungsten—produces hardened cutting tools.

- Chromium—increases the wear resistance and improves the appearance of steel.

- Manganese—makes carbon steel easier to roll and forge.

- Vanadium—increases the shock resistance of steel, such as for driveline shafts and bearings.

- Silicon—increases the hardness and toughness of steel and is a major alloying element for improving steel's casting and forging properties.

- Molybdenum—adds hardness and toughness to steel.

- Nickel—increases hardness and improves resistance to corrosion in steel.

- Zinc—often used to coat metals, including steels, to prevent corrosion. (*Galvanizing* is a process of immersing steel in molten zinc to form a coating of zinc and iron alloy. When heated, galvanized steel can produce zinc oxide, which is hazardous to breathe.)

Cast iron is a ferrous metal with a very high percentage of carbon. Cast iron has a carbon content of about 2.00 to 4.00 percent. It has many uses including engine blocks and gearbox housings.

## NON-FERROUS METALS AND ALLOYS

Non-ferrous metals are those metals that do not contain iron. Alloys of non-ferrous metals, such as brass, are very common.

Aluminum is a common non-ferrous metal. Its alloys are used in agriculture for many applications. Aluminum is lightweight and somewhat easy to work while cold. However, aluminum can be difficult to work hot.

Aluminum is a good conductor of electricity and has excellent heat transfer properties. It is used for heating, air conditioning, and refrigeration equipment. Aluminum is lightweight and, therefore, used for machines and equipment, such as trailers, airplanes, and food handling equipment.

Copper is an excellent conductor of electricity and heat. Copper is used for water pipes, wires, and heat transfer equipment, such as radiators. Copper is generally considered easy to solder and shape.

17-4. Aluminum (left) and copper (right) are non-ferrous metals.

Lead is a heavy and somewhat soft metal. It has been used for liquid cell electrical batteries and different kinds of soldering applications. Lead is considered a health hazard. Therefore, it should be used with care. Always wear protective clothing when using lead.

Magnesium is very similar to aluminum and is often mistaken for aluminum. It is one third lighter than aluminum. Magnesium is used where a light weight is desirable, such as wheels, trailer beds, and lawn mower frames. However, magnesium will burn and produces magnesium oxides, which are a serious health hazard.

Copper alloys are commonly made of copper, tin, and zinc. One of the most common alloys is brass. Brass is made by adding up to 40 percent zinc to copper. Brass is harder than copper and has good machining properties. Many hinges, screws, and other hardware are made from brass. Bronze is a copper alloy made of copper and tin. Bronze is tough and wear resistant. It is used for machinery parts, such as bearings. Bronze has an attractive appearance and is highly resistant to corrosion.

# PROPERTIES OF METALS

*Metallurgy* is the study of the chemical and physical properties of metals. Physical metallurgy is the study of the properties and characteristics of metals and can be divided into two broad areas—physical properties and mechanical properties. The properties of alloys can be quite different from the properties of the parent metallic chemical elements. Understanding the basic principles of metallurgy and the properties of metals is important when fabricating metals.

## PHYSICAL PROPERTIES

Metals have a wide range of physical properties. ***Physical properties*** are those characteristics of metal that do not change during fabrication. For example, the melting point of a metal does not change as it is worked. To change the melting point, the chemical characteristics of the metal must be changed.

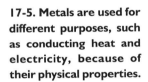

17-5. Metals are used for different purposes, such as conducting heat and electricity, because of their physical properties.

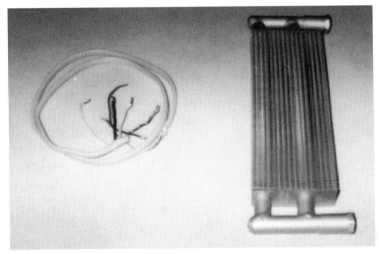

The ***melting point*** of a metal is the temperature at which the metal changes from a solid state to a liquid state. A pure metal will melt at a specific point. However, some alloys will melt in a ragne of temperatures.

***Specific gravity*** is a measure of the density of a metal. Water is used as the standard for specific gravity, with an assigned specific gravity of 1.00.

***Corrosion resistance*** of a metal is its ability to resist oxidation. Gold, platinum, and silver are most resistant to corrosion. Copper, tin, lead, and nickel are somewhat corrosive resistant. Zinc is commonly used as a coating to protect steel from corrosion. Magnesium and aluminum will corrode, however, they do tend to form a surface layer of oxidation, which protects the metal underneath.

***Electrical conductivity*** is the ability of the metal to allow electrical current to flow through it. Silver, copper, and aluminum are considered to be very good conductors of electricity. The term "conductor" refers to a metal that has good electrical conductivity. Materials that do not allow electricity to flow easily are called insulators.

*Thermal conductivity* is the ability of metal to transfer heat. The terms "insulator" and "conductor" are also used when referring to thermal conductivity.

## MECHANICAL PROPERTIES

*Mechanical properties* are those characteristics encountered when working with metal. They include hardness, ductility, toughness, tensile strength, and compression strength.

*Hardness* is the ability of a metal to resist indentation, scratching, or filing. A metal becomes more brittle as it becomes harder. Metals can be identified based on the degree of hardness. A file, hacksaw, or a hammer and center punch can be used to determine the relative hardness of a metal. Hardness can be measured by how far a probe can be pushed or forced into a metal sample. A Rockwell hardness tester is commonly used to precisely determine the hardness of a metal. It uses a diamond penetrator to determine the relative hardness. The Rockwell "C" scale is used for determining steel hardness.

17-6. The hardness of a metal can be measured using a file or hacksaw.

*Ductility* is the property of a metal to be formed into shapes without breaking. Copper is considered to be a ductile metal, as it can be made into tubes and wire easily.

*Toughness* is a measure of a metal's ability to resist impact. Many machinery parts, such as axles and internal engine parts, need to have toughness.

*Tensile strength* is the property of a metal to withstand a pulling force. Tensile strength is very commonly used to determine the strength of a metal. Tensile strength is expressed by the amount of force required to pull the metal apart. *Yield point* is the amount of force required to stretch

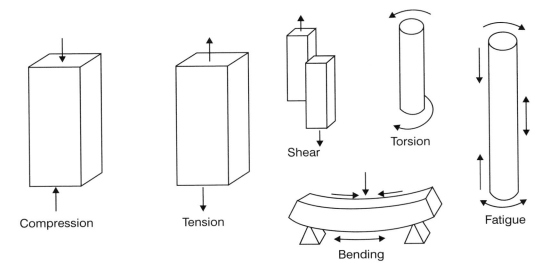

Compression    Tension    Shear    Torsion    Bending    Fatigue

**17-7. Mechanical properties determine the ability of a metal to withstand various load forces.**

the metal until it is permanently deformed. *Ultimate strength* is the point at which the metal fails.

*Compression strength* is the ability of a metal to withstand a compression force. Compression strength is used for determining the load bearing ability of structural metals in bridges and machinery frames.

# IDENTIFYING METALS

One of the very first steps in metalworking is to identify the metal. With so many different kinds of metals and alloys, correctly identifying a metal can be a difficult task. Distinguishing the physical properties of various metals and alloys is useful for identification. First, learn to categorize different basic metals and alloys. To identify specific metals, especially different alloys based upon their chemical composition, involves chemical analysis of a sample.

A good strategy for identifying metal materials is to keep labeled samples of a known metal for comparison.

General methods used to identify metals are:

1. Use: The use of a metal is one of the most practical ways to identify it. For example, steels are often used for structural supports, aluminum for heat transfer, and copper for water pipes.

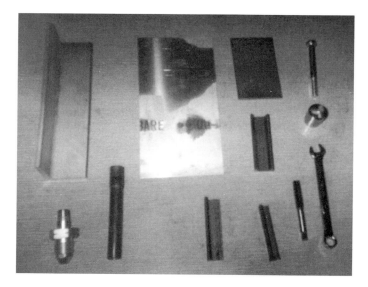

17-8. Metals can be identified by their use, weight, hardness, and other characteristics.

2. Magnetic test: Generally, a ferrous metal will be magnetic and a non-ferrous metal will not be magnetic. There are some exceptions—some stainless steels are not magnetic.

3. Weight: Cast iron and lead are relatively heavy, whereas, aluminum and magnesium are very light.

4. Hardness: A file or center punch can be used to determine a material's hardness.

5. Appearance: Some metals, such as cast iron and galvanized steel, have distinct surface appearances.

6. Heat conductivity: Copper and aluminum are good heat conductors.

7. Spark test: Metals containing varying carbon levels and certain alloying elements produce sparks with distinctive colors and shapes when held against a grinding wheel.

## METAL SHAPES

Metals come in many different shapes for many different uses. Refer to Figure 17-9 for common steel shapes.

Steel may be "hot rolled" or "cold rolled." Hot rolled steel is formed while it is hot. Cold rolled steel is formed after it has been cooled. Hot rolled steel generally is less expensive to purchase and is used for many structural purposes. Cold rolled steel has a more consistent grain structure. It is easier to machine and has higher tensile strength, ductility, and a much brighter finish.

| | | Sizes Commonly Used | How Dimensioned (Thickness x Width x Length) (T x W x L) |
|---|---|---|---|
| 1/8" ⟵3/4"⟶ | Band iron | 1/8" to 1/2" thickness 1/4" to 2" wide | 1/8" x 3/4" x L |
| ⟵1/8" 1/2" ⟵1/2"⟶ | Angle iron | 1/8" to 1/4" wall thickness 1/4" to 3" wide | 1/8" wall x 1/2" x L |
| 3/4" ⟵1/8" | Square tube | .030" to 1/4" wall thickness 1/4" to 3" wide | 1/8" wall x 3/4" x L |
| 3" ⟵1/8" | Round tube and pipe | .030" to 1/4" wall thickness 1/4" to 3" diameter | 1/8" wall x 3" x L |
| 3/4" 1/8" ⟵3/4"⟶ | Channel iron | 3/4" x 1/2"–1/8" wall thickness 3" x 1-1/2"–1/8" wall | 1/8" wall x 1/2" x 3/4" x L |
| 1" | Round | 1/8" to 2"–diameter | 1" diameter x L |
| 1" | Square | 1/4" to 1"–square | 1" x L |

**17-9. Metal products come in many different shapes for different purposes.**

Extruded metal refers to metal that has been forced through a die to form various shapes. Aluminum window frames can be extruded.

Casting refers to metals that are formed from a liquid state in a mold. Many metals can be cast. Examples include cast engine blocks of either aluminum or cast iron.

Forging refers to metals that are shaped by a hammering process. Many tools and engine parts are forged. Forging is usually while the metal is heated, however, some cold forging is done.

# METALWORKING PROCESSES

Metalworking processes can be divided into two categories—cold metalworking and hot metalworking. Cold metalworking means to work with metals that are not heated. Hot metalworking is working metal that is heated.

## COLD METALWORKING PROCESSES

Many processes can be performed on metals and alloys without heating the material. Metal can be cut, shaped, drilled, threaded, and fastened. These processes are often the best to use because they tend not to deform, strain, stress, or distort the materials. Cold metalworking processes can also be used to fasten and fabricate metals with other types of materials, such as plastics and wood. However, the cold metalworking process can be time consuming and difficult to perform. Whether to use cold or hot metalworking processes will vary for different metals and applications.

### Safety Practices for Cold Metalworking

Always follow the specific recommended safety practices for any equipment being used. Be familiar with the manufacturer's recommendations and always follow those safety guidelines.

Safety practices to follow when working with cold metal processes are:

1. Always wear personal eye protection.

2. Make sure that fire extinguishers are available and operational.

3. Wear hearing protection when operating power equipment.

4. Always provide adequate ventilation.

5. Wear appropriate clothing to protect you from chips and sparks.

6. Make sure all electrical equipment is properly grounded.

7. Always make sure that any pieces of metal being worked are secure.

8. Wear appropriate footwear to protect you from metal that may fall or be stepped on.

9. Make sure all equipment is in good operating condition.

10. Always keep the work area clean and orderly.

11. Make sure that everyone in the metalworking area has expertise in safe metalworking practices.

12. Do not allow children to play in a metalworking area at any time.

13. When leaving the work area, make sure all equipment is turned off and all metal has been properly stored.

## Cutting Metal

The most basic cold metalworking process is cutting metal. Metal can be cut with a saw, shear, or other kind of tool. Hand tools, portable power tools, or stationary power tools are used. Equipment can be driven by electrical, hydraulic, or pneumatic power, or can simply multiple mechanical force.

Bandsaws are often used to cut metal. Bandsaws have a continuous saw blade, called a band, to cut the metal. Bandsaws can be portable or stationary. Stationary bandsaws can be mounted vertically or horizontally. These saws can cut a variety of metals. However, very hard metals are

17-10. A bandsaw is used to cut metal.

not easily cut. Many times a cutting fluid is used to help cut metal. The *cutting fluid* helps to keep the metal and blade cool, keep the saw blade clean, and lubricate the moving parts.

"Cut-off" saws use a circular abrasive saw blade to cut metal. Generally, these types of saws are not as accurate as others, but cut metal quickly. Because of the abrasive nature of these saws, they tend to heat the metal. Abrasive saws work best with harder metals, such as steel; softer metals tend to coat the blades. Abrasive saws are widely used when welding is a part of fabrication. Since metals will be heated during the welding processes later, heat from cutting with a "cut-off" saw has only a minimal effect on strength.

Metals can also be sheared. Hydraulic and mechanical presses can be used to shear metal. Shears can cut metal very quickly, however, they tend to leave a rougher material edge then saws.

17-11. An abrasive saw can cut metal easily. (Courtesy, American Welding Society)

## Drilling and Punching Metal

One of the most important cold metalworking processes is drilling or punching round holes, slots, or other shapes in metal. Many metal fabrication processes use bolts, rivets, screws, or other types of fasteners to hold metal together. These fasteners require some type of hole in the metal. Round holes can be drilled or punched through metal. Drilling produces a more accurately sized and shaped hole. Punching holes in metal can be much faster than drilling. To get accurately sized and shaped holes, a ream should be used.

17-12. A drill press is often used to drill holes in metal. (Courtesy, Glen Miller, University of Arizona)

Drilling involves using a drill bit to bore or cut the hole. Drill bits come in a variety of types and sizes. They tend to be very hard and, therefore, can also be brittle and easy to break. Drill bits are made from hardened alloy steels and will lose hardness, if overheated. Portable drills are widely used. They can be electric, pneumatic, or hydraulically driven. Stationary drills can also be used and drill presses are a common type of stationary drill. They tend to be faster than portable drills and produce more accurately sized holes. When drilling holes, cutting fluids are often used to reduce heat and friction and to keep the drilling process clean.

Holes can also be punched through metal. Punches can be hand-operated, hydraulic or pneumatic, or mechanically driven. Hydraulic presses are very common because of the large amount of force generated. A variety of punch dies can be used to punch a variety of shapes through metal.

## Threading and Tapping

A common method of mechanically fastening metal is to use threads. Threads are cut outside on a round stock of metal with a die. Inside threads are cut with a tap. Dies and taps can be turned manually or mechanically.

There are different types of threads. The spacing and size of the thread is called the ***thread pitch***. The most common pitch of threads are referred to as national fine (NF), national coarse (NC), and pipe threads (NPT). Threads can be based upon the United States measurement—the number

| National Coarse and National Fine Threads and Tap Drills | | | |
|---|---|---|---|
| Size | Threads per inch | Tap drill 75% threaded | Clearance drill |
| 2 | 56 UNC | 50 | 42 |
|   | 64 UNF | 50 | 42 |
| 3 | 48 UNC | 47 | 36 |
|   | 56 UNF | 45 | 36 |
| 4 | 40 UNC | 43 | 31 |
|   | 48 UNF | 42 | 31 |
| 6 | 32 UNC | 36 | 26 |
|   | 40 UNF | 33 | 26 |
| 8 | 32 UNC | 29 | 17 |
|   | 36 UNF | 29 | 17 |
| 10 | 24 UNC | 25 | 8 |
|   | 32 UNF | 21 | 8 |
| 12 | 24 UNC | 16 | 1 |
|   | 28 UNF | 14 | 2 |
| 1/4 | 20 UNC | 7 | G |
|   | 28 UNF | 3 | G |
| 5/16 | 18 UNC | F | 21/64 |
|   | 24 UNF | I | 21/64 |
| 3/8 | 16 UNC | 5/16 | 25/64 |
|   | 24 UNF | Q | 25/64 |
| 7/16 | 14 UNC | U | 16/32 |
|   | 20 UNF | 25/64 | 29/64 |
| 1/2 | 13 UNC | 27/64 | 17/32 |
|   | 20 UNF | 29/64 | 33/64 |
| 9/16 | 12 UNC | 31/64 | 19/32 |
|   | 18 UNF | 33/64 | 37/64 |
| 5/8 | 11 UNC | 17/32 | 21/32 |
|   | 18 UNF | 37/64 | 41/64 |
| 3/4 | 10 UNC | 21/32 | 25/32 |
|   | 16 UNF | 11/16 | 49/64 |
| 7/8 | 9 UNC | 49/64 | 29/32 |
|   | 14 UNF | 13/16 | 57/64 |
| 1 | 8 UNC | 7/8 | 1-1/32 |
|   | 14 UNF | 15/16 | 1-1/64 |
| 1-1/8 | 7 UNC | 63/64 | 1-5/32 |
|   | 12 UNF | 1-3/64 | 1-5/32 |
| 1-1/4 | 7 UNC | 1-7/64 | 1-9/32 |
|   | 12 UNF | 1-11/64 | 1-9/32 |
| 1-1/2 | 6 UNC | 1-11/32 | 1-17/32 |
|   | 12 UNF | 1-27/64 | 1-17/32 |

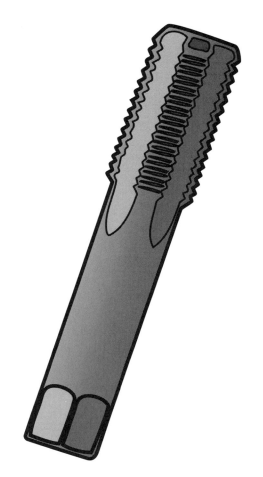

17-13. A chart of different size and pitch taps.

of threads per inch—or the International Standard (metric)—the spacing of the threads in millimeters. There are also specialized threads that are designed for specific purposes.

Taps are used to cut threads in holes. The holes must be precisely drilled or reamed to the proper size. Dies are matched to the diameter of the metal. Threading requires precision and correct methods. Thread-cutting fluids are used to lubricate, cool, and clean the threads during cutting.

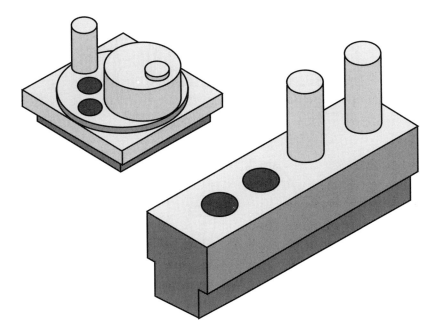

**17-14. Two types of bending jigs used to shape metal.**

## Bending and Shaping Metal

Many metals can be shaped without being heated. A grinder is one tool used to shape metal. Grinders may be portable or stationary. Hand tools, such as files, are also used. Metal can be bent to form different shapes. The most common way to bend metal is to use a hammer and vise. Bending jigs are sometimes used to shape metals. They can be manually or mechanically operated. Hydraulic bending jigs are often used to bend pipe and other types of metal.

## Fastening Metal

Metals can be fastened together mechanically by using bolts, screws, rivets, and other cold metalworking methods. These types of fasteners hold the metal materials together by friction. The same methods are used to fasten metal to other materials, such as wood or plastic. These methods are widely used because they are easy to fabricate, can be used in a variety of situations, and may be designed to be disassembled and then re-assembled.

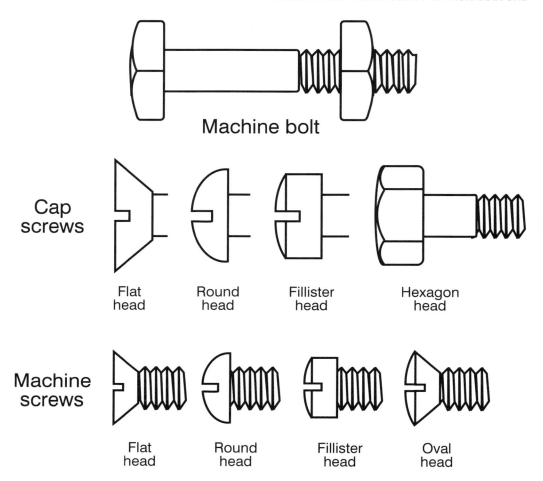

17-15. Fasteners used in metalworking include screws and bolts.

## Metal Machining

*Machining* is the process of precisely shaping metal. Metal can be machined with lathes, milling machines, and other equipment. These machines require considerable skill to operate.

A lathe spins the metal and uses a stationary tool to cut and shape the metal. Specialized lathes are used to "turn" crankshafts, brake drums and rotors, and other components. Milling machines hold the metal stationary and the tools rotate. Both lathes and milling machine can be operated by computers. This is referred to as computer aided machining or CAM. The computer can also be used to design a part—computer aided

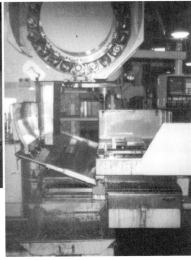

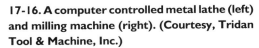

17-16. A computer controlled metal lathe (left) and milling machine (right). (Courtesy, Tridan Tool & Machine, Inc.)

design or CAD. The combination of computer aided design and machining is sometimes referred to as CAD/CAM.

## HOT METALWORKING

Hot metalworking processes use a heat source to prepare the metal for the selected metalworking processes. Some metalworking processes are easier or more economical to perform on heated metal than cold metal.

There are two basic ways to heat metals: combustion and electricity.

Propane and acetylene fuel gases are common heat sources. A more intense heat can be produced if pure oxygen is used with the fuel gas for

17-17. Eye, ear, face, and head protective equipment. (Courtesy, American Welding Society)

combustion. Electricity can also be used as a heat source. Heat is generated by creating resistance to the flow of electricity.

## Safety Practices for Hot Metalworking

Always follow the specific recommended safety practices for hot metalworking equipment. Be familiar with what the manufacturer recommends and always follow those safety guidelines. Safety practices to observe when working with hot metal processes are:

1. Always wear personal eye protection.
2. Make sure that fire extinguishers are available and operational.
3. Wear hearing protection when operating power equipment.
4. When working with welding equipment wear the recommended shade lenses for eye protection. As a general guideline for gas welding and cutting, a number 5 is suggested. For arc welding, a number 10 or 12 is appropriate.
5. Always provide adequate ventilation.
6. Wear appropriate clothing to protect from harmful rays, heat, and sparks.
7. Always keep all gas storage cylinders securely fastened in a vertical position.
8. Never leave hot metal unmarked and unattended.
9. Properly store all flammable materials. Do not store rags, paper, gasoline, kerosene, diesel fuel, and other similar materials in a hot metalworking area.
10. Always keep the work area clean and orderly.
11. Make sure that everyone in the metalworking area has expertise in safe metalworking practices.
12. When leaving the work area, make sure all equipment is turned off and all hot metal has been properly cooled.

## Heat Treating

**Heat treating** is used to change the properties of metal by controlling the heating and cooling of the metal. Heat treating includes five basic processes: hardening, annealing, stress relieving, normalizing, and tempering. The heat treating processes are used to change the grain structure, tensile strength, machinability and hardness, and relieve the internal stress forces of metal. Both ferrous and non-ferrous metals and alloys can be heat treated. However, most of the heat treating processes are used to change the properties of carbon steel and steel alloys.

The structure of steel can be changed under varying heating and cooling conditions. Steel is made of iron and carbon. The higher the percentage of carbon in the steel, the harder the steel. The carbon atoms fit between the iron atoms forming an additional chemical compound called cementite ($Fe_3C$). Cast iron contains the highest percentage of cementite. Cementite is a very hard substance. Pearlite is a mixture of cementite and ferrite. Ferrite has a very low percentage of carbon.

Heat treating processes work because iron and steel change their crystal structure when heated and cooled. Iron melts, turns from a solid to a liquid at about 2800°F. The higher the content of carbon, the lower the melting point. As a liquid, the atoms are randomly arranged. As the metal solidifies, the atoms arrange themselves to form a crystal structure. Each

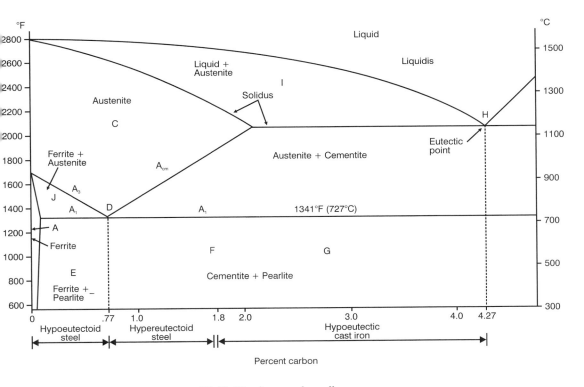

**17-18. The iron-carbon diagram.**

atom occupies a specific location or space. The pattern of the atom arrangement is called a space lattice. When iron first solidifies, it forms a body-centered, cubic space lattice form. This means there is one atom at each corner of the cube and one atom in the center of the cube. This body-centered cubic of iron between the temperatures of about 2800 and 2200°F is called Delta iron.

As the iron continues to cool, the atoms rearrange themselves into a different pattern called a face-centered cubic. In iron, this is called gamma iron or austenite. The atoms are arranged on each corner of the cube, but atoms are now located in the center of each cube face, with no atoms in the centers of the cubes. As the cooling continues, another change occurs at below 1600°F as the atoms arrange themselves as body-centered cubics. These cells are called alpha iron. Ferrite is alpha iron with small amounts of carbon. As the iron drops below 1400°F, the iron becomes capable of attracting a magnet.

As the crystal changes, these changes are called allotropic changes. The process of the allotropic changes is called transformation. The temperatures at which these changes occur are called critical temperatures.

*Hardening* is a heat treating process that increases the relative hardness of the steel. Steel with a carbon content of more than 0.30 percent can be hardened by proper heat treating. The steel is heated to above its alpha iron critical temperature (1341°F) and will turn a bright red color. The steel is then cooled very quickly. Tempering oil or water is used to quench the steel. The liquid should be stirred to speed cooling. The hardening process "freezes" the crystal structure in a state of stress producing a hardened steel.

*Annealing* is the opposite process of hardening. The steel is again heated to a bright red color, but allowed to cool very slowly in an insulating medium, such as dry sand or a non-flammable insulation. This allows the crystal structure of the steel to arrange itself in very "stressless" structure producing a softer steel.

*Stress relieving* is a form of annealing. The stress relieving process is to heat the metal to just below the critical temperature, allow the heat to be maintained for a long period of time, possibly for hours, and then allowed to cool very slowly. This process is used to relieve stress points of metal frames. One technique is to heat the metal in a furnace for several hours, turn the furnace off, and leave the metal in the furnace for one to several days as it slowly cools. The metal will not fully soften, since it was not heated to the austenite stage.

*Normalizing* is similar to annealing except the metal is allowed to cool in the open air. This produces a metal that has been stress-relieved, while not quite as soft as annealing, but more machinable then hardening.

*Tempering* is a process to reduce the hardness of a hardened metal by relieving a desired level of internal crystal structure stress. The process of tempering is to reheat a hardened metal to a desired temperature. Polished steel can be tempered based upon the color of the oxides as they appear on the steel. However, a temperature-controlled tempering furnace will be a more accurate process. Once the steel is reheated to the desired level, it is again quenched in a cooling solution.

## Welding

*Welding* is the process of joining materials by melting the metals, allowing the metals to flow together, and then returning the materials to a solid state. Metals need to be protected from atmospheric gases while they are molten. Exposure of molten metals to oxygen, nitrogen, and other atmospheric gases can change the physical and chemical properties of the metals. A common technique is to use a shielding gas to protect the molten metal. Carbon dioxide is often used as a shielding gas for a variety of welding , cutting, and other hot metalworking processes. Shielding gases should not react with molten metals. The shielding gas may be supplied from a gas cylinder or tank. Flux from an electrode can also be used to create a shielding gas.

**Gas Metal Arc Welding.** Gas metal arc welding (GMAW), also called *metal inert gas welding* (*MIG*), is a very popular form of welding. MIG welding uses a continuous supply of relatively small diameter metal wire, inert gas, and an electrical current to weld metals together. The metal wire is usually a solid wire that is of the same composition as the metal being welded. Direct current electricity is supplied through the welding wire and the base metal. Heat is produced as the electrical current jumps the gap between the welding wire and the metal being welded. The inert gas provides a shield that protects the molten metals and stabilizes the electric arc.

*Inert* means that the materials will not readily react with other elements. Inert gases can be found to the far right of a chemical element periodic table. These gases, called noble gases, have all of the their electron positions full. Therefore, they cannot react with other elements since they have no open electron positions. Other gases, such as carbon dioxide, have characteristics similar to the noble gases and are considered inert gases for welding and hot metalworking processes. Argon is used a great deal in MIG welding. Carbon dioxide and helium are also used. These gases are also mixed with argon. The type of gas used is based upon the type of metal to be welded.

The MIG welding process uses a welding machine that produces direct electrical current. These machines are designed to maintain a constant

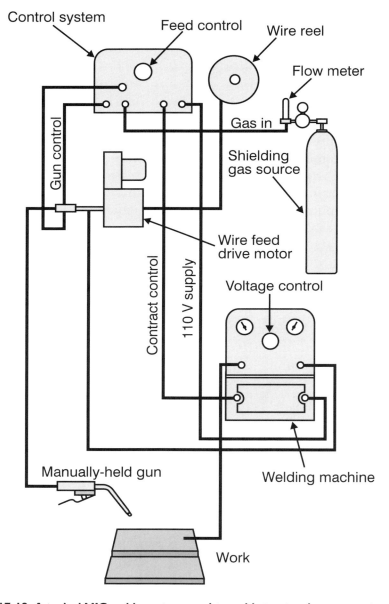

**17-19. A typical MIG welder set-up used to weld structural components.**

electrical voltage or pressure. This is referred to as a constant voltage or constant potential welder. The welders vary the current flow, or amperage, to maintain the constant voltage. When compared to other welding proc-esses, MIG welding is generally considered to be one of the easiest to learn and most practical. Very clean welds are produced with relative ease. MIG welding is relatively safe, however, the welder must wear protective clothing, a suitable welding helmet with the recommended shade lenses, usually a number 10 or 12, and welding gloves.

To weld with a MIG welder:

1. Select the proper kind of welding filler wire.

2. Select the proper wire size.

3. Set the recommended voltage.

4. Adjust the gas flow rate (cubic feet per hour).

5. Adjust the feed rate of the electrode wire.

6. Set the electrode extension or "stick-out".

7. Control the welding torch movement.

MIG welding has grown in popularity, especially for sheet metal and other smaller welding applications. MIG welding is used extensively for robotic welding applications and other automated welding processes.

17-20. A MIG welder being used to weld structural com-ponents. (Courtesy, Jasper S. Lee)

**Flux Core Arc Welding.** Flux core arc welding (FCAW) is very similar to MIG welding. The same kind of welding equipment is used. A continuous wire electrode is used. There is a flux core in the center of the wire, hence the name. Sometimes, a shielding gas is also used, but usually the flux in the wire provides sufficient shielding action. FCAW does not produce a weld as clean as the solid wire used in MIG welding. The completed weld usually will be coated with a slag coating, which should be chipped or brushed clean. However, FCAW does not require the constant use and handling of a shielding gas. This makes it a good choice for field repairs. The skill level required for FCAW is higher than for most forms of MIG welding.

The procedures and safety precautions for flux core arc welding are basically the same as for MIG welding.

**Tungsten Inert Gas Welding.** *Tungsten inert gas welding* (*TIG*) is also called gas tungsten arc welding (GTAW). TIG welding can produce very high quality, clean welds on many different kinds of metals. The tungsten inert gas welding process uses an electric arc, a non-consumable tungsten electrode, an inert gas shield, and, possibly, a non-coated metal welding rod.

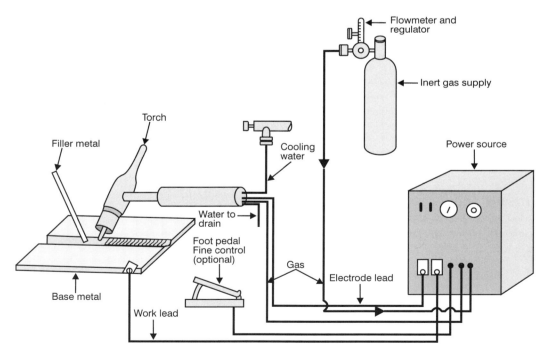

17-21. A typical TIG welding set-up.

TIG can be used to produce high quality welds on aluminum, steel, stainless steel, and other metals. The most common shielding gas used is argon. The tungsten electrode is used to conduct the electrical current and create the arc. The tungsten electrode is not consumed in the molten metal. There are several different types of tungsten electrodes. As a general rule, a pure tungsten electrode is used for welding aluminum and other similar metals. For aluminum, high frequency alternating current is used with a ball-shaped tungsten electrode. For steel and other similar metals, straight polarity direct current is recommended with a pointed thoriated tungsten electrode. Always check and follow the manufacturer's recommendation for the type of electrical current and electrode to use.

The TIG welding torch body or handle is held in one hand and the filler welding rod in the other. Some torch handles are water-cooled because of the intense heat produced by TIG welding. Most TIG welding operations use a variable amperage control that is either hand- or foot-operated. The variable control is used to start and stop the arc as well as save shielding gas. The process of holding the torch body, the welding rod, and operating the variable amperage control as well as completing the actual weld, requires considerable skill, expertise, and practice.

TIG welding uses an AC-DC welder, with a high frequency control. A flow control valve is used to turn the inert gas flow on and off. A flow regulator is used to regulate the amount of inert gas that is flowing. The manufacturer will recommend inert gas flow rates as the number of cubic feet per hour (cfh). The torch body holds the tungsten electrode and allows the inert gas to flow around the electrode and form a protective gas shield. Set the welder according to manufacturer's instructions based on the type of

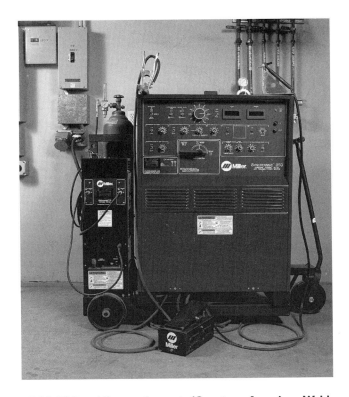

**17-22. TIG welding equipment. (Courtesy, American Welding Society)**

metal being welded and the thickness and condition of the metal. The
TIG welding process is very similar to the gas welding process, in that a
molten weld area, called a weld puddle, is created. You need to carefully
strike an arc, create a weld puddle, and add the welding rod to the weld
puddle. The TIG welding process produces a very clean weld bead having
an excellent appearance as well as good penetration.

**Shielded Metal Arc Welding.** Shielded metal arc welding (SMAW)
has been and continues to be a very popular form of welding. SMAW is
as commonly called "stick" welding or just arc welding. This type of
welding has been popular because of the many different kinds of metals
that can be welded. A large amount of production type welding is now
done as MIG welding. However, SMAW is still used for many repairs and
small production welding applications in agriculture. Also, arc welding
equipment is not complicated to operate and maintain. However, arc
welding does requires a moderate skill level. Some metals, such as aluminum, are very difficult to weld with the SMAW process, while low carbon
steel is relatively easy.

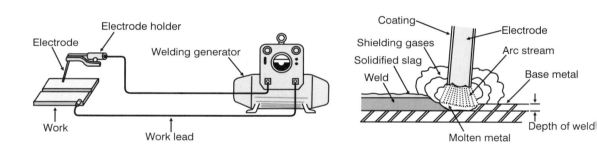

**17-23. A typical electric arc and gas shield of the welding process.**

Shielded metal arc welding uses a welding electrode, which is a core
wire coated with flux. The core wire is made of metal that matches the
base metal being welded. There are many different kinds of electrodes to
weld a wide variety of metals. The flux coating on the electrode provides
a gas shield to protect the molten metal until it solidifies and also stabilizes
the electric arc. Electrodes are sized by the diameter of the core wire—1/8
and 5/16 inch electrodes are common sizes. Select the size of the electrode

to match the thickness of the base metals. As a general rule, an electrode will penetrate into the base metal a distance equal to its core wire diameter. Also, it will produce a weld bead as high as the diameter of the core wire. Another general rule is that the bead width should be about 3 to 4 times the electrode core wire diameter. By changing welding speed, amperage, and using electrode movements, such as weaving, specific welds for different applications can be produced.

An electrode produces a coating on the completed weld. This coating is called *slag*. The slag protects the molten metal as it cools and solidifies. The slag coating should be chipped off the weld once it has cooled. The slag coating should be cleaned off of a bead if another bead is to be made on the previous weld.

Electrodes are identified by classification systems established by the American Welding Society (AWS). The classification systems vary from one type of electrode to another. The AWS electrode classification system for carbon steel electrodes is described here. The systems for electrodes for other metals, such as stainless steel and aluminum, are similar.

The AWS uses the letter "E" to designate an electrode. The E is followed by usually two, but sometimes three, digits that indicate the tensile strength of the core wire metal in pounds per square inch. The next digit indicates the welding position(s) in which the electrode can be used. Generally, a "1" is most common as those electrodes are designed to weld in all positions. A "2" means the electrode can be used only to make flat or horizontal fillet welds. The last digit refers to the specific welding characteristics of the electrode based on the type of flux on the electrode.

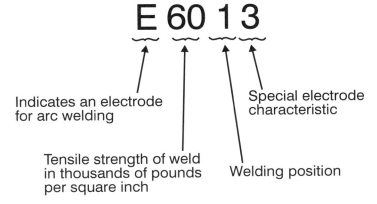

**17-24. The AWS electrode identification system for steel welding electrodes.**

E 60 1 3

Indicates an electrode for arc welding

Tensile strength of weld in thousands of pounds per square inch

Welding position

Special electrode characteristic

The electric arc between the electrode and the base metal produces the heat required to melt the electrode core wire and the base metals. The arc length is the distance the electrode is held from the base metals being welded. Arc length must be maintained at a constant distance to generate consistent heat. The heat is produced by the resistance of the electricity to flow across the arc. The flux helps to stabilize the arc. Electrodes can be difficult to get started. They tend to stick to the base metal as you "strike" the electrode to the base metals to produce an arc. Also, some electrodes are easier to weld with because some fluxes produce more stable arcs then others. However, these electrodes may not produce suitable metal cleaning and weld penetration characteristics. Select the type of electrode to best suit welding skill, the type of metal, and the desired bead characteristics.

The amount of heat produced is controlled by the welding amperage output of the welder. Amperage refers to the rate of flow of the electrical current. Too much amperage will melt too large an area of the base metal. Amperage that is too low will not generate enough heat to melt the metal and the electrode. The welders used for SMAW are considered to be constant current welders. Set the desired amperage according to the recommendations of the specific electrode and the welder will maintain that amperage.

Either direct current or alternating current can be used for different welding applications and electrodes. These type of welders are based on step down transformers—they step down the voltage, which will step up the amperage. A welder that is turned on, but not welding, will have an open circuit voltage of about 70 to 80 volts. While welding, the voltage will drop to about 20 to 30 volts.

The *duty cycle* of a welder refers to the relative amount of welding time compared to total time. It is a form of efficiency measure. For example, a welder with a 20 percent duty cycle is designed to be used no more than 2 out of every 10 minutes when welding at the rated amperage. Rated amperage is usually the maximum amperage rating of the welder. This allows the transformer in the welder to cool. Many welders actually have electric fans to keep the welder cool.

**Gas Welding.** Gas welding is the process of melting metals together with the heat produced by burning fuel gases and oxygen. Gas welding is also called "oxy-fuel" welding or fuel gas welding (FGW). It is often called oxy-acetylene welding (OAW) when acetylene is used as the fuel gas. Gas welding is still used to some extent, however, the advancements in MIG and TIG welding have decreased its use. Many fabrication shops use oxy-acetylene for cutting, brazing, and soldering purposes. So, the gas welding equipment is often readily available and used because of the convenience. It should be noted that gas welding requires considerable skill and expertise to perform quality welds.

Gas welding uses a fuel gas to produce the heat for welding. Acetylene is used because of the relative amount of heat the flame will produce. An oxygen-acetylene welding flame produces a temperature of about 6000°F at the tip of the blue, inner flame cone. Acetylene is a very unstable gas. A molecule of acetylene is made of two carbon atoms and two hydrogen atoms. The molecule creates a triple bond between the carbon atoms. Triple bonds, when released through combustion, produce a great deal of heat energy. Warning! A triple chemical bond is very unstable and acetylene may explode if it is

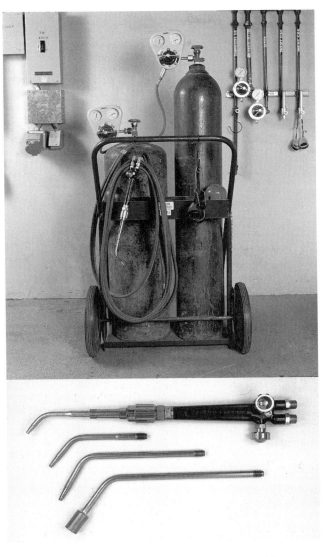

17-25. Oxy-acetylene welding equipment. (Courtesy, American Welding Society)

mishandled. Acetone is added to help stabilize acetylene. Pure acetylene becomes unstable if pressurized more than 15 psi.

The combustion of acetylene produces carbon dioxide, which acts as a shielding gas to protect the molten metals. Carbon dioxide is an excellent shielding gas for welding low carbon steel. Use a welding flux to help protect other types of molten metals. Gas welding can be performed with or without a filler metal. It is often a good idea to practice welding without

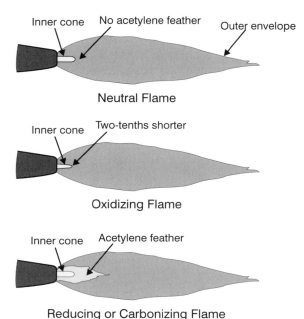

17-26. A diagram of the carburizing, neutral, and oxidizing oxygen-acetylene welding flames.

a filler metal rod when first learning to gas weld. Gas welding is often used on sheet and other thinner forms of metal. Increase and decrease the amount of heat for welding by using different size welding tips. The tips have different size holes in the end to allow more or less fuel gas and oxygen to flow through. The temperature of the flame is determined by the kind of fuel gas. The amount of heat produced is determined by the size of the welding tips. Always follow the welding equipment manufacturer's recommendations for selecting the proper size welding tip based upon the thickness of the metal being welded. Select the proper gas pressures based upon the recommendations for the tip size selected.

The gas pressures are set by the pressure regulators. Different pressure regulators are used for the fuel gases and the oxygen.

The welding torch flame creates a molten circle of metal called a **puddle**. In welding, a small circular movement with the torch controls the size and shape of the puddle. The puddle is moved ahead with a circular pattern. The flame of the torch should remain at a constant height, with the inner flame cone about $1/8$ of an inch above the molten metal. Moving too fast, keeping the torch too high, or welding in a windy environment can expose the puddle to the air and create a poor weld.

**Plasma Arc Cutting.** Plasma arc cutting uses an electrical arc and fast-moving ionized gases to cut metals. A plasma arc can cut aluminum, stainless steel, and most other metals. A tungsten electrode conducts the DC electricity to create an arc, which produces heat to melt the metal. Forced air blows the molten metal away. Plasma arc is rapidly becoming more popular as the preferred method of cutting metal, especially thinner sheets that tend to warp when heated.

**17-27. Plasma Arc Welding. (Courtesy, American Welding Society)**

Plasma arc cutting requires personal protective equipment, including hearing protection, as the forced air and electric arc create a noisy work environment. Operators should wear gloves, protective clothing, and suitable eye protection similar to that required for gas welding and cutting.

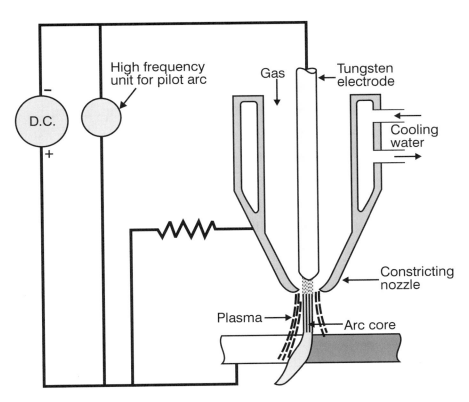

**17-28. A cross-section of plasma arc cutting equipment in operation.**

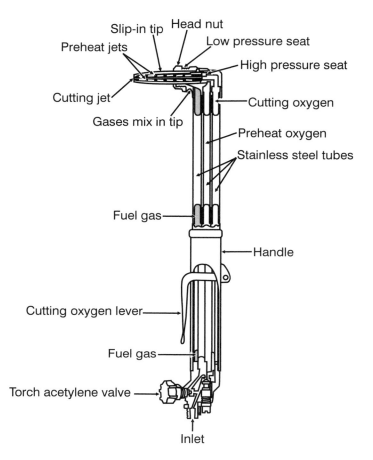

**17-29. Parts of an oxygen-acetylene torch used to cut steel.**

**Oxygen Fuel Gas Cutting.** Oxygen fuel gas cutting is a hot metalworking process of cutting metal by rapidly oxidizing the metal. This type of metal cutting is used for cutting ferrous metals and carbon steels. The basic process is to heat the carbon steel metal to above its critical temperature (about 1400°F). The iron changes structure and, by adding pure oxygen, will rapidly oxidize or burn. Gas cutting is a very fast way to cut metal and is still a popular way to cut carbon steel, especially thicker stock. The plasma arc cutting process has replaced some of the gas cutting applications for thinner metals.

Acetylene is a very common fuel gas for cutting. MAPP gas, methylacetylene propadiene, is also used as a fuel gas for cutting. The pressure of the oxygen stream is set at a higher pressure for cutting than for gas welding. This increased pressure forces the molten metal out of the cutting area. The type of cutting tip is based upon the type of fuel gas used and the type of cut desired. Select the proper cutting tip size based on the thickness of the metal. Set the line pressures according to the manufacturer's recommendations. Always check and follow the manufacturer's recommendations for the equipment.

The basic process of gas cutting is:

1. Set-up the oxygen-acetylene cutting equipment.

2. Set the preheat flame as a neutral flame.

3. Preheat the metal, preferably on an edge.

4. Once the steel has reached a bright red heat, open the pure oxygen valve to allow a steady stream of oxygen to rapidly oxidize the metal.

5. Move the cutting torch along at the proper speed and tip height to maintain a constant cut.

6. When completed, and the torch safely shut-off, observe the cut metal edge to determine if the cut was made correctly.

Cutting steel with a fuel gas torch can be done manually or with an automated torch assembly. Using a simple straight edge or jig, such as a piece of angle iron, can greatly increase the quality of a cut by helping to keep the torch tip steady.

## Hot Metal Shaping

Many metals can be shaped, bent, and formed more easily when heated. Carbon steels change structurally as they are heated and are actually easier to bend and shape while they are heated. Gas torches with heating tips are often used to heat metal to be shaped. Coal forges have been used for many years, but gas furnaces are used more for industrial type applications.

Heated metals, such as steel, can be placed in a vise and twisted or bent to the desired shapes. As the metal cools to below its critical temperature, it will harden again and should be reheated or tempered. Various types of jigs can be bought or made to shape heated metals. Not all metals

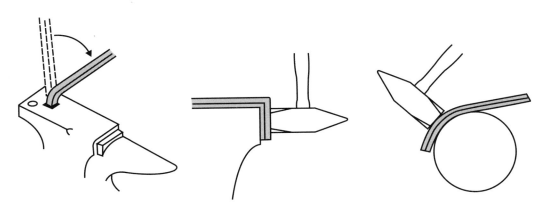

**17-30. Hot metal being bent to form desired shapes.**

respond to heating to make the metal more ductile and malleable. For example, aluminum is relatively soft at room temperature and has a narrow heat range of transformation so that it may be damaged by heating. Consider the properties of the metal to determine whether heating will be appropriate for hot metalworking.

## Soldering

**Soldering** is fastening base metals with another filler metal that melts at temperatures below 840°F. The filler metal is called a solder. The molecules of the solder adhere or "stick" to the surfaces of the base materials. This process is adhesion. Soldering is not as strong as welding for tensile strength. However, soldering produces a tight, leak-proof bond that is often used to seal two pieces of metal together.

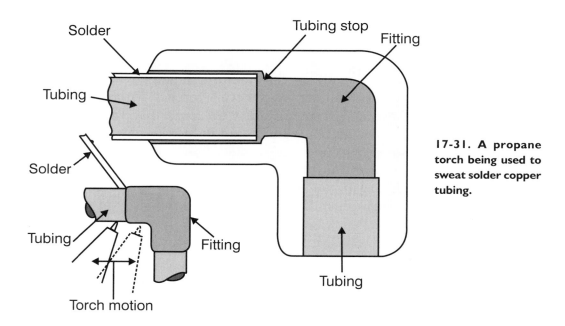

17-31. A propane torch being used to sweat solder copper tubing.

Different kinds of solders are used for different applications. Select the appropriate solder for the type of metal and application. In the past, an alloy of tin and lead was a very popular solder. It is still available, but should not be used for soldering food or water handling systems because of the health hazards associated with lead. Other soldering materials include mixtures of silver, tin, zinc, and aluminum.

The soldering process requires the use of a flux to clean the soldering area of oxides and prevent molten solder from oxidizing. Wetting refers to the action in which a flux or solder flows easily and adheres in a thin, continuous layer. There are two basic types of soldering fluxes, organic and rosin. Organic fluxes are very good reactive cleaning agents. However, they tend to be corrosive. Take care when using the organic acid and base fluxes. Rosin fluxes are less corrosive, but they are less active than organic acids. Use rosin fluxes when soldering electrical connections.

A wide variety of heat sources are used for soldering. Electric soldering guns or irons are common for small applications. Propane and other types of torches are used for larger jobs. *Tinning* is the process of applying a very thin protective layer of solder. The term is derived from the process of thinly coating the inside of cans with tin. *Sweating* refers to the capillary action by where the solder alloy flows throughout a tight joint. Copper pipe and fittings used in plumbing are sweated together when soldered.

The general process for soldering is to:

1. Clean the base metals to be soldered.

2. Apply the correct flux to match the solder and metals.

3. Heat the joint or metal area until the solder alloy begins to melt.

4. Reduce the heat so the base metals heat up slowly and allow the solder to flow easily. Do not add solder until the base metals are hot enough to melt it.

5. Allow the metal to cool. Clean the soldered joint.

## Brazing and Braze Welding

*Brazing* refers to the processes of joining metals by heating them to a temperature below their melting point while the filler metal is melted at a temperature above 840°F but below the melting temperature of the base metal. The filler metal is distributed between the base metal surfaces by capillary action between the tightly spaced surfaces. Brazing is sometimes called hard soldering. The brazing filler metal is usually a metal alloy. Generally, melting point is the temperature at which material starts to turn to a liquid from a solid. The flow temperature is usually higher than the melting point and represents the temperature at which a material will flow easily.

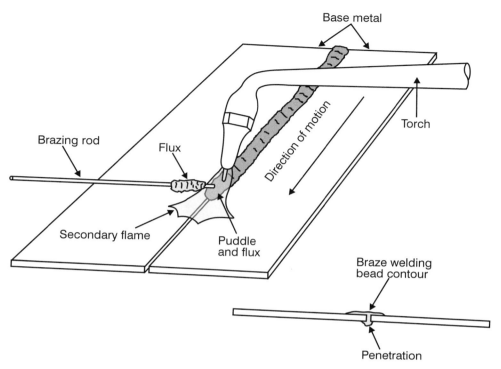

**17-32. An oxygen-acetylene torch used to braze weld low-carbon steel.**

Braze welding is similar to brazing in that the same temperature levels are used, and the same materials used, but capillary action is not used. In braze welding, a bead is formed from the brazing filler metal similar to the welding process.

In both brazing and braze welding, the base metals are held together by the molecular bonding action of the filler metal with surfaces of the base metals. Brazing does not produce bonds as strong as the welding process. However, brazing and braze welding can be used to join dissimilar metals and form a leak-proof seal. Both processes require brazing fluxes to help the filler metal bond with the base materials.

Silver soldering, by definition, is a brazing process—the silver-based filler metal melts and flows above 840°F. Silver brazing is actually a better description then silver soldering.

As with soldering, brazing and braze welding require clean, well-prepared metals. The brazing materials should be matched to the base metals. Usually, an oxygen-acetylene torch with welding tips is used as the heat source. Other heat sources, such as propane or a furnace, can be used. The general process of brazing is very similar to soldering.

# SUMMARY

Fabricating metals involves shaping, joining, and cutting to produce useful products. Successful fabrication begins with proper identification of the kind of metal. This often involves using principles of metallurgy.

Metalworking may be cold or hot. Common cold metalworking includes cutting, drilling and punching, threading, bending and shaping, fastening, and machining. Hot metalworking includes heat treating, welding, cutting, shaping, soldering, and brazing.

The skills and expertise needed to fabricate projects from metal are some of the most rewarding and challenging you can learn. This chapter only briefly described the basic concepts and procedures commonly used to work with different kinds of metals. You will find that working with metals, following the various manufacturer's recommendations, and working safely, will produce good results.

# REVIEW QUESTIONS

1. What are the common types of metals used in agriculture?

2. How can you distinguish ferrous and non-ferrous metals and alloys?

3. What are the chemical and physical properties used to describe metals?

4. What are the basic mechanical properties of metals?

5. How can you identify common types of metals used in agriculture?

6. What are the basic cold and hot metalworking processes?

7. What are the general safety practices for performing cold and hot metalworking processes?

8. What are the common hot metalworking practices and processes used in agriculture?

9. What are the metal heat treating processes used in agriculture?

10. What are the most common metalworking processes?

11. How do the basic gas welding and cutting processes work?

12. How does the soldering process work?

13. How do the braze welding processes bond metal together?

# APPLYING THE CONCEPTS

1. Make a collection of metal samples. You can learn to identify different kinds of metals by collecting different samples and then using the samples to identify metals as you work with them.

2. Learn how to safely cut metal using the different types of metal cutting equipment you have on-hand. Be sure to accurately measure and then cut the metal to size. Learn which equipment does the best job cutting different kinds of metals.

3. Practice safely drilling and threading metal. Being able to make accurate threads in different kinds of metals is one of the basic metalworking practices which you can master.

4. Metal can be safely bent and shaped using the cold metalworking practices. Many metalworking projects require that the metal be shaped. Practice using different jigs and equipment to accurately shape metal.

5. Practice safely performing basic MIG and FCAW welding processes. Once you have mastered the basic skills, build a metalworking project which uses these welding processes.

6. Learn how to safely perform basic TIG welding processes. TIG welding requires considerable practice, however, once mastered, you can apply the skills and practices to many different situations.

7. Learn how to safely perform SMAW processes. SMAW can be used to safely build a variety of projects and is widely used in agriculture.

8. Use the plasma arc cutting process to cut different kinds of metals. Determine which metals are best cut using this process.

9. Learn how to safely perform basic gas welding and cutting practices. Gas welding and cutting requires considerable practice and you must practice being a safe worker.

10. Practice safely performing the basic soldering and braze welding operations. Use these practices to design and construct a sheet metal project.

# 18

# WOOD AND MASONRY STRUCTURES

Many kinds of structures are used in agriculture. Some are needed to house livestock and their products. Others are used to store feed, equipment, supplies, and materials. Each structure is designed for a particular use and must meet the needs of a unique environment.

Wood, concrete, and masonry materials are often used in building the structures. Careful planning and proper construction procedures must be used to assure an efficient, durable structure. Using the wrong materials or procedures can result in an unsatisfactory structure.

People in agriculture often design and construct simple facilities themselves. Larger, more complex facilities involve using the services of a professional designer and skilled builder. With either approach, fundamental knowledge is important to successful construction.

18-1. A modern horse barn. (Courtesy, Jasper S. Lee)

551

# OBJECTIVES

This chapter covers the fundamentals of using wood, concrete, and masonry materials in agricultural construction. After completing this chapter, you will:

1. Explain how to plan and design an agricultural structure.

2. Describe how to prepare a site for a structure.

3. Explain how to design a structure to withstand loads.

4. Describe floors, walls, and roofs used on agricultural structures.

5. Identify major wood materials and describe how they are produced and used.

6. Explain how concrete is made and used.

7. Describe important practices in maintaining structures.

**TERMS**

air-entrained cement
bird's mouth cut
board foot
cambium
clear span structure
concrete
concrete masonry building
dead load
engineered grade
equal gabled roof
fascia plumb cut
fiber saturation point
footing
foundation wall
gambrel roof
grade stamp
gypsum board
hardboard
heartwood
hydration
linear foot
live load
lower plumb cut
particleboard
phloem
ply
pole building
Portland cement
purlins
ridge cut
rigid arch building
rise
roof slope
run
sapwood
stickers
structural grade
stud frame building
subgrade
tail cut
3, 4, 5 triangle corner method
upper plumb cut
veneer
whole systems planning
xylem

# TYPES OF STRUCTURES USED IN AGRICULTURE

Many different kinds of structures made from a variety of materials are used in agriculture. The four most common types of agricultural structures are stud frame construction, pole frame construction, rigid frame construction, and concrete masonry construction. They may be used in combination with each other. The kind of structure used is based upon local building codes, the planned use of the structure, costs, and practical construction considerations, such as location, available supplies, labor, and equipment.

## POLE BUILDINGS

Pole building construction is common for livestock, equipment, and material storage. Pole buildings are considered relatively low cost to construct, very versatile, and provide many different uses for the same structure. A *pole building* is a structure made using wooden poles as the foundation and major frame components. These structures are generally single story, rectangular in shape, with low to moderately sloped roofs.

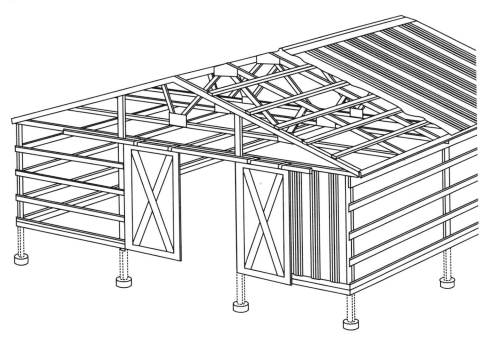

18-2. Pole buildings have many uses in agriculture and are very popular.

The support poles are spaced according to the load design of the structure. Many pole buildings are designed as *clear span structures*—there are no poles in the center of the building, only along the perimeter or outside walls. Pole buildings are usually designed for low-load type roofs made of materials such as sheet metal or fiberglass. The types of floors used in pole buildings are varied. Earthen and concrete floors are common in pole buildings. Sometimes, the floor is left as exposed soil until a later date, when a concrete floor is poured. Some pole buildings are constructed with both soil and concrete floors in different areas.

In colder climates, pole buildings may be enclosed on all four sides, or one of the longer sides may be left open for easy access by livestock and equipment. In moderate and arid climates, two or more of the sides may be left open for ventilation.

In some commercial and residential areas, pole type building construction is restricted or not allowed. Check local building codes to ensure compliance.

## STUD FRAME BUILDINGS

Stud frame buildings are common in residential construction. In agriculture, stud frame construction is used for relatively small buildings or

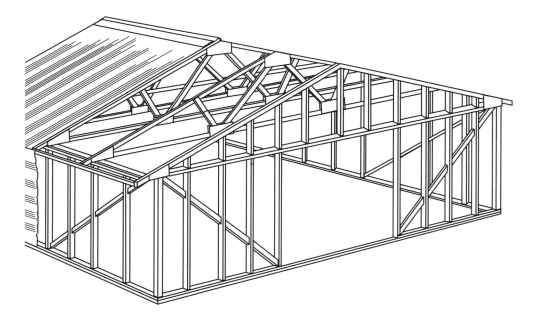

**18-3. Stud frame construction is used for some agricultural structures, but is more widely used for residential type construction.**

buildings that have a low ceiling height, such as poultry and swine farrowing houses. A *stud frame building* is a structure made primarily of sawed lumber constructed on a concrete or masonry foundation. Plywood, particle board, and other materials may be used on the lumber frame. Climate control is relatively easy in a well constructed stud frame building. However, the overall cost per square foot of building space is usually higher for stud frame structures.

Generally, stud frame structures are constructed by placing a concrete and/or masonry footing and foundation around the perimeter of the building. Concrete or wooden platform floors are commonly used in stud frame buildings. A placed concrete floor is often used for livestock and equipment buildings. Wooden platform floors are common for residential type buildings.

The walls are built using studs, which are usually spaced either 16 or 24 inches apart. Lumber studs are most common, however, metal studs can be used. A variety of outside and inside wall materials are used. Outside walls can be covered with aluminum, wood, vinyl, or galvanized sheet metal siding. Inside walls can be covered with wood, aluminum, sheet metal, vinyl, plastic, gypsum board or sheet rock, or left uncovered leaving the studs exposed. Stud frame buildings usually have ceilings, except when used for agricultural purposes. Stud frame buildings also use a variety of roofing materials, including fiberglass shingles, aluminum, sheet metal, wood shingles, clay shingles, and others. The type of material used is often determined by the load capacity of the roof supports.

## CONCRETE MASONRY BUILDINGS

A *concrete masonry building* uses either poured concrete, concrete block, tile, or brick for floors and walls. Concrete structures are often used in dairy, livestock, and food processing applications where the walls and floors need to be kept clean and sanitized. The concrete can be sealed to help provide surfaces that are easy to clean. Concrete structures also have a very long lifetime. Concrete masonry type structures are sometimes required by building codes for food processing structures.

Concrete masonry structures last a long time. These structures generally require lower maintenance than other structures and maintain their value for many years. Skill is required in building concrete masonry structures. Often it is more economical and practical to subcontract the concrete and masonry work to experienced construction crews.

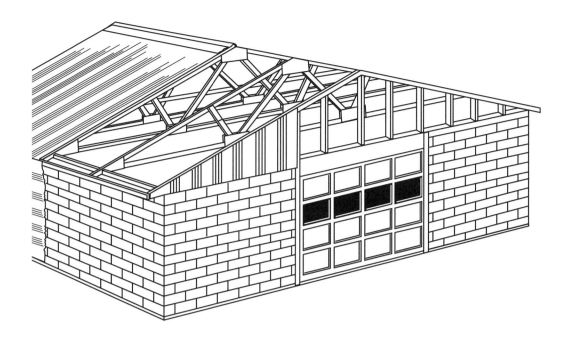

**18-4. Concrete construction can be found in many agricultural applications.**

## RIGID ARCH BUILDINGS

A *rigid arch building* uses a series of wall and roof arch units to form the building construction. The arches can be made of wood or metal materials. This type of construction is used for machinery sheds, green-houses, and many other applications. The arches may be built at the construction site or purchased as preconstructed units. The preconstructed arches are a popular form of construction. At the building site, the arches are spaced according to the building design and erected on a foundation or slab floor.

Rigid arch construction is also called rigid frame construction. It is a popular form of building because it is relatively easy to construct. Arch frame construction is often used on small buildings. Builders also like the predesign and preconstruction characteristics of the arches. These charac-teristics permit sturdy, consistent structures to be built quickly and effi-ciently. Rigid arch structures also tend to have lower construction costs than other types of structures. However, the placement of the arches often

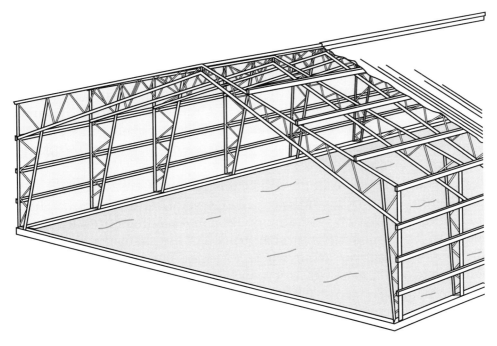

**18-5. Rigid frame construction is often used for smaller agricultural structures.**

requires the use of a crane, which may be a limiting factor. As with other types of structures, often, it is more economical and practical to get prefabricated, rigid frame structural components and have experienced construction crews assemble the structural frame than it is to design and build the structure yourself.

# PLANNING AGRICULTURAL STRUCTURES

Just as there are many different kinds of agricultural structures, there are many different factors to consider when planning structures. Consider whether you will do most or all of the planning, design, site preparation, purchasing of materials, and actual construction, or if someone else will do all or part of the construction processes. The first and most important step is to do a complete job of planning. Consider the long term goals and immediate needs. This kind of planning is best described as *whole systems planning* or management. Agricultural structures are often planned for an expected life of 50 or more years. Consider as many factors as possible to ensure that the structure will be useful for many years.

Cost is always an important consideration. Consider the costs associated with site preparation, utilities, meeting local codes, construction materials, and maintenance. Obtain construction bids from at least three sources, even if you are considering doing most of the work yourself. It may be more cost effective to have a contractor do the construction. Contractors have access to better equipment and expertise and may provide some form of structural warranty.

Site considerations are important. Consider access to water, electricity, waste handling, and other utilities. Find several local sources of helpful site planning information including professional planners from utility companies as well as construction design firms. For large construction projects, get different perspectives about where to locate new structures or how to go about renovating existing structures.

Environmental concerns are also important considerations. Investigate the possible impact that permanent or temporary structures may have on water quality, air quality, and general quality of life. Local building codes may dictate the size and type of structure as well as the materials used. Use care when planning for structures that house livestock, in which food products are handled, that provide storage for agrichemicals, or may be used by the public.

Consider future space needs. Often, the sizes of equipment, crop yields, livestock requirements, and future needs are not factored into the construction plan. Consequently, structures become obsolete long before they deteriorate structurally.

These broad considerations need to be addressed when planning agricultural structures. The key is to get information from several sources. Good planning saves time and money and results in a better structure.

# SITE PREPARATION

Good site preparation is an important aspect of construction. Select a site convenient to utilities, with good environmental qualities such as drainage, and that meets local codes and restrictions.

First, determine the best location for the structure. There are many factors to consider, such as soil type, degree of slope, access to the structure, and local codes. Do some basic surveying and measuring. Small structure sites can be determined by using tape measures, long boards with builders' levels, and some nylon string. You can establish 90 degree corners by using the *3, 4, 5 triangle corner method.* For example, measure along one side of the planned structure a distance of 12 feet. Then, measure along the other side of the corner 16 feet. By aligning the measured points so the hypotenuse of the triangle formed is 20 feet, you will create a 90-degree angle, or corner. The 3, 4, 5 method is used by multiplying by a factor of 4. This works well in most applications. However, take care on sloped areas that the measurements are made on a flat, horizontal plane.

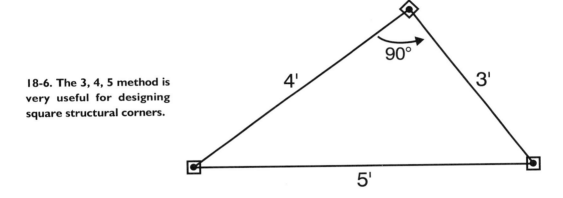

**18-6. The 3, 4, 5 method is very useful for designing square structural corners.**

For larger structures, it will be best to use a builder's level or transit to level and establish the position of the structure. Establish several key reference points and with the level or transit quickly reestablish the planned structure position.

If a site has a slope, cut and fill the slope to get a suitable building site. The top soil should be removed. Top soil usually has too much organic material and will tend to be "spongy," which can create problems with concrete and lumber. This may require excavation equipment on larger sites. Fill soil should be clean—free of excess organic material and large boulders and rocks. Use construction equipment to pack the fill. Also, any site where the soil is exposed must be contained with fences, straw, or other material to prevent erosion.

After the location of the structure is known, use a series of batter boards to establish the corners and sides of the structure. If the site is fairly level and accessible, establish the batter boards prior to any excavation work. However, if the site requires considerable cutting and filling for the sub-grade, establish a rough building site, and then position the batter boards.

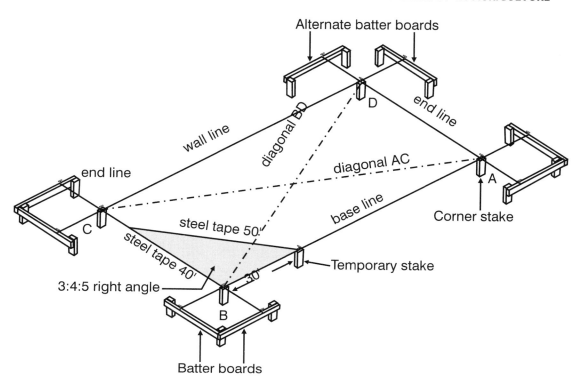

**18-7. Batter boards are used to establish and reestablish a structure's corners and dimensions.**

Batter boards should be at least one foot from the planned building lines. Batter boards allow quick reestablishment of the building lines once construction has begun. Simply connect the points (nails) on the batter boards with a string.

Agricultural structures require a suitable subgrade. The **subgrade** is the area upon which the structure will be placed. Crushed stone, sand, and gravel are good subgrade materials for concrete. Level and compact the subgrade. If the planned floor is to be exposed soil, subgrade fill material may not be required. However, it is much easier and more efficient to remove the topsoil and level the site prior to any poles or foundations being set.

Pole type buildings will require that the holes for the poles be measured and bored. Those buildings set on a concrete slab will need the subgrade leveled and prepared for pouring the slab and foundation. Sections of the slab that will support any load carrying walls will need to be thicker and should extend below the frost line. Those structures built on a foundation will need to have the foundation excavated and the footing and foundation placed below the subgrade. The footing is used to support the foundation walls. The footings and foundation walls are made from concrete, concrete blocks, and treated wood. The poles, footings, and foundation should be placed below the frost line. In those climates not susceptible to freezing temperatures, the foundation should be set deep enough on firm subsoil to support the structure.

# STRUCTURAL LOADS

The various loads a building must withstand are important in design. A safety factor should be designed into any structural load. For example, a safety factor of 100 percent, means that the structure is being designed to handle twice the expected maximum load. Local building codes may specify certain safety factors for some structures.

## LIVE LOADS

A *live load* is the load that, under normal conditions, changes as the structure is being used. In designing a trailer to carry livestock or grain, the weight of the livestock or grain is considered the live load. Likewise, in the design of an equipment storage structure the weight of the equipment on the floor is a live load.

## DEAD LOAD

The weight of the structure itself is called the *dead load*. Dead loads are calculated by adding the weights of all the

18-8. Livestock, grain, machinery, and people are considered live structural loads.

structural materials together. Computer programs can quickly and effectively determine dead load weights. Dead loads are also important when designing equipment, such as trailers and wagons, for handling livestock and commodities.

## SNOW LOADS

Snow loads can add large amounts of weight to the roof of a structure. As an example, for the middle latitude portion of the United States, an estimated snow load of 20 pounds per square foot of horizontal roof projection area downward is used for a roof slope of 4/12. The snow load

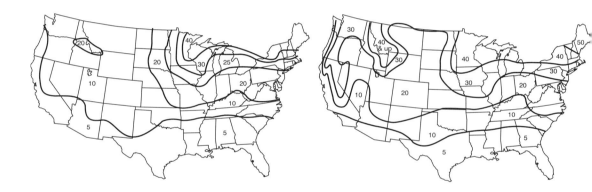

**18-9. A map can be used to determine structural snow loads, however, you may need to consult local building codes and recommendations.**

decreases as the roof slope becomes steeper. Generally, a minimum snow load estimate is 10 pounds per square foot. This is due to the threat of freezing rain and should be used in all parts of the United States, except for the extreme southern area where freezing rain does not occur. In most parts of the country, snow loads should be calculated on a state or local basis depending on local weather history. Use the estimated 50-year snow load for most structures, and the 25-year snow load estimate for temporary structures. Some northern and mountainous areas should use estimated snow loads of 50 pounds per square foot. In these areas, steeper roof slopes are recommended.

## WIND LOADS

Wind loads push against the walls and roofs of structures. Winds tend to push against outside walls and may cause a weak structure to collapse sideways. Winds will also push against the side of steeply sloped roofs. For flat roofs, the winds will tend to lift the roof off the structure flipping the roof over. Most agricultural buildings are designed with relatively flat roofs, so the structures tend to "blow up" under severe wind conditions. Therefore, it is necessary to adequately fasten the roof down. Wind loads are generally a local site consideration. Windbreaks can significantly reduce the threats of severe wind damage. Most parts of the United States can expect wind loads to be 20 pounds per square foot of area normal to the roof. Structures in areas prone to hurricanes or on the downward slopes of mountains should be designed for local conditions based upon a recommended 50-year frequency factor. It should be noted that it is impractical to design a structure for wind loads that can be expected to fully withstand the direct force of tornado winds.

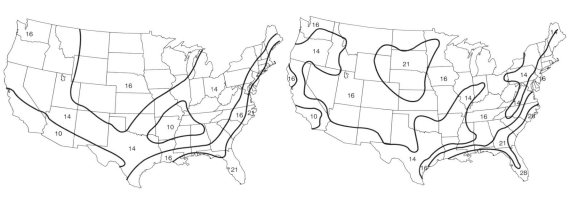

18-10. Wind loads should also be considered when planning agricultural structures.

# FOOTINGS AND FOUNDATIONS

Footings and foundations provide the base support for a structure. Pole buildings use sturdy wood or metal poles placed in firm soil to support the structure. Some applications will recommend that the poles be set in concrete or with a gravel base. The poles can also be set in or on supports.

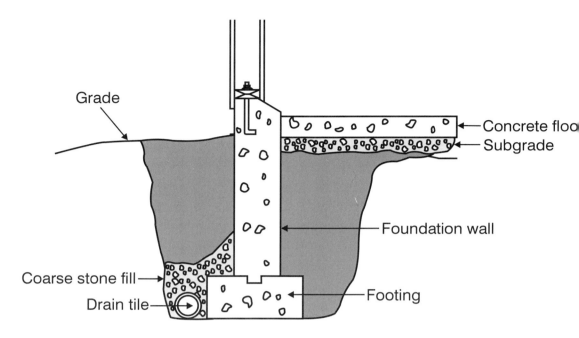

**18-11. The footing and foundation are very important building structures.**

These supports may be called pilasters or pillars and are often made from placed concrete or concrete blocks.

Slab concrete construction uses a placed concrete floor with a thickened edge or perm to support the structure. Slab construction is used for small scale, single story structures with limited dead and virtually no live structural loads.

A *footing* is often made with placed concrete. The footing provides the main structure support. Footings are placed on firm soil below the frost line. Many geographic areas will also require suitable drainage at the base of the footings. As a rule, footings should be at least twice as wide as the foundation wall. The footing should be at least as thick, or high, as the wall. For example, the minimum footing of a single story structure using 8 inch concrete blocks as the foundation wall should be 16 inches wide and 8 inches high. Check local building codes and consider the type and condition of the supporting soil before designing a footing. Often, structural plans will indicate a recommended footing size. However, that may not be adequate for the structure you are building. Steel reinforcing materials are usually needed for concrete footings.

A *foundation wall* supports the structure from the footing to the above grade wall. Concrete blocks are often used for foundation walls. Poured concrete and wood structures can also be used for the foundation wall. Reinforcing materials may be added to foundation walls to provide additional strength in unstable soil conditions or earthquake prone areas.

# FLOOR STRUCTURES

Select a floor based on use of the structure. The best type of floor for an agricultural structure may be no constructed floor at all. Good, well-graded soil may serve as a very effective floor surface. Soil is an inexpensive flooring material. Soil floors require periodic maintenance. Clean and grade the soil from time to time to reduce dust and mud. Livestock will prefer soil to other types of flooring materials. Soil does present some serious concerns related to sanitation. Also, it does not make the best surface for working on equipment or machinery.

Concrete floors are one of the most common types of floors used in agriculture. Concrete is durable, strong, and relatively easy to keep clean. The concrete is placed over a sand or gravel subgrade. Concrete floors are usually 4 or 6 inches thick. Welded wire fabric is used in concrete floors to help control cracking.

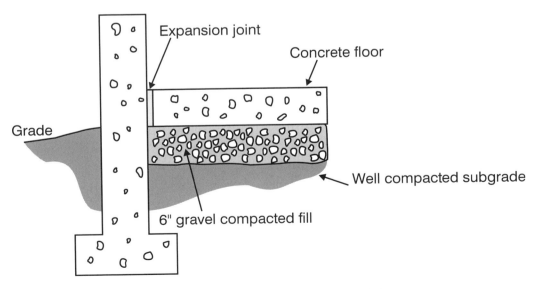

18-12. Concrete is often used for agricultural floors.

Wood floors are more commonly found in office and residential structures. However, wood is often used in agricultural structures for flooring in second stories. This is a good use of wood because of the relatively light weight and ease of installation. The wooden floors are supported by floor joists. The joists can be made of solid lumber such as 2 × 8 structural lumber. Solid lumber is often used for short floor spans or when there is additional floor support. Floor truss joists can be designed or purchased. Designed floor joists are often more economical and provide more support than solid lumber floor joists. If you are constructing a wood floor, you should consider both options and chose the best for the particular application.

Floors can be covered with a variety of materials. Concrete floors often need to be sealed with a concrete sealer. However, concrete floors can be painted or covered with other flooring materials, such as ceramic tile. Wooden floors are also very common. Wooden floors can be made from plywood or structural type manufactured wood products, such as particle board. Be sure to use the proper grade of flooring material. Floors can be covered with vinyl materials. These materials are not very common for agricultural applications other than food processing structures.

# WALL STRUCTURES

Pole buildings may use panels or siding materials for the walls. The wall materials may be made from wood, metal, fiberglass, or plastic. The materials are attached, with either screws or nails, to the wall purlins. *Purlins* are horizontal structural pieces that go across or are perpendicular to the poles. Lumber is the most common material used for purlins, however, metal can also be used.

Stud frame construction uses vertical structural pieces, called studs, to create the wall structure. Studs can be made from wood, metal, or plastic materials. The studs are spaced, usually 16 or 24 inches on center, between a top and bottom plate to create the wall. Common wall studs are 2×4 and 2×6 lumber. The wall materials are then fastened to the wall studs. The stud walls may be assembled on a flat surface and then tilted up into place. Sometimes, prefabricated walls can be purchased, ready to be set in place, complete with outside siding and insulation.

Many kinds of materials can be used to cover interior and exterior walls. Metal is commonly used for walls for agricultural structures. Wood siding material is also used. Plastic and vinyl sidings are common in residential and commercial applications. Maintenance costs and expected life should be considered when selecting siding material.

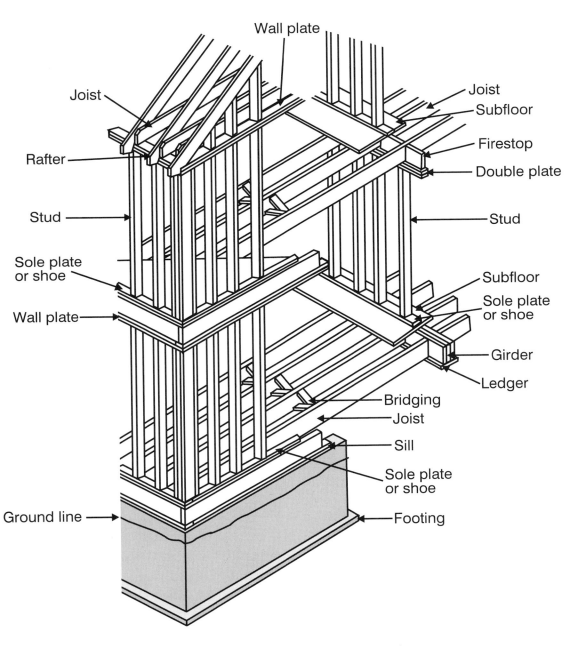

**18-13. The basic parts of a stud wall construction.**

# ROOF STRUCTURES

Many different styles of roof structures are used for agricultural buildings. Roof styles often provide picturesque as well as practical applications. The variety of roof structures found in rural settings can lend to the beauty and character of an area.

Gable and gambrel roof styles are two of the most often used for agricultural structures. Gable roofs are often used for single-story structures that have a relatively low slope. Lower sloped roofs require less materials to construct, however, they are not designed to carry heavy snow, live ceiling, or dead loads. Gambrel roofs are often used for two-story structures. Gambrel roofs are also used in areas where heavy snow loads can be expected. Because gambrel roofs have more surface area, they will require more roofing materials.

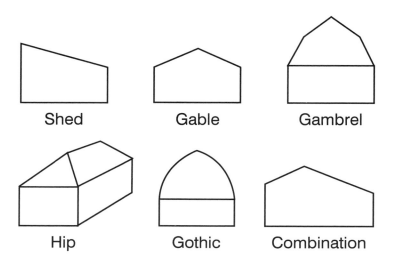

18-14. Many different kinds of roofs are used.

## RAFTER CONSTRUCTION

Rafter construction is often used for smaller shed, gable, gambrel, and combination style roofs. The angle of the roof is called the roof slope or roof pitch. **Rise** is the height of the roof and **run** is the horizonal length of the roof slope. **Roof slope** is the inches of roof rise per foot of roof run. Roof slope is expressed as a fraction with a denominator of 12. Common roof slopes used for agricultural buildings are 3/12, 4/12, 5/12, and 6/12. A 4/12 slope means the roof rises 4 inches for every foot of roof run. An *equal gabled roof* means that both roof slopes are the same. A *gambrel roof* uses two different slopes on each side of the roof. The steeper first slope with a flatter second slope provides for a greater second story volume. The roof pitch is defined as the inches of roof rise over twice the roof run. Roof pitch is expressed as a reduced fraction. For example, a 1/4 pitch roof has a slope of 6/12.

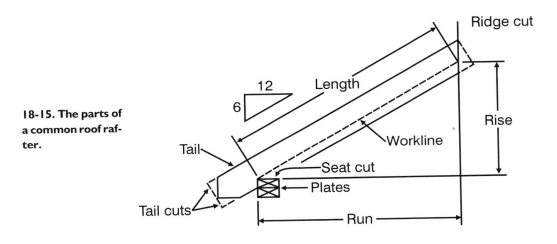

**18-15. The parts of a common roof rafter.**

A simple roof rafter is designed and cut based on the roof slope. The roof slope is made by using a framing square. Using a framing square to design rafters and angles is a useful skill. Carpenters like to use the tongue of the framing square for the base 12 roof slope and the blade of the square to measure the rise in inches. Note, that a 12/12 triangle is an isosceles triangle and forms 45 degree angles.

The top cut of a common rafter is called the **upper plumb cut** or the **ridge cut**. The lower end rafter cut is called the **lower plumb cut**, **tail cut**, or if a fascia board is going to be used, a **fascia plumb cut**. A notch is cut in the rafter for it to set on the top plate of a stud wall or the girder of a pole type building. This notch is often called the **bird's mouth cut**. It is made of the heel cut and the seat cut. These cuts are designed by using the slope triangle created by the framing square based on the roof slope. A simple shed or gable roof will only use one roof slope. However, a gambrel roof will use two slopes to design two rafters, which will be fastened together.

The length of the common rafter can be determined in three basic methods. The first method is to simply use the Pythagorean theorem to determine the rafter length based upon the rise and run. Determine the length of the hypotenuse of the triangle by taking the square root of the sum of the squares of the legs of the triangle. For example, if an equal gable roof has a span of 20 feet and a rise of 4 feet, the slope is a 4/12, the pitch is 1/6, and the runs are 10 feet each. The rafter length is determined by:

$Y^2 = A^2 + B^2$, where,

$Y$ = the hypotenuse or rafter length,

and A and B are equal to the lengths of the legs of the triangle, the rise and run.

$$Y^2 = \sqrt{(3.33)^2 + (10)^2}$$
$$Y^2 = \sqrt{111}$$
$$Y = 10.54 \text{ feet or } 10 \text{ feet } 6.5 \text{ inches}$$

The second method is to use a framing square to "step" the length of the rafter. Use the slope triangle, in this case 4/12, to "step off" the number of feet of run, which for our example is ten. Accuracy is essential when using this method, as a small error can be multiplied into a much larger one.

The third method of determining rafter length is to use a rafter table. There are two basic types of rafter tables. One kind actually gives you the length of the hypotenuse of the slope triangles. A common example of such a rafter table is the Stanley rafter table. For example, the rafter table gives the rafter length per foot of run. In this example, the table value is 12.65. Multiply this value by the run, 10 feet, to get 126.5 inches. This can be converted to feet, inches, and sixteenths of an inch by:

1. Dividing by 12, 126.5/12 = 10.54 feet.

2. Multiplying the remainder by 12, to get it back to inches, .54 × 12 = 6.48 inches.

3. Multiplying the remainder by 16, to convert to sixteenths of an inch: .48 × 16 = 8/16 or 1/2 inch.

4. Therefore, the length of the rafter is 10 feet, 6 and 1/2 inches.

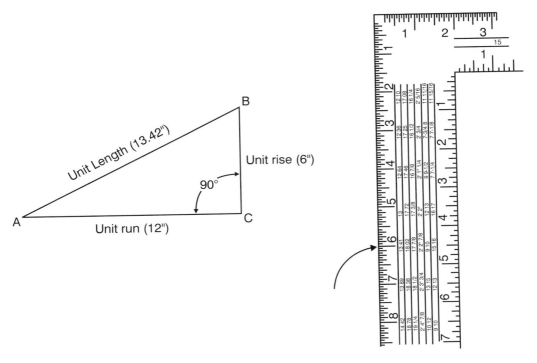

**18-16. This is an example of the information provided on a rafter table found on a framing square.**

Another type of rafter table provides actual rafter lengths for selected slopes and given runs. The Shapliegh rafter table is an example. Metric rafter tables are also available.

When designing rafters, keep several practices in mind. Add length to the rafter for any overhang of the roof beyond the wall. Overhangs of 12, 18, and 24 inches are common. Keep in mind, that the overhang has slope, so use the slope value to determine how much to lengthen the rafter. For example, 12 inches of roof overhang would add 12.65 inches to the overall length of the rafter in our example. Consider if a ridge board will be used at the roof peak, or fascia and soffits at the lower end of the rafter. You will need to account for these board thicknesses. Also, check all measurements and the design prior to making a series of cuts.

Always lay out and cut one or two pattern rafters. (For a shed roof, only one pattern will be required; for a gable roof, "left" and "right" pattern rafters will be required.) If the pattern rafter(s) fit, they can be used as templates for marking the remaining rafters.

Cutting rafters for special roof applications, such as hip and valley roofs, as well as gambrel roofs, requires considerable skill and accuracy. However, with careful planning and the use of rafter tables and a calculator the needed calculations and measurements can be made. It is always a good idea to lay out a model in chalk on a concrete floor or driveway to make sure everything fits.

## TRUSS RAFTER CONSTRUCTION

A truss rafter is an assembly of the roof structural members designed and constructed as a single unit. Truss rafters are designed to support the roof loads and provide a clear building span. A clear building span means that the building has no center supports and the roof is supported by the outside walls. Generally, truss rafters are used for structures with spans from 24 feet to 60 feet. Truss rafter designs can be used for low, moderate, and heavy load types of roofing materials and many different slopes. Truss rafters are used for many structures in agriculture. Sometimes, building plans will provide detailed instruction for designing and constructing the truss rafters. Consult an engineer and truss rafter design plans before building truss rafters. It is important to properly design and construct the truss rafters according to the characteristics of the structure. It may be more economical and safer to buy manufactured truss rafters, than to build them.

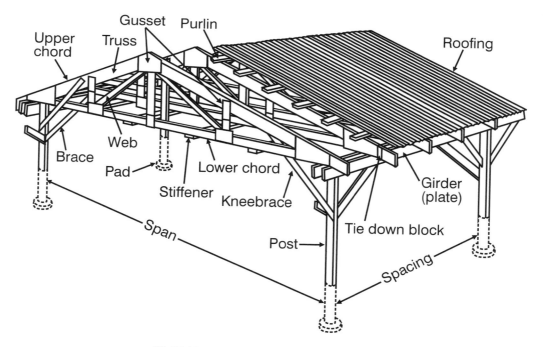

18-17. The parts of a truss rafter assembly.

When selecting or designing truss rafters, consider the type of structure to be built. What type of roofing materials are to be used? Will a ceiling, or second-story area be included? What is the building span and will it have a clear span, or use center support walls or poles? What snow, wind, dead, and live loads are expected on the roof and ceiling to support? Truss rafters must be designed and constructed based upon these considerations to provide a safe design load strength.

There are several basic kinds of truss rafters. The king post design is often used for short roof spans and is also recommended for some ceiling applications. The "w" truss assembly is very common for agricultural structures. It is often used for short and medium span structures, usually less than 40 feet. The scissor truss is used where a high ceiling clearance is needed. Other types of trusses or multiple truss assemblies are used for large span structures, from 40 to 60 feet, or wider.

Truss rafters are designed with top chords, which are the rafters and support the roofing materials. The bottom chords provide stability to the structure walls. The bottom chords help to transfer the downward force of the roof to the outside walls and keep the walls from "pushing out." The column members connect the top and bottom chords together. The truss members are fastened together using gussets. The gussets may be made from either metal or wood, depending on the design and desired construction techniques.

Use good plans in building trusses. Truss rafter plans will specify the structural grade of lumber, plywood, fastener, and glue to use. Use a flat surface area to layout and construct the trusses. A construction jig will need to be set up. The jig can be placed on a concrete floor. A jig can be made using ¾ inch or thicker floor materials. A series of chalk lines and positioning blocks will help place the truss members in the proper position. The gussets can be installed, either by nailing, stapling, or gluing plywood gussets, or by driving in place metal gussets.

Truss rafters are installed using 2, 4, or 8 feet spacing. The spacing is largely based upon the expected loads on the roof. Truss rafters used for agricultural structures usually have either a 4/12 or 5/12 slope. The 4/12 slope is very common for most applications. The 5/12 slope is recommended for heavier snow loads. The 3/12 slope trusses are often used in warmer climates where little or no snow loads are expected. Truss rafter assemblies can be designed for slopes greater than 5/12, and for combination and gambrel roof designs. The trusses are usually set in place with a construction crane. Smaller span trusses can be set by hand, using several workers to properly position the truss rafter. Cross bracing will need to be constructed to position and support the trusses in place. Also, knee braces will need to be constructed for pole buildings or long structures, over 36 feet, where end walls are not being used or will not support the entire structure.

## ROOFING MATERIALS

There are basic roof materials used for agriculture structures: sheathing and shingles. Metal sheathing is probably the most common roofing material used in agriculture. Galvanized or painted steel sheet metal provides a very durable, attractive roof. These materials are installed as roof panels. They are generally considered economical and relatively easy to install.

Shingles are commonly used for residential type construction. They are a very attractive style roofing material. Shingles can be made of wood, asphalt, fiberglass, or ceramic materials. Shingles make durable roofs. However, shingled roofs can have high dead loads (especially, ceramic style shingles) and, therefore, require considerable roof frame structures for support. The type of roofing material to be used must be considered when designing the wall and roof structures.

# WOOD CONSTRUCTION

Wood is one of the oldest building materials. Wood is used extensively because of its relative strength, ease to work, wide range of uses, and it is a renewable resource. As a natural product, wood is environmentally "friendly." It can be cut, shaped, and fastened together to construct a variety of projects and structures.

There are two basic types of wood—softwoods, which come from coniferous trees, and hardwoods, which come from deciduous trees. Generally, conifers have needle-like leaves year around and deciduous trees have broad leaves that fall off during winter. However, softwoods are not necessarily softer than hardwoods. The relative degree of hardness is more dependent on the species. Softwoods are widely used for structural lumber because the conifers have been developed to grow quickly and uniformly, which is important for commercial lumber production. Hardwoods tend to grow slower and are used for more specialized applications, such as flooring, furniture, and other uses.

# HOW WOOD IS PRODUCED

Wood, by definition, is produced from trees. Trees grow in height by terminal buds and in diameter by a layer of growth cells inside the bark called the *cambium*. The cambium layer produces new "wood" cells on the inside and new "bark" cells on the outside. The inner bark, also called the *phloem*, transports the plant food produced by photosynthesis to other parts of the tree. The outer bark was once inner bark, but now serves primarily to protect the tree. Inside the cambium layer is the *sapwood*, or *xylem*. The sapwood moves water and plant nutrients from the roots to the other parts of the tree. The center of the tree trunk and branches is the *heartwood*. Heartwood was once sapwood but is not as active in the movement of nutrients as the sapwood. Tree growth rings are produced by the annual growth patterns of the cambium layer. During warm growing seasons, a lighter-colored, less dense sapwood (spring growth) is produced. When the growing season slows, the sapwood growth produces a more dense wood structure (summer growth), hence, the darker wood growth rings.

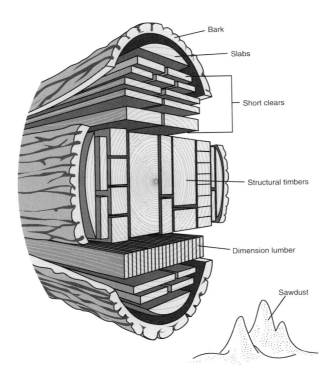

**18-18. Wood is produced as a tree grows from the cambium layer.**

The tree is cut into boards at the sawmill. Depending on the species and condition of the logs, various sized boards will be produced. First the log is "squared" and then cut into slabs, which are then cut into boards. This process is often used to cut softwood boards known as "plain-sawed" lumber. Some hardwood logs are cut into quarters, then sawed into boards to get a more favorable board end-grain structure. This is called "quarter-sawed" lumber.

Once cut, the wood should be seasoned. Seasoning removes excess water from the wood. Wood can be air dried or kiln dried. To air dry, the boards are stacked with crosspieces called *stickers* to form air spaces between the layers of boards. Air dried wood should have a moisture content of 19 percent or less. Kiln drying uses an oven to heat the wood and dry the lumber.

It is important to dry wood to decrease the chances of decay. Wood decay is caused by microorganisms that live in the wood. The water in wood can be found in the cell walls, absorbed water, or in the cell cavities, free water. The free water will be the first water to be dried from the wood. Once the water is only in the cell walls this is called the *fiber saturation point*. For most types of wood, the fiber saturation point is from 23 to 30 percent with 28 percent being typical. When wood is dried below its fiber saturation point, the cell walls will begin to shrink as they lose water. This shrinking can cause wood defects, such as checks, splits, and warps, which include bows, crooks, and cups. Always look at boards to determine if there are any natural defects. For example, bows and crooks, should always be placed up when used for rafters, floor, and ceiling joists. Look at the end of a board to determine if a cup will occur as a board drys.

Lumber and wood products are sold by the piece, linear foot, or by the board foot. *Linear foot* means that the product is priced per each foot of length. Some wood products are sold by the board foot. A *board foot* is a one foot square that is 1 inch thick. One board foot is any combination of thickness, width, and length totaling 144 cubic inches.

## LUMBER GRADING

Lumber is wood that has been cut to specific dimensions for structural construction. The lumber is cut from logs into various dimensions. Lumber for structural construction is cut to standard dimensions for uniformity in design. The cut lumber is dried either by natural ventilation (air-dried) or by a heat source, such as a kiln. The lumber may be used as surfaced

S-GRN
**CONST**
EASTERN
HEM-TAM

NELMA

18-19. An example of a lumber grade stamp.

lumber—the wood has smooth surfaces—or as rough lumber—the wood has saw-cut surfaces. Common structural lumber is softwood, such as spruce, pine, or fir, that has been kiln dried and surfaced on all four sides to structural dimensions.

Structural lumber can be identified by the lumber grade stamp. The **grade stamp** will indicate the species of the tree, the drying process, the mill that processed the lumber, the group or association that graded the lumber, and the actual grade. The grades are based upon the relative quality of the wood. Different grades are used for softwoods and hardwoods. Also, different dimensional lumber may be graded differently, such as for boards and structural lumber. The wood may be graded by appearance. A board graded "CLR" indicates that the board is free, or clear, of any knots. The appearance grades may be words, such as clear, or number grades, such as "No. 2."

Wood may also be graded based on its relative strength. These grades are sometimes called **structural grades**. The strength will be stamped on the lumber to indicate the load carrying capacity of the lumber. These grades are often used for commercial structures that may be expected to hold varying loads, such as livestock or people. The building architect or designer may specify a minimum strength lumber to ensure that the floor, or other component, will be able to safely carry the expected load.

## MANUFACTURED WOOD PRODUCTS

Science and technology have developed a variety of wood products. These products are manufactured from raw or processed wood materials. The most common ones used for agricultural construction are plywood, laminated lumber, and wood particle type boards.

## Plywood

Plywood has been widely used in agricultural construction for many years. Plywood is made of alternating layers of wood veneers. **Veneers** are thin layers of wood. Veneers are made by turning a log and cutting, or "peeling" a thin continuous layer of wood from the log. These veneers are graded based upon their quality and appearance. The veneers are then glued together alternating the direction of the wood grain for each layer, or **ply**, hence, the name plywood. The outside veneers on the plywood sheets are called the face veneers. The grains of the face veneers on a sheet of plywood will go in the same direction along the longest sides. Plywood is widely used because of its dimensional stability, exact size, and strength qualities.

Plywood will be graded and stamped according to the appearance grade of the veneer or the structural strength of the ply. One of these grades will be stamped on the plywood sheet. Appearance grades will be designated by a pair of letters. The letters usually are N, A, B, C, and D, with N being the best, "no knots or defects" in the face. The D grade will indicate some large knots and possible defects. When large knots and defects are repaired, these are called "plugged" grades and are usually produced as C- and D-plugged grades. Both sides of the plywood sheet are graded. For example, an AC plywood has an A grade veneer on one side and a C grade veneer on the other. The grade stamp will appear on the "lesser" (lower grade) side or edge of the sheet. Some plywood sheets have the same grade of veneer on both faces, as an example, BB.

Some plywood and other manufactured wood products are graded based on their application as sheathing materials for floors, roofs, and walls. These are called **engineered grades** with an identification index. The

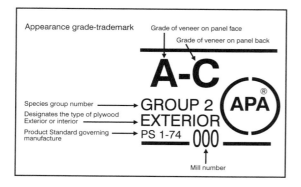
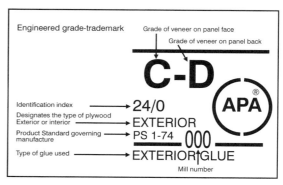

**18-20. A plywood grade stamp provides very useful information.**

identification index on the grade stamp will indicate the maximum spacing for rafters and floor joists. An example would be a 48/24 identification index, which means that a roof rafter spacing of 48 inches and a floor joist spacing of 24 inches are acceptable. These spacings are based on a roof load value of 35 pounds per square foot of area and a floor load of 100 pounds per square foot.

The engineered grades of plywood will also indicate the species of wood by a group classification. There are five basic groups, with Group 1 being the highest strength down to Group 5, which is the lowest strength. The engineered grades include Structural I and II. Structural I grade uses Group 1 species, and Structural II grade uses Group 1, 2, and 3 species. The structural I and II grades will indicate the type of glue used as "interior" or "exterior," which is based upon the exposure of the application. For almost all agricultural applications, "exterior" glue plywoods are recommended. There is an engineered grade called "CDX" that has interior rated plies, but uses exterior type glues.

There are several speciality type plywoods available. Plyform is one type designed to be used for concrete forms. There are also medium density overlay (MDO) and high density overlay (HDD) panels, which are used for table tops, cabinets, and other smooth surface applications. Generally, MDO is used when the surface is to be painted, and HDO is used when the surface is not going to be painted. Marine plywood is high quality and water resistant. A variety of flooring, inside wall paneling, and outside wall siding plywood sheets are also produced for many different applications.

## MANUFACTURED WOOD MATERIALS

There are many different kinds of manufactured wood products. The two most often used in agriculture are hardboards and particleboards. **Hardboards** are made by pressing wood fiber mats together under very high pressure and temperature. This process causes the natural glues in the wood to bind the fibers together. These natural wood glues are called **lignin**. Hardboards are more dense than natural wood. Hardboard panels are prefinished or ready to be finished.

**Particleboard** is made when wood chips are bonded with synthetic resins. Particleboards are very uniform and have a smooth finish. Particleboards are often used as floor and roof sheathing materials. Also, they are used as core stock for cabinets, tables, and walls where a decorative finish material, such as a vinyl coating, is glued on the particleboard.

580

MECHANICAL TECHNOLOGY IN AGRICULTURE

## OTHER MANUFACTURED CONSTRUCTION MATERIALS

There are many different kinds of manufactured construction materials made from substances other than wood. Several used in agricultural structures include gypsum board, plastic panels, fiberboards, and insulation boards.

*Gypsum board* is sometimes called sheet rock or drywall. Gypsum board is used extensively for interior walls. However, gypsum is made of $CaSO_4$ $2H_2O$ with paper coatings on both sides. Gypsum boards contain about 21 percent water and are not very practical for use in high moisture areas. Special water-resistant gypsum board panels are available, which can be used in some agricultural applications.

Plastic panels and plastic laminated boards are used for special applications in agriculture, especially where walls and ceiling need to be cleaned and sanitized. Dairy and other food handling facilities often require surfaces that will not absorb water and are easy to keep clean.

Fiberboards and insulating boards are often used to insulate structures. Fiberboards are generally made from wood and other natural fibers. Some insulating boards are made from fiberglass, polyurethane, or other type of material. These materials are primarily used as insulating materials. Fiber and insulating boards are not dense enough to provide adequate strength for structural purposes.

## CONCRETE CONSTRUCTION

Concrete is used in agricultural construction to build floors, foundations, footings, walls, driveways, roads, and walkways. Concrete is durable and strong. Concrete structures can easily last 50 years or longer if properly maintained. Concrete is used in the food processing industry because it provides a surface that is relatively easy to clean and maintain.

*Concrete* is mixture of a paste and aggregates. The cement paste bonds the aggregate particles together to form a rocklike construction material. The concrete paste is made from a mixture of Portland cement and water. *Portland cement* is very finely ground powder made from limestone, shale, clay, and iron materials. Lime (CaO) makes up about two-thirds of the raw materials used to make cement. Cement is made by heating a mixture of these ingredients in a kiln and then grinding the materials to produce a very fine powder-like material. Cement was first patented in the early

18-21. Concrete has many applications in agriculture, such as this greenhouse foundation and floor (left) and aquaculture raceway (right). (Courtesy, Jasper S. Lee)

1800's by John Aspdin of England. The name Portland cement comes from the Isle of Portland in England where a popular form of cement was made from calcium.

The paste of cement and water hardens due to the chemical reaction of hydration. Once the cement is mixed with water, the hydration reaction begins to occur. *Hydration* is the process of a material combining with water to form a hydrate. The hydrate formed from the cement paste is very hard and rocklike. The chemical hydration process produces heat; therefore, concrete will not harden properly under very cold conditions. The best temperature for concrete to harden is about 70°F. If the temperature is too hot, the concrete will set too fast and will not reach its full strength potential. It is important that concrete not "dry" to become set or hard, but rather use up water in the chemical process of hydration. Therefore, keep concrete wet or moist to get high strength, good quality concrete. Hot, sunny, windy conditions tend to evaporate the available water for hydration. Under these conditions, the concrete should be kept wet. The hydration process will continue for several days or weeks as long as water is available. Concrete will reach about 80 to 90 percent of its strength potential in seven days if it is kept moist. The concrete will reach 90 to 95 percent of its strength after a month. Keep concrete moist and the concrete forms in place for a week to get good quality concrete.

## TYPES OF PORTLAND CEMENT

Several different types of cement are used in agricultural applications. The different types allow for the construction of agricultural structures under various conditions. The five basic types of Portland cement are indicated by Roman numerals. *Air-entrained cements* are indicated by an "A" after the type designation. Air-entraining cement improves resistance of the concrete to frost and freezing conditions. Air-entraining additives are put in the cement to produce microscopic air bubbles. Air-entrained cement type IA, IIA, and IIIA are very common for agricultural applications.

Type I is called normal Portland cement. It is used for many applications including floors, driveways, tanks, and other uses.

Type II is called modified Portland cement. It is often used for large construction applications where heat buildup in the concrete is a concern. This type is used when the concrete is being poured in hot, summer conditions.

Type III is called high-early strength Portland cement. Type III is used when it is important to get concrete set quickly. This type of cement allows us to get equipment or livestock on the concrete sooner.

Type IV is called low-heat Portland cement. This type is used for large concrete pours where heat buildup may be a problem. Type IV is seldom used for concrete applications in agriculture.

Type V is a called sulfate resistant Portland cement and is used where the concrete is exposed to highly alkali soils.

### Aggregates

Concrete is a mixture of cement paste and aggregates. The cement paste bonds the aggregate particles together. Concrete is made of 60 to 80 percent aggregates. Aggregates are classified based upon the size of the particles. The smaller size aggregates are called sand and are screened through a 1/4 inch screen mesh. The larger aggregates are called gravel. Concrete can be no stronger than the relative strength of the aggregate particles. It is very important to use clean, strong, properly sized aggregates for quality concrete.

When concrete is mixed, the cement paste flows between the aggregate particles. The paste fills the voids between the aggregate particles. A good aggregate will have the best ratio of different-sized particles to reduce possible void areas. The smaller sand aggregate particles will fill the voids around the larger gravel particles. The concrete paste will cover all of the

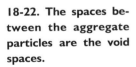
18-22. The spaces between the aggregate particles are the void spaces.

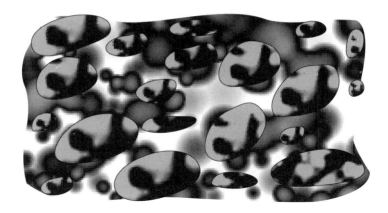

aggregates and bond the different-sized particles together. Proper mixing of the right size aggregates and the best proportions of cement, water, sand, and gravel produces the highest quality concrete.

An interesting activity is to mix several different-sized aggregates together and see how the volumes of the materials are changed by different particle sizes. Use 1- and 5-gallon buckets. Carefully measure and mix in the 5 gallon bucket 2 gallons of dry sand, 2 gallons of dry gravel, and 1 gallon of water. The mixture should be a total of 5 gallons. Will the mixture fill the 5-gallon bucket? Gravel has large void spaces of air, which become filled with the sand, and the sand has smaller-sized void spaces, which are filled by the water.

Estimate void spaces in a material, such as sand, by determining the volume of water that can be mixed in a known volume of material. Another interesting activity is to take a measured volume of very dry sand and add a small amount of water to see the effect of the coating of the sand particles with water. Note that as small amounts of water are added, the sand "bulks" and will not go back into the same container. How does this work? As the water is mixed in the sand, the sand particles become coated with water and are separated by a thin film. Next, observe that as more water is added the sand will fit in the container again, and will even take less space. Why does this happen? There are several things going on with the sand and the water. As the sand particles become fully saturated, the air spaces are lost as the air is forced out. Also, the sand particles become lubricated by the water and will move or "settle" in the container as they move to points of least resistance. Therefore, saturated sand will take less space.

## DESIGNING CONCRETE MIXES

Concrete is known for its compressive strength, resistance to abrasion, and durability. It is an excellent construction material for floors and supporting structures, such as building foundations and footings. Generally, concrete is very heavy when compared to other construction materials. Therefore, concrete construction requires very solid subgrades and forms.

The relative strength of concrete is determined by the quality of the materials used, the way the concrete is placed and cured, and the water-cement ratio of the concrete mixture. The water-cement ratio is described by one of two methods. First, by the gallons of water per cubic foot of cement and second, by the pounds of water in a mix for each pound of cement, which is expressed as a proportion (decimal). The proper water-cement ratio is based upon the intended use of the concrete.

A 5-gallon mix (.44 ratio) is used for very severe wear applications. An example would be the possible contact with agrichemicals. The 5-gallon mix means that 5 gallons of water are used for each cubic foot of cement. Six-gallon mixes (.53 ratio) are very common and are used for floors, driveways, walks, storage tanks, and structural concrete. Seven-gallon mixes (.62 ratio) are used for foundation walls, footings, and large masses of concrete. The lower the water-cement ratio, the higher the expected strength of the concrete.

Concrete mixes will often be expressed as a series of numbers. An example being a 1, 2, 3-6 mix, which means 1 volume (cubic foot) of cement, 2 volumes of sand, 3 volumes of gravel, and 6 gallons of water. You could determine the water-cement ratio by converting the gallons of water to a weight (water weighs 8.3 pounds) and a cubic foot of cement weighs 94 pounds. Therefore, 49.8 lbs./94 lbs. yields a .53 water-cement ratio.

The concrete will also have a yield factor, which is used to determine how much actual volume of concrete the mix will produce. A common value of 60 percent, or .60, is used as a general yield correction factor. This means that 10 cubic feet of individual materials gives 6 cubic feet of concrete mix. Therefore, add all of the volumes together. One cubic foot of water has 7.5 gallons, so 6 gallons of water have a volume of .8 cubic feet. To get the actual yield of the concrete, multiply the yield factor of .60 by the total materials volume. If the percentage of solids or voids in the materials are known, the absolute volume can be calculated. However, for most common mixes, the .60 yield factor will be satisfactory.

Determine how much the concrete will weigh by using the weights of the materials:

I cubic foot of cement (94 lbs./cubic ft.) = 94 pounds

2 cubic feet of sand (100 lbs./cubic ft.) = 200 pounds

3 cubic feet of gravel (100 lbs./cubic ft.) = 300 pounds

6 gallons of water (8.3 lbs./gallon) = 49.8 pounds

Total weight of 4.08 cubic feet of concrete = 644 pounds

## DETERMINING THE STRENGTH OF CONCRETE

The relative strength of concrete is measured and expressed as the compression strength in pounds per square inch. The relative strength can be estimated based on the water-cement ratio:

5.0 gallon mix ( .44) about 6000 psi

6.0 gallon mix ( .53) about 5000 psi

7.0 gallon mix ( .62) about 4000 psi

Note: These estimated values are based on type I, non-air entrained concrete cured for 28 days.

The strength of concrete can be tested by making test cylinders or slabs. Commercial concrete construction projects often use test cylinders to test the concrete used for buildings, bridges, dams, roads, and airport runways. Pour 2 inch diameter cylinders about 4 inches long and test them in a hydraulic press. A shock absorbent type gage is needed to measure the force require to break the cylinders. Keep in mind, that well cured, low water-cement cylinders will take several tons of force to break. Use adequate shielding as these cylinders may "explode" from the force. Test dry and wet cures, the length of time cured, water-cement ratios, and other variables.

A second test is to pour small concrete slabs. Good test sizes are 1 inch thick, 2 inches high, and 12 inches long, or 2 inches thick, 4 inches high, and 24 inches long. Use a lever beam tester and a spring scale to measure the amount of force required to break the slab. This method is safer and the tester is easier to build.

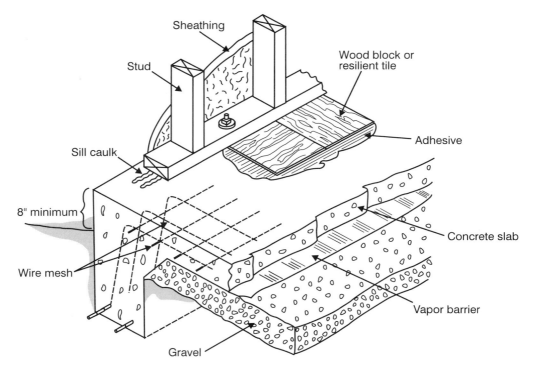

**18-23. A diagram of a concrete slab floor.**

The relative strength of concrete can be improved by adding steel reinforcing materials. High tensile strength steel rods (commonly called re-bar) are often placed in concrete footings, foundation walls, sills, columns, and beams to increase the tensile strength of the concrete. Proper placement of the steel reinforcing rods is important. As a rule, place the rods down 2/3 of the thickness of the concrete in floors. Position the rods at least 2 inches from the edge of the concrete. Concrete floors tend to crack, so welded wire mesh is often added to keep the concrete slab from separating and shifting.

## DETERMINING THE AMOUNT OF CONCRETE NEEDED

Determining how much concrete is needed for a structure or project is based upon the volume of concrete needed. The basic method is to determine the number of cubic feet of space to be poured (Formula 18-1). As an example, assume a concrete slab 20 feet long, 10 feet wide, and 6 inches thick is to be poured.

Volume = length × width × thickness

$$\boxed{\text{Formula 18-1.}}$$

    Volume = (20 feet) × (10 feet) × (6 inches) × (1 foot/12 inches)

    Volume = 100 cubic feet.

In mixing concrete, use the volume in cubic feet to measure and mix the concrete. Be sure to use the yield corrected batch volume.

Our 1, 2, 3-6 gallon mix, with a 4.08 yield, would require 25 "batches." Therefore, use 25 cubic feet (bags) of cement, 50 cubic feet of sand (2.5 tons), and 75 cubic feet of gravel (3.75 tons), and 150 gallons of water.

In using ready-mixed concrete ordered from a concrete plant, base the order on the cubic yards needed. One cubic yard has 27 cubic feet. Therefore, convert to cubic yards using Formula 18-2.

Volume in cubic yards = (cubic feet needed
                 × (1 cubic yard/27 cubic feet)

$$\boxed{\text{Formula 18-2.}}$$

Volume = (100 cubic feet) × (1 cubic yard/27 cubic feet)

Volume = 3.7 cubic yards

   Note: It is a good idea when ordering concrete materials to order 5 percent extra on larger jobs and up to 10 percent extra on small jobs, to be sure there will be enough to finish the job. When working with concrete, it is better to have a little too much, rather than not enough. Any excess concrete can usually be used for small projects or repairs.

**18-24. Concrete is often ordered as ready-mix, which is poured from the truck at the construction site.**

18-25. Concrete forms, braces, and reinforcement wire mesh in place for a floor.

When ordering ready-mix concrete, be sure to provide the following information: when to deliver, how many yards, what is being built, the maximum size aggregate, the water-cement ratio, and any special conditions, such as if a quick-setting concrete is needed.

## WORKING WITH CONCRETE

As with all construction processes, pouring concrete involves knowledge and skill. Each concrete project will require a series of tasks to get good quality concrete. Make adjustments and adaptations for each job. To produce quality concrete, follow these basic steps.

1. Carefully plan the concrete structure. Many decisions related to the size, site, materials, availability of equipment, and project contract-

18-26. Concrete is being poured at a prepared construction site.

ing need to be made before beginning the construction. The first step is to make a job schedule and bill of materials.

2. Select and prepare the site. Concrete structures are designed to be permanent, so good site preparation is essential.

3. Prepare the subgrade structure. Be sure that the soil is firm, free of organic material, and has suitable drainage. Use good quality subgrade materials, such as sand or gravel, to form a structural base. Use properly designed concrete forms.

4. Determine the proper mix of concrete materials. Decide if you are going to mix the concrete on the job site or order ready-mix concrete. Remember, determine the amount of concrete needed, the size and amount of aggregates, reinforcing materials, and other important factors.

5. Place the concrete. Make sure enough workers are available to get the concrete poured, placed, floated, and finished before it sets. Get the concrete evenly distributed to all parts of the form.

6. Screed the concrete level. Use a straight edge, such as a 2×4 board, to work the concrete even with the top of the form.

7. Float the concrete. Use either wood or metal (aluminum or magnesium) concrete floats to smooth the concrete surface.

8. Allow the concrete to take an initial set, then finish trowel the concrete smooth. It usually will take one to two hours for the concrete to take its initial set. Concrete has usually set enough if the surface water, called bleed water, has been absorbed back into the fresh concrete. Another technique for determining whether con-

18-27. Fresh concrete being smoothed with a bull float. (Courtesy, John Childs, Illinois)

18-28. A trowel is used to smooth the concrete after it has an initial set. (Courtesy, John Childs, Illinois)

crete is set is to stand on the concrete or attempt to make a firm hand print. If your shoe heel or your hand can make only about a 1/4 inch imprint, then the concrete is ready to be trowel finished. Trowel finishing is a skill that demands fast, yet precise work to get a good smooth finish. Power trowels are recommended for large jobs. Troweling forms a layer of smooth, dense concrete on the surface. However, too much troweling will lead to cracking and scaling of the surface.

9. Apply a suitable finish material or appearance. Use a broom or brush to get a rough, granular surface, which will prevent slips. A straight edge can also be used to create ridges on slopes to help livestock and equipment achieve good traction.

10. Be sure to allow the concrete to properly cure. Concrete should be kept moist for at least seven days if possible. Flood or sprinkle the concrete daily to keep it wet. Concrete can also be covered to prevent evaporation. However, covers tend to leave areas of discoloration and marks on the concrete.

## CONCRETE MASONRY MATERIALS

Concrete masonry is a popular type of agricultural construction. Masonry construction is often used for food processing structures, such as dairies, wineries, canning plants, and meat processing facilities. Concrete blocks do not rot, are easy to keep clean, fireproof, and are not affected by some pests, such as rodents and termites.

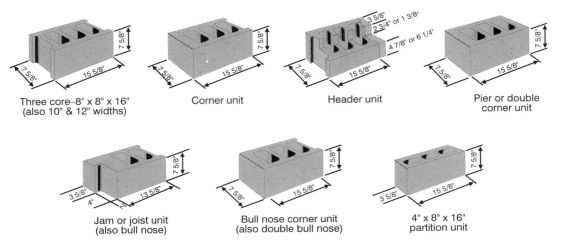

Three core—8" x 8" x 16"
(also 10" & 12" widths)

Corner unit

Header unit

Pier or double
corner unit

Jam or joist unit
(also bull nose)

Bull nose corner unit
(also double bull nose)

4" x 8" x 16"
partition unit

**18-29. Many different kinds of concrete masonry blocks are used for agricultural structures.**

There are two general types of concrete masonry materials, hollow and solid. These materials may be made from Portland cement, water, and standard aggregates, which are considered standard weight. A standard weight 8 × 8 × 16 inch concrete masonry block will weigh from 30 to 50 pounds. Lightweight units are made from Portland cement, water, and either a natural or fabricated aggregate, such as pumice, coal cinders, or plastics. A lightweight unit will weigh about half as much as a standard unit with the same dimensions.

Concrete masonry units are made in even number widths (4, 6, 8, 10, and 12 inches) and heights (4 and 8 inches). The 8 × 8 × 16 inch concrete block is widely used to build agricultural structures. Note, the actual block dimensions are about 3/8 of an inch smaller than the nominal block sizes to allow for a 3/8 inch mortar joint. When planning for concrete block construction, always try to get the wall and other building dimensions to even feet. This will eliminate cutting any blocks to build the structure.

Many styles of concrete masonry blocks are available. The most common styles are standard blocks, corner units, pier or double corner blocks, jamb and joist blocks, header blocks, and others. Also, concrete masonry blocks can be used to build headers or lintels to go over open passages or windows; pilasters, which provide stiffness and stability to walls and structures; and foundation walls and supports.

Most concrete masonry construction uses mortar to hold the blocks together. Some structures, such as concrete silos, use solid concrete units with interlocking edges that are held together with rods or bans. They often use some type of surface bonding material, like a plaster, to seal the cracks.

Masonry cement is usually mixed with water and sand to make mortar. A common mix is one volume of masonry cement and 2.5 to 3 parts sand, with enough water to make the mortar plastic-like and consistent. When masonry cement is not available, you can use 2 volumes of Portland cement with 1 volume of lime and mix with 4 to 5 volumes of sand. It will take about 7.5 cubic feet of mortar to joint 100 (8 × 8 × 16 inch) blocks. A 100 square foot wall (112.5 blocks) will take about 8.5 cubic feet of mortar. Both estimates are based upon 3/8 inch mortar joints.

The process of laying concrete blocks requires considerable know-how and skill. Often concrete masonry work is subcontracted to professional construction crews. You will need to start with clean, dry blocks; water; sand; masonry cement; and tools. The blocks must be placed on a firm footing or foundation. Start by setting at least two building corners and laying the blocks in between. The corners will allow the use of a string

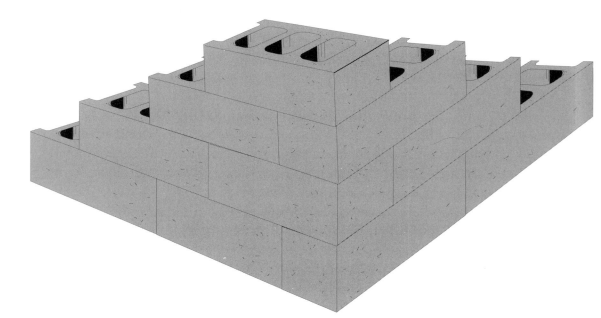

**18-30. Concrete blocks are set from the corners of the structure.**

to align the blocks. Each block must be square and level. The mortar joints must be consistent to get a sturdy, attractive structure. The mortar joints will need to be cleaned and grooved. A round or v-shaped groove is often used for appearance and to help seal the joints.

Tilt-up concrete units are also used to build agricultural structures. Some bunker silos and materials handling structures use poured concrete slabs, which are lifted or tilted in place. The concrete slabs should be reinforced and properly cured. They must also be securely fastened and supported.

## STRUCTURAL MAINTENANCE

Structures need to be maintained regularly. Make periodic checks of structures to look for possible problem areas. The most common area of concern is damage from insects, plants, and animals. Also, check for weather and climate related damage. Foundations may be weakened by freezing weather or the erosion of supporting soil and subgrade materials. Roof damage may occur from wind, snow, and rain. Structures should be checked regularly for deteriorating paints and finishes; structural failures, such as sagging roofs and floor cracks; and possible electrical problems, such as wiring failures.

Make seasonal inspections of all structures. It is generally recommended that you annually employ an inspector to look for pests and structural problems. Inspect all structures after any severe weather. Install and maintain smoke and fire detection equipment on all structures, especially those that house people and livestock. Store flammable materials and agrichemicals in safe areas and make regular inspections for safety.

Keep accurate records for all structures. Record any maintenance, inspections, or improvements that have been made. For future planning, it is very helpful to know when structures were painted, repaired, or cleaned. Good records can help to predict when further maintenance practices will be needed.

## SUMMARY

Many structural problems can be avoided or corrected with minimal costs if regular periodic inspections are made and accurate records are kept.

Structures of all types serve very important functions in agriculture. We use structures to store agricultural commodities and produce, house livestock, and store and protect equipment and machinery. They may also serve as facilities where the production, processing, selling, consumption, and enjoyment of agricultural products occur. There are many different kinds of structures used for many different purposes.

Wood and masonry are commonly used in agricultural construction for a wide range of structures. Common types of structures include pole, stud frame, concrete masonry, and rigid arch buildings.

Essential activities include planning, site preparation, design, and construction. Load influences design and materials selection. Regular inspection and periodic maintenance are essential to keep buildings in good condition.

# REVIEW QUESTIONS

1. What are the four basic types of structures used in agriculture?

2. What are the factors to consider when planning agricultural structures?

3. How do you prepare a site?

4. What are the different kinds of structural loads for agricultural structures?

5. How do you design basic structural footings and foundations?

6. What are the different kinds of floors used for agricultural structures?

7. What are the different types of wall structures?

8. What are the different types of roof structures and roof materials?

9. How do you design common rafters?

10. How do you basic construct a truss rafter?

11. How is wood produced?

12. How do air and kiln wood drying techniques differ?

13. What are some different kinds of wood products?

14. How is concrete made?

15. What are the types of Portland cement?

16. How do you design concrete mixes?

# NDIXES

## APPENDIX A

### INTERNATIONAL SYSTEM OF MEASUREMENT

The International System of Measurement is based on units of 100, which can best be compared to our money system of dollars and cents. Different units are used for measuring length, volume, weight (mass), and temperature. Converting units within SI is extremely simple since in effect, changes are made by moving the decimal point. Initially, it is essential to learn the metric prefixes and which units are used for measuring length, volume, weight, and temperature.

### Length

Length is the distance from one point to another. The SI unit of length is the meter. In making measurements, it is often more convenient to report Length in terms which signify a portion or combination of meters. The following prefixes are used with the main unit meter to specify measurements of length.

| Prefix | Symbol | Meaning |
|--------|--------|---------|
| kilo- | km | 1,000 meters |
| hecto- | hm | 100 meters |
| deca- | dam | 10 meters |
| meter | | |
| deci- | dm | 0.1 meter |
| centi- | cm | 0.01 meter |
| milli- | mm | 0.001 meter |

### Volume

Volume is the amount of space a substance occupies and is based on measurements of length (i.e. length × width × height). The SI unit of volume is the cubic meter; however, this measurement is too large for most scientific work, so scientists normally use cubic decimeters (0.1 of

597

a meter)$^3$ to measure volume. One cubic decimeter (1 dm)$^3$ is equal to 1 liter (1). The following prefixes are used with the main unit liter to specify measurements of volume.

| Prefix | Symbol | Meaning |
|---|---|---|
| kilo- | kl | 1,000 liters |
| hecto- | hl | 100 liters |
| deca- | dal | 10 liters |
| liter | | |
| deci- | dl | 0.1 liter |
| centi- | cl | 0.01 liter |
| milli- | ml | 0.001 liter |

## Weight

Weight is a measure of the pull of gravity on an object. The SI unit of weight is the newton. Since the pull of gravity differs when you leave the earth and experiments are now conducted in space, scientists commonly measure the mass of an object which is how much matter is in something. (For example, the moon's gravity is approximately one-sixth that of the earth.) The SI unit of mass is the gram. The following prefixes are used with the main unit gram to specify measurements of mass.

| Prefix | Symbol | Meaning |
|---|---|---|
| kilo- | kg | 1,000 grams |
| hecto- | hg | 100 grams |
| deca- | dag | 10 grams |
| gram | | |
| deci- | dg | 0.1 gram |
| centi- | cg | 0.01 gram |
| milli- | mg | 0.001 gram |

## Temperature

Temperature is the amount of heat in something. The SI unit for measuring temperature is degrees Kelvin. One degree Kelvin is equal to one degree Celsius which is the common unit of measurement for the metric system. The metric system of measuring temperature is also based on 100. In this case there are 100 from the temperature at which water freezes to the temperature at which water boils. Common temperature measurements in Celsius are 18° Celsius—room temperature, 37° Celsius—body temperature.

## Area

Area is based on measurements of length (i.e. length × width). The SI unit for area is the square meter (m$^2$). However, when measuring plots of land for agricultural purposes, the hectare (ha) is normally used instead of the square meter. 1 hectare = 10,000 square meters.

## Conversion Factors for Acceptable Units

| To convert Column 1 into Column 2 multiply by | Column 1 Acceptable Unit | Column 2 SI Unit | To convert Column 2 into Column 1 multiply by |
|---|---|---|---|
| **Length** | | | |
| 0.304 | foot, ft | meter, m | 3.28 |
| 2.54 | inch, in | centimeter, cm ($10^{-2}$m) | 0.394 |
| 25.4 | inch, in | milimeter, mm ($10^{-3}$m) | $3.94 \times 10^{-2}$ |
| 1.609 | mile, mi | kilometer, km ($10^{3}$m) | 0.621 |
| 0.914 | yard, yd | meter, m | 1.094 |
| **Area** | | | |
| 0.405 | acre | hectare, ha | 2.47 |
| $4.05 \times 10^{3}$ | acre square | meter, $m^2$ | $2.47 \times 10^{-4}$ |
| $9.29 \times 10^{-2}$ | square foot, $ft^2$ | square meter, $m^2$ | 10.76 |
| 2.590 | square mile, $mi^2$ | square kilometer, $km^2$ ($10^{3}$ m)$^2$ | 0.386 |
| **Volume** | | | |
| 35.24 | bushel (dry), bu | liter, L | $2.84 \times 10^{-2}$ |
| 28.3 | cubic foot, $ft^3$ | liter, L | $3.53 \times 10^{-2}$ |
| $3.83 \times 10^{-2}$ | cubic foot, $ft^3$ | cubic meter $m^3$ | 35.3 |
| $1.64 \times 10^{5}$ | cubic inch, $in^3$ | cubic meter $m^3$ | $6.10 \times 10^{4}$ |
| 3.78 | gallon, gal | liter, L | 0.265 |
| $2.96 \times 10^{-2}$ | ounce (liquid), oz | liter, L | 33.78 |
| **Mass** | | | |
| 28.4 | ounce | gram, g | $3.52 \times 10^{-2}$ |
| 454 | pound, lb | gram, g | $2.20 \times 10^{-3}$ |
| 0.454 | pound, lb | kilogram, kg | 2.205 |
| 907 | ton (2,000 lb), ton | kilogram, kg | $1.10 \times 10^{-3}$ |
| **Yield and Rate** | | | |
| 35.84 | 32-lb bushel per acre | kilogram per hectare | $2.79 \times 10^{-2}$ |
| 53.75 | 48-lb bushel per acre | kilogram per hectare | $1.86 \times 10^{-2}$ |
| 62.71 | 56-lb busher per acre | kilogram per hectare | $1.59 \times 10^{-2}$ |
| 67.19 | 60-lb bushel per acre | kilogram per hectare | $1.49 \times 10^{-2}$ |
| 9.35 | gallons per acre | liter per hectare | 0.107 |
| 1.12 | poun per acre | kilogram per hectare | 0.893 |
| **Temperature** | | | |
| $5/9(F - 32)$ | Fahrenheit, F | Celsius, C | $(9/5C) + 32$ |

# APPENDIX B
# STANDARD HYDRAULIC SYMBOLS

## LINES AND LINE FUNCTIONS

- Line, working
- Line, pilot (L>20W)
- Line, drain (<5W)
- Connector
- Line, flexible
- Line, joining
- Line, passing
- Direction of flow, hydraulic pneumatic
- Line to reservoir
  - above fluid level
  - below fluid level
- Line to vented mainfold
- Plug or plugged connection
- Restriction, fixed
- Restriction, variable

## PUMPS

- Pump, single fixed displacement
- Pump, single variable displacement

## MOTORS

- Motor, rotary fixed displacement
- Motor, rotary variable displacement
- Motor, oscillating

## CYLINDERS

- Cylinder, single acting

## CYLINDERS (cont.)

- Cylinder, double acting
- Cylinder, differential rod
- Cylinder, double end rod
- Cylinder, cushions both end

## MISCELLANEOUS UNITS

- Direction of rotation (arrow in front of shaft)
- Component enclosure
- Reservoir, vented
- Reservoir, pressurized
- Pressure gage
- Temperature gage
- Flow meter (flow rate)
- Electric motor
- Accumulator, spring loaded
- Accumulator, gas charged
- Filter or strainer
- Heater
- Cooler

## MISCELLANEOUS UNITS (cont.)

- Temperature controller
- Intensifier
- Pressure switch

## BASIC VALVE SYMBOLS

- Check valve
- Manual shut off valve
- Basic valve envelope
- Valve, single flow path, normally closed
- Valve, single flow path, normally open
- Valve, maximum pressure (relief)
- Basic valve symbol, multiple flow paths
- Flow paths blocked in center position
- Multiple flow paths (arrow shows flow direction)

## VALVE EXAMPLES

- Unloading valve, internal drain, remotely operated
- Deceleration valve, normally open
- Sequence valve, directly operated, externally drained
- Pressure reducing valve

## VALVE EXAMPLES (cont.)

- Counter balance valve with integral check
- Temperature and pressure compensated flow control with integral check
- Directional valve, two position, three connection
- Directional valve, three position, four connection
- Valve, infinite positioning (indicated by horizontal bars)

## METHODS OF OPERATION

- Pressure compensator
- Detent
- Manual
- Mechanical
- Pedal or treadle
- Push button
- Lever
- Pilot pressure
- Solenoid
- Solenoid controlled, pilot pressure operated
- Spring
- Servo

# GLOSSARY

**3-way switch**—an electrical switch with three terminals and no marked on or off positions; always used in pairs, allowing a load to be controlled from two locations.

**3, 4, 5 triangle corner method**—a method for establishing a right angle based on the Pythagorean Theorem.

**4-way switch**—an electrical switch with four terminals and no marked on or off positions; always used with a pair of 3-way switches to control a load from three or more locations.

**absorption dynamometer**—a device for measuring power output.

**accessory system**—engine systems not essential to engine operation.

**agrarian**—based on agriculture.

**agricultural mechanization**—the use of power and machinery to produce food and fiber.

**air intake system**—the engine system that causes air or an air–fuel mixture to enter the combustion chamber during the intake stroke.

**air-entrained cement**—a type of cement containing additives that produce microscopic air bubbles in the concrete, improving its resistance to damage by frost and freezing.

**alloy**—a metal composed of two different chemical elements.

**alternating current (AC)**—an electrical current that reverses direction of flow periodically.

**ambient (amb.) temperature**—temperature of the air around an object.

**ammeter**—a meter used to measure current in an electrical circuit.

**ampacity**—the current carrying capacity of a conductor or other electrical device.

**ampere (A)**—the unit of measure of current in an electrical circuit.

**analog (linear) integrated circuit**—an electronic circuit that produces, amplifies, or responds to a continuous electrical signal.

**Andrus, Leonard**—early partner of blacksmith and inventor John Deere.

**annealing**—a heat treating process that reduces internal metal stresses, making the metal less hard and brittle.

601

**apparent power**—the power in an AC electrical circuit calculated as the product of voltage times amperage.

**armature**—the rotating component of a DC electric motor.

**atom**—the smallest unit of an element that retains the properties of the element.

**avalanche voltage**—the reverse-bias voltage required to cause a zener diode to conduct.

**axial piston pump**—a type of hydraulic pump where the pistons are parallel to the pump's drive shaft.

**backwiring**—a technique for connecting a circuit conductor to an electrical device by inserting the conductor into a spring-loaded hole in the device.

**balanced load**—connecting 120-volt electrical loads at the service entrance panel so that the amperage loads between both ungrounded service conductors and the grounded service conductor are the same.

**balanced vane pump**—a type of hydraulic pump designed to prevent excessive side-loading of the rotor shaft and bearings.

**bar chart**—a type of graph that represents values and amounts by the relative length of two or more bars.

**battery**—two or more chemical cells connected together that produce electricity by chemical reactions.

**battery ignition system**—a type of engine ignition system that uses energy from a battery or alternator to produce the ignition spark.

**bidirectional triode thyristor (TRIAC)**—a solid-state electronic switch that will allow current flow in both directions.

**bipolar transistor**—a type of transistor consisting of three alternating layers of p- and n-type semiconductor material.

**bird's mouth**—notch made in a rafter to fit the plate.

**bleed**—the process of removing air from a diesel fuel system.

**board foot**—a unit of measure for lumber consisting of a volume equal to 144 cubic inches.

**boost**—the increase in an engine's intake air pressure produced by a turbocharger.

**bottom dead center (BDC)**—piston position at the exact bottom of its stroke.

**bow instrument**—mechanical drafting tool device for producing circles and arcs.

**Boyle's Law**—physical law describing the relationship between the pressure and volume of a gas at constant temperature.

**branch circuit**—electrical circuit from the last overcurrent protection device to the utilization equipment.

**brazing**—a non-fusion welding process.

**breadboarding**—assembling and testing a temporary electronic circuit prior to constructing a permanent version.

**bridge rectifier**—a four diode network used to change both halves of an incoming AC sine wave into DC electricity.

**BTU (British Thermal Unit)**—a measure of heat energy; 1 BTU is the quantity of heat required to raise the temperature of 1 pound of water 1 degree Fahrenheit.

**building service conductors**—electrical conductors that supply electricity from the central distribution point to individual load centers.

**cable**—two or more electrical conductors enclosed in a protective outer sheath.

**cable ripper**—an electrician's hand tool used to slice the outer sheath of a cable.

**cambium**—the layer of growth cells between the wood and bark of a live tree.

**capacitance (C)**—a measure of the ability to store electrical energy in an electrostatic field.

**capacitive reactance**—opposition to the flow of AC current due to capacitance; causes the voltage in the circuit to lag the current.

**capacitor**—a device that stores electrical energy in an electrostatic field.

**capacitor-start capacitor-run motor**—type of AC induction motor that develops a high starting torque while drawing a moderate starting current.

**capacitor-start induction-run motor**—type of AC induction motor that uses a capacitor for starting but not when running.

**carburetor**—engine fuel system component that meters and atomizes the fuel and mixes it with the intake air on some spark ignition engines.

**Case, J. I.**—early manufacturer of a machine, called the combine, for threshing, separating, and winnowing grain crops.

**central point distribution system**—a common electrical distribution system where electrical service for dispersed load centers originates from one central location.

**centrifugal switch**—a switch that opens by centrifugal force.

**cetane number**—a measure of the ignition quality of diesel fuel.

**circuit**—a complete pathway for the flow of electrons.

**circuit breaker**—a device commonly used to protect electrical circuits and loads from overcurrent conditions.

**circuit overload**—excessive current flow in an electrical circuit.

**clamp-on ammeter**—a type of ammeter that can be used without connecting it directly into the electrical circuit.

**clear span structure**—a building with no center posts.

**closed circuit**—a complete pathway from the voltage source to the load(s) and back to the voltage source.

**combine**—a machine for harvesting and threshing grain.

**combustion**—the chemical process of oxidation that produces heat.

**commodities**—agricultural products such as corn, wheat, livestock, etc.

**compass**—a mechanical drafting device for drawing circles, arcs, and ellipses.

**compound pressure relief valve**—a pressure limiting hydraulic valve that operates in two stages.

**compression**—a reduction in the volume occupied by a substance; the second stroke of the four-stroke engine cycle.

**compression gage**—a tool used to measure the pressure developed in an engine combustion chamber.

**compression ignition engine**—a type of engine where the fuel is ignited by the heat of compression in the combustion chamber; another name for a diesel engine.

**compression ratio**—the ratio of the volume of the combustion chamber with the piston at BDC to the volume with the piston at TDC.

**compression rings**—piston rings designed to seal between the piston and cylinder wall to prevent loss of pressure in the combustion chamber.

**compression strength**—the ability of a material to withstand a compressive force.

**compression system**—the primary internal combustion engine system involved in creating compression and producing power from the combustion of an air–fuel mixture.

**computer assisted design (CAD)**—the use of computer hardware and software to produce drawings.

**concrete**—a rock-like construction material formed from a mixture of paste and aggregates.

**concrete masonry building**—a structure built primarily from concrete blocks.

**condenser**—an engine ignition component that functions as a capacitor.

**conduction**—the transfer of heat through the interaction of molecules or atoms without the conducting material itself being moved.

**conductor**—a substance that has low resistance to the flow of electrical current.

**conduit**—a channel or tube through which electrical conductors are run in order to provide the conductors with mechanical protection.

**connected load**—the total amperage of all loads connected to a building's service entrance panel, usually calculated on a 240-volt basis.

**connector**—a fitting used to join one piece of hydraulic piping to another piece of piping or to a hydraulic component.

**continuous signal**—an electrical signal that can vary between a range of values.

**convection**—the transfer of heat to or from an object by a gas or liquid.

**conventional theory**—posits that electricity is the flow of positively charged particles through a conductor, and that flow is from positive to negative.

**coolant hydrometer**—a device for measuring the freeze protection of an engine coolant mixture based on the specific gravity of the mixture.

**corrosion resistance**—the ability of a substance to resist oxidation.

**cosine**—a trigonometric term indicating the ratio of the adjacent side of a given acute angle in a right triangle to the hypotenuse.

**counter voltage**—an induced voltage that opposes any change in the current flow in a circuit.

**covalent bonding**—the type of chemical bond between two atoms when they share electrons in pairs so that each atom provides half of the electrons.

**cracking pressure**—the pressure at which a hydraulic pressure relief valve first begins to open and divert oil flow to the reservoir.

**cradle scythe**—a hand-held grain harvesting tool having a long, curved blade attached to a long, bent handle.

**cranking amperage**—electrical current flow required for starting an internal combustion engine.

**crankshaft throw**—offset on an engine crankshaft that converts linear piston movement to rotary crankshaft motion.

**crystal lattice**—arrangement of atoms in an orderly, repeating, three-dimensional patten.

**cutting fluid**—a liquid used in many metal cutting operations to keep the saw blade and metal cool, clean, and lubricated.

**cycle**—a complete set of events recurring in the same sequence.

**cycle time**—in a hydraulic system, the amount of time required for one complete set of events to occur.

**cylinder block**—primary engine structural component housing the reciprocating engine components.

**cylinder leakage test**—a test used to determine the extent and source of engine compression losses.

**DC motor**—a motor designed to operate on direct current electricity.

**dead load**—the weight of the structural components of a building.

**Deere, John**—blacksmith and manufacturer of the self scouring steel plow.

**demand load**—the maximum amperage electrical load expected to operate at any one time, usually calculated on a 240-volt basis.

**depletion region**—a region depleted of electrical carriers.

**design function**—the purpose for which a structure has been created.

**dielectric**—the insulating material separating the plates of a capacitor.

**differential cylinder**—a hydraulic cylinder having unequal piston areas exposed to fluid pressure during the extension and retraction strokes.

**digital integrated circuit**—an electronic circuit that produces, amplifies, or responds to signals having two values—on or off.

**direct acting pressure relief valve**—a pressure limiting hydraulic valve in which fluid pressure acts directly against a spring loaded check ball.

**direct current (DC)**—a type of electricity having a constant voltage and polarity with respect to time.

**disconnecting means**—a device for opening the circuit between all ungrounded electrical conductors and a motor and motor controller.

**discrete semiconductor component**—an individual electronic component made from semiconductor material.

**divider**—mechanical drafting tool used to transfer measurements and spacings from one location to another.

**dome**—top of a piston; also called the piston head.

**doping**—adding elements to pure silicon to alter its electrical characteristics.

**double-pole circuit breaker**—a type of circuit breaker that simultaneously opens or closes two ungrounded circuit conductors.

**drafting machine**—a mechanical drafting device that takes the place of the T-square and triangles.

**drawbar power**—tractor power available for pulling a load attached to the drawbar.

**drawing board**—a wooden board to which drafting paper is attached in order to make mechanical drawings.

**ductility**—the degree to which a metal can be cold formed without breaking.

**duplex convenience outlet (DCO)**—an electrical device having two receptacles on a single strap.

**duration**—the length of time that an engine valve is open, based on the number of degrees of crankshaft rotation.

**duty cycle**—the relative amount of a 10 minute period during which a welding machine can operate at its rated amperage.

**dwell**—number of degrees of crankshaft rotation that mechanical breaker points are closed.

**electric shock**—occurs when electrical current flows through the body.

**electrical circuit**—a pathway for the flow of electrons.

**electrical conductivity**—the relative ability of a material to allow electrical current flow.

**electricity**—the flow of electrons from atom to atom in a conductor.

**electrodes**—dissimilar metals used in a chemical cell for producing electricity.

**electrolyte**—a chemical solution containing ions.

**electromagnet**—a soft iron core surrounded by a coil of wire, that temporary becomes a magnet when electrical current flows through the wire.

**electromotive force**—the electrical force or pressure that causes or tends to cause current to flow in a circuit; commonly measured in volts.

**electron**—a negatively charged atomic particle that orbits the atom's nucleus.

**electron theory**—posits that electricity is the flow of negatively charged particles (electrons) and that flow is from negative to positive.

**electronics**—the use of semiconductors to manipulate electrical signals.

**element**—substances that cannot be reduced into simpler substances using ordinary chemical means.

**enclosure**—the housing or covering of an electric motor.

**end bell**—the removable end-coverings of an electric motor.

**energy**—the capacity to do work.

**engine**—a device that changes heat energy to mechanical energy.

**engine coolant**—a mixture of antifreeze and water used in liquid cooling systems to transfer heat from engine components to the surrounding air.

**engine cooling system**—system designed to maintain the optimal temperature of an internal combustion engine.

**engine displacement**—the total swept volume of an engine's cylinders as the engine completes one stroke.

**engine timing**—proper sequencing of the intake, compression, power, and exhaust events of an internal combustion engine.

**engineered grade**—plywood grade based on approved uses for the material.

**equal gabled roof**—a gable roof with the same slope on both sides of the roof.

**equipment grounding**—connecting conductive equipment and surfaces not intended to carry electrical current to the earth.

**equipment grounding conductor**—the conductor used to connect conductive, noncurrent-carrying parts of equipment, raceways, and other enclosures back to the system grounding electrode.

**equivalent simple circuit**—a circuit in which all series and parallel loads are combined to form a single load having the same resistance as the original circuit.

**exhaust**—the process of removing spent combustion products from the engine combustion chamber; the final stroke of the four-stroke engine cycle.

**exhaust system**—auxiliary engine system that removes exhaust gases and particles from the combustion chamber.

**farad (F)**—unit of measurement of capacitance.

**fascia plumb cut**—a cut at the bottom end of a rafter to which a fascia board is attached.

**feeder circuit**—an electrical circuit that originates at a service entrance panel and supplies electrical power to a sub-panel.

**ferrous**—containing iron (Fe).

**fiber saturation point**—moisture condition in which all water, except that in the cell walls, has been removed from wood.

**fibrillation**—rapid, uncontrolled contractions of portions of the heart muscle resulting in irregular heartbeat.

**field-effect transistor (FET)**—a voltage controlled transistor.

**filter**—a device that removes small particles from a fluid.

**firing order**—denotes the sequence of power strokes in the various cylinders of a multicylinder engine.

**fixed capacitor**—a capacitor having a set, non-adjustable capacitance value.

**fixed displacement pump**—a pump in which the volume of the pumping chamber cannot be changed while the pump is in operation.

**fixed resistor**—a resistor having a set, non-adjustable resistance value.

**flat head**—type of cylinder head that does not house the valves.

**floor plan**—drawing that depicts the overall layout of a building.

**fluorescent light**—a type of bulb consisting of a glass tube filled with a gas and having a filament in each end.

**footing**—the projecting base under a wall or column that spreads weight and helps prevent settling.

**force**—a push or pull that tends to start, stop, or change the direction of motion of an object.

**forward-biased**—the condition where the anode of an electronic device is more positive than the cathode.

**foundation wall**—structural supporting component from the footing to the above grade wall.

**frame**—the primary housing of an electric motor.

**frame number (FR)**—number found on a motor nameplate that, divided by 16, gives the number of inches from the center line of the motor shaft to the bottom of the motor mounting.

**free electrons**—electrons not tightly held in orbit around the nucleus of an atom.

**friction**—resistance to motion of two objects or surfaces that are in contact.

**friction power ($P_f$)**—the power an engine consumes in overcoming friction; the difference between an engine's indicated power and brake power.

**fuel cell**—device for producing electricity from the reaction of chemicals supplied to the fuel cell from an outside source.

**fuel combustion meter**—engine analysis instrument designed to determine the percentage of a fuel gas actually burned by the engine.

**fuel system**—engine auxiliary system designed to meter and deliver clean fuel to the combustion chamber.

**full-flow pressure**—the pressure required to completely open a hydraulic pressure relief valve.

**full-wave rectification**—the process of changing both halves of an AC sine wave into DC electricity.

**fuse**—a device commonly used to protect electrical circuits and loads from overcurrent conditions.

**galvanizing**—the process of applying a thin coating of zinc to the surface of a metal to inhibit oxidation.

**gambrel roof**—a type of roof where two different roof angles are used on each side.

**geographic information system (GIS)**—a computerized field mapping process where fields are divided into grids and then mapped for physical attributes per grid.

**germanium**—a chemical element having four electrons in the valence ring.

**global positioning system (GPS)**—a system of high altitude satellites orbiting the earth and having the capability to provide exact geographic locations on the earth's surface.

**governing system**—the engine auxiliary system that maintains a constant engine speed under varying load conditions by controlling fuel flow to the engine.

**governor**—the primary sensing and control mechanism of an engine's governor system.

**grade stamp**—a stamp indicating the quality of lumber or manufactured wood products.

**grades of hardness**—a method for designating the lead hardness of drawing pencils.

**ground-fault**—an extremely dangerous electrical circuit condition where a current-carrying wire makes electrical contact with a conductive object that is grounded.

**ground-fault circuit interrupter (GFCI)**—an electrical device intended to protect persons from electrical shock by de-energizing the circuit almost instantaneously when a ground-fault occurs.

**grounded conductor**—circuit conductor intentionally connected to ground at the service entrance.

**grounding**—direct or indirect electrical connection to the earth.

**grounding electrode**—serves as the terminal or connection to earth for an electrical grounding system.

**gypsum board**—a manufactured construction material used primarily for interior walls; also called sheet rock or drywall.

**half-wave rectification**—the process of changing only one half of an AC sine wave into DC electricity.

**hand hacksaw**—a hand powered tool for cutting metals.

**hardboard**—a manufactured wood material made by pressing wood fiber mats together under high temperature and pressure conditions.

**hardening**—a heat treating process that increases the relative hardness of a metal.

**hardness**—the relative ability of a metal to resist indentation, scratching, or filing.

**heartwood**—the wood at the center of a tree or branch.

**heat treating**—the process of changing the properties of a metal by controlling the heating and cooling process.

**henry (H)**—the unit of measurement for inductance; 1 henry is the inductance required to induce 1 volt in a coil when the current changes its rate of flow by 1 ampere per second.

**hertz (Hz)**—indicates the number of cycles per second for AC electricity; electricity in the U.S. is generated at 60 Hz.

**horsepower**—the unit of measure for power in the U.S. system of measurement; the amount of power required to do 33,000 foot-pounds of work in one minute.

**horsepower rating (HP)**—the rated horsepower output for an electric motor or internal combustion engine.

**hour meter**—panel instrument that records the hours of operation for many agricultural machines, especially tractors.

**hydration**—the chemical process of a material combining with water to form a hydrate.

**hydraulic actuator**—a hydraulic device for converting fluid energy into mechanical energy.

**hydraulic cylinder**—a type of hydraulic actuator that produces linear motion.

**hydraulic motor**—a type of hydraulic actuator that produces rotary motion.

**hydraulics**—the branch of physics dealing with the mechanical properties and applications of liquids in motion.

**hydrocarbon fuel**—engine fuels consisting of hydrogen and carbon.

**hydrodynamic lubrication**—a method of engine lubrication where movement of the lubricant is by adhesion to moving or sliding surfaces.

**hydrodynamics**—use of liquids at high flow and low pressure to perform work.

**hydroelectric**—a method of generating electricity using the energy of moving water to turn the generator turbine.

**hydrostatic lubrication**—a method of engine lubrication where movement of the lubricant is due to a pump.

**hydrostatics**—use of liquids at low flow and high pressure to perform work.

**ignition system**—engine auxiliary system for initiating the combustion of the air and fuel mixture.

**ignition timing**—the point in the engine cycle when combustion of the air and fuel mixture occurs.

**impedance**—the total opposition to current flow in a circuit.

**in-phase**—condition existing in an AC electrical circuit when voltage and amperage reach peak positive and negative and zero values at the same time during the cycle.

**incandescent light**—a type of lamp that glows because of the heat produced as current flows through a high resistance tungsten filament.

**indicated power ($P_i$)**—the theoretical power output of an engine based on mean cylinder pressure, engine displacement, and engine operating speed.

**individual branch circuit**—a branch circuit that serves a single electrical load.

**inductance (L)**—the property of an electrical circuit that opposes any change in current flow.

**induction motor**—a type of AC electric motor where current flow in the rotating motor component is caused by induction.

**inductive reactance**—the amount of opposition to change in current flow produced by an inductor.

**inductor**—a coil placed in an electrical circuit to produce a desired amount of inductance.

**inert**—an element or compound that does not readily react with other elements or compounds.

**input device**—computer hardware used to enter information into the computer; for example, a keyboard or mouse.

**insulated-gate field-effect transistor (IGFET)**—a type of field-effect transistor that operates at high speed with low power requirements.

**insulation class**—system used with electric motors to indicate the maximum safe operating temperature that will not cause premature damage to the insulation on the internal windings.

**insulator**—a substance that has an extremely high resistance to the flow of electrical current.

**intake**—the process of bringing a new air or air–fuel mixture into the engine combustion chamber; the first stroke of the four-stroke engine cycle.

**integrated circuit**—a complete electronic circuit contained entirely on a single chip.

**interactive process**—a non-linear process where decisions made at one point may impact previous decisions while altering the basis for future decisions.

**intercooler**—a heat exchange device.

**internal combustion engine**—a device for converting heat energy into mechanical energy by combusting fuel inside the engine.

**International System (SI)**—the formal term used for the metric measurement system.

**inverse-time characteristic**—the characteristic of an overcurrent protection device whereby it opens the circuit faster as the overload is greater.

**ion**—an electrically charged atom or group of atoms.

**isometric projection**—a pictorial drafting technique in which the object being drawn is shown in a three-dimensional perspective.

**junction diode**—an electronic device made by joining a piece of n-type and a piece of p-type semiconductor material together; current will flow only when the p–n junction is forward-biased.

**junction field-effect transistor (JFET)**—a type of voltage-controlled transistor.

**kilo**—metric prefix for one thousand (1,000).

**kilowatt (kW)**—1,000 watts.

**kilowatt-hour (kW-hr)**—commonly used unit of electrical energy use; 1 kilowatt-hour is the equivalent of using 1,000 watts of electrical power for one hour.

**kinetic energy**—energy of motion.

**KVA code letter**—code found on an electric motor nameplate; indicates the approximate kilovolt-amperes (KVA) per horsepower consumed by the motor under locked-rotor condition.

**lands**—part of the piston that provides support to the piston rings.

**landsat**—satellites that make photographs of the earth and plot the earth's resources.

**laser**—a device that produces coherent light.

**Law of Charles and Gay-Lussac**—states that the volume of a gas varies directly with its absolute temperature, provided the pressure remains the same.

**Law of Conservation of Energy—** states that energy can neither be created nor destroyed, although it can be transformed from one kind to another.

**light-emitting diode (LED)—**a special type of diode that emits light when forward-biased.

**line graph—**a type of graph showing the relationship between two continuous variables.

**linear actuator—**a hydraulic device that produces straight-line motion, such as a hydraulic cylinder.

**linear foot—**denotes a length of 12 inches, without regard to thickness or width.

**live load—**a load on a structure that changes under normal building use.

**load—**any electrical device that consumes power, such as a lamp or motor.

**lobe profile—**refers to the shape of the camshaft lobe.

**lower plumb cut—**the cut made on the lower end of a rafter.

**lubrication system—**engine auxiliary system that keeps engine parts lubricated.

**machining—**a cold metal working process for shaping metal.

**magnetic induction—**the process of producing current flow in a conductor by the relative motion of the conductor and a magnetic field.

**magneto-type ignition system—**a type of engine ignition system that produces electricity for the ignition spark by magnetic induction.

**main disconnect—**The overcurrent protection device/switch that limits amperage and allows all electrical service provided through a main or building service entrance panel to be disconnected.

**main journal—**crankshaft bearing surfaces that hold the crankshaft in proper alignment within the engine block.

**maintenance interval—**manufacturer's recommendation for periodic machine service; given as hours of use and/or length of time.

**mass—**quantity of matter in an object.

**mathematics—**the branch of science dealing with quantities, magnitudes, and their relationships through the use of numbers and symbols.

**McCormick, Cyrus—**patented and manufactured the horse-drawn reaper.

**mechanical drawing—**a drawing made with the aid of mechanical drafting tools such as T-squares, triangles, etc.

**mechanical efficiency—**the ratio of the power delivered by a machine to the power produced by the machine.

**mechanical property—**characteristics of a metal including hardness, ductility, toughness, tensile strength, and compression strength.

**melting point—**the temperature at which a substance changes from a solid to a liquid.

**messenger—**the neutral wire conductor in a triplex cable.

**metal—**any of a class of chemical elements characterized by ductility, malleability, luster, and conductivity of heat and electricity.

**metal inert gas welding (MIG)**—a type of gas metal arc welding using a continuous wire as the electrode and an inert gas to shield the molten puddle.

**metallic conduit**—metal tubing used to support and protect a number of individual electrical wires which are run through it.

**metallurgy**—the study of the chemical and physical properties of metals.

**metric system**—the international system of measurement based on the gram, meter, and liter as the basic units of weight, length, and capacity, respectively.

**milli**—metric prefix meaning one one-thousandth (.001).

**milliampere (mA)**—unit of current flow equal to one one-thousandth (.001) of an ampere.

**model number**—manufacturer's identification number for a specific product, such as electric motors or engines.

**motor**—a device for converting an energy input into a mechanical energy output.

**motor controller**—a switch or other device that is normally used to start and stop a motor by making and breaking the electrical current to the motor.

**motor duty cycle**—an electric motor rating indicating whether the motor is designed for continuous or intermittent operation.

**motor rotation**—the direction of rotation of the motor shaft.

**multimeter**—a type of electrical meter that can be used to measure two or more electrical circuit characteristics.

**multiplication of force**—the transformation of a small input force into a larger output force, accompanied by a proportional decrease in output distance or speed.

**nameplate**—tag located on the frame of an electric motor that provides specialized information about the motor.

*National Electrical Code (NEC)*—comprehensive set of electrical safety standards published by the National Fire Protection Association and updated every three years.

**National Fire Protection Association (NFPA)**—nonprofit organization devoted to promoting and improving the science and methods of fire protection; publishes the *National Electrical Code.*

**neutral bar**—connection point in the service entrance panel that is intentionally connected to earth.

**neutron**—the part of the atomic nucleus having no electrical charge.

**Newbold, Charles**—obtained the first U.S. patent for the plow.

**nominal voltage**—standard voltage classification which may differ slightly from the actual or measured voltage; most common are 120V or 240V.

**non-differential cylinder**—a double-acting, linear hydraulic actuator having both sides of the piston fitted with a cylinder rod.

**non-ferrous**—a metal that does not contain iron (Fe).

**non-positive displacement**—a type of pump where the fluid volume delivered per cycle decreases with increases in outlet pressure.

**nonmetallic conduit**—nonmetal tubing used to support and protect a number of individual electrical wires which are run through it.

**normalizing**—a metal heat treatment process where the metal is heated to just above the transformation temperature, maintained for a time, and then allowed to cool in open air.

**oblique projection**—a mechanical drawing showing three sides of an object, with the near side drawn at a 90-degree angle.

**Occupational Safety and Health Administration (OSHA)**—agency of the U.S. Government responsible for formulating and enforcing workplace safety standards.

**octane number**—standardized rating of the ignition quality of gasoline.

**odometer**—panel instrument that records the cumulative miles traveled by a vehicle.

**ohm**—the basic unit of electrical resistance.

**ohmmeter**—a device used to measure electrical resistance.

**Ohm's Law**—basic electrical law stating the relationship between voltage, amperage, and resistance in a circuit.

**oil ring**—bottom piston ring(s) intended to control the amount of oil on the cylinder wall.

**open circuit**—a circuit condition where a complete circuit from the source to the load and back to the source does not exist.

**operating system**—engine system required in order for the primary engine system to operate.

**orthographic projection**—a type of mechanical drawing that shows two or three separate views of the object drawn.

**output device**—computer hardware that transfers computerized information onto paper or other media.

**overcurrent**—level of current flow in a circuit above the maximum safe level.

**overhead valve cylinder head**—type of cylinder head housing the intake and exhaust valves.

**parallel circuit**—electrical circuit having alternate paths for current flow.

**particleboard**—manufactured wood product made by bonding wood chips with synthetic resins.

**Pascal's Law**—basic law of hydraulics; states that pressure applied to an enclosed fluid is transmitted equally and undiminished in all directions, acts with equal force on equal areas, and acts at right angles to the walls of the container.

**pen plotter**—computer input device that allows a person to transfer an image into the computer by tracing or drawing.

**pentavalent element**—any chemical element having five valence electrons.

**perforated board (perf board)**—nonconductive board with pre-drilled holes often used for assembly of permanent electronic circuits.

**permanent-split capacitor motor**—a type of capacitor-start motor where the capacitor and auxiliary windings remain in the running circuit while the motor operates.

**phase angle**—the angle describing the shift between the voltage and amperage in a circuit.

**phloem**—inner tree bark that transports plant food produced by photosynthesis to other parts of the tree.

**photovoltaic effect**—phenomena by which certain materials, such as cadmium sulfide, convert light energy into electrical energy.

**physical property**—characteristics of a metal that do not change during fabrication.

**pictorial drawing**—a type of drawing that shows an object as a unified whole.

**piezoelectric effect**—the phenomena by which certain quartz crystals produce electricity when subjected to pressure.

**piping**—the general term for pipes and/or hoses used in a hydraulic system.

**piston**—reciprocating primary engine component that compresses air or and air–fuel mixture in the combustion chamber and which receives the force from the expansion of these gases.

**piston blow-by**—the movement of combustion gasses around the piston and into the engine crankcase.

**plow**—a piece of primary tillage equipment used to break or turn over the soil.

**ply**—an individual layer in a sheet of plywood.

**points of carbon**—method used to indicate the carbon content of steel.

**polarity**—the condition of being positive or negative with respect to some reference point.

**pole**—the moveable contact in an electric switch.

**pole building**—a type of building structure that uses wooden poles as the major structural support components.

**Portland cement**—a finely-ground powder made from limestone, shale, clay, and iron materials that, when combined with water, forms the paste that bonds concrete together.

**port**—a plumbing connection that allows flow into and/or out of a device.

**position**—refers to the number of discrete positions the valving element in a hydraulic system directional control valve can assume in directing fluid flow.

**positive displacement**—a type of pump where the same volume of fluid is delivered per cycle, regardless of the output pressure.

**potential energy**—energy due to position.

**potentiometer (pot)**—a variable resistor having three terminals.

**power**—the time rate of doing work.

**power-take-off**—external tractor shaft for delivering rotary power to implements or other machines.

**power factor**—cosine of the phase angle; ratio of true power to apparent power in an electrical circuit.

**precision farming**—information-based farming techniques where production inputs such as seed, fertilizer, and chemicals are applied only in affected areas and only in the amounts needed.

**pressure override**—in a hydraulic system, the difference between the cracking and full-flow pressures for a pressure relief valve.

**pressure tester**—a diagnostic tool used to pressurize a liquid coolant system to test for leakage.

**preventive maintenance**—periodic maintenance practices intended to keep equipment in good working condition.

**primary battery**—batteries that are not designed to be recharged.

**primary system**—internal combustion engine system directly involved in creating compression and producing power.

**prime mover**—in a hydraulic system, the device that powers the hydraulic pump.

**printed circuit (PC) board**—nonconductive board with pre-drilled holes connected by copper traces; often used for assembly of permanent electronic circuits.

**proton**—the positively-charged portion of an atom.

**protractor**—a mechanical drafting tool for checking and establishing angles.

**PTO power**—power available at a tractor's power-take-off shaft.

**puddle**—the molten pool formed when welding.

**purlins**—horizontal structural building supports running perpendicular to poles or rafters.

**quartz crystal**—silicon dioxide ($SiO_2$).

**radial piston pump**—a type of hydraulic piston pump where the pumping chambers are perpendicular to the pump's drive shaft.

**radiation**—heat transfer through electromagnetic waves.

**ram**—a single-acting hydraulic cylinder with a rod diameter nearly equal to the cylinder bore.

**reaper**—an early piece of farm equipment used to cut and gather grain crops.

**rectification**—to convert alternating current to direct current.

**refining**—the removal of unwanted impurities.

**remote sensing**—gathering and recording data from a distance.

**repulsion-start induction-run motor**—a type of wound-rotor AC electric motor capable of starting very heavy loads.

**reservoir**—hydraulic system component for storing and cooling hydraulic fluid.

**resistance**—characteristic of any material that opposes the flow of electricity; measured in ohms.

**resistor**—electrical or electronic component intended to introduce resistance into a circuit.

**reverse-biased**—the condition where the cathode of an electronic device is more positive than the anode.

**rheostat**—a variable resistor having two terminals.

**ridge cut**—the cut made at the top end of a rafter; also called the upper plumb cut.

**rigid arch building**—a type of building where a series of wall and roof arch units form the building structure.

**rise**—the height of a roof.

**roof slope**—the rise per foot of run for a roof.

**root mean square (rms)**—the effective voltage of AC electricity equal to 0.707 times the peak voltage; the type of voltage measured by most AC voltmeters.

**rotary actuator**—a hydraulic device that produces rotating motion, such as a hydraulic motor.

**rotor**—the rotating component of an AC electric motor.

**run**—the horizontal length of the roof slope.

**running winding**—the main winding on the stator of an AC electric motor.

**sapwood**—the softwood between the inner bark of a tree and the heartwood; also called xylem.

**saturated hydrocarbon fuel**—fuels, such as gasoline and diesel, that contain the maximum possible number of hydrogen atoms and that contain only single covalent bonds.

**scale**—a drafting term indicating the relationship between the dimensions of the drawing and of the drawn object.

**scavenging**—the process of removing burnt gases from an engine combustion chamber.

**schematic drawing**—a type of graphic communication that uses standardized symbols, or schematics, to represent objects.

**schematic symbol**—a standardized symbol that represents an object.

**science**—the systemized knowledge of nature and the physical world.

**secondary battery**—a battery that can be recharged.

**semiconductor**—a material that is neither a good insulator or conductor.

**series circuit**—an electrical circuit containing two or more loads and having only one path for the flow of current.

**series-parallel circuit**—an electrical circuit containing both series and parallel electrical loads.

**service conductors**—electrical conductors from the service point to the service disconnecting means.

**service drop conductors**—overhead electrical conductors originating at the utility company service transformer.

**service entrance equipment**—the components of the electrical system needed to carry current form the building service conductors to the point of origin of branch and feeder circuits within the building or load center.

**service entrance panel**—the main control and cutoff means for the electrical service in a specific building or load center.

**service factor (SF)**—indicates the continuous overload capacity of an electric motor.

**service laterals**—underground conductors supplying electrical service to individual residences and businesses.

**service point**—the point of connection between the electrical utility's wiring system and the individual customer's wiring system.

**sickle**—a sharp, curved metal blade fitted with a short handle; used to cut grain.

**silicon**—a chemical element having four valence electrons; extensively used in manufacturing electronic components.

**silicon-controlled rectifier (SCR)**—a current-controlled solid-state switch that allows current flow in only one direction.

**simple circuit**—an electrical circuit containing only one load.

**single-phase electricity**—a type of AC electrical service having one source voltage applied over two conductors.

**single-pole circuit breaker**—a type of overcurrent protection device used to protect a circuit having one ungrounded conductor.

**site specific crop management (SSCM)**—the use of satellite, electronic, and variable rate technologies to automatically apply the correct production inputs to each specific field location.

**sketch**—a freehand drawing.

**skirt**—the bottom portion of a piston.

**slag**—the protective covering that forms over the weld bead when using certain welding processes.

**sleeves**—replaceable cylinder liners used on some internal combustion engines.

**solar cell**—a device for converting light into electricity through the photovoltaic effect.

**soldering**—a non-fusion joining of metals using a filler metal (solder) that melts at a temperature under 840°F.

**solid state**—a term designating electronic components without moving parts that can control current.

**spark ignition engine**—a type of internal combustion engine that requires an ignition spark to ignite the air and fuel mixture at the beginning of the power stroke.

**special purpose outlet (SPO)**—a receptacle outlet installed to serve a specific electrical machine, appliance, or device.

**specific gravity**—the ratio of the weight or mass of a given volume of a liquid to the same weight or mass of the same volume of water.

**speed**—the rate at which a body moves.

**split-phase motor**—a type of squirrel cage AC induction motor developing fairly low starting torque while drawing a high starting current.

**squatting**—settling on public or other unoccupied land.

**squirrel cage rotor**—a type of rotor commonly used in AC induction motors.

**starting system**—the engine auxiliary system that turns the engine crankshaft for engine starting.

**starting winding**—the auxiliary winding on the stator of an AC induction motor; used only when the motor is starting.

**stator**—stationary motor component consisting of a laminated steel core holding coils of copper wire in place.

**stickers**—crosspieces placed between layers of boards being air dried in order to allow air movement between layers.

**strainer**—a coarse filter that traps particles larger than the strainer openings.

**stray voltage**—small voltage difference existing between two surfaces, such as a metal waterer and the earth.

**stress relieving**—a form of annealing where the metal is heated to just below its critical temperature, held for an extended period, and then cooled very slowly.

**stroke**—the movement of the engine piston from top dead center (TDC) to bottom dead center (BDC) or from BDC to TDC.

**structural grade**—lumber grade based on relative strength.

**stud frame building**—a structure made primarily of sawed lumber and constructed on a concrete or masonry foundation.

**subgrade**—a layer of earth and/or crushed stone and gravel leveled and graded for a foundation.

**sulky**—a light, two-wheeled carriage seating one person.

**supercharger**—a mechanically driven air pump used to increase the volumetric efficiency of an internal combustion engine.

**sweating**—the capillary action by which solder flows throughout a tight joint; the process of joining copper tubing by soldering.

**switch**—a device for opening and closing an electrical circuit.

**switch loop**—that part of a circuit from a light fixture located in the center of the run to the switch located at the end of the run, controlling the light fixture.

**synchronous alternator**—device commonly used in electric power plants to generate electricity.

**system grounding**—the intentional connection of current-carrying portions of the electrical system to earth.

**system objective**—a statement describing the desired goal or outcome of a design project in measurable terms.

**system operating parameter**—the conditions under which the system objective must be met.

**T-square**—a mechanical drafting tool that forms a 90-degree angle with the left or right edge of the drawing board.

**tachometer**—a device for measuring the speed of a rotating shaft in revolutions per minute (rpm).

**tail cut**—cuts made at the lower end of a common rafter.

**tempering**—heat treating process that reduce the hardness of a hardened metal by relieving a desired amount of internal stress.

**template**—an outline pattern from which letters and symbols can be traced.

**tensile strength**—the ability of a material to withstand a pulling force.

**terminal board**—the board at which electrical connections are made to an electric motor; usually located in one of the end bells.

**thermal conductivity**—the relative ability of a material to transfer heat.

**thermal efficiency**—the ratio of the mechanical power produced by an engine to the amount of heat energy consumed.

**thermal protection**—a motor overload protection technique relying on heat production to open the motor circuit in case of an overload.

**thermocouple**—a device consisting of a junction of two dissimilar metals that generates a voltage when the junction is heated.

**thermodynamics**—the branch of physics dealing with heat flow.

**thermopile**—an electrical-generating device consisting of a number of thermocouples connected in series to increase output voltage.

**thread pitch**—refers to the spacing and size of the threads on threaded connectors, taps, and dies.

**three-phase electricity**—electrical service consisting of three interrelated voltages for which the phase difference is 120 degrees.

**throw**—refers to the number of paths provided for current to flow out of a switch.

**thyristor**—a class of semiconductor switching device.

**time-delay**—a fuse or circuit breaker that will tolerate a small, temporary overload without opening the circuit.

**tinning**—the process of applying a very thin layer of solder to a base metal.

**top dead center (TDC)**—piston position when the piston is at the top of its stroke or when combustion chamber volume is at a minimum.

**torque**—a twisting or rotating force.

**toughness**—measure of a metal's resistance to impact.

**transistor**—a semi-conductor device used for amplification and switching applications in electronic circuits.

**triangle**—mechanical drafting tools used either alone or in pairs to produce a variety of angles.

**triplex cable**—a cable consisting of three conductors twisted together; commonly used for overhead service drops.

**trivalent element**—a chemical element having three valence electrons.

**true power**—the amount of electrical power actually consumed.

**tungsten inert gas welding (TIG)**—electric arc welding process using a non-combustible tungsten electrode, an inert shielding gas, and possibly a non-coated filler rod; also called gas tungsten arc welding (GTAW).

**turbocharger**—a turbine-type air pump, driven by engine exhaust gasses, designed to increase the volumetric efficiency of an internal combustion engine.

**Type S fuse**—a type of fuse designed to prevent "over-fusing" a circuit; also called a "non-tamperable" fuse.

**ultimate strength**—the point at which a metal fails due to an applied force.

**unbalanced vane pump**—a type of hydraulic vane pump where the pump rotor and drive shaft are subjected to unbalanced forces.

**Underwriters' Laboratories, Inc. (UL)**—a nationally recognized non-profit organization that provides a voluntary product testing and listing program for electrical (and other) materials and devices.

**ungrounded conductor**—a circuit conductor not attached to the ground; commonly called a "hot" conductor.

**unit factors**—ratios whose actual value equals unity, or one.

**United States Customary System (US)**—the system of measurement commonly used in the United States based on the pound, foot, and gallon as the basic units of weight, length, and capacity, respectively.

**universal motor**—a type of wound-rotor electric motor that can operate on AC or DC electricity.

**unloading valve**—a type of hydraulic valve which by-passes pump output to the reservoir when a set pilot pressure is maintained.

**upper plumb cut**—cut made at the top end of a rafter; also called the ridge cut.

**vacuum gage**—a diagnostic tool used to test the engine intake system.

**valence ring**—the outermost electron orbit of an atom.

**valve clearance**—the gap between the valve tappet and the valve stem.

**valve face**—the angled surface of the engine valve that seals against the valve seat.

**variable capacitor**—a type of capacitor whose capacitance value can be adjusted.

**variable displacement pump**—a type of pump where the volume of fluid pumped per cycle can be changed while the pump is in operation.

**variable rate technology (VRT)**—automatically varying the rate of application of production inputs, such as feed, seed, and fertilizer, without stopping.

**variable resistor**—a type of resistor where the resistance value can be adjusted.

**velocity**—speed of motion.

**veneer**—thin layers of wood made by peeling a continuous layer of wood from a log.

**viscosity**—a measure of a liquid's resistance to flow.

**volt (V)**—the unit of electrical pressure, or electromotive force.

**volt meter**—an instrument for measuring voltage.

**voltage drop**—the reduction in voltage that occurs as electricity flows through a resistance.

**voltage source**—the origin of the electromotive force in a circuit; for example, a battery or alternator.

**volumetric efficiency**—a measure of the air-pumping ability of an internal combustion engine.

**waste gate**—a device that controls the amount of boost produced by a turbocharger.

**wattmeter**—an instrument for measuring the power in an electrical circuit.

**watts (W)**—the basic unit of electrical power.

**way**—refers to the number of paths for oil flow through a directional control valve, including reverse flow.

**welding**—the process of joining materials by fusion.

**whole systems planning**—a planning system in which specific decisions are made based on a holistic, global perspective.

**wire nut**—a common type of connector for making solderless splices in electrical conductors.

**wire stripper**—an electrical wiring handtool for removing insulation from individual conductors.

**wire wrapping**—a solderless technique for assembling permanent electronic circuits.

**with diversity**—electrical loads in a building or other load center not expected to operate at the same time as the loads without diversity in the same building.

**without diversity**—electrical loads in a building or load center which, under normal conditions, will all operate at the same time.

**work**—the movement of a force through a distance.

**xylem**—the softwood between the inner bark of a tree and the heartwood; also called sapwood.

**yield point**—the point at which a metal being stretched becomes permanently deformed.

**zener diode**—a type of diode designed to conduct in reverse direction when its breakdown voltage is reached, maintaining a relatively constant voltage despite variations in current.

# BIBLIOGRAPHY

Althouse, Andrew D., Carl H. Turnquist, William A. Bowditch, and Kevin E. Bowditch. *Modern Welding.* South Holland, Illinois: Goodheart-Willcox Co. 1988.

Boyd, James S., and Carl L. Reynolds. *Practical Farm Buildings: A Text and Handbook*, Third Edition. Danville, Illinois: Interstate Publishers, Inc. 1993.

Buriak, Philip, and Edward W. Osborne. *Physical Science Applications in Agriculture.* Danville, Illinois: Interstate Publishers, Inc. 1996.

Burke, Stanley R., and T.J. Wakeman. *Modern Agricultural Mechanics*, Second Edition. Danville, Illinois: Interstate Publishers, Inc. 1992.

Cochrane, William. *The Development of Modern Agriculture*, Second Edition. Minneapolis, Minnesota: University of Minnesota Press. 1993.

Dugger, William E., Jr., and Howard H. Gerrish. *Electronics Technology.* South Holland, Illinois: Goodheart-Willcox Co. 1994.

Goering, Carroll F. *Engine and Tractor Power*, Third Edition. St. Joseph, Michigan: American Society of Agricultural Engineers. 1992.

Gustafson, Robert J. *Fundamentals of Electricity for Agriculture*, Second Edition. St. Joseph, Michigan: American Society of Agricultural Engineers. 1988.

Holt, Michael. *Understanding the National Electrical Code®*, Second Edition. Albany, New York: Delmar Publishers. 1995.

Jacobs, Clinton O., and William R. Harrell. *Agricultural Power and Machinery.* New York, New York: McGraw-Hill Book Company. 1983.

621

Lee, Jasper S., and Diana L. Turner. *Introduction to World AgriScience and Technology.* Danville, Illinois: Interstate Publishers, Inc. 1997.

Lindley, James A., and James H. Whitaker. *Agricultural Buildings and Structures.* St. Joseph, Michigan: American Society of Agricultural Engineers. 1996.

Mimms, Forrest M. *Getting Started in Electronics.* Fort Worth, Texas: Radio Shack. 1983.

*National Electrical Code®* (1996 Edition). Quincy, Massachusetts: National Fire Protection Association, Inc. 1995.

Phipps, Lloyd J. and Glen M. Miller. *AgriScience Mechanics.* Danville, Illinois: Interstate Publishers, Inc. 1998.

Phipps, Lloyd J. and Carl L. Reynolds. *Mechanics in Agriculture*, Fourth Edition. Danville, Illinois: Interstate Publishers, Inc. 1992.

Stetson, LaVerne E., Gerald R. Bodeman, and Jack L. Schinstock. "Electrical Wiring Methods and Materials for Agricultural Buildings," *Applied Engineering in Agriculture,* Volume 5(1): March, 1989.

Sullivan, James A. *Fluid Power: Theory and Application.* Reston, Virginia: Reston Publishing Company, Inc. 1982.

Surbrook, Truman C. *Interpreting the National Electrical Code®,* Fourth Edition. Albany, New York: Delmar Publishers. 1997.

Surbrook, Truman C., and Ray C. Mullins. *Agricultural Electrification.* Cincinnati, Ohio: South-Western Publishing Co. 1985.

_____. *Agricultural Wiring Handbook,* Eleventh Edition. Columbia, Missouri: National Food and Energy Council. 1996.

_____. *Farm Buildings Wiring Handbook*, Second Edition. Ames, Iowa: Midwest Plan Service. 1992.

_____. *Fundamentals of Motor Control.* Raleigh, North Carolina: Square D Automation and Control. 1991.

_____. *Industrial Hydraulics Manual*, 25 Printing. Troy, Michigan: Vickers, Inc. Technical Training Center.

_____. *Selecting and Using Electric Motors.* Washington, DC: United States Department of Agriculture, Farmer's Bulletin No. 2257. 1974.

# INDEX